MW00616359

Why Mom Deserves a Diamond®

The Encouraging Branch

Gallery of diamonds
Publishing

Newport Beach, California USA
www.galleryofdiamonds.com

Our nine diamonds from L to R: Tram Diep, Guita Afzali, Sandra Babic, Janey Perone, Claudia Elliott, Jeanette Rodriguez, Michael Campos, Carmen and Michael Watson.

Other books by Michael C. Watson and Gallery of Diamonds:

Adopted Like Me - Chosen to Search for Truth, Identity, and a Birthmother
In Search of Mom- Journey of an Adoptee
WHY MOM DESERVES A DIAMOND® - The Crystal Heart
WHY MOM DESERVES A DIAMOND® - Sparkling Treasures
WHY MOM DESERVES A DIAMOND® - Beyond the Goddess Venus.
WHY MOM DESERVES A DIAMOND® - Words of Love
WHY MOM DESERVES A DIAMOND® - Twelve Years of Love
WHY MOM DESERVES A DIAMOND®- The Legendary Contest
WHY MOM DESERVES A DIAMOND® -10th Anniversary of the Greatest Contest on Earth
WHY MOM DESERVES A DIAMOND® - The Greatest Contest on Earth
WHY MOM DESERVES A DIAMOND®- A Millennium Mother's Day Tribute
WHY MOM DESERVES A DIAMOND® - Seventh Anniversary Edition
WHY MOM DESERVES A DIAMOND® - 2,002 Essay Winners for 1998
WHY MOM DESERVES A DIAMOND® - 1,002 Essay Winners for 1997
WHY MOM DESERVES A DIAMOND® - 732 Essay Winners for 1996
WHY MOM DESERVES A DIAMOND®- 391 Essay Winners for 1995
WHY MOM DESERVES A DIAMOND® - In Remembrance of Mother's Day 1994
WHY MOM DESERVES A DIAMOND® - In Remembrance of Mother's Day 1993

Published by:

Gallery of Diamonds Publishing

Plaza Newport Shopping Center
1000 Bristol St.North, Suite 8
Newport Beach, CA 92660 U.S.A.

www.galleryofdiamonds.com
www.whymomdeservesadiamond.com

Copyright © 2009 by Michael C. Watson and Why Mom Deserves a Diamond, Inc . First Printing 2009.

WHY MOM DESERVES A DIAMOND® is Patent Pending and is a registered trademark of Why Mom Deserves a Diamond, Inc.

WHY MOM DESERVES A DIAMOND®– The Encouraging Branch
ISSN 1535-8445
ISBN 978-1-891665-41-7
Copies may be ordered directly from the publisher for $34.95 plus $6.95 for shipping (California residents add 8.75 sales tax.)
For terms in volume quantities, please contact the publisher.

This book contains the winners of the Orange County, California students that participated in the 2009 Gallery of Diamonds, WHY MOM DESERVES A DIAMOND® writing contest. A portion of the proceeds from the sale of this book is donated to the Orange County Public Library to supplement their educational materials on creative writing, world religions, astronomy, physics, biology, ecology, and resource books for members of the adoptive triangle, which include adoptees, adoptive parents, and birthparents. No part of this book may be reproduced or transmitted in any form or by any means, electronic or mechanical, including photocopying, recording or by any retrieval system without written permission and expressed consent from the authors contained herein. Every effort was made to correctly reproduce each students work. We apologize for any mistakes.

Book Cover by Tram Diep.

Martha Velia Watson

March 15, 1920 - September 14, 2006

Contents

School Index

In Honor of *all* Moms

Dearest Reader,

Seventeen years have passed since Margaret Ketchersid came to Gallery of Diamonds to claim her grand prize in the first WHY MOM DESERVES A DIAMOND® contest. Like buried treasure, her enchanting poem sparkled deep within the mound of essays on my desk. I will never forget that beautiful morning on Mother's Day, 1993, as she presented the precious gem to her mother.

No one realized, including myself, that the contest originally established in honor of my adoptive mother and birth mother would resound throughout the world as a ministry to honor *all* mothers.

This year's 6,300 winners were judged from a mountain of submissions that reached the ceiling. The book is the result of hundreds of thoughtful hours, the devotion and expertise of our associates, and the dedication of nineteen contest panel judges. Since every winner was required to recite his or her words, the book eternally preserves that magical moment between every mother and her child.

The book you are holding is extraordinary, for it contains 6,300 letters of love!

Each winner was awarded a genuine gemstone. Garnet winners are in regular type and amethyst winners are in bold. There were also two grand prize Diamond Winners.

I hope you receive much joy in reading how these kids expressed their appreciation for their mothers. Win or lose, an exercise that invites us to reflect on how our moms are important must be beneficial for our society.

When we know we are loved, we learn to love ourselves. When we love ourselves, it is easier to love others. When we love others, our world becomes our beautiful home. That is the conviction of Gallery of Diamonds.

Michael Watson

President

The Greatest Tribute to Mom

In 1993, Michael Watson started a mother's appreciation contest. He was adopted as a child, and although he had very loving parents, he was always curious to know about the woman who gave birth to him. This contest would be in honor of his adoptive mother and his birth mother. It would also give kids a chance to show their appreciation for their own moms.

Watson invited kids to write an essay entitled, WHY MOM DESERVES A DIAMOND®. The most creative contestant would receive a quarter-carat diamond now valued at $600. The contest would be an exercise on love.

Gallery of Diamonds received two hundred and fifty entries from students who poetically illustrated why their moms should merit the gem. It was fascinating to read how each student expressed his or her unique appreciation. Reviewing each labor of love gave Watson a feeling of wholeness that was indescribable. With vibrant imagination, this assignment was approached as a once-in-a-lifetime chance to honor one's mother.

On Mother's Day, Margaret Ketchersid was declared the first-place Diamond Winner. It was a quiet, yet heartwarming ceremony as Margaret presented the diamond to her mother, Ruth. Afterwards, Watson re-read that mound of essays, feeling it would be unfair for the remaining students to receive nothing. Therefore, he selected fifty runners-up, choosing to award them a beautiful red garnet from Africa.

The next day, Watson called each second-place winner to receive his or her gemstone prize. The gallery soon became filled with people. Each student recited their composition. Using jewelers tweezers, each child seized a garnet from a parcel of gems, and placed a stone into their mother's palm. An anthology of the winning entries was assembled and saddle-stitched into a book entitled, *In Remembrance of Mother's Day - 1993*. Now winners were also published authors!

Nowadays, Mother's Day submissions invade Gallery of Diamonds by the thousands.

What began as a tribute for Watson's own mothers evolved into a commemoration in which thousands of kids are recognized for their achievements while becoming a little closer to their moms. Writers are motivated to do their very best, and mothers receive a gem that endures as a symbol of their child's appreciation.

Gallery of Diamonds gives thanks for its extraordinary staff, who work tirelessly organizing the thousands of submissions. It is this incredible devotion and cheerful attitudes that are responsible in making the contest a rewarding and magical experience for every gemstone winner and their mom. We also thank the fourteen Orange County teachers who were selected as contest panel judges. Each teacher spent much time sorting and reading each essay.

As a final note, after searching for nearly twenty years, Watson found his biological family and discovered the identity of his own birth mother. He never met her, for she died in 1981. The autobiography, *Adopted Like Me*, details Watson's wonderful adventure and how it helped create the greatest mother's appreciation contest in the nation. A copy is free with any purchase.

Since 1993, thousands of kids have participated in this annual celebration of love, and millions of people have been positively touched. We are certain that a type of moral has been instilled in all to understand more fully the value of mom in our lives.

We believe the greatest gift is a wonderful memory. We hope that every mother and child that came to Gallery of Diamonds took home a wonderful memory that will last a lifetime.

Who Invented Mother's Day?

The person associated with creating Mother's Day is **Anna Jarvis**. It was first celebrated at Andrews Methodist Church in West Virginia on May 10, 1907, to honor the memory of her own mother who died three years earlier. The church bell rang 72 times for each year of her mother's life. In 1914, President Woodrow Wilson declared Mother's Day a national holiday.

Anna Jarvis was an early reformer of women's rights. She was a teacher in Grafton, West Virginia, cared for her blind sister, was a literary editor, and participated in the temperance and suffrage movements.

Nearly fifty countries honor their mothers with a special day. Although International Mother's Day is May 11, the United States always celebrates this holiday on the second Sunday of May.

The Gemstone Prizes

Grand Prize - Diamond

A Diamond Winner holds the highest honor of the contest and receives the most precious of gems to give to mom. Since 1993, 48 kids have been DiamondWinners.

The diamond is the subject of countless legends. The Hindus believed that this brilliant gem was created when bolts of lightning struck rocks. To be effective as a talisman, the gem would have to be given as a token of love or friendship.

A symbol of innocence, justice, faith, and strength, the diamond was believed to make its wearers courageous and victorious over their enemies.

This incredible gem began life millions of years ago, deep beneath the Earth's surface, when enormous heat and pressure squeezed together carbon atoms into the hardest substance known, and a crystal that is a playground for light.

How much pressure does it take to make a diamond? Imagine the Eiffel Tower turned upside down, with all its weight resting on a plate 5 inches square!

First Prize - Amethyst

Since only highly creative contestants are chosen for this prize, it is a great honor to be an Amethyst winner.

This is a beautiful purple gemstone in the quartz family. Some early legends about amethyst included the belief that it sharpened intelligence and rendered the owner shrewd in business, protected the soldier and gave him victory, aided hunters, protected against disease, and controlled evil thoughts. The ancient Greeks believed it would protect one from the effects of wine! Amethyst is also the birthstone for February.

Second Prize - African Garnet

It is very honorable to receive this special gem. The type that comes from Africa is known for its deep, brilliant red color. Garnets have been used as amulets against accidents in travel, and were believed to  promote sincerity and cure anger. All garnets have high refractive indices, having high lustre and brilliance. Garnet is also the birthstone for January.

Diamond, garnet and amethyst are durable gems that give its wearer many years of enjoyment. Since they are natural gemstones, any small inclusions should not be considered as a defect.

The Legend of Gallery of Diamonds

Michael Watson was adopted into a family of loving parents who lived in the small town of New Albany, Indiana. Although curious about his birth origins, Michael learned that it is the person that gives love, nurture, and caring instruction that is one's true mother.

Michael began his profession at the age of seventeen, when he was hired at a small jewelry store. His duties were simply to sweep the wooden floors and deliver repairs to the goldsmith. He would be handed a small brown paper bag, told never to open it, and deliver it across the town. He never dreamed of the precious jewels it contained!

Years later, Michael was hired by a diamond importer in Kentucky. He quickly attained a love affair with rare and beautiful diamonds and was promoted to manage a store in Kansas. In 1989, he journeyed to California to become a gemologist and open a diamond business.

Determined to build a jewelry company that offered timeless designs at lower prices than competitors, Watson purchased loose diamonds then hired master jewelers to set the diamonds into unusual gold mountings. He quickly learned the secret to offer fine jewelry at lower prices:

1. Select the best diamonds.
2. Set them by trained master setters.
3. Eliminate the fees of the middleman.

In 2006, the headquarters of Gallery of Diamonds moved to a larger facility in Newport Beach. The company continues to specialize in fine diamond jewelry and is the leading manufacturer of mother's jewelry. The gallery has master jewelers, appraisers, and designers.

Customers are invited to watch the fascinating process of appraisals performed by a GIA gemologist. These appraisals are included with every diamond purchase and include a color photograph and a description of quality and value.

Throughout the lively history of Gallery of Diamonds, the store has provided over 25,000 families with a magical experience.

First store in 1991.

Near the contest deadline, mail carrier P. J. Medina delivers thousands of contest entries.

The quest of Gallery of Diamonds is to combine excellent service with its lifetime jewelry, and to make sure every child gets the chance to tell their moms how much they love them in the legendary, WHY MOM DESERVES A DIAMOND® contest.

Trademarks

WHY MOM DESERVES A DIAMOND®, THE LEGENDARY CONTEST®, and MOON OVER MOUNTAINS™ are registered trademarks of Gallery of Diamonds. Gallery of Diamonds conducts its contests in every state in the United States and protects its trademarks, trade dress, and business methods.

Secret Jewelry Cleaning Formula

The best way to clean jewelry at home is by mixing one part ammonia, three parts water, and a few drops of dishwashing liquid. Use an old toothbrush to scrub underneath the gemstones and around prongs. Rinse with water.

Do not use bleach. Do not use for opal or pearl jewelry Do not drop jewelry into sink!

Our secret formula is a hot solution of lemon scented ammonia, water, and Spic and Span®.

2009 Diamond Winners

Eyes glittering with flawless light.
Face perfect as an angel.
She guides me in wisdom.
She is my encouraging branch.
She's my gem of life.

David Duplissey
Grade: 4
Ambuehl Elementary
San Juan Capistrano, CA

Diamond Teacher: Jennifer Sullivan
Contest Panel Judge: Karen French

David and mother, Deanne.

My mother loves as passionately as a fire in the forge, melting the iron surrounding our hearts, filling us with golden compassion and silver kindness.

Cheryl Bond
Grade: 6
Oak Middle School
Los Alamitos, CA

Diamond Teacher: Wendy Hearn
Contest Panel Judge: Kathi Manuel

Cheryl and mother, Alyssa.

Diamond Winners Since 1993

Since 1993, nearly 250,000 kids have submitted words of love in our renowned contest. Following is a compilation of Diamond Winners since 1993 and some interesting statistics. Notice how the length of the entries has been gradually reduced to the current limitation of 25 words. As the contest has grown, this stricter requirement was necessary to read and judge the thousands of entries we receive annually. This has certainly increased the challenge of creatively expressing the love of mom in a few chosen words.

1993

Margaret and mother Ruth.

Her love is not blind, it is clear and forgiving
Her touch is all-knowing, her joy is life giving
This angel, my mother, gives of herself
And illuminates me with compassion's true wealth

A symbol of courage and strength she remains
And understands all my joys and pains
To gaze at my mother, who strives beyond duty
Is to see radiate her unique, warming beauty!

The sweet voice of mother, her strong, safe, embrace
I long to possess her pure, natural, grace
My Mother, my Guide, and gemstone so rare
Deserves out of likeness a diamond as fair

Margaret Ketchersid
Grade 10
Edison High
Huntington Beach, CA

The grand prize:
1/4 carat diamond.

1994

Alison and mother, Sandy.

No one knows what it's like
To walk in her shoes
When every game she played with me
She always seemed to lose

And the note from Santa Claus
Seemed to look the same
As the writing on the lunchbags
Where she wrote my name

In all the falls I took, and the cuts I made
She fixed me up with only a kiss
And a purple band-aid

In all the things I didn't do
And all the things she knew
I'd never thought I'd seen the day
I saw us moving further away

But of all the things she ever said
And all the nights sleeping in my bed
I promised I'd give her the diamonds in the sky
When all she said she ever wanted
Were the diamonds in my eyes

Alison Murphy
Grade 10
Capistrano Valley High
Mission Viejo, CA

1995

Whether I stand on land or shore
I know I couldn't love my mother more
Always caring, always there
In times that are good, in times of despair
Magical lands we like to explore
When she reads aloud from classical lore
I thank you, Mom, at each day's end
You really are my best friend

Scott Kircher
Grade 6
Harbor Day
Corona Del Mar, CA

Scott
and
mother, Valerie.

Megan and mother, Lornna.

A Mother Recipe

Million gallons of love, two pinches of creativity, twelve cups of niceness, two gallons of understanding. Million drops of unique and beautifulness, any other items that might make your mother wonderful.
Mix well, bake two seconds.
I guarantee my mother!

Megan Darakjian
Grade 4
Cordillera
Mission Viejo, CA

Lauren and mother, Kathleen.

Shadows flickering, dancing about
Even the moon is terrified
I lie wide awake, petrified as the distant silhouettes come dancing toward me
Then suddenly they disappear
As she flicks on the light
Her soothing smile, her comforting voice
And the monsters are all gone

Lauren Kiang
Grade 7
La Paz Intermediate
Mission Viejo, CA

Genevieve and mother, Sherry.

Burning sands, ever shifting
Desert of life I must pass through
When I sink, two hands are lifting
Helping me to start anew
She's the oasis where I may rest
She, who always knows me best
Diamond in the rough

Genevieve Slunka
Grade 11
Irvine High
Irvine, CA

Jessica and mother, Dianne.

My Mom is a cozy place. Like a warm cup of cocoa. Or a pillow trimmed with lace
My Mom's love is all mine. I can always depend. She's more than a mom.
She's my best friend

Jessica Barraco
Grade 4
Eastshore Elementary
Irvine, CA

In Memory
of Dianne Barraco

Orange County Winners from 1993 to 2009				
Year	Winner	Grade	School	City
1993	Margaret Ketchersid	10	Edison	Huntington Bea
1994	Alison Murphy	10	Capistrano Valley HS	Mission Viejo
1995	Scott Kircher	6	Harbor Day	Corona del Mar
1996	Megan Darakjian	4	Cordillera	Mission Viejo
1996	Lauren Kiang	7	La Paz	Mission Viejo
1997	Jessica Barraco	4	Eastshore	Irvine
1997	Genevieve Slunka	11	Irvine High	Irvine
1998	Jason Kirstein	3	Westwood Basics	Irvine
1998	Tawnya Ravy	7	Bernardo M.S.	Yorba Linda
1999	Blair Perkins	5	Taft Elementary	Orange
1999	Paula Kim	7	Los Alisos	Mission Viejo
2000	Sandy Enriquez	5	Gilbert Elem.	Garden Grove
2000	Tiffany Lamanski	7	St. Pius V	Buena Park
2001	E. J. Debowski	4	John Malcolm	Laguna Niguel
2001	Alyssa Connella	7	La Paz	Mission Viejo
2002	Harry Hudson	2	Bathgate Elem.	Mission Viejo
2002	Amanda Wheeler	7	Los Alisos	Mission Viejo
2003	Aris Simsarian	2	De Portola Elem.	Mission Viejo
2003	Logan Cluttey	8	Los Flores M.S.	R. Sta. Margarit
2004	Tyler Buttle	5	Reilly Elementary	Mission Viejo
2004	Erica Haggerty	8	St. Angela Merici	Brea
2005	Analyse Groton	4	Linda Vista Ele.	Orange
2005	Jason Punzalon	8	Servite High	Anaheim
2006	Kevin Banifatemi	5	De Portola Elem.	Mission Viejo
2006	Laura Chae	7	Sierra Vista M.S.	Irvine
2007	Grace Penner	5	Brookhaven Ele.	Placentia
2007	Michael Glidden	11	Capistrano Valley HS	Mission Viejo
2008	Sophia Vazquez	2	Jim Thorpe Fund.	Santa Ana
2008	Linda Huynh	7	Fred Moila	Fountain Valley
2009	David Duplissey	4	Ambuehl Ele.	San Juan Capis
2009	Cheryl Bond	7	Oak Middle School	Los Alamitos

National Diamond Winners

Year	Winner	Grade	School	City	State
1998	Vicki Ann Blood	4	St. Pancratius	Lakewood	CA
1998	Jennifer Plankenhorn	8	Arroyo Seco	Valencia	CA
1999	Roberto Ruiz	5	St. Malachy	Los Angeles	CA
1999	Chris Olsen-Philips	6	Binford Elementary	Bloomington	IN
1999	Brice Tomlinson	6	Trinity Christian Academy	Addison	TX
2000	Rachel Tomberlin	7	St. Timothy Episcopal	Apple Valley	CA
2000	Victor Taylor	5	St. Mary	New Albany	IN
2000	Ashley Goodell	8	Chippewa M.S.	Okemos	MI
2000	Laura Cataldi	10	Nardin Academy	Buffalo	NY
2000	Ashley Kreidler	11	St. Johns	Delphos	OH
2000	Jennifer Scruggs	5	Sleepy Hollow Elementary	Amarillo	TX
2001	Jesus Hernandez, Jr.	12	St. Thomas High	Houston	TX
2002	Matthew W. Scott	11	Heartland High	Belton	MO
2003	Travis Dziad	6	St. Mary's	Greenville	SC
2004	Lindsey Croft	12	Nevada Union High	Grass Valley	CA
2005	Emily Magers	6	Timberview M. S.	Colorado Spgs	CO
2006	Sera Choi	7	Becker M.S.	Las Vegas	NV

In 1998, the contest was expanded to the entire state of California. To date, kids from nearly every state in the United States have submitted their essays to Gallery of Diamonds.

1998

Jason and mother, Heather.

A diamond has all the colors of the rainbow.
My mom deserves a diamond because she is all the colors in my life.

Jason Kirstein
Grade: 3
Westwood Basics Plus
Irvine, CA

Vicki Ann and mother, Kathy.

My mother deserves a diamond because she's unique, priceless, perfect, pure, precious, dazzling, flawless and rare. She sparkles with love and glistens with knowledge. She is a gem to me.

Vicki Ann Blood
Grade: 4
St. Pancratius
Lakewood, CA

Jennifer and mother, Janet.

A heavenly calm, and pure state of grace. A lovely expression falls on her face. A whisper of words, like velvety lace. Soft summer's glow, in securing embrace.
My Mother.

Jennifer Planenhorn
Grade: 8
Arroyo Seco Junior High
Valencia, CA

Tawyna and mother, Nancy.

Her lips are roses, her complexion is cream. She understands my deepest thoughts and dreams. She is my angel with a halo of gold. She is my mother.

Tawyna Ravy
Grade: 7
Bernardo Yorba M. S.
Yorba Linda, CA

1999

Blair and mother, Wendi.

Her touch- like breezes on a warm summer day. Her laugh- like one million tears being dried away. Mom is her name for which there is no other. Mom- mine forever.

Blair Perkins
Grade 5
Taft Elementary
Orange, CA

Paula and mother, Michelle

A rose, pure and true. Movements of a rainbow. Voice like silk, and laughter like the drumming of raindrops. Diamond of life. Sparkling and glittering with unimaginable beauty. My mother.

Paula Kim
Grade 7
Los Alisos
Mission Viejo, CA

The salt of my life is my mom, which gives taste in all the recipes of life. She is the ingredient that gives inspiration in my journey to my goals.

Roberto Ruiz
Grade 5
St. Malachy
Los Angeles, CA

Roberto and mother, Margarita

Gem of my heart, fair as can be. A star from heaven brought to earth. A precious jewel beyond compare. Deserving this diamond is my angel, my mother.

Chris Olsen-Phillips
Grade 6
Binford Elementary
Bloomington, IN

Chris and mother, Deb.

My mother has a heart of gold. Her love is the most precious thing I hold. And when I look at her I see. An angel sent to protect me.

Brice Tomlinson
Grade 6
Trinity Christian Academy
Addison, TX

Brice and mother, Jackie

2000

She is like a wave.
As tribulations appear in my
life, the tide rises and she
flows to my side. Her flowing
nature calms my storm.
Mom, my refuge.

Ashley Kreidler
Grade: 11

St. Johns
Delphos, OH

Ashley and mother, Mary Jo.

A flower that blossoms
everyday
A stream that always flows
An adventure that has just
begun
A book that never ends
A candle that will never die
Mother.

Tiffany Lamanski
Grade: 7
St. Pius V.
Buena Park, CA

Tiffany and mother, Pauline.

My mother is an angel. This
is true, I know. She's an
everlasting hug, that'll never
let me go. Knowing that I'm
loved, because she told me
so.

Ashley Goodell
Grade: 8
Chippewa Middle School
Okemos, MI

Ashley and mother, Cheryl.

A glorious angel sent from
heaven, with beauty like a
dove.
Her voice drains all sadness.
A brilliant star shining
through the darkness. My
friend, my mom.

Jennifer Scruggs
Grade: 5
Sleepy Hollow Elementary
Amarillo, TX

Jennifer and mother, Laura

My mother's love is like a
blanket, shielding me from
cold winds of harm.
Embraced within her soft
touch, I am safe. Sacrificing
all, she comforts me forever.

Laura Cataldi
Grade: 10

Nardin Academy
Buffalo, NY

Laura and mother, Pauline.

The soothing sound of her
voice melts away my
sorrow. The gentleness of
her touch relieves my
deepest pains. The warmth of
her sparkling eyes
penetrates my soul. Mom.

Rachel Tomberlin
Grade: 7
St. Timothy Episcopal
Apple Valley, CA

Rachel and mother, Cathy.

A vast lake sparkling with
sunlight. A pure meadow
with the gentlest breeze. My
mother is more beautiful
than all of these. My angel. My
mother.

Victor Taylor
Grade: 5
St. Mary
New Albany, IN

Victor and mother, Lisa.

Her hair like the swaying sea
cradling a sunset,
Eyes like two blue sparkling
sapphires. Hands as
smooth as gold silk. A voice
soft like the gentle
wind. Mom.

Sandy Enriquez
Grade: 5
Gilbert Elementary.
Garden Grove, CA

Sandy and aunt, Emma.

2001

E. J. and mom, Lisa.

A beautiful rose that blooms in July. With bright golden sapphires - those are her eyes. Her hair is black, like the calm, silent night. That's my mom all right!

E.J. Debowski
Grade: 4
John Malcom
Laguna Niguel, CA

Jesus and mom, Carmen.

Behold the ark that bears the covenant of conception. From her womb the living bond arose. And so it is I must behold, my mother, the temple of creation.

Jesus Hernandez, Jr.
Grade: 12
St. Thomas High Sch.
Houston, TX

Alyssa and mom, Michele.

Mom is a masterpiece created with love, Her sparkling smile shines from above. Bountiful in kindness she proceeds with great care. Without knowing how much I appreciate her there.

Alyssa Connella
Grade: 7
La Paz Intermediate
Mission Viejo, CA

My mother is a river
meandering in and out,
flowing into every part
of my life.
Her banks overflow
with love, kindness,
gentleness and
patience.

**Amanda Wheeler
Grade: 7
Los Alisos
Intermediate
Mission Viejo, CA**

Amanda and mom, Kelly.

My beautiful rose is
fresh from the garden.
Her eyes sparkle like
the dew on the soft
petals.
Her smile glistens like
a rainbow.
She is my charming
mother.

**Harry Hudson
Grade: 2
Bathgate Elem.
Mission Viejo, CA**

Harry and mom, Mahgabien.

She is a saint, whose
love is great
Giving of herself, she
knows not hate
Kind her eyes, and soft
her touch
Because of her, I have
so much.

**Matthew Scott
Grade: 11
Heartland High Sch.
Belton, MO**

Matthew and mom, Kathy.

Contest Statistics						
Entries Submitted and Gemstones Awarded						
Year	Entries	Max Words	Diamond	Sapphire	Amethyst	Garnet
2009	19,734	25	2	0	2,100	4,200
2008	16,148	25	2	0	1,650	3,350
2007	15,521	25	2	0	1,333	2,667
2006	15,462	26	2	0	1,333	2,667
2005	22,629	27	2	0	1,333	2,667
2004	21,253	27	2	0	1,333	2,667
2003	24,850	27	2	0	1,333	2,667
2002	14,375	29	2	0	1,000	2,000
2001	14,050	29	2	0	1,000	2,000
2000	15,225	29	2	0	1,000	2,000
1999	14,150	30	2	0	500	1,865
1998	10,650	30	2	0	300	1,700
1997	5,025	40	2	25	0	975
1996	4,675	45	2	30	0	700
1995	2,016	70	1	40	0	350
1994	1,425	100	1	10	0	200
1993	250	100	1	0	0	50

2003

My Mom is like jewels glimmering through the night sky.
Her eyes sparkle like rain dropping from the clouds.
I love you mom, all the time.

Aris Simsarian.
Grade: 2.
De Portola Elementary
Mission Viejo, CA

Aris and mother, Anne Marie

Essence of happiness in this gray world.
She taught me to respect life, while leaving my footprint.
But in comparison, mine are as oarstrokes upon the water.

Logan Cluttey
Grade: 8
Los Flores Middle School
Rancho Santa Margarita, CA

Logan and mom, Carole.

My mother - a rock, silent and firm. My mother - a river, peaceful and calm.
Mother - the Sun, warm and loving.
She is the greatest wonder of creation.

Travis Dziad.
Grade: 6. St. Mary's School
Greenville, SC

Travis and mom, Denise

My mother's blue eyes are magical fountains in heaven. Her voice calls upon the angels to sing. The sunset is a sign that she is in my heart.

**Tyler Buttle.
Grade: 5.
Reilly Elementary
Mission Viejo, CA**

Tyler and mom, Jodi

Her voice- a chorus of angels. Her kisses- a butterfly's whisper. Her spirit- a gentle summer breeze. Her love- a deep sea. My mother...a precious diamond.

**Erica Haggerty.
Grade: 8.
St. Angela Merici
Brea, CA**

Erica and mom, Judith

Eyes sparkling, like iridescent drops of rain. Smiles warm, as hot cocoa on frigid rosebud lips. Loving, deeper than all the oceans and seas. Mother...my sanctuary.

**Lindsey Croft.
Grade: 12. Nevada
Union High School
Grass Valley, CA**

Lindsey and mom, Lynne

2005

Analyse and mother, Patricia

My mother's eyes are like two fireflies glistening in the moonlit sky.

Her kiss is like a big blue wish.
Mother is Nature's way of saying "Hooray!"

Analyse Groton.
Grade: 4.
Linda Vista Elementary
Orange, CA

Jason and mother, Lucrecia

You're spring's showering rain of care.
You're summer's shining smile.
You're autumn's sweater of warm comfort.
You're winter's beauty.
You're my mother, the seasons of love.

Jason Punzalan.
Grade: 9.
Servite High School
Anaheim, CA

Emily and mother, Kyong

Her voice, a nightingale.
Her touch, butterfly wings
Her heart, overflowing with love
Her kisses, flawless bubbles
Mom, a perfect gem.a gift forever

Emily Magers.
Grade: 6.
Timberview Middle School
Colorado Springs, CO

The definition of love will show her face.
And speak of endless giving and grace.
You'll ask me who this woman is.
She's my flawless mother!

Kevin Banifatemi
Grade: 5.
De Portola Elementary
Mission Viejo, CA

Eyes that shine like brilliant stars.
Smile that glows like that of Mars.
Beauty beyond the goddess Venus.
Perfect, my mother, like Earth beneath us.

Laura Chae.
Grade: 7
Sierra Vista Middle School
Irvine, CA

Kevin and mother, Mojdeh

Laura and mother, Sue

Feeling of safety in her palm.
A touch of warmth in her heart.
Endless love in her eyes.
All points to mom, my pure guiding light.

Sera Choi
Grade: 7 Becker Middle School
Las Vegas, NV

Sera and mother, Mi Keong

2006

2007

Sparkling gold treasures, snow white doves. That's mom, shining beyond and above. Clear as a raindrop, plain to see. Mom deserves this diamond, it's destiny.

Grace Penner
Grade:5 Brookhaven Elementary
Placentia, CA

Grace and mother, Tara

She gave my breath its heat
She gave my heart its beat
She allowed love
and life to meet
Without my mom I am incomplete.

Michael Glidden
Grade:11 Capistrano Valley High
Mission Viejo, CA

Michael and mother, Gerlyn

A little bit of moonlight
A dab of sun
Then the crystal heart
will be yours
The twinkling light shines like
mom's wonderful eyes

Sophia Vazquez
Grade: 2
Jim Thorpe Fundamental

Sophia and mother,: Luz

Her eyes gaze into my soul
Her heart forged
completely of gold
Her voice melts into
crystals of compassion
My mother...the gem of me.

Linda Huynh
Grade: 7
Fred Moiola
Diamond Mom: Kimberly

Linda and mother, Kimberly

"There is a universal power called love. Whether it is born from our hearts, our mothers, or a Master Diamond Cutter, we have witnessed it from the lips of thousands of kids. Following are 6,300 winning essays selected from this years 20,000 submissions.

Dedicated to the one who molds and shapes us, and helps us become who we are- mom."

The 2009 Orange County Winners

Adams Elementary
Costa Mesa

Teacher: Diane Bonthius

Angela Cortes   Grade: 02
My mom is special because she is very nice. She looks like a pretty flower. She is very nice to me and helps me.

Vivian Jorge   **Grade: 02**
My mom looks like a beautiful flower from a garden and smells like a rose. She is as cute as a diamond. She's so beautiful.

Stephen Mack   **Grade: 02**
She is pure love. My mom is like a flower. She cares for people and her eyes shine. She has pure health. Pure love.

Michelle Monroy   Grade: 02
My mom is special because she is as pretty as a beautiful rose. Her eyes sparkle in the dark and the sunlight. She is cool!

Jeremy Nacion   Grade: 02
My mom deserves a diamond because she takes care of me. She is very special. She is a very nice mom.

Alondra Ochoa   Grade: 02
My mom is special to me. She's always nice to me. She gives me surprises that open like a rose flower.

Diana Rendon   Grade: 02
My mom deserves a diamond because she is very special. She takes care of me. My mom deserves a diamond because she cooks so good.

Timothy Shannon   **Grade: 02**
My mom deserves a diamond because she is very, very nice. Her eyes are like two stars on a starry night. She deserves a diamond.

Teacher: Tim Christiansen

Janette Medero   Grade: 02
My mom helps me make cupcakes. She also helps me make cookies. She helps me on my homework.

Leslie Pacheco   Grade: 02
My mom shows me how to read. My mom helps me sing. My mom kisses me every day when it's night or time for school.

Andrea Ramos   Grade: 02
My mom is a good mom to me. She does good things for me and I love my family.

Diana Rodriguez   Grade: 02
My mom deserves a diamond because she shine like a star. My mom is also very special to me because she gives me love.

Martin Valladares   Grade: 02
My mom lies me. I play with my mom. My mom gives me pizza.

Teacher: Casandra Flemer

Kayla Brockman   **Grade: 03**
My mommy's eyes sparkle and her smile lights up the room just like a beautiful diamond. That's why my mom deserves a diamond.

Dane Cannon   Grade: 03
My mom is as beautiful as a diamond sparkling in the sunlight and her smile shines as pretty as a rare jewel.

Myrka Carrillo   **Grade: 03**
My mom deserves a diamond because she looks pretty like the sun glowing in the water. My mom smells like a flower growing in the summer.

Araceli Orozco   Grade: 03
Because she is sweet and nice. She is the best mom ever. I love her so much. I hope she gets a diamond.

Julie Ann Sumalpong   Grade: 03
My mom deserves a diamond because she took care of me when I needed someone, and I want to thank her for loving me.

Stephanie Villegas   **Grade: 03**
She loves me, she takes care of me. She is always there at any time I need her. She knows me more than anyone else.

Teacher: Joni Lanfield

Kelang Anterea   Grade: 03
My mom is great. She's sweet as she can be. When I need some help, I know she's always there for me.

Rane Dongworth   **Grade: 03**
My mom's eyes sparkle like moonlight. She sounds like a bird singing in my ear. Her smile shines like a diamond.

Brandon Escoto   **Grade: 03**
My ,mom is as beautiful as a star. Her eyes shine like the sun. Her lips taste like a rose; her face like a flower.

Julian Escutia   Grade: 03
My mom is special. She sparkles like the sun. Her eyes shine like the full moon. She wakes up and the birds sing.

Giselle Gayosso   **Grade: 03**
My mom is so pretty. She shines like the sun. She glows like the moon. She is beautiful.

Miguel Guardado   Grade: 03
My mom deserves a diamond because she is sweet. Her eyes shine like the moonlight. She is as beautiful as a butterfly.

Samantha Shepard   **Grade: 03**
Her eyes sparkle in the light. She is so beautiful and kind. My oh my, she shines like a star! I love mom very much.

Joan Toledo   Grade: 03
Your love is all I need. I see a thousand sunsets. Beautiful, loving and kind. I love you, Mom.

Teacher: Lori Shepler

Vinny Clements   **Grade: 03**
My mom deserves a diamond because her heart glistens and her teeth glow.

Evelyn Garcia   Grade: 03
My mom deserves a diamond because she shines like one when she's happy. My mom is a great person. She deserves a diamond.

Sienna Hume   Grade: 03
My mom is the best. She sparkles like a diamond. She is like a red rose that grows when it snows.

Anthony Morales   Grade: 03
My mom deserves a diamond because her hands protected and are for me for eight years. My mom's heart is a crystal.

Alderwood Basic Plus Elementary
Irvine

Teacher: Dan Grubb

Jordan Barbieri   Grade: 06
Her eyes twinkle like the sky, brighter than the stars at night. Her hair waves like shiny gold. Her voice is melody in my soul.

Tyler Doan   Grade: 06
Her eyes sparkle like a moonlit sea. Her smiles are like a cup of hot tea. There is nothing more important to me.

Anjani Iman   Grade: 06
My delightful mother, for sure, cherishes and cares, loves and hugs, kisses and always misses when we're apart. My extraordinary, admirable mother cannot be beat!

Teacher: Peggy Landon-Koustik

Yauss Agahi   Grade: 06
My mom is an angel on Earth. Her smile is breathless, her eyes pure diamonds. You would be in heaven to believe she is yours.

Suea Andersson   Grade: 06
Love, soft like a pillow. Tall and dainty like a willow. My mother is great to me, she lets my soul be safe and free.

Naria Quazi   Grade: 06
My mother is intensely bright, she shines like the most radiant star. The light of my sky, her brilliant rays guide me through the night.

Teacher: StefanieSacket-Mowers

Nitya Bhardwaj   Grade: 06
She holds my hand every step of the way, telling me everything's going to be okay. Just like a diamond, our bond will last forever.

Alex Dao   Grade: 06
She sparkles with love and glistens with compassion. Through time she made me see what life is meant to be. I'll always love my mom.

Alysse LeFevre   Grade: 06
Her eyes shine like Heaven above, her spirit makes her glow. The melody of her voice, flows through my soul.

Monica Son   Grade: 06
Her eyes twinkle like there's a dark world with one glistening moon. Her smiles are so flawless like a shining sun. Best of all, she cares.

Jerin Tomy   Grade: 06
A caring hand, a gentle feel. A loving face, shining in appeal. A protecting hug, a quiet kiss. I love my mom with endless bliss.

Kevin Yen   Grade: 06
Bright as stars, fresh cookies in jars, her twinkling eyes remind me of sings. About life, give us no strife. The star in my path.

Aliso Niguel High
Aliso Viejo

Teacher: Diane Kent

Aislinn Anaya   Grade: 10
She's like a lily. Always bright. Her petals are never sad and her smell is so good. She never dies down. My flower, Elsa.

Chase Anderson   Grade: 10
My mom cares for me. She take much pride in what she does. I know that she would do anything for me. I love her.

Julie Artemov   Grade: 10
Eyes behind her head, feet that don't rest and helping hands. Nurturing care that heals all wounds. Hair of gold to match her heart.

Edward Bennett   Grade: 10
Hardest working woman I know. Most loving mother I've ever known. She takes me from place to place and really deserves a diamond one day.

Jason Borras   Grade: 10
My mother is my hero. She's a single parent with two children. We have been through the best and worst. My mother deserves a diamond.

Katie Brantley   Grade: 10
Without you, how could I be? Lost along a darkened sea. All I know is that to me, your love and support have made thee.

Austin Burkett   Grade: 10
My mom has been with me, through good and bad times. She has a heart of gold. Nobody, could ever replace her in my heart.

Alexis Colacchio   Grade: 10
For who I love and care for. Love me unconditionally. The thought of her love for me. Overwhelming… No, but instead, embraced into my heart.

Nieko Decker   Grade: 10
My mom deserves a diamond. She's always there for me. Feeds and watches me, and no one can replace her. I love her too much.

Vincent Dominguez   Grade: 10
My mom deserves a diamond because she is the nicest, sweetest person in the world. She always thinks of others and puts herself last always.

Raynee Donaldson   Grade: 10
She gives you light in darkness, love when you feel unloved. When you're weak, she makes you strong. Her love the best love you'll have.

Toni Dymon   Grade: 10
My mom is not just an ordinary mom. She is my best friend, my provider, and someone I will always be there for me.

Omar Ellaboudy   Grade: 10
My mom is very helpful and supportive. Whenever I need her help or support, she's always there to provide whatever I need.

Benny Garcia   Grade: 10
If one person deserved a diamond, it would be my mom. Everything she does for me. She's caring, loving and all around an amazing person.

Kevin Gomez   Grade: 10
Sacrifice is all she has ever done. She gave her family an unforgettable life. My mom deserves a diamond and everything in the whole world.

Krista Green   Grade: 10
My mom means everything to me. She has made the world a better place. Perfect in every way, making me who I am today.

Hannah Haboian   Grade: 10
She loves and cares about me. She will help me whenever I need help. Without her, I wouldn't be who I am. She's my mom.

Johnny Hallam Grade: 10
Wakeboarding, snowboarding, and surfing is fun. However, my mom is better than the sun, and her smile lights up the sky. Shining brightly like stars.

Gerrit Hill Grade: 10
Ever since I was born, you've loved and cared for me. Every day and night, you deserve so much from me. I'll love you forever.

Maxi Jones **Grade: 10**
A heart filled with love, a mind filled with wisdom. My mom beams with a smile and laughter is always near. Her support never ends.

Amanda Kachevas Grade: 10
Always has a bright big smile. Never strict, yet always keeps her kids in check. Never thinks about herself, only the things that help others.

Sara Lacson Grade: 10
Mom, my best friend, she deserves many things, not just a diamond. All that she has done and gave up, she deserves anything she wants.

Taylor Lajoie Grade: 10
My mom never stops loving me. The best, most caring, loving and all. She loves me, heals me, supports me and cries for me.

Ziching Lim **Grade: 10**
Outrageously stunning, precious and clean cut, not worth losing or ignoring for life. So important I can't live without. She is my loving mother.

Jessie Mancilla **Grade: 10**
A garden in her heart. Where precious memories grow. Simple, yet unique. Mother always knows. A place in her life, she calls me her own.

Vivian Meisami Grade: 10
No ,matter what, mom is always there, always so happy, loving and caring. She gives so much. Wouldn't trade her for anything in the world!

Amanda Monteleone **Grade: 10**
You are more than a mom, and unique in every aspect. Light shines through you, such a strong, loving, amazing person. My best friend.

Hayley Mueller Grade: 10
Motherly touch, lovable personality, extremely outgoing, fun to be around. A mother, wife, friend, a hero. Without her, everyone's life would not be the same.

Dana Mullaney **Grade: 10**
Understanding and loving, beautiful and wise, protective and angelic. Affection never dies. Providing my welfare, necessities and care. You're my inspiration. Mom, you're always there.

Axel Navarro Grade: 10
My mom is amazing and fun, she works very hard and is loving, she is caring and understanding, I will always love you mom.

Hayley Noll Grade: 10
Always cleaning the house with a smile on her face. She puts us before herself. In the end, my mom deserves more than a diamond.

Kamran Qadeer Grade: 10
A shiny new diamond. Boy, does she deserve it. Helping others before serving herself. Homemade cooking every night. Her vibrant caring eyes. Likewise that diamond.

Marcia Rocha **Grade: 10**
Looking up at your smile, everything's okay. You look down to me and give me the strength of the day. Amazement, love, comfort and home.

Zachary Rosas Grade: 10
My mother is a diamond for her never ending sacrifice. Her underlying love is forever like a diamond shining bright.

Michelle Ruiz **Grade: 10**
My mom helps me to succeed. When I need her and being the best she can be.

Emily Shapland **Grade: 10**
Kind, respectful and honest woman. An angel from above. A strong, hardworking, single parent. She fills me with her love. My hero, savior, my mom.

Phillip Spitler Grade: 10
My mom is amazing. She has a heart as big as the sun. She has raised three boys on her own. She has sacrificed everything!

Lauren Thayer Grade: 10
She's like a mystery to me, my mother. Chestnuts and creams abound her face, like candy. Yet, her heart and mind are spicy… like cinnamon.

Robert Valdez Grade: 10
My mom goes all out for the family. Gives 100% and more at work. Proud of herself. Never asks for anything, she deserves a diamond.

Scott Wendy Grade: 10
Every tumble, you came through. Helped raise me to be the man I was meant to be. No diamond equates to you, you still sparkle!

Chloe Xoza Grade: 10
Lovingly brought me to this world, taught me everything I know, so selfless she'd give anything to make me smile, she's always there for me.

Conrad Zimmer **Grade: 10**
Unexpressed it hides, never seen by her. I really do appreciate, I really do love her. If only I told her, I loved you more.

Malcolm Brown **Grade: 11**
Delicate flower of grandeur and grace. This is my mother , ma mere, le fleur. Anyway you say it, she is beautiful like a diamond. Love.

Morgan Williams **Grade: 11**
A diamond has many facets, my mother, too. For she cares, wonders and hopes. She's tough, yet kind. Diamonds are forever and so is she!

Aliso Viejo Middle School
Aliso Viejo

Teacher: Sally Engelhardt

Sara Beygi Grade: 06
Diamonds are long-lasting and so is her love. I think she was sent from Heaven above to shower us with her everlasting love.

Will Hickson Grade: 06
Moms are the help we need in school, the soul in our heart, the strength in our knowledge, the extra push we need in life.

Manue Lopez **Grade: 06**
Hard working like a builder, sweeter than sugar, encouraging like a leader, smart like a teacher. Those are the things that make up my mom!

Brian Moore Grade: 06
My mom's eyes like twinkling stars in the night. My mom's heart as big as Jupiter. My mom, worth more than any diamond.

Crystal Ramos Grade: 06
I don't say "I love you" enough to my mom. She says it to me in any way possible. I love you mom.

*

Most Frequently Used Words

Look what we found by plugging the 2007 winning entries into the computer. If this contest were limited to one word it would be *love*, for this word showed up 2,288 times. Here are some selected words and the frequency in which they occur.

Compiled by Alicia Giersch.

Top 5 words

Love	2,288
Eyes	793
Heart	661
Beautiful	588
Smile	320

Moms in the kitchen

Candy	44
Chocolate	31
Cupcake	5
Lollipop	2
Pumpkin	2
Bubblegum	1
Chestnuts	1
Gobstopper	1
Krispy Kreme	1
Meatloaf	1
Pepperoni	1
Beef Stroganoff	1

Moms in Nature

Butterfly	65
Dove	43
Ladybug	5
Dragonflies	2
Antelope	1
Ferret	1
Flamingo	1
Koala	1
King Kong	1
Lovebird	1
Mink	1
Unicorn	1

Anatomy 101

Eyes	821
Heart	675
Smile	320
Hands	39
Arms	32

Lips	24
Teeth	17
Ears	9
Toes	5
Ankle	1

Physical affection

hug	100
kiss	68
touch	57
spank	1

Moms in Space

Sun	304
Stars	215
Sky	186
Moon	98
Universe	28
Galaxy	13
Mars	13

The many professions of Mom

Angel	266
Queen	27
Cook	16
Clown	9
Princess	6
Doctor	5
Chef	4
Superhero	3
Driver	3
Encyclopedia	3
Mermaid	3
Healer	2
Comedian	2
Judge	2
Scientist	2
Painter	2
Actress	1
Advisor	1
Artist	1

Athlete	1
Author	1
Baker	1
Ballerina	1
Braider	1
Caregiver	1
Caretaker	1
Chauffer	1
Cinderella	1
Coach	1
Counselor	1
Disciplinarian	1
Firefighter	1
Gardner	1
Magician	1
Maid	1
Mathematician	1
Officer	1
Pitcher	1
President	1
Seamstress	1
Therapist	1
Traveler	1
Trooper	1
Tutor	1

Moms around the World

World	196
Ocean	77
Sea	49
Paradise	4
Exotic	2
Battlefield	1
Congo	1

Moms as Plants

Rose	152
Sunflower	7
Daisy	7
Orchid	2
Petunia	1

Precious Objects		Beautiful Mom!			
gold	106	beautiful	588	patient	48
jewel	65	sweet	329	compassionate	37
gem	36	gentle	210	intelligent	33
ruby	15	friend	200	graceful	30
pearl	12	happy	155	gorgeous	21
sapphire	11	wonderful	24	amazing	17
emerald	6	fun or funny	116	awesome	17
		generous	61	goddess	8
				supermodel	1

Which Winner Said This?

She is as brave as a noble dragon.

I love her like Oreos love milk and tuna loves mayonnaise.

Her hugs feel like you swallowed a gulp of hot soup

She's my saddle on my horse. She keeps me on my course.

She is a magician in the kitchen.

She sparkles like a fireball of prettiness.

Her face hangs in my gallery of art.

Her eyes are lagoons of love.

A music note; tall lean and elegant.

When I came out of her tummy she was so beautiful.

My mom is the ketchup on my hotdog, the pickles on my hamburger, and the parmesan cheese on my pasta. She is my favorite condiment.

She is as alert as an alarm clock.

Her long blonde hair is like a river of love.

I'm the pie, she's the baker. She's the god, I'm the priest.

Sometimes she's a sloth sleeping quietly.

Like a dog, fast and fearless. Mom, a wall, hard but cracking down.

A child at heart. Instead of making my lunch, she plays with the puppy.

She says loving a teenager is like loving a cactus.

She's the fluff in my pillow.

She can end world hunger with her fajitas.

Like the earth, she keeps me grounded.

She gave up her fun and young life to be a mother.

She is as good a cook as McDonalds.

Hardworking like a volcano, pushing lava up to erupt with love.

She jumps on the trampoline and my next door neighbor's mom doesn't.

She supplies me with food, water, and other things I need for special occasions.

She always makes sure we have plenty of clothes and food on the table.

Christian Rios   Grade: 06
My mom is the one who complete me, loves me, cares for me, and the one who will permanently be at hand for me.

Andrew Zapala   Grade: 06
My mom deserves a diamond. She lets my roots grow and makes perfect decisions for me, so I can grow into a nice flower.

Sarah Zia   Grade: 06
Mom is one of a kind, irrespective of events of time. She takes care of me day and night, in my gloom, she's my sunlight.

Ambuehl (Harold) Elemen.
San Juan Capistrano

Teacher: Heidi Caestecker

William Burks   Grade: 02
My mom deserves a diamond. She brings my lunchbox if I forget it. She even brings me to school on time everyday.

Shane Gerrity   Grade: 02
My mom should get a diamond because she keeps a roof over our heads. When I'm sick, she takes good care and give me medicine.

Rachel Hall   Grade: 02
The reason my mommy deserves a diamond is she always keeps me company and plays with me too. And whenever I'm sad, she comforts me.

Mabel Keeler   Grade: 02
My mom deserves a diamond because she is kind and caring and special. She's the best mom I could ever have.

Jonathan Khachadoorian   Grade: 02
I think my mom deserves a diamond because she is very special to me, and I love her.

Ashlee Stoffel   Grade: 02
My mom deserves a diamond because her eyes sparkle like a diamond. She kisses me and tucks me in. My mom deserves a diamond.

Allison Teas   Grade: 02
My mom is very loving and sweet. She brings happiness to my family. I love my mom so much just like a rose.

Teacher: Marilee Carroll

Gustavo Barajas   Grade: 03
My mom smells like a beautiful flower in the sky. She sparkles like stars. My mom is the best mom I could ever have!

Grace Bologna   Grade: 03
Glowing light breeze, that's my mom. Her eyes are like the dew on a daffodil. An intelligent lady. She is the love of my life!

Morgan Creek   Grade: 03
She's calm like the still sea. Her eyes sparkle like an amethyst in the sunlight with dew drops. Perfect in every way! I love my mom!

Angel Dominguez   Grade: 03
You're always there for me when I need you in my life. You're the gem, the shining stars in the night. She knows no hate.

Joshua Eck   Grade: 03
My mom is like the moon and the stars. She fills my heart with love. I love my mom!

Emily Friess   Grade: 03
She's Mother Earth to me. Her love is as powerful as five burning red suns. You can find her in Heaven. She is an angel.

Kameryn Laureano   Grade: 03
Glistens like the shimmering moon, mystical and compassionate describes you. Majestically as a queen, she is a stupendous enchanted mom!

Kailynn Martinez   Grade: 03
My mom is my moon glistening through the night. My mom is my heart. She's my world to me. I love my marvelous mom.

Chase Rettberg   Grade: 03
Mom is dazzling and cuddles best in the world. She loves me very much and talks softly. My mom sparkles like the stars.

Madyson Siu   Grade: 03
An enchanted rose, shaped as a sapphire. Her heart is made of gold and she glistened like a gemstone. She is the love of my life.

Danielle Stockton   Grade: 03
She's a beautiful rose, river of love, angel of gold. She has sapphire eyes and owns the colors of my life. My mom is exquisite.

Teacher: Suzanne Devaney

Amir-Hadi Boroumand   Grade: 01
My mom's eyes are a diamond of joy. I love my mom even if she is mad at me. My mom's heart beat is so big!

Tommi Carvalho   Grade: 01
I love her and she makes my eyes sparkle. Her heart sparkles in my eyes. My mom's skin is as beautiful as snow.

Gage Doble   Grade: 01
My mom's eyes are like diamonds. Her voice is calming like running water. Her skin feels like a soft blanket. I love her.

Ella Friess   Grade: 01
My mom is a big diamond to me. I think her sparkling eyes are so beautiful. My mom deserves a diamond.

Taylor Kellermann   Grade: 01
She makes my eyes glitter. She is the best. She is the diamond of my heart. She is my mom forever.

Nicole Leick   Grade: 01
She has beautiful sparkling eyes like jewelry and gold. She makes my eyes sparkle like a dragon's wing. My mom is as sweet as a cherry.

James Luke   Grade: 01
My mom's heart is like gold. Her eyes are like the ocean. She brings me joy.

Isaiah Matthews   Grade: 01
When I look into my mom's eyes they sparkle so much. They look like a diamond.

Madison Smith   Grade: 01
She is beautiful and makes my heart sing. I love her, she makes me happy.

Teacher: Victoria Goodhue

Cameron Aroz   Grade: 03
My mom's eyes shine like the sun shining down at me. Her heart is as big as a lake. She is as lovely as a gem!

Evan Aswegan   Grade: 03
My mom is so playful, loving and hilarious too. I can hear her laughter in my heart which will always remind me of her.

McKenzy Church   Grade: 03
My mom is a gem to me because she is not like anyone else. She has a golden heart as big as the world!

Louis Harden   Grade: 03
Her eyes blaze like the sun. She's as gentle as a butterfly landing on the ground. I would be nothing without my mom. She's amazing!

Kaleb Marschall   Grade: 03
My mom is as gentle as a flower petal. She is always joyful to everyone in our family. My mom deserves a diamond!

Kayla Mazzotti   Grade: 03
She is as dazzling as a gem, humorous as a comedian and sweet as a candy apple. That's my mom!

Madison Sedgewick   Grade: 03
My gorgeous mom is like a brilliant diamond! When it comes to homework, she is ingenious. It's delightful to have her around!

Brianna Urrutia   Grade: 03
She's thoughtful, kind and cheerful. I love her and she's so important to me. Her laughs are music to my ears. What a marvelous mother.

Linnea Wright   Grade: 03
She's the apple of my eye. Busy like a bee. She cares about me. When I cry, I sleep with her. Gorgeous like a diamond.

Teacher: Jennifer Sullivan

Jarrod Baldasare   Grade: 04
Dark hazel eyes stare into my eyes. Sunshine reflects off her smile. Moonlight shines upon her hair. She's as lovely as an angel.

Naomi Burks   Grade: 04
Her sparkling brown eyes gaze at me like the warmth of the sun. Her wavy black hair is like a dark pool of love.

Serenity Church   Grade: 04
A face like an angel, hair like the sparkling snow, tears filled with joy. She is the diamond that guides me through my life.

Jacob Dahl   Grade: 04
My mom is loving. Her eyes are glowing. She fills everyone with joy. She is a very wonderful mom.

Haley Dorris   Grade: 04
Flawless, sparkling eyes in the summer light, heart made of pure gold, brown eyes a brilliant sight, a touch of her skin soothes my soul.

David Duplissey - DIAMOND   Grade: 04
Eyes glittering with flawless light. Face perfect as an angel. She guides me in wisdom. She is my encouraging branch. She's my gem of life.

Chase Gustafson   Grade: 04
She has a joyful smile and shiny hair that glistens. Her heart is like a gleaming gem. Mom guides me through tough times.

Kendall Kupferberg   Grade: 04
Soft laugh, sparkling eyes…when she gazes at me, if fills my heart with love. She is the diamond sent from Heaven above.

Carson Marchello   Grade: 04
Eyes shining like a bluebird. She guides me with her wisdom. She's the one that makes me a better person. She's my mom forever.

Grace McCurdy   Grade: 04
Her loving, warm laughter fills the air. Her fun, caring words make me want to fly. She is the one that makes stand high. Mom.

Jon Erik Moyles   Grade: 04
Her safe, cozy hugs offer me warmth. Her sparkling, glimmering brown eyes always watch out for me. She's my shining star.

Riley Murphy   Grade: 04
I know a girl…crystal brown eyes, hair like spun gold, a warm loving smile. She makes me feel like Heaven. She makes me whole.

Alexis Ortiz   Grade: 04
Her radiant heart wakes up the sun. Her sweet smile shines like the moon in the sky. She is my Mother Earth.

Juam Ramirez   Grade: 04
My number one mom…you fill my heart with love. I feel safe and sound with you by my side. My mom, my love!

Braeden Schmitt   Grade: 04
Her loving, peaceful hugs warm me. Her eyes are like the shining star that guides me. She's the crystal of my heart.

Katya Vazquez   Grade: 04
You are the sunshine of my heart. Your eyes shine like a glimmering star. Your sparkling smile makes me giggle. You are the joy in my life.

Rayna Wright   Grade: 04
You are loving as the wind whispers "Mama". Your beautiful smile in the morning brings the shiny sun to warm me. I love you, Mama.

Andersen (Roy O.) Ele.
Newport Beach

Teacher: Tim Reese

Catherine Black   Grade: 04
Eyes that twinkle in the sunlight, a heart so caring for others. Yes, that's my mother! And yes, I love her!

Christopher Cottrell   Grade: 04
My mom is beautiful like the heavens. Her heart is full of love. When a shooting star falls, I think it's my mom from Heaven.

Madelyn Deverian   Grade: 04
My mom deserves a diamond. When she puts me to bed and turns around and says good night, my heart is filled with love.

Maddie Green   Grade: 04
My mom deserves a diamond because she is the best mom ever! She helps me with my homework and anything else I need help on!

Lisa Hamilton   Grade: 04
My mom flows into my heart and soul, just like a flawless river of gold. She brightens up my life, just like a beautiful morning light.

Kyle Hatch   Grade: 04
My mom has a heart that shines like the sun and a face that sparkles like a diamond.

Jordan Lamb   Grade: 04
My mom is a hardworking woman, if you know her. At night, when she tucks us in, she kisses me on the forehead.

Quinn McCardle   Grade: 04
She's always up late taking care of our family. No matter how tired she is, she has a smile so gorgeous that it brings smiles to all.

Elizabeth McKenzie   Grade: 04
My mom is pretty and she's nice. She helps me with my work. I love the twinkle in her eyes. They always make me smile.

Kate Ramm   Grade: 04
My mom's hart is made of gold. Her soul is as bright as a star. She loves her kids and her husband.

Layson Savant   Grade: 04
I would see her eyes sparkle in the reflection. I would hear her heart beat with love. I would feel the comfort of her love.

Paige Solaas   Grade: 04
When I see my mom, I feel warm and soft. I hug her and my soul is comforted with love. I feel loved by her.

* Amethyst winners in bold.

Anderson Elem. (H. B.)
Garden Grove

Teacher: Juliann Dodosh

Maria Alvarez — Grade: 06
Your eyes are as black as the night sky. Your heart is as red as a cherry. But, your love is as big as the Earth.

Vanessa Mondragon — Grade: 06
You're the master of all tasks, your arms are open when I'm blue. I love you so much, I want to be just like you.

Julie Phoummavanh — Grade: 06
My mom shines like a diamond, shaped in so many ways. Her smile, her kisses, her laughter puts a smile on my face everyday.

Alexya Salcedo — Grade: 06
When I see my mother, I feel sunshine through my body. She makes me feel warm in my heart. Yes, my mother is the best!

Teacher: Dana Eber

Laura Cruz — Grade: 04
My mom's eyes twinkle, her lips are luminous. My mom's heart is generous, it is attractive and her hugs are a ring of love.

Bao Dinh — Grade: 04
My mom is wise as a teacher. Like a diamond, my mom is gorgeous. Like a diamond, my mom is bright

Daywna Giron — Grade: 04
My mother's love is forever. Her eyes shimmer and sparkle like a diamond. Her hair is as yellow as the sun.

Melissa Gomez — Grade: 04
My mom shines like the moon. Her eyes are like the stars and she looks like a gorgeous diamond. I love her like a star.

Ann Gutierrez — Grade: 04
My mother is made out of love and kindness. Her eyes gleam like two diamonds twinkling in the sky. She fills my heart with warmth.

Sophia Hoang — Grade: 04
Her eyes twinkle like sunlight. She talks with full compassion. My mother always brightens my life. She is always gleaming like the moon and sun.

Angel Lopez — Grade: 04
My mom is radiant. Her eyes twinkle like the stars. My mom is as pretty as a rose. Her heart is bright like the sunlight.

Michelle Maya — Grade: 04
My mom is as luminous as the sun and as faithful as the moon. She is trusting like an angel and brilliant like polished gold.

Tommy Nguyen — Grade: 04
My mom is so precious. The most incredible mom you'll ever find. She works hard for me. So she has a sparkling personality.

Peter Nguyen — Grade: 04
My mom's eyes are luminous that they light my life. My mom's heart shines like crystal. She has compassion. She loves me with her heart.

Alexis Nunes — Grade: 04
My mom shines like a diamond in the night sky. When I see the sky, I can see her gorgeous eyes. She smells like roses.

Tylor Pham — Grade: 04
My mom is like a diamond and her love is forever. Her eyes sparkle like the shining sun. Her heart is like the lovely diamond.

Agustin Ramirez — Grade: 04
My mom's eyes are luminous and she is radiant all day. She is fascinating and her black hair shines like her eyes.

Lizbeth Valencia — Grade: 04
My mom is as luminous as the morning sun. My mom is special. When my stars at dawn, she shines, at night, she twinkles.

Teacher: Mary Ferraro

Yesenia Flores — Grade: 05
"Mother" is such a simple word, but to me the meaning is seldom heard. For everything I am today, my mother's love showed me the way.

Priscilla Le — Grade: 05
Your smile brings hope. Your eyes bring truth. Your heart brings love, pure and true. All the essentials to a true mom.

Michelle Nguyen — Grade: 05
Her heart shines as the sun. Her eyes twinkle as the stars. She's the gem of flawless ideas. That will never run out of delightment.

Howard Quach — Grade: 05
My mom is the light of my life. The light that cares for me. She works to give me life, and will shine for eternity.

Alize Smith — Grade: 05
My mom is a star shining in the night sky, she makes my soul glow, I love looking in her eyes.

Teacher: Franny Landman

Sean Ho — Grade: 05
Her face shines in the morning sun. Her voice sounds like nature's song. She makes me feel better when I'm sad. She is my mom.

Nikki Jimenez — Grade: 05
Mom is sweet and pretty too, like a diamond in my little view. She is shiny and bright. Mom, the diamond in ,my little view.

Dorothy Luong — Grade: 05
In the light, your eyes shine. Your heart, as pure as gold. Your love for me is very divine because you are my mother.

Tin Nguyen — Grade: 05
The earth is big, wonderful and old, but not as big and wonderful as my mom's heart of gold.

Jasmine Nguyen — Grade: 05
Her eyes shine like two diamond rings. Her jewels shine brightly in the sun. Her beauty makes most jewels melt. She is my mommy.

Chris Parrish — Grade: 05
A star lights her eyes. I see a diamond in the sky. Her mouth melts into gems of love. She's beautiful like the sky above.

Alvis Pham — Grade: 05
Crystals shine and diamonds glitter just like my mom's glistening eyes. Music is smooth, cotton is soft and so is my mom's beautiful voice.

Anthony (Susan B.) Ele.
Westminster

Teacher: Michelle Hanson

Quynh Ngan Le — Grade: 01
My mom should get a diamond because she is a doctor. She gets my tooth out.

Melissa Sanchez — Grade: 01
She is nice. She helps people. My mom is nice to me. My mom is beautiful.

Lillian Thao — Grade: 01
My mom should get a diamond because she is smart and tells us what to do.

Chloe Tran — Grade: 01
Mommy, gorgeous long hair, loving, proud, cheerful, magnificent.

Teacher: Carolyn Kim

Gerardo Alvarez   Grade: 01
My mom should get a diamond because she is helpful. She is helpful because she loves me so much.

Lan Do   Grade: 01
My mom should get a diamond because she helps me when I do something wrong. I love her very much.

Sopha Ngo   Grade: 01
My mom should win a diamond because when I fall and I have a boo boo on my lap, she cares for me. I love my mom.

Kyle Nguyen   Grade: 01
My mom should get a diamond because she works hard and she is honest and helpful and nice. I love my mom a lot.

Jenny Nong   Grade: 01
My mom should get a diamond because she cooks good fish. She is very helpful. She loves me a lot.

Anne Pham   Grade: 01
My mom should get a diamond because she is helpful. She is nice. She is hard working. She is the best mom.

Marianna Ramos   **Grade: 01**
My mommy cooks for me and she really loves me. My mom is very beautiful, I love my mom.

Katrina Sam   Grade: 01
My mom should get a diamond because she is hard working and she is helpful because she cooks food for me and I love her.

Destiny Vieyra   Grade: 01
My mommy should get a diamond because she makes the best spaghetti.

McKenzie Williams   Grade: 01
My mommy should get a diamond because she works hard in school. I love her.

Teacher: Michele Stevens

Phuc Huynh   Grade: 01
Mommy, black hair and short, cheerful, helpful, giving, loving, kind, caring, special.

James Mau   **Grade: 01**
Mom, red hair is beautiful, loving, proud, caring, incredible.

Kayla Pham   Grade: 01
My mom is nice. My mom loves me. My mom is pretty, pretty. My mom is cute.

Aborland Montessori
Fullerton

Teacher: Marty Shepard

Justin Oh   Grade: 01
My mom loves diamonds and her eyes sparkle like jewelry. She always gets a gift from me because she is special. That's my great mom!

Paula Sanchez   **Grade: 01**
My mom is like a diamond heart. She's graceful like an angel. She's kind and says I love you, sweetheart. She's my best mom!

Meilana Valdez   Grade: 01
My mom is special. My mom loves me. My mom is a special gift that I love very much.

Priscilla Truon   **Grade: 02**
She is more than a diamond, she fills my heart. Her eyes shine like stars. She is my mom, the most beautiful person on Earth.

Franki Ysais   **Grade: 02**
My mom is like a diamond. She's so pretty. Her eyes sparkle when she make me dinner. She loves me and I always hugs her.

Nikita Lad   Grade: 03
My mom's hair is like silk. She lets me help her clean. She reads me a book and puts me to sleep. I love her.

Nathan Sebial   **Grade: 03**
My mom is like a precious diamond, because my mom helps me on my homework. My mom cares for me. She's a gift from above.

Samantha Van Praet   **Grade: 03**
My mom is my good luck charm. Whenever I'm upset, she'll cheer me up. She's always there for me. She is my heart.

Teacher: Cynthia Van Praet

Danyal Mohammad   **Grade: 01**
My mom's hair looks like a chocolate fountain. Her eyes look like hot cocoa. She always smells like grapes. I'm glad she's with me forever.

Justina Guo   Grade: 02
My mom's eyes sparkle like glitter. My mom helps me in math. She smells like roses. I love her more than my favorite toy.

Meredith Liou   Grade: 02
Her face is like a beautiful rose. She checks my homework everyday. My mom is my angel from heaven. She is the best.

Elijah Collins   Grade: 03
My granny is my mom. She watches me play football. She makes the best tacos. She smells like sweet cinnamon. I love her.

Justine Lin   Grade: 03
My mom's hair is as soft as my pillow. Her smile shines in the sun. I love my mom. I will never leave her.

Arianna Lopez   Grade: 03
My mom comforts me when I'm scared. Her hugs are warm and cozy. Her skin is as soft as a blooming rose. I love her.

Derek Min   Grade: 03
My mom's eyes are like dark chocolate. Her hair is soft like cotton. She smells like a garden of roses. I love her.

Harrison Quinn   **Grade: 03**
My mom's eyes sparkle like fireworks in the night sky. Her teeth glow like diamonds in a treasure chest. I love you Mom.

Arovista Elementary
Brea

Teacher: Laurie Brown

Jorge Altamirano   **Grade: 05**
My mom is like the rising full moon, beautiful and pretty. Her eyes shine like it too. And that's why my mom deserves a diamond.

Zachary Arnold   **Grade: 05**
My mom is very thoughtful, always cheers me on, and encourages me to succeed. She is ravishing and is always there for me lovingly.

Danielle Bauer   Grade: 05
My mom is the nicest, most helpful, and kindest mom ever. She is very caring. Her eyes sparkle like stars. She deserves a diamond.

Dustin Buell   Grade: 05
My mom deserves a diamond because she does just about everything for me. She is giving, caring, loving and the greatest mom ever.

Jada Gutierrez   **Grade: 05**
My mom deserves a diamond because she gives me a warm home. When she kisses me goodnight, you can see a diamond in her eyes.

Michael Hannum   **Grade: 05**
There is a stunning lady, she is dazzling daily. She loves me a bunch though. I'm a bit much, this great lady is my mom.

* Amethyst winners in bold.

Sophia Lincoln Grade: 05
My mom is a gem. Her smile is as bright as a diamond. She's as precious as a pearl with a loving heart.

Maxwell Menzies Grade: 05
My mom is a beacon of light. In my dark times, she leads me to love. If I'm in despair, she shines up my day.

Jose Rodriguez Grade: 05
I think my mom is loving, caring, and absolutely awesome. She is the best mom in the world. That's why she deserves a diamond.

Linda Ruiz Grade: 05
My mom deserves a diamond because she is beautiful. My mom has pretty eyes. She is a diamond. That's why she deserves a precious gem.

Ryan Sims Grade: 05
My mom's caring. She's always sharing. Her kisses are as soft as a feather pillow, and her hair is as straight as an arrow.

Zachary Tellez Grade: 05
My mom deserves a diamond because she is so sweet. Her kisses are like candy, sweeter than syrup. I love my beautiful mom.

Eli Wheaton Grade: 05
My mom deserves a diamond because she is the world's greatest mom to me. She is loving and generous. She is also a genius.

Teacher: Leslie Corbett

Constance Bravo Grade: 04
My mom, her eyes sparkle like a star. I thank her for all she does for me. Her smile is so shiny, I get blinded.

Abigail Foster Grade: 04
Mom is everything to me. She's like a shining star that everyone should meet. That's why she's a great mother to me.

Duke Hansen Grade: 04
My mom is very sweet. My mom is very kind. It's hard to find a mom like mine. She's one of a kind.

Julia Robles Grade: 04
My mother is sweet and charming too. My mother is special and shines like light too! I love you, Mom.

Mark Toriz Grade: 04
My mom's smile sparkles in the light, along with her sweet smile. Her hugs always make me feel better, whenever I feel sad.

Teacher: Debbie Hathaway

Miranda Martinez Grade: 02
My lovely mother deserves a diamond because she shines like sparkly sparkles. And she always makes me dinner. My mom is kind to me.

Athena Molina Grade: 02
My lovely mother deserves a diamond because she sparkles like a star. She is my hero because she is the best. I love my mom.

Alexa Worthy Grade: 02
My angel mother deserves a diamond because she is a loving and caring mother.

Teacher: Nicole Lanfranco

Ernesto Castruita Grade: 04
Your eyes are like the sparkling moon, your hair is like a jet black diamond, your heart is pure beauty. You're my one and only mom.

McKenna Duffy Grade: 04
Her eyes sparkle like a sparkling moon. Her hands feel as soft as silk, she's a loving person whose love never ends. She's my mom.

Anahi Garcia Grade: 04
Her hair is like wind, her smile is so warm, you look at her, you could tell she's nice, and you could trust her, Mom!

Kaitlyn Garcia Grade: 04
M for my best friend. O for on my side. M for my beautiful mom. I think my mom deserves this diamond because she's one.

Ethan Lee Grade: 04
Her hair gleams in the sun. Together we have fun. If I'm down, she'll help me feel better. Her eyes sparkle in bad weather. Mom.

Lucero Ramirez Grade: 04
Her eyes are as shiny star, she is the most beautiful mom and she is also kind and nice. She is my mom.

Garrett Rias Grade: 04
Her eyes are like blossoms. Her face is as soft as water. Her hair is like the wind. I love my mother. Mother.

Joshua Ryan Grade: 04
My mom is as beautiful as a rose. Her eyes shine like a star. Every time I see my mom, I love her more.

Matthew Spink Grade: 04
My mom is so special, so happy and true. She makes my life easy, and loves me too!

Matthew Wang Grade: 04
She has hair that looks like the waves of the sea. She has the scent of the flower on the plains. That's my mom!

Teacher: Tammi O' Rourke

Jacob Albee Grade: 02
My mom deserves a diamond because she cares about people. She helps friends and family and takes good care of my brother and I.

Jaeden Barajas Grade: 02
My mom deserves a diamond because she sparkles like one. She's caring and loves me no matter what. I will love my mom forever.

Jack Hannum Grade: 02
My mom deserves a diamond because she is very pretty and makes the best cookies.

david Jovellanos Grade: 02
My mom is the best. She never lies to me. She loves me. I love her. She takes care of me.

Cameron Legendre Grade: 02
My mom should win a diamond because she is the nicest mom in the whole world. Because she helps us with our homework.

Faith Luevanos Grade: 02
My mom deserves a diamond because her eyes sparkle like one. My mom deserves a diamond because she's careful with rare things.

Robby Moreno Grade: 02
My mom deserves a diamond because she is special, a hardworking mom. Also, she is a good cook.

Joan Neri Grade: 02
My mom deserves a diamond because every time I get stuck on my homework, she helps me. She also gives me lots of love.

Karlie Pascuzzo Grade: 02
My mom should win a diamond because when I'm hurt, she will always be there for me, so special, and I love her. Yes!

Garrison Raine Grade: 02
My mother is like a flower, so pretty who cooks so great and love me forever. She shines like a diamond in my heart.

Kaylee Serna   Grade: 02
My mom deserves a diamond because she is always there when I need her and because she taught me to love and care for others.

Omar Taylor   Grade: 02
My mom deserves a diamond because she is just like one. She is brilliant and she sparkles everyday to me and my family.

Nathan Wyse   Grade: 02
My mom deserves a diamond because she protects me and loves me and she makes me food and does the dishes too. She loves her family.

Kevin Young   Grade: 02
My mom deserves a diamond because she helps to take care of me and makes sure I am safe.

Teacher: Shannon Robles

Colin Ansari   Grade: 04
Mom, you are so pretty. You're just like a blossom. Your hair blows in the wind, just like the leaves.

Lizzy Ilten   Grade: 04
Mom, you are so pretty, your eyes glitter in the sun. Your sweet and really fun, I love you mom!

Dallin Luedte   Grade: 04
My mom is a hero to me. She is pretty and nice, as if she sis charmed. She sparkles. My mom deserves a diamond.

Yesenia Marquez   Grade: 04
Mom , you are so pretty. Your eyes glimmer in the light. You are as sweet as a bee. I love you mom!

Delaney Stewart   Grade: 04
Mom has a star, it's up in the sky. You can see it at night. It's the star next to your heart!

Jordynn Stom   Grade: 04
My mom has eyes like a blue bird. She teaches me how to cook. She helps me with laundry. My mom is graceful. I love mom.

Teacher: Patricia Romero

Will Burgess   Grade: 05
My mom's the best at everything she does. She always loves me, just because!

Evelynn Burt   Grade: 05
Her voice is like the non-stop ocean. Her beauty is like the endless rainbow after a beautiful rain. Her eyes twinkle like the stars.

Ashlee Camacho   Grade: 05
She deserves a diamond for all the care she gives. If you meet her, you will see that she's the perfect mom for me!

Daniel Franz   Grade: 05
I love my mom. Her eyes glisten like jewels. Her love is like an infinity pool. She helps me everyday in each and every way.

Jordan Lomardo   Grade: 05
My mother is gentle like a loving lamb. She's a bubble waiting to burst with love and care! I love my mother.

Summer Wright   Grade: 05
My mom deserves a diamond because she is loving, takes care of me, and listens to me when I have problems to talk about.

Arroyo Elementary
Santa Ana

Teacher: Donna Anderson

Brianna Barragan   Grade: 03
My mommy deserves a diamond because she is hard working, beautiful, kind, caring and sweet. Everyday I thank God for giving me my amazing mommy.

Derek Benjamins   Grade: 03
My mom deserves a diamond because she makes sure that we have food and that we to go bed at 8:00!

Zoe Edwards   Grade: 03
My mom always helps me with homework. She is very careful. She works very hard cleaning and making meals. And she always says she loves me.

Amanda Francis   Grade: 03
I think my mom deserves a diamond because when I need her, she comes for me.

Jack Frodyma   Grade: 03
My mom deserves a diamond because she is wonderful. I love my mom. She takes care of me all the time. I love you!

Hailey Jackson   Grade: 03
My mom is very special to me. She always takes good care of me. She loves me and I love her back. I love my mom.

Issac Woolem   Grade: 03
My mom deserves a diamond because she makes me food when I am hungry, and she makes me feel better when I am sick.

Teacher: Nancy Brucker

Samuel Brown   Grade: 02
My mom deserves a diamond because she helps me with my homework everyday. She is as valuable as a shiny diamond to me!

Trevor Kodzis   Grade: 02
I think my mom deserves a diamond because she is as rare as a diamond. She is as beautiful as a diamond and as precious.

Saige Smith   Grade: 02
My mom deserves a diamond because she is like one. She is hard to find, but she is my very special diamond!

Hayes Wilson   Grade: 02
My mom deserves a diamond because she is very nice. She always backs people up. Also, she is very pretty.

Presley Campbell   Grade: 03
Why does my mom deserve a diamond? She deserves a diamond because she shines like one. She is valuable and rare like one too.

Riley Esterhalt   Grade: 03
My mom deserves a diamond because she cares for me. When I am hurt, she will help me. She helps me with my homework.

Molly O'Brien   Grade: 03
My mom deserves a diamond because she is always caring. She watches out for me. She always helps me, and she always loves me.

Cory Smith   Grade: 03
My mom deserves a diamond because she is nice and caring. She is as beautiful as a diamond. She always helps others.

Teacher: Robin Chillingworth

Mason Dosher   Grade: 02
I love my mom because she is very nice. My mom is very smart. She always cleans all the rooms. My ,mom deserves a diamond.

Theron Genovese   Grade: 02
My mom needs a diamond because she loves me and she does nice things for me. My mom is a sweet mom to me.

Sierra Hughes   Grade: 02
My mom deserves a diamond because she does all the chores in my house and she plays with me. She makes me food to eat.

* Amethyst winners in bold.

Nicollete Maniatis — Grade: 02
My mom deserves a diamond because she's so sweet! My mom is super special. She knows a lot of math. My mom is awesome!

Christopher Mykkanen — Grade: 02
I love my mom because she helps me with homework. I love my mom because she cheers for me at swim meets. I love her.

Lauren Paz — Grade: 02
My mom deserves a diamond because she's so very sweet. She always treats me right.

Salil Tantamjarik — Grade: 02
My mom deserves a diamond because she will always love me. My mom will take me to a lot of places. I love my mom.

Hunter Till — Grade: 02
My mom is sweet and nice. She is awesome. My mom is the best cook in the world. I love her to pieces.

Teacher: Stephanie Lukkes

Liam Beran — Grade: 02
My mother deserves a diamond because she is special. She loves me and takes very good care of me.

Mason Davis — Grade: 02
My mom deserves a diamond because she loves me and takes care of me. I love her so much. I like when she is happy.

Jared Disbrow — Grade: 02
My mom deserves a diamond because she cares for me, and loves my family too. That's why I'd like to give my mom a diamond.

Elizabeth Forkey — Grade: 02
Mother I love, oh, I love her so much. To give my mom a diamond would mean a lot to me! Helpful, Energetic, Really great!

Francesco Nepite-Temblador — Grade: 02
My mom deserves a diamond because she provides for my family and she is always happy!

Justin Soliman — Grade: 02
My mom deserves a diamond because her eyes are like gems! And because she watches over our family and says "You're the best!"

Ruby Tafoya — Grade: 02
My mommy deserves a diamond because she is friendly and polite. She is pretty and takes care of me.

Teacher: Wendy Miller

Sarah Bubier — Grade: 02
My mom is very caring. She protects me. She is thoughtful. She loves my sisters, my brothers, my dad and me at all times.

Colin Chillingworth — Grade: 02
She takes care of me. She makes me breakfast, lunch and dinner. She is the best mom in the world. She makes cool snacks.

Isabella Cisneros — Grade: 02
My mom nurtures me. My mom helps me get better when I'm sick. My mom loves me. My mom is very beautiful.

Zachary Fielding — Grade: 02
She takes good care of me. My mom makes the best dinner ever. She's the best mom in the world.

Scott Leandro — Grade: 02
My mom cares about me and loves me. She takes care of me. She takes me to my favorite restaurant and makes yummy food too.

Eli McKenzie — Grade: 02
She tries her best at everything, especially on her cooking. She always makes us happy when we are sad. She helps us when we are sick.

Riley Osborn — Grade: 02
My mom is so beautiful, smart, helpful, caring and she is the nicest mom in the world. I love my mom!

Emilio Padilla — Grade: 02
She bakes me cookies. She takes care of me. She cleans my room. She also makes a fantastic dinner too. That's why!

Cameron Sotoodeh — Grade: 02
She lets me do the fun things. She does good things to people and me. She is so pretty and beautiful. She loves me so much.

Tyler Warren — Grade: 02
My mom is the best mom in the world! She is very funny! She cleans my room for me. She is outstanding!

Arroyo Vista Elementary
Rancho Santa Margarita

Teacher: Laura Gates

Talia Bernacohi — Grade: 01
My mom's smile makes me feel good. I thank God that she is made. My mom's smile makes me feel better. My mom is loveable.

Ethan Hockman — Grade: 01
My mom's heart warms me up. Her eyes sparkle and shine. She helps me with my homework. I love my mom because she tucks me in.

Sydnie Magala — Grade: 01
My mom is nice. My mom's smile warms my heart. I love when my mom tucks me in. I love my mom. She's the best.

Christopher Patrick — Grade: 01
My mom is a playful mom. She makes a good lunch for me and she helps me with my homework. She's a really good mom.

Max Vega — Grade: 01
My mom's loving. My mom's the best. She helps me with everything. My mom works hard for our family. I am thankful for my special mom.

Brandon Xim — Grade: 01
My mom is loveable. My mom is pretty, she always looks her best. I love my mom. She loves me. She's so nice.

Teacher: Beth Renz

Jack Lawson — Grade: 01
She is wonderful because she helps and loves me. Sometimes my mom cooks for me and takes care of me. She is the best mom.

Emma Northcutt — Grade: 01
I love my mom because she cooks my favorite foods. Every day she makes lunch for me. She is wonderful because she helps me clean up.

Nick Werfelmann — Grade: 01
My mom is the best ever. I love my mom so much. My mom cooks for me. She is so happy.

Amelia Windal — Grade: 01
My mom is the best ever. Everyday she cooks the best breakfast in the world. I love my mom because she cares for me.

Teacher: Mary Samis

Michael Brungardt — Grade: 01
My mom is as pretty as a rose. My mom is the best because she gives me the best hugs.

Cole Cruz — Grade: 01
My mom is as clean as a flower. My mom is as sweet as a cupcake. She is the best in the whole entire world.

Ryan Irwandy — Grade: 01
My mom is as sweet as honey. My mom works as hard as a rock. My mom is pretty.

Paige Japlit — Grade: 01
Mom is as sweet as a cherry. She helps kids because she is a teacher. My mom is as beautiful as a rainbow.

Justin Limlengco — Grade: 01
My mom is as beautiful as a rose. My mom is as sweet as cherries. My mom is as cuddly and sweet as can be.

Madison Marchant — Grade: 01
My mom is sweet as a pink blanket. My mom is sweet as a cherry. I love mom.

Clara Meade — Grade: 01
My mom is funny as a clown and she is sweet as honey.

Jenna Mierczynski — Grade: 01
My mom is as shiny as a diamond. My mom is as cuddly as a teddy bear. My mom is as kind as a puppy.

Makenzie Moncrief — Grade: 01
She is sweet as a cherry. My mom is funny as a puppy. My mom is beautiful as a sparkly diamond.

Margaret Pham — Grade: 01
My mom is as sweet as a sugarplum. My mom is as beautiful as a sunset.

Avila (Don Juan) Elem.
Aliso Viejo

Teacher: Mary Wilson

Trevor Hart — Grade: 01
I love my mom because she is the best in history. She is special because she's cool. I should give her a giant hug.

Skylar Machnikowski — Grade: 01
My mom is as sparkly as sparkly as a diamond. My mom deserves a diamond because she's lovely, she's special, so she deserves it, okay.

Natasha Riding — Grade: 01
I love my mom because she's the best mom and she is the special also she really wants a diamond.

Carter Watson — Grade: 01
My mom is awesome as a dazzling diamond because she is the best and because she is my mom. I love her the most.

Barcelona Hills Elementary
Mission Viejo

Teacher: Patricia Budig

Julia Davis — Grade: 05
Roses are red. Violets are blue. My mom deserves that diamond from you. She is the most smartest, prettiest, hardworking mom in the world.

Haylee Gasser — Grade: 05
My mom's eyes sparkle like the sun, sparkles on the sea. Her smile lights up the whole world. She's as beautiful as a rose blooming.

Devyn Hughes — Grade: 05
My mom is hardworking and helpful. She is as beautiful as a flower and has a voice like a bell ringing. She is the best mom.

Kiana Krzycki — Grade: 05
My mom deserves a diamond because she is like the sun that brightens my day and she's like the moon shining in the night sky.

Amber Solomon — Grade: 05
My mom deserves a diamond because she is so amazing. When I see her, it's like a light glowing through my soul. She's very graceful.

Lauren White — Grade: 05
She's as busy as a bee. Her teeth are as white as snow. She's outgoing as a sunflower blooming. Her eyes shine like the moon.

Teacher: Gail Gilpin

Hana Baichtal — Grade: 02
My mom has a smile that glows like the morning sun. When she gives me hugs, it makes me feel loved. I love her.

Peyton Dewers — Grade: 02
My mom is as sweet as chocolate chip cookies. She is so kind. I love her kisses and hugs when I get hurt.

Shawn Flores — Grade: 02
Her smile sparkles in the sun. My mom is very special. She has a cute and pretty face. She makes me feel happy.

Leanne Grant — Grade: 02
When I got hurt, she helps me get up. When she reads, I feel loved and happy. Her smile sparkles like the sun.

Madison Griggs — Grade: 02
My mom is our family hero. Her smile brightens our hearts. Her eyes are beautiful. She gives the best hugs and kisses in the world.

Christine Honda — Grade: 02
My mom's eyes sparkle like diamonds. My mom helps me with my homework. She helps me get it right. My mom's hugs feel warm inside.

Andrew Isaac — Grade: 02
My mom's hugs make me really happy. She is as pretty as Cinderella. Some of her food tastes so good. My mom is so special.

Kendall Kearns — Grade: 02
When my mom smiles, it makes me smile back. When I fall, my mom pays attention to me. She is special. She is great.

Spencer Rubio — Grade: 02
My mom's hugs make me feel happy. When I have a bad day, she gets me a treat. Her sparkling smile always cheers me up.

Skyler Whitcher — Grade: 02
My mom's hugs make me feel like I'm in Heaven. My mom's food makes me feel like I never want to stop eating.

Teacher: Karen Thompson

Samer Abulaban — Grade: 02
She has eyes like a clear river. My mom is as pretty as a shining star. She is the best thing that happened to me.

Aaron Bergen — Grade: 02
My mom is very gentle. Her eyes are like a waterfall sparkling in the sun. She's as beautiful as a rose.

Jack Celaya — Grade: 02
Eyes that sparkle like snow, as gentle as a shimmering river. Heart like the golden sun. As beautiful as a precious ruby.

Ryan Chisholm — Grade: 02
My mom's eyes are beautiful as the moon. She is lovely. She is nice. She has a nice heart. She is very beautiful.

Maiya Contreras — Grade: 02
Eyes twinkle like stars. Heart as big as a rainbow. As playful as a dolphin. As lovely as a diamond. I love my mom.

* Amethyst winners in bold.

Dornaz Danesh   Grade: 02
Her smile and her heart are gifts to me. She means a lot to me, my beautiful mommy. She loves me, I love her.

Payton Dodd   Grade: 02
My mom's eyes sparkle like dazzling rivers. Her skin is soft as rose petals. She's as beautiful as a shimmering sunset and lovely as diamonds.

Grace Dunscombe   Grade: 02
My mom's eyes are like sparkling stars. Her heart is like a beautiful rose. Her hair like twirling snowflakes. Her smile like a sparkling diamond.

Nolan Helfrich   Grade: 02
My mom has sparkling blue diamond eyes and delightful tan skin. She's the cool breeze that I breathe. Funny as a clown. Soft as a rose.

Ethan Ludwig   Grade: 02
She's as sweet as candy. Her eyes sparkle like stars. She smells as good as a rose. She rises like the sun. She is my mom.

Jayden Lupis   Grade: 02
My mommy's eyes are like shimmering waves. She's as nice as a butterfly and funnier than a puppy. She's as sweet as a puppy too.

Michael Morizono   Grade: 02
She's as funny as a clown. She is nice and she cares like a Koala bear. She is as sweet as a flower.

Christina Polcuch   Grade: 02
She is a beautiful red ruby in a clear river, as generous as a Church priest, and her heart is as big as the sun.

Garrett Sandzimier   Grade: 02
She is beautiful as a flower. She sings like beautiful birds. Her sweet heart is as kind as a deer.

Samantha Volpe   Grade: 02
Eyes that sparkle like a drop of golden sun. Hair that shines like the morning sun. She's like an angel. I love my mother.

Charlie Wright   Grade: 02
Her eyes are like beautiful tulips in the hot sun. As pretty as a shimmering river. Heart as beautiful as the colors of the sunset.

Bathgate Elementary
Mission Viejo

Teacher: Kelly Anderson

Anthony Fernandez   Grade: 05
She shines her way through my life like my little guardian angel. She makes bad times good and always looks at the beauty in things.

Ivy Galloway   Grade: 05
Her smile is like the moon lighting any dark weather. Her heart is like an everlasting diamond I will always treasure.

Selah Gilmore   Grade: 05
My mom is like the sun in the morning, so beautiful and bright. Her eyes sparkle in the moonlight. She is a diamond to me.

Mallika Gummuluri   Grade: 05
Her dark hair is like the night. Her smile is very bright. Her eyes are like gems. We both like M
Ms.

Devlin Hamidjaja   Grade: 05
My mom's eyes are special like a sun setting. She's the most special person in the universe. She's as pretty as a diamond and ruby.

Nathan Harriott   Grade: 05
My mom is like a brightening star, as perfect as can be, sending down love and joy down to me. I repay her by giving love.

Olivia Jarvis   Grade: 05
My mom is the light of my life. She sparkles like a diamond all my life. Her heart is like two hearts all melted together.

Karishma Kumar   Grade: 05
Her body is like the ocean and she never stops moving. Her eyes sparkle like rubies. She glows like the sun and is my star!

Brendan Mitchell   Grade: 05
In the morning when I see her, her eyes shimmer like the ocean. Whenever I'm sad, I think of her and my sadness goes away.

Katelyn Moye   Grade: 05
Her smile is a banana as ripe as can be. She shines like the night sky and is as nice as cherry berry pie.

Calvin Pring   Grade: 05
My mom makes me happy whenever I'm sad. Her eyes shine like the shiny blue ocean, and she is the best mom anyone can have.

Helena Shipley   Grade: 05
Her hair shines like the sun. She is as sweet as candy. Her smile brightens up my day. She always takes care of the family.

Lindsey Southworth   Grade: 05
Moonlight shimmers against her unique mane. As she does sweltering work to help our family, her days are packed like a tornado of labor.

Travis Yagi   Grade: 05
Loving, caring, and nice. My mom is all of those things. I think she is like a diamond. She is priceless. She is the best.

Tony Zhou   Grade: 05
Her eyes are as bright as a full moon. She is the beauty of life. She means the whole universe to me.

Beatty (Gordon H.) Elem.
Buena Park

Teacher: Jennifer Turner

Aileen Chua   Grade: 05
My mom is graceful and unique. Her face is beautiful and smiling. When she wakes, the sun rises above. She's my role model!

David Cisneros   Grade: 05
Her hair like golden feathers and her eyes like crystals. Her warm smile like rubies. Her hug like warm blankets. Her love like never ending warmth.

Ariadna Espinoza   Grade: 05
My mother is like a flower that blossoms and hugs me everyday. She is like a book that never ends and knows I am safe.

Serena Mann   Grade: 05
She's the sun that shines above. A heart like candles that will never burn out. Passion you couldn't describe. My mom is to love forever.

Adrian Ramirez   Grade: 05
I love her shiny face in the morning. Like the sun, her face is like a crystal heart. Her hands, soft like the wind.

Christina Seo   Grade: 05
She is the Angel of Love. Her eyes are sweet as honey. I am helpless without her. My magical mom!

Jessica Baek   Grade: 06
My mom is like a blanket that warms my soul. Whenever I am depressed, she gives me an everlasting hug. Guardian Angel, a friend - Mom.

Sam Cho   Grade: 06
An angel sent from Heaven. As graceful as the angels flying around in the skies. She is the gift of love, Mom.

Genesis Gonzalez   Grade: 06
She's sent from Heaven. Her heart is rich like gold. Her voice sweet like candy. Without her, my life will be empty. My mom!

Grace Kim   Grade: 06
My mother is like a bright star glimmering from the sky. Hand as soft as sand. Eyes flowing like the waters. Mom.

James Kim   Grade: 06
My mother, her heart as light and delicate as a feather. When she is with me, she can always change the weather in my heart.

Oriana Kroschuk   Grade: 06
She is beautiful as the morning sunrise. Warm as a summer sun. Loving and caring. Soft as a cloud and sweet as candy. My mother.

Brittany Mc Mullen   Grade: 06
Her eyes as deep as the ocean blue. The reason for my life. She inspires me so. She knows I love her. She is my mother.

Kimberly Rodriguez   Grade: 06
Her hugs and kisses warm me up every time. She protects me from danger. She is the love of my life. My mother.

Kurt Shin   Grade: 06
With hands so soft and hair so find, something I can't define. With a beautiful voice, loud and clear, something that I love to hear.

Tricia Anne Yuvienco   Grade: 06
Delicate as a pink rose, just as beautiful. Wondrous royalty, but more than a queen or princess. Serene spirit, great-hearted lady. Noble angel. My mom.

Beechwood Elementary
Fullerton

Teacher: Blair Levine

Robby Bower   Grade: 03
She is like a diamond, as pretty as a gem. If you ever see her, she's the best of all of them.

Matthew Cho   Grade: 03
Your eyes sparkle and dazzle like diamonds. Your hair is flawless and shiny. Your hands are the color of peaches.

Haley Grant   Grade: 03
My mom is my guardian diamond, who shines through the moonlight. Her eyes twinkle like the stars at night time.

Angela Lankenau   Grade: 03
Every song seems to have your blessing. Everyone seems to love you. I love you so very much, Mama.

Kristi Rho   Grade: 03
When my mom smiles at me with love, her face shines like a diamond!

Bayley Weber   Grade: 03
With a lot of love and joy and her lovely heart is in my heart with a lot of peace.

Benedict (Truman) Elem.
San Clemente

Teacher: Lori Crandall

Brooke Hendrickson   Grade: 05
Loving, laughing, full of life. Caring and kind to everyone. Helping and always holding my hand. Mom is better than any word. I love mom!

Kira Nemeth   Grade: 05
Why my mom deserves a diamond is because she cares about me just as much as God and sparkles even more than a diamond.

Jason Risdana   Grade: 05
Her eyes glisten in the sunlight. Her hair is like a stream flowing on the river. Her face is like a painting. This is my mom.

Ryann Wagner   Grade: 05
My mom deserves a diamond because she works hard and gets nothing back. She is huge help. She is the one person who deserves it.

James West   Grade: 05
My mom, her hair is as soft as silk, her eyes the color of a buffaloes' hair and the heart as pretty as a diamond.

Teacher: Julia Ferguson

Nora Foss   Grade: 04
Mom. Her eyes are like diamonds and she loves me like the world. My mom's love is glowing like the sun. I love my mom.

Shawn gocke   Grade: 04
My mom is sweet, shines like the sun, smiles like the stars up above. She's the pot of gold at the end of the rainbow.

Ethan Grubbs   Grade: 04
My mom is beautiful and loving and works hard. She has eyes as blue as the sea. I'll never forget her love for me.

Lauren Knight   Grade: 04
My mom is the reason the sun rises in the early morning sky. She is as beautiful as a blossoming rose. She loves me always.

Colby Lacher   Grade: 04
Mom. Helpful and loving. Busy as a bee. Sweet as an apple. I'll never forget her love for me.

Kate Lopez   Grade: 04
My mom. Her eyes are as green as an emerald. Her smile sparkles like the sun. I love my mom! She is the best!

Victoria Reardon   Grade: 04
She is as beautiful as the sky and the sunset. Her love is as strong as the Earth itself. She is my mom.

Nikki Rutherford   Grade: 04
Mom. Your smile is like twinkling stars. You're as pretty as an angel. I'll never forget how much you care for me!

Blake Winston   Grade: 04
My mom shines like a star. She is sweet like honey. I will never forget how much she loves me.

Alice Zhang   Grade: 04
Mother. My mother is why the world has lively creatures and flowing rivers. She is as gorgeous as an aqua canary. My mom deserves diamonds.

Teacher: Jan Mc Gaffin

David Haynes   Grade: 03
My mom's eyes sparkle like the ocean and her heart is as big as the world. She says funny jokes. She's the best mom ever.

Camryn Ostrander   Grade: 03
Violets are blue, roses are red, I love you mommy even when I'm in bed. Your eyes are beautiful, sparkling with glee. I love you.

Bailey Phillips   Grade: 03
My mom is as pretty and beautiful as a sparkling star in the sky and she is glittery as a rose. She is gorgeous.

Kane Sheckler   Grade: 03
Her eyes are sparkling bright. Her eyes are as beautiful as roses. She is an elegant runner.

* Amethyst winners in bold.

Elijah Usui   Grade: 03
My mom's eyes are sparkling like diamonds in the morning and my mom's heart is as warm as an oven.

Teacher: Cynthia Murphy

Claire Garrity   Grade: 04
My mom is very sweet. She is a good person to be with. She does a lot for me and she is always helpful too.

Jett Jordan   Grade: 04
I think my mom is the most loving mom in the world. She'd give her heart to me. She's so sweet. She deserves a diamond.

Eric Kearns   Grade: 04
My wonderful mother is a great cook. She does laundry for everyone in my family. She is very nice. She loves my family a lot.

Jacki Romney   Grade: 04
My mom is generous, kind, sweet and very loving and I love her very much. That is why my mom deserves a diamond.

Ava Schwab   Grade: 04
My mom deserves a diamond because she takes care of me whenever I'm sick. She cares for me, loves me, and protects me.

Benson (Barbara) Elem.
Tustin

Teacher: Rosalind Brookes

Ephraim Liu   Grade: 03
My mom is special in every way. She cares for me every day. She is like the treasures of the sea.

Aimee Sung   Grade: 03
She is a loving mother. She works hard for money for me and my brother. This is why she deserves a diamond.

Teacher: Christine Burns

Savannah Spears   Grade: 01
My mom deserves a diamond because she always protects me. Also, I think she is very playful and she tickles me!

Simon Yarnall   Grade: 01
My mom deserves a diamond because she is pretty and teaches me. Also, I think she is the most beautiful woman!

Teacher: Tom Coffey

Olyvia Hutchins   Grade: 03
My mom deserves a diamond because the diamonds sparkle will match my mom's green eyes. She is a special diamond to me.

Kaitlyn Martinez   Grade: 03
My mom deserves a diamond because she has heart full of love, sweet shining eyes and sweet smiles everyday. Also, because she is sweet.

Anthony Valdivia   Grade: 03
Her eyes sparkle like brown crystals and her heart is filled with love that we share together.

Teacher: Kim DeBenedetto

Kade Adams   Grade: 03
She's as pretty as a green emerald. Her love is priceless. Her eyes sparkle like a diamond. She's so attractive.

Ryen Diaz   Grade: 03
She's beautiful in every way. I look at her sparkling eyes everyday. She's got the brightest smile. She's my mother and I love her.

Gavin Feist   Grade: 03
My mom's eyes shine in the moonlight. They glisten in the sunlight. She is so lovely. She is a diamond.

Aly Ramirez   Grade: 03
My mom is lovely like a shining star. Her eyes are chocolate like a brownie. She deserves a diamond because she works hard for me.

Anthony Vargas   Grade: 03
Her brown hair is shining, gleaming in the night sky. Her green eyes are very shining. That is my sweet mom. Sweet and grand.

Naomi Wattanasarn   Grade: 03
My mom deserves a diamond because she talks pleasant words. Her eyes are brown like sweet chocolate. My mom reminds me of a sparkling gem.

Camille Yost   Grade: 03
Her hair shines in the light and her eyes sparkle like a diamond. She is very beautiful like a butterfly.

Teacher: Junka Ezaki

Mariah Bohorquez   Grade: 01
My mom is special because she takes me to really fun places.

Shannon Moore   Grade: 01
My mom is special to me because she takes me to the park.

Teacher: Felisa Gibbs

Lily Andoh-Kesson   Grade: 04
My mom is a remarkable and terrific mother. She has the most outstanding voice ever! I really adore her so much. She is the best.

Flor Zinzun   Grade: 04
My mom deserves a diamond because she is beautiful, she is always there for me. She is really smart and also dazzles like a charm.

Teacher: Courtney Jones

Alexandria LaRossa   Grade: 05
My mom works so hard for us. I wanted to show her how much I appreciate and care about her by giving her a gift.

Emily Mc Mahon   Grade: 05
My mom teaches me to smile and have hope even in difficult times. She inspires me through her tremendous kindness. Her intelligence outshines the stars.

Morgan Stalder   Grade: 05
My mom helps me be a better person. She shows me the importance of doing my best always. She's a magnificent, hardworking, single mom.

Bergeson (Marian) Elem.
Laguna Niguel

Teacher: Nicole Koopman

Nyiri Gharakhani   Grade: 05
My mom is hardworking and always pampers us with tender love and care. A diamond would show the sparkle she brings to our lives.

Sara Mehrinfar   Grade: 05
My mother deserves a diamond because she provides the world with so much beauty and its time she receives something beautiful in return.

Parker Romo   Grade: 05
Roses are red, violets are blue, my mom deserves this diamond because she loves us, works hard, plays with us, and is our mom.

Ada Zhang   Grade: 05
My mom is very flawless. My mom is very fine. That's why she deserves a diamond. A diamond that will shine.

Teacher: William Paine

Verinia Gillebaard   Grade: 02
My mom shines like the sun. Her eyes glitter like a star and she smells like a violet. She is as stunning as a precious diamond.

Mari Grodahl   Grade: 02
My mom's voice is like birds chirping. My mom's eyes twinkle like shooting stars. My mom's heart is like a diamond. I love her!

Logan Layral   Grade: 02
My mom is beautiful. Her eyes are like diamonds. She shines like the sun. She's like shiny gold in the wind.

Gabriel Peransi   Grade: 02
My mom is like a crystal in the sky, she is kind. She takes care of me, she loves me, I love her very much.

Ximena Salazar   Grade: 02
My mom is a beautiful angel with a sunny smile. She is very funny with me and I love it and she's always pretty.

Teacher: Holly Wiseman

Logan Gresko   Grade: 05
My mom is a loving, hardworking mother. She is blissful and calm. She does so much for me and helps me when I'm confused.

Lauren Mahdi   Grade: 05
My mommy is lovely, kind hearted, always there for me and supports me. I couldn't be more thankful for having such a fantastic mommy!

Remi Petit   Grade: 05
My mom's love is like a diamond, it shines and sparkles, and will last forever. She deserves a diamond because she's hardworking, thoughtful, and compassionate.

Emily Vees   Grade: 05
My mom loves me whether I am good or bad. My mom is always there for me in good times and in bad times.

S. Blake Vom Steeg   Grade: 05
My mom is beautiful, kind and loving too. She helps me with school, it's true. She loves me, so that's why she deserves a diamond!

Bethany Christian Aca.
Westminster

Teacher: Renee Shinn

Sydney Alferos   Grade: 06
Her soft voice speaks to my soul. Personality is an ocean of compassion. Glorious Angel sent from above. Stands with me through thick and thin.

Darcie Bierrer   Grade: 06
My mother's caring touch comforts. Her eyes shine like diamonds. Her amazing love overflows. My life would be broken if I couldn't see her face.

Derek Caldwell   Grade: 06
My Mother is loving and kind. She makes me feel better when I'm sad. She makes me well when I'm sick. I love my mom.

Chase Coulombe   Grade: 06
Mom, she's so kind. She always knows what's on my mind. When I'm sad, she's right there to show that she cares. Mommy is awesome!

Ashton Kauwe   Grade: 06
More loving than you can imagine. She's stronger than a rock. Nothing could ever replace her. A diamond in my heart, my mom.

Kristy Nguyen   Grade: 06
The soft gentle words. The glisten in her eyes. The gracefulness in her touch. Her smile that lightens the day. One very simple word, AMAZING.

Cassidy Prince   Grade: 06
My mom is so pretty, as pretty as a diamond. She has a sparkle in her eyes. She is light that leads me to God.

Christian Rost   Grade: 06
Beautiful mom. My mom shines like a star in the beautiful night sky. She loves me like a momma bear loves her cub.

Elizabeth Vo   Grade: 06
Attitude is godly, voice speaks softly. Always seems happy, more precious than diamonds. No one can replace her, I am so blessed to have her.

Chianna Westaway   Grade: 06
My mom's smile brightens my day, the least I can do is obey. All I have to say is "I love you very much, Mom."

Blessed Sacrament
Westminster

Teacher: Lori Stanley

Paul Cao   Grade: 03
My mom shines a path of joy in my life. All her tears flow into my soul. She rejoices with lovely passion. I love her.

Tisa Do   Grade: 03
My mom's eyes look sweet and loving. Her smile looks nice and pretty. Her words bring kindness to the world. I love her a lot.

Katie Doornek   Grade: 03
Her hair is as great as a horse's mane. Her eyes sparkle like the stars and her love and kindness comes from the light inside.

Cynthia Garcia   Grade: 03
My mom is beautiful and great. Her heart is like the shining stars in the sky. She is gorgeous and kind. I love her. She is mine.

Jeffrey Hermans   Grade: 03
My mom deserves a diamond because she cooks well. My mom is loving and kind. My mom is helpful and playful.

Jennifer Nguyen   Grade: 03
My mom has a diamond heart because she is kind to me. Her eyes sparkle like a gem because she loves me very much.

Katlinh Nguyen   Grade: 03
Her eyes twinkle with love. Her kindness is like a dove. Her smile cannot be sold. Her heart is made out of gold.

Ivy Nguyen   Grade: 03
My mom is a kind woman who has beautiful eyes. She has a wonderful heart with lots of love in her. Her eyes have stars.

Vanessa Nguyen   Grade: 03
My mom is the beautiful light that shines on me. Her life is my joy and love. She is fully bright. Her love is wonderful.

Allen Ninh   Grade: 03
Her voice melts into my crystals of compassion. A little of her sparkle makes me happy. Her eyes gaze into my soul. I love her.

Karen Pham   Grade: 03
Her love to me is like a dove. Her smile is always from Heaven above. Her words of God bring me up from down.

Annaysa Sanchez   Grade: 03
My mom is a shiny girl and twinkles in my eyes, with sparkles of her beautiful face and love of her spirit.

* Amethyst winners in bold.

Daniel Tran   **Grade: 03**
My mom's smiles are like the clouds in the sky. Her heart is the light of the candle. Her spirit is in the air.

Dominic Tran   Grade: 03
My mom's eyes sparkle like diamonds in the sun. Her laughter sounds like beautiful music. Her love for me and my brother is everlasting.

Brea Country Hills Elem.
Brea

Teacher: Shinobu Hirota

Aidan Gillanders   **Grade: 02**
My mom is always helpful, always open to give. She plays games with me. She takes me camping. She helps me when I'm sick.

Erika Iligan   Grade: 02
My mom always works hard for us. She gets us ready before she takes care of herself. She loves us very much.

McKenzie Johnson   **Grade: 02**
My nice mom loves me. She makes my lunch and plays games with me. She buys me clothes. She makes this world a better place.

Zoya Khan   Grade: 02
My mom is very nice to people. She cooks very good food for me. She helps me get better.

Choyun Lee   Grade: 02
My mom, kind, good, caring, loving, cooking nice and loving to me everyday. A perfect person.

Rachel Lindbo   Grade: 02
My mom is nice, friendly, and funny. She looks out for me. She helps me with homework. She loves me so so so much.

Melanie Oliva   Grade: 02
My mommy loves me. She cares for me. My mommy is great to everyone especially her family. She helps me when I can't do something.

Raveen Rajakaruna   **Grade: 02**
Mom, loving, nice, sweet, friendly, funny. I like her and she likes me.

Teacher: Carrie Thomas

Brock Denbo   Grade: 02
My mom sparkles as bright as the sun. She is so kind and thoughtful. I love her so much and she loves me too!

Aron Hernandez   Grade: 02
My mom is nice since the day I was born. She hugs me and squeezes me and throws me up in the air.

Natalie Kim   Grade: 02
Light is bright but bright light cannot be as my mom's crystal eyes and her diamond heart.

Jenna Matiasevich   **Grade: 02**
She is the light of my soul. Her eyes shine up to the moon. I love her so much and she loves me too!

Sally Min   Grade: 02
My mom is a diamond because she is nice, pretty and supportive.

Rilee Price   Grade: 02
I have a big diamond that is my mommy and she sparkles like the morning sun. She looks so very pretty when she sparkles.

Jackson Swindle   **Grade: 02**
As my mom's eyes sparkles, I shall love her heart as much as she loves mine. My mom's heart is as big as God. Mom.

Andrea Zhang   **Grade: 02**
My mom sparkles. My mom is a friend of mine. But most of all, she loves me. I shall give her my love too.

Brea Junior High
Brea

Teacher: Jennifer Bruner

Andrew Baffa   Grade: 07
My mom deserves a diamond because of all that she's done for me, cook, care, love and always listens to what I have to say.

Samantha Cortes   Grade: 07
My mom is a full time teacher and is super caring. She doesn't care how you're dressed. She'll love you how you are. The best!

Michelle Maceda   Grade: 07
My mom deserves a diamond because my mom is one in a million. There's no other mom that's as caring or loving. She's the best!

Victoria Park   Grade: 07
My mom deserves a diamond. The diamond equals mom. She shines the world, just like crosses symbolize Jesus. My mom needs something to represent her.

Alondra Sandoval   Grade: 07
I think my mom deserves a diamond because she's hardworking, big heart, cares for others. She deserves to be noticed.

Nicholas Williams   Grade: 07
My mom does so much for me and my family. It would be awesome to give her something in return. She is my precious gem.

Luz Cruz   **Grade: 08**
Mom deserves a diamond because she is special like one, but most of all, she deserves my love. The love to give mom, diamond.

Teacher: Kara Dietz

Rebecca Brannon   **Grade: 07**
My mom works hard to provide even though she doesn't feel good. She puts everyone before herself. I love my mom!

Elizabeth Davis   Grade: 07
She works. She cleans. She helps. She loves. She does it all. With rare pleases and few thank you. We'll always love her the best.

Karen Her   **Grade: 07**
When my mom, my guiding light, sits there and holds me tight. Her simple touch is my comfort, her love means we'll be together forever.

Megan Ortiz   **Grade: 07**
My mom is funny, nice and cares for me when I'm sick. She's the one I turn to when I need help for anything.

Chris Richey   Grade: 07
My mom never sits. She does laundry all day. The jewelry store key is too much to pay. So a diamond is a good surprise!

Teacher: Maria Gonzalez

Christopher Arellanez   Grade: 07
My mom's eyes are like diamonds, they glisten in the sun. She flies like a beautiful butterfly gracefully through the air.

Makena Dandley   Grade: 07
Mom deserves a diamond because she cares, helps, loves me, my friends and family, been there through thick and thin, made me who I am today.

Uche Ewenike   Grade: 07
My mom deserves a diamond because she is hardworking, always smiling, single mom who takes care of me and my brother without any help.

Michelle Hoang   Grade: 07
My mom deserves a diamond because she takes me to ice skating practice in the morning, doesn't complain about it. Also, cares and loves me.

Farrah Lee   Grade: 07
She has always been my best friend and had always cared for me. She is a marvelous mom and is outstanding at her job!

Seth Luce   Grade: 07
When you take on the title, "Mom", all that means is compassion. You watch out for your children always. That, to me, deserves a reward.

Anna Monros   Grade: 07
Without her, I would be alive. We were one for nine months. She is my best friend. My loving mother and my world.

Miles Robertson   Grade: 07
My mom deserves a diamond because I can always go to her for advice and when I am down, she turns my frown upside down.

Breeana Salinas   Grade: 07
Sacrifices her life for mine, committed herself to a family, loved me and raised me through life, believes love is endless, a remarkable woman "mom".

Ajay Shanmugham   Grade: 07
Enthusiastic, puts me before her, works hard for me, Trojan spirited, soft heart, makes a greater person, gives 110%, humble, devoted, brilliant.

Michelle Tjoa   Grade: 07
My mother is my angel that watches over me and helps me when my wings forget how to fly. She guards me with her love.

Fayaaz Virani   Grade: 07
My mother deserves a diamond because she has nurtured me since I was small. She has made me the person I am today.

Brea-Olinda High
Brea

Teacher: Laurel Batchelor

Joseph Chang   Grade: 12
She brings love, joy and peace and is the rock to our family. My mother is patient and can withstand more pressure than any diamond.

Abbie Mendoza   Grade: 12
"A-me-rrri-ka", mom said. Accent strong. I laughed. Then suddenly recalled her compassion, tolerance, and realized that in her I can find the better me.

Sean O'Connor   Grade: 12
Everyday mom takes on the world for us, to give us all she can. Her sacrifice is pure love. She deserves so much more.

Kendall Rodriguez   Grade: 12
My mom is beautiful inside and out. She never thinks about herself and constantly is seeking to do good things for our world. She's loving!

Drew Rosell   Grade: 12
My mom is always helping me. Even when I can't see what she wants me to be. That's why she deserves a diamond from thee.

Brethren Christian JR/SR
Huntington Beach

Teacher: Janet Niswonger

Madison Caffey   Grade: 07
My mom deserves a diamond because I love her. She is amazing, hardworking and I admire her for that. My mom deserves the diamond.

David Glover   Grade: 07
The reason my mom deserves a diamond is that she is fine. But my favorite thing about her is she is mine!

Dawson Hoppes   Grade: 07
Like a buried treasure at the bottom of the sea with no flaw that you can see. That's my mom!

Jeremy Jorgensen   Grade: 07
I am blessed with the best. I thank God each day for my mom that loves me more and more each day. My amazing mom!

Jessica Lee   Grade: 07
My mom is a sweet and loving person. She cares about everyone and as perfect and pure as a diamond.

Hailey Lee   Grade: 07
Like a discovered diamond helps a pioneer to live a better life. Like a lighthouse leads a boat from the harsh sea ---- This is my mom.

Bonnie Lundin   Grade: 07
A fallen angel from above, she gives me all her greatest love. I am so proud to call her mom.

Connor Mahoney   Grade: 07
My mom deserves a diamond because she is loving, caring, dazzling, and is a glistening gem to me.

Jack McInally   Grade: 07
We're all blessed with one, but mine is like no other. She showers me with love; she's kind, she is my mother.

Frederick Okamoto   Grade: 07
Funny, loves animals, loves God, and is brave; these are the words that describe my best friend in the world, my mom. She loves me.

Hayden Rahman   Grade: 07
My mom is awesome. She is loving and kind, always knows what is on my mind. She doesn't deserve a diamond; she deserves much more.

Cyrus Read   Grade: 07
Someone is as bright as the sun, her heart is made of pure gold. She is as giving as God...that someone is my mom!

Sierra Starke   Grade: 07
Loveable, unique, rare, and special in so many ways. A person like this doesn't come around often. My mom shines the brightest in my eyes.

Katie Swanson   Grade: 07
My mom deserves a beautiful diamond because she glistens everyday and whenever the sky is gray, just as a diamond, she lights up the day.

Jordan Thomas   Grade: 07
Because she knows me so well. She puts up with my moods and knows how to cheer me up. I love her so much!

Jonathan Wong   Grade: 07
My mom deserves a diamond because of her unconditional love, compassion, and being there for me when I need her.

Brookhaven Elementary
Placentia

Teacher: Karen Aleksic

Sydney Andersen   Grade: 04
Mom, is the most loving person just like God that came from Heaven. Also, the happiest in the world because she has two loving children.

Hannah Cardenas Grade: 04
My mom loves me more than the universe. She has a heart as big as a boulder. She is so shiny as a star, I love you.

Jacob Ek Grade: 04
She loves me with all her heart. She pushes me in a shopping cart. She gives me a lot to eat.

Nathan Estabrook Grade: 04
My mom's heart is as sweet as sugary cheesecake. My mom's smile is as shiny as all of God's light. She is special to me.

Marcus Hubner Grade: 04
My mom is so bright. She will never let me out of sight. You love me so much you can call me a boo.

Eddie Kitahara Grade: 04
My mom deserves a diamond because she is the most loving, tenderness and honorable that anyone could have as a mom.

Melissa Mejia Grade: 04
My mom's love for me is as big as Russia and everything in it. Also, my mom's heart sparkles like a diamond in the sun.

Garrett Stark Grade: 04
My mom is sporty, loving and sweet. She makes yummy food to eat. USC is her favorite team. Her eyes have a brown special gleam.

Teacher: Jamie Grijalva

Diya Borooah Grade: 02
My mom deserves a diamond because she always tells me to do right things. Also, she gives me breakfast with love and care.

Charissa Chang Grade: 02
My mom deserves a diamond because when she looks at me I feel I want to kiss her. That's why my mom deserves a diamond.

Ryan Evans Grade: 02
My mom deserves a diamond because she helps out in our classroom. She also makes my lunch for home and school. I love my mom!

Aviva `Gelfer-Mundl Grade: 02
My mommy deserves a diamond because she does many things for me. She always makes me a spectacular lunch. She is sweet as a strawberry.

Noah Holland Grade: 02
My mom deserves a diamond because she cares about me deeply like when she gives me special kisses when I go to bed!

Teacher: Deneen Kniess

Thomas Anderson Grade: 02
Like a daisy in a garden, she makes me feel like nothing can be better. She cares for me. It is my wonderful, great mom.

Emily Estabrook Grade: 02
A star shines like a sparkling light in my mom's eyes. She breathes like the smell of oranges and is as pretty as a rose.

Brandon Gomez Grade: 02
Eyes like underground seashells. A heart as tall as a tree. A voice as sweet as the seas and always there for me.

Neil Kamdar Grade: 02
Glows like the stars. Just like the moon. Like a rose, shiny and bright. My grateful mom is full of night.

Teju Ramani Grade: 02
Her hair is dark black as the night sky shines. She blooms when the sun rises. She will always be in my heart everyday.

Joeli Schwartz Grade: 02
Eyes that twinkle like the stars in the sky. Her smile as pretty as the rainbow and when I need her, she is there.

Ethan Wynn Grade: 02
The moon is beautiful as my mom's eyes. The sunlight is pretty as my mom's lips. A rose is beautiful as my mom's hair.

Teacher: Tara Leifeste

Chris Hasrouni Grade: 04
My mom deserves a diamond because she studies with me, she gives me good food and finally she is very loving and very, very caring.

Taylor Hoffman Grade: 04
Her words are sweet as nightingale. Her heart is warm and pure; that's why my mom deserves a diamond and that I know for sure.

Ryan Mulrooney Grade: 04
My beautiful mom deserves a diamond because she's the best mom in the whole universe and is loving and caring.

Selina Nicoletti Grade: 04
My mom deserves a diamond because she always keeps her promises. Also, she never lies. She is a hard worker. My mom deserves a diamond.

Alexandria Owens Grade: 04
My mom deserves a diamond because she is a loving and kindly mom. She has been there for me all my life. I love her.

Garrett `Seiler Grade: 04
I think my mom deserves a diamond because she is nice, kind and helpful. Also, because she helps me when I'm stuck on my homework.

Samantha Steinbrecher Grade: 04
The color of her eyes are as sweet as chocolate. Her personality is as bright as the sun. That is why mom deserves a diamond.

Zachary Taylor Grade: 04
My mom deserves a diamond because she is giving and helps others. She is very thoughtful. She watches me like a pretty angel in heaven.

David Thorpe Grade: 04
My mom deserves a diamond because she is a loyal teacher and has a passion for others. Her eyes are darker than the darkest night.

Teacher: Steve Nakanishi

Noor Arbab Grade: 05
She's the only sparkling star I see in the gleaming moonlight. My life revolves around her. She brings love, care and happiness to our lives.

Paige Bakkers Grade: 05
Her hair glistens in the early morning sun. Her heart is as sweet as sugar on my tongue. Her love for me is something indescribable.

Karlie Bennett Grade: 05
Her golden heart, her sparkling eyes. My mom, really deserves a prize. I love her, she loves me. I'm compassionate about my mom, Lori B.

Sarah Caycho Grade: 05
My mom is the sun that shines on me. She's the one that makes me feel important to her. She is my world.

Laurel Faher Grade: 05
She's kind and considerate very nice. Her eyes do sparkle with delight. Her mouth always smiling with joy and that's why I love my mother.

Tiffany Fukunaga Grade: 05
Her eyes glitter like ice crystals. She warms my heart with joy. She loves me like a little star. My mom deserves a diamond.

Rachel Garner   Grade: 05
Hearts are big, hearts are huge, but my mom has the biggest heart of all. That heart is filled with love and care.

Luke Helmbold   **Grade: 05**
Her eyes remind me of fireworks coming down like red and blue showers. Her hug as warm and tranquil as a bed of flowers. Mom.

Rio Iizuka   Grade: 05
My mom's bright eyes sparkle like the sun. Her sparkle mean something wonderful. She is always surrounded by happiness.

Lexi Jarvis   Grade: 05
My mom is the key to my heart as she glistens, glows and sparkles through the path that she unlocked in my heart.

Rachel Lackmann   **Grade: 05**
My mom is like the sun, while I am like the earth. Every day she smiles at me and loves me. She means so much.

Victoria Lemieux   **Grade: 05**
My mom is the golden token of my heart and the person that keeps the love and compassion within me every single day I live.

Milan Patel   **Grade: 05**
When you stare into her brown eyes, engraved in them is, "I love you". Her hands gently wrap around you and all is safe.

Cierra Robinson   Grade: 05
I know my mom deserves a diamond because her bubbly personality fills you with joy. If she was a flower, you would surely pick her.

Cole Smith   Grade: 05
She is as beautiful as diamond. Her eyes glisten like the moon shining on the water. Her smile is as captivating as a butterfly.

Jade Telles   Grade: 05
Her eyes sparkle like the brightest stars. When you're sick, she treats you with medicine, love and care. I love her and she loves me.

Elizabeth Thanos   **Grade: 05**
A cold winter breeze, a roaring fire, and cup of cocoa. My mom stays by my side creating perfect memories for life.

Katie Thanos   Grade: 05
A gleaming gem polished by sunlight with a beauty more powerful than Aphrodite herself.

Dylan Valdez   Grade: 05
A seed in my heart grows to a rose as my mind if filled with passionate thoughts of her. It will stay forever.

Brywood Elementary
Irvine

Teacher: Freddi Siegel

Sergio Anand   Grade: 06
My mom deserves a diamond because she is valuable than the biggest diamond in the world.

Derek Castellano   **Grade: 06**
Mom deserves a diamond because she has to love, care for, and most of all, put up with a whole family. We LOVE our mother.

Rylee Charrette   Grade: 06
My mom deserves a diamond because she is a kind, caring, and hardworking person. I'm proud to say she's my mother. I love mom!

Katrina Dang   **Grade: 06**
My mom deserves a diamond because she's a great role model. She teaches me how to love, and she always says she's grateful for me.

Megan Raye Enciso   Grade: 06
My mom deserves a diamond because she is a hardworking mom. I treasure her and I am very proud of her.

Kameron Johnson   Grade: 06
My mom deserves a diamond because I appreciate the dozens of kind things she does for me and the people around her.

Hibah Kareem   Grade: 06
I think my mom deserves a diamond because like diamonds, she is very rare to find and the best mom ever! I love her!

Joanne Kim   Grade: 06
My mom works consistently with all her heart to make me happy with a smile on her face even when she gets stressed out.

Sue Kim   Grade: 06
I think my mom should get a diamond because she truly makes me believe that I am a special, unique person that she loves.

Andres Martinez   Grade: 06
I know my mom deserves a diamond because she is the most supportive, hardworking, loving, caring, appreciative, kind, generous, and wise mother I know.

Lauren Muniz   Grade: 06
My mom deserves a diamond because she cares for my whole family. My life seems more beautiful when she is with me.

Elijah Saldana   Grade: 06
I think my mom deserves a diamond is because she is nice, funny, smart and that she is friendly. She is also special.

Suriya Tanjasiri   **Grade: 06**
My mom deserves a diamond because she is a good influence and she is confident in everything she does. My mom is a role model.

Monica Vaca   **Grade: 06**
My mom is thoughtful, hardworking and dedicated woman. I love her so much and care for her, and I know she does too.

Matthew Yi   Grade: 06
My mom deserves a diamond because she teaches me right from wrong. She made me the person I am today. She is very special.

Nathan Zaldivar   **Grade: 06**
My mom is dedicated to my happiness. When I have bad days, she's always there for me, and helps me through it. She's very special.

Calvary Chapel Jr. High
Santa Ana

Teacher: Aimee O' Connor

Noah Alderson   Grade: 07
My mom deserves a diamond because she has taught me to become what I want to do. She has unending love and I appreciate it.

Riley Alexander   Grade: 07
My mom deserves a diamond because she's smart, funny and hardworking. On top of that she drives at least two hours a day for us.

Tripp Aversa   Grade: 07
My mom deserves a diamond because she sparkles. Her faith is solid as a diamond, and diamonds are the hardest gem ever knows to man.

Bryce Bastian   Grade: 07
When I was three years old, my mom gave up her job, where she was a boss, because taking care of me was more important.

* Amethyst winners in bold.

Caleb Bush   Grade: 07
Amazing, hard worker, cooks great meals, trustworthy, honest, smart, organized, servants heart, loves the Lord, loves children. This is why mom deserves a diamond.

Tanna Fernow   Grade: 07
My mom works extremely hard to support me. She loves me very much and always thinks about me before herself. I love her so much.

Emily Lopez   Grade: 07
My mom is the greatest. She dedicates her time to me and puts me before her. I want to show appreciation to her in everything.

Kellie Mendres   Grade: 07
My mom's wonderful, she will surf in 50 degree water just to make me smile. She'll make funny food and we will together eating it.

Jamie Nelson   Grade: 07
My mom is the most diligent person you could find. She's a selfless mother that never does anything for herself. She has a golden heart.

Rachel Nelson   Grade: 07
My mom is nice, fun, awesome and cool and she spends time with me which really rules and that's why she deserves a diamond.

Brooks O'Hea   Grade: 07
I've been convinced my mom is an angel, spiritually covered in diamonds. I give her a diamond and everyone will see her as an angel.

Brooke Self   Grade: 07
My mom deserves a diamond because she's hardworking and takes care of us because she loves us. I love her and thinks she deserves it.

Calvary Christian School
Santa Ana

Teacher: Chambles

William Bucher   Grade: 05
My mom deserves a diamond because she teaches me how to be a man and she encourages me to make the right choices.

Teacher: Lori Flores

Katelyn Bobo   Grade: 01
My mom deserves a diamond. She cleans me. She feeds me. She loves me. She hugs me. That's how my mom deserves a diamond.

Matthew Campbell   Grade: 01
My mom deserves a diamond. She makes me rolls. She goes with me to get pizza. She is excellent.

Joshua Diaz   Grade: 01
My mom deserves a diamond. She helps my teachers and she helps the teacher do groups. She makes good food.

Allen Esmaeili- Tehrani   Grade: 01
My mom deserves a diamond. She takes good care of me and my two brothers. She is a good gardener. She plays games.

Jaden Gorman   Grade: 01
My mom deserves a diamond. She is excellent at sewing. She is excellent at skiing. She is excellent. She is excellent at running.

Hope Markley   Grade: 01
My mom deserves a diamond. She is a great cook. She loves me. She is a great writer.

Ethan Parks   Grade: 01
My mom deserves a diamond. She does nice things for my friends. She gives me hugs and kisses. She is awesome. My mom is perfect.

Kate Rodebaugh   Grade: 01
My mom deserves a diamond. She does everything right. My mom loves God. She can do amazing things. I love my mom.

Teacher: Cherie Hutchens

Brendan Hughes   Grade: 03
I think my mom should win the diamond because she's funny, kind, loving, and she is the best mom in the entire world.

Abraham Nuno   Grade: 03
Because she helps me do my homework and she is nice and kind and helps at church and helps me with math and cursive.

Griffin Selby   Grade: 03
The reason my wonderful mother deserves a diamond is because she is a loving, smart, helpful and beautiful young woman. She will love this gift.

Tony Snyder   Grade: 03
She deserves a diamond because she is kind and she takes care of all four kids. You can trust her and she is very loving.

Daphne Sullivan   Grade: 03
My mom deserves a diamond because she helps me through hard times. She is my mom and a friend. She has a great personality.

Teacher: Ann Klein

Andrew Beggs   Grade: 02
My mom deserves a diamond because she always helps me with my homework and always, goes to my baseball games. She loves me very much.

Egan Bosch   Grade: 02
My mom deserves a diamond because she is brave, loving, kind, true, and she tries to help in any way. She deser4ves a diamond.

Hope Bryson   Grade: 02
My mommy deserves a diamond because she's as sweet as an angel and she makes the world smile. She is my hero.

Jamie Horton   Grade: 02
My mom loves me and I love her too, and when she smiles, my heart goes wild. I just know she deserves a diamond.

Andrew Vercueit   Grade: 02
My mom deserves a diamond because she is very nice. She lets me play computer every Friday after school and after piano practice every week.

Mikaylee Whitmarsh   Grade: 02
My mommy deserves a diamond because her eyes twinkle in the sum like stars at night. She always finds stuff I can't find.

Teacher: Amber Mitchell

Megan Diaz   Grade: 01
My mom deserves a diamond. My mom really, really loves me and she helps everybody very much.

Alana Mc Cormick   Grade: 01
My mom deserves a diamond because she is pretty and she is good at cleaning.

Ciera Rasmussen   Grade: 01
My mom deserves a diamond because she does a lot of things. She takes us a lot of places. She loves us. She is fantastic.

Aubrey Rynders   Grade: 01
My mom deservers a diamond because mom's won't let anything happen to us and mom's never let us down.

Alexa Velasquez   Grade: 01
My mom deserves a diamond because she is very loving and kind. She is the best mom in the world. She is spectacular.

Teacher: Joyce O'Brien

Sara Chao   Grade: 02
My mom deserves a diamond because she is running our home. She is loving, helpful and caring. She believes in God very well.

Tosh Landis   Grade: 02
She is the best mom you could have. She is loving. She is very nice and caring and is very fine.

Jhaelynn Myers   Grade: 02
My mom is so faithful. I appreciate the gifts she gives me. I would give her millions and millions of love. She is a sunshine.

Celeste Santarrosa   Grade: 02
My mom is so, so wonderful to have around. She is so caring. She never ever had a diamond. She really sparkles like a diamond.

David Sawada   Grade: 02
Because she is helpful, she takes us to school everyday. She is really friendly. I appreciate her a lot.

Teacher: Tracy Robinson

Jeremy Bharwani   Grade: 02
My mother deserves a diamond because she helps with everything. I think she is the best mom ever. She has been team mom seven times.

Lindsey Cho   Grade: 02
My mother is sweet, nice and takes good care of me. She's fun to play with and reads me the Bible.

Ethan Pittman   Grade: 02
My mom deserves a diamond. She makes me dinner, lunch and breakfast and she tucks me in bed. And let's me play with my friends.

Kailey TeSelle   Grade: 02
My mom is a realtor. I think she deserves a diamond. She is a great cook. She reads a lot of books. She is really great.

Joshua Walker   Grade: 02
My mother deserves a diamond because she loves me a lot. My mom cuddles with me. My mom loves me as much as she can.

Teacher: Libby Rowley

Maddi Baker   Grade: 05
My mom is the best. She helps me study for my tests. My mom sparkles like a jewel. She picks me up from school.

Robert Garcia   Grade: 05
My mom deserves a diamond so if the world ends, she will have a heavenly smile.

Joshua Jones   Grade: 05
My mommy deserves a diamond because she is nice and helps me with my homework. That's why my mom deserves a diamond.

Jacob Lewis   Grade: 05
My mom deserves a diamond because she's the kindest person I know and the best mom in the world. My mom's one of a kind.

Joy Orr   Grade: 05
My mom deserves a diamond. She's kind and nice. She always thinks of me. She says I'm her baby. My mom is all I need.

Jackson Reese   Grade: 05
My mom deserves a diamond because she obeys the golden rule everyday. I hope I die before she does because I love her so much.

Emily Rojas   Grade: 05
My mom is so nice and neat. Did I mention she's also sweet and deserves this diamond as a treat.

Josh Sepetjian   Grade: 05
My mom deserves a diamond and here's the reason why. She feeds and she treats me like a really special guy.

Cole Spear   Grade: 05
My mom deserves a diamond because she earns it because she is always a hard worker and she is the one who gets me gifts.

Teacher: Amy Slazas

Cassie Brubaker   Grade: 06
My mom deserves a diamond because she shines like one. She is flawless like one too. She deserves a diamond that shines like her personality.

Rachel Duffy   Grade: 06
My mom is like a thousand stars glistening in the sky. I can tell she is so very kind when I look into her eyes.

Jordin Lavigne   Grade: 06
My mom deserves a diamond because she's a wonderful woman of God. She does anything for anybody, now I want to do something for her.

Teacher: Wilma Taylor

Joshua Biddle   Grade: 04
She is the love my life. She would give up her life for someone in need. She is heart warming. I love her.

Sofia Megna   Grade: 04
My mom deserves a diamond because she's always thinking about others first and she is so kind. God has put grace on my mother.

Ashley Park   Grade: 04
Every time my mom gives me a hug, my heart rings like a chime. I love her and she loves me, a perfect harmony.

Cami Sorrells   Grade: 04
My mom deserves a diamond because she is the most kindest, lovingness mom anyone would want to have. She knows how to cure sadness.

Teacher: Libby Vande Wydeven

Christina Baker   Grade: 03
My mom deserves a diamond. It will add to her sparkle. She always helps me when I need her. She never lets me down.

Jake Bobo   Grade: 03
My mom deserves a diamond because when I'm sad, she always cheers me up. She always helps me when I need it. She helps everyone.

Caleb Cummings   Grade: 03
My mom deserves a diamond because she is always there for me when I'm sad, and she tells me to do my own personal best.

Drea DeFord   Grade: 03
My mom deserves a diamond because she is a mom. She cheers me on at all my softball games. She's the best!

Drew Ganahl   Grade: 03
My mom deserves a diamond because she would do anything for me. She would even give her life for me just like Jesus did.

Deanna Hullings   Grade: 03
My mom deserves a diamond because she is the best mom. She washes my clothes and feeds me. She said she loves me very much.

* Amethyst winners in bold.

JT Miller Grade: 03
My mom deserves a diamond because she is kind to everyone she sees. She loves me and my brothers and everyone. My mom loves.

Hallia Rolph Grade: 03
My mother deserves a diamond because she is the most beautiful person in the whole world. Jesus made her just for me to love.

Teacher: Jennie Whitsell

Hanna Boyd Grade: 06
Mom gives love to who, everyone she knows. When, everyday, all the time. My mother loves and cares for everyone. I love my mom.

Harold Cooper Grade: 06
My mom is super awesome. She is outrageous, super fast and cooks super magnificent. She is better than Bobby Flag.

Everett Cox Grade: 06
My mom deserves a diamond because she's loving and kind. She helps me with my homework and loves me when I'm sad.

Sean Ely Grade: 06
My mom's the best. My mom takes me everywhere I go. My mom makes me every meal. But most of all my mom loves me.

Kelly Sullivan Grade: 06
The queen of my heart. My mother is a queen, with beauty divine. She deserves the best I can give and she is all mine.

Sabrina-Faire Trujillo Grade: 06
My mom is the smartest person I've ever met. Over most moms, she has a difficult job. My mom forgives me when I do wrong.

Kristen Vande Wydeven Grade: 06
My mom is omnipresent. Whenever I see her, my mom is awesome and very supportive of my dancing.

Canyon View Elementary
Irvine

Teacher: Virginia Bergguist

Amanda Chang Grade: 03
My mom deserves a diamond because she takes care of my animals and lots of people. I think she deserves a present, a good diamond!

Andrew Lee Grade: 03
I think my mom deserves a diamond because she helps me go to sleep when I'm sick and pray. She should deserve a good diamond.

Brianna Oh Grade: 03
My mom deserves a diamond because she is very nice to us and she also makes healthy food, she explains nicely when things are wrong.

Sarah Rubin Grade: 03
My mom deserves a diamond because she doesn't need diamonds or money to make her happy. She only needs my sister, my dad, and me.

Kerenna Samynathan Grade: 03
I think my mom deserves a diamond because she is brave to climb Diamond Rock, she completes our family.

Matthew Shaftar Grade: 03
My mom deserves a diamond because she is respectful to me. And she lets me be free.

Justin Shin Grade: 03
My mom deserves a diamond. She works on everything. She works with my dad, my brother, and even me. She had endured birth without anesthetic.

Brooke Tuchman Grade: 03
My mom deserves a diamond because she works very hard every day and every day she does something important for the family.

Canyon Vista Elementary
Aliso Viejo

Teacher: Christina Cunningham

Evan Cronkhite Grade: 05
My mom is great even though she needs a break. I think my mom deserves it because she is a diamond herself.

Karena Diep Grade: 05
My mom deserves a diamond. She is loving, caring and the best mom ever. That's why she deserves a diamond.

Barrett Greene Grade: 05
My mom deserves a diamond that is what I say. She can play all day without even getting tired.

Linnea Holmen Grade: 05
My mom is the best, she isn't a pest. She is super kind, she is always on my mind.

Jared Inouye Grade: 05
My mom deserves a diamond because she works hard and helps me do my homework and cleans our house almost everyday.

Emily McCormick Grade: 05
My mom deserves a diamond because she helps me so. My mom deserves a diamond because she's awesome wherever she goes. I love my mom so.

Alexandra Morcos Grade: 05
My mom deserves a diamond because she is awesome! She has nothing for herself just so my brother and I can. She works hard everyday.

Jacob Rork Grade: 05
My mom deserves a diamond because she is the best loving mom in the entire universe. She is caring and deserves a treasure.

Karina Sanchez Grade: 05
Hey mom, you rock! You're the coolest mom on the block. Just because you're so cool, here's a diamond just for you.

Aguste Sharma Grade: 05
My mom's name is Upasna, she likes really good pasta. She's really kind and caring. She teaches me sharing. She deserves a diamond.

Jake Sichley Grade: 05
My mom deserves a diamond because she's special in every way possible and enchants everybody she meets.

Tiffany Tran Grade: 05
Mom teaches me the ups and downs of the world and the good in all things.

Teacher: Juliean Hansen

Melissa Borboa Grade: 05
My mom deserves a diamond because she is sweet as candy but most of all, I love to hold her special hand.

Christian Bowcutt Grade: 05
You can compare my mom to rain, always helping us grow. She cleanses our home just like rain cleanses the earth.

Briana Cialdella Grade: 05
My mom is calm and beautiful, just like a collage of an orange and yellow leaf gracefully drifting onto earth's cold, brown soil.

Jeela Fakhriravari Grade: 05
She has been always available for me. No matter what. She is the most responsible, caring, and kind mom. That's why she deserves a diamond.

Everett Ferer — Grade: 05
My mom deserves a diamond because she is like the sun's rays hitting your face when you see it. I really love my mom.

Emily Jarvis — Grade: 05
My mom is a shining star from heaven above. She fills my heart with joy and makes me cry happy tears. Light shines upon her!

Summer Jorgensen — Grade: 05
Mom deserves a diamond, bright and clean because she does everything kindly for me. She dusts an folds and is never mean. Mom loves me.

Alexandra Marx — Grade: 05
She gives me life. She is as gracious as a star dancing in the night. Her love shines at the darkest times. She is mine.

Tula Masterman — Grade: 05
My mom, a very kind soul indeed. She's always looking out for me. Caring, kind and always helpful. I love my mom.

Casey Olson — Grade: 05
Mommy deserves a diamond neat and fine because she's done a lot for everything that's mine. Very flawless, not a mess, really fancy, with a dress.

Arlene Pastrana — Grade: 05
My mom deserves a diamond because she fills my heart with happiness, love, and care. My mom also deserves a diamond for everything she's done.

Riley Peters — Grade: 05
My mom deserves a diamond because she provides for my family, is very kind and caring and helps me with anything I need.

Drew Rappaport — Grade: 05
My mom is the one thing I'll have if that's it. She protects, encourages and loves me. I'd probably be nothing without my mom!

Ryan Robinson — Grade: 05
My mom deserves a diamond because she is loving and takes good care of me like feeding me every day and helping me with homework.

Kelly Shaw — Grade: 05
Her touch is like beautiful butterfly wings. Her smell is gorgeous and pink. Her heart overflows with warmth. Her love is so perfect for me.

Lexi Shulman — Grade: 05
My mom is like a rose, so very sweet and fine. My mom is like a butterfly, small and delicate, yet so strong and divine.

David Weinberg — Grade: 05
You let me know you love me in so many ways. I'm thankful that you're here for me every single day. Mom, you are so special.

Teacher: Tracey Heuer

Sarah Bluestone — Grade: 05
Mothers are awesome, they are as sweet as blossom. I want to see the bright light in her shiny eyes when she gets the diamond.

Taylor Burton — Grade: 05
My mom deserves the diamond and I'll tell you why. My mom's the best because she always tries.

Mason Coppi — Grade: 05
My mom deserves a diamond. She takes care of me when I'm sick. She also takes care of my dog and baby sister.

Gregery Lee — Grade: 05
My mom deserves a diamond because she is very nice and she sparkles like a star throughout day and night.

Riley Monarch — Grade: 05
My mom deserves a diamond because she is very nice, generous and caring and even to the mice! P.S. She is very scared of mice!

Matthew Padre — Grade: 05
My mom is as pretty as a flower and as sweet as tea. She is awesome like a superhero and super as a mom.

Carson Skoropadd — Grade: 05
My mom deserves a diamond because she's been working hard her whole life and helping others.

Teacher: Vanessa Knox

Maryam Al-hassani — Grade: 05
My mom deserves a diamond because she is as bright as one. She helps us grow, play and go. Mom, you're number one!

Avery Avzu — Grade: 05
My mom deserves a diamond, she is very nice to me. Her love is like the air I can't live a second without it.

Adrianna Boutros — Grade: 05
My mom is always there for me. She sparkles like a diamond in the rain or shine. She would give her life to me.

Alex Bretana III — Grade: 05
My mom is sometimes sad, never gets mad. She loves me always, never stops caring, never stops working. She gets better, never worse.

Melisa Gulsen — Grade: 05
My mom loves and cares for me. She never gets mad which makes me glad that she is my family.

Kevin Hine — Grade: 05
In rain or shine, she's there for me. When I fail, she lifts me up to the heavens. She is my diamond.

Andrew Hodges — Grade: 05
My mom deserves a diamond, so very fine, because a hero like her will always shine. I love her. My hero.

Abbey Huffer — Grade: 05
I see you every morning when I wake up. Your eyes glistening like the sun. With you and I'm always surprised. I love her.

Ricardo Ioera — Grade: 05
My mom is the sparkle in my eyes. My hero. My mom is as beautiful as real beauty to make a son like me.

John Kim — Grade: 05
My mother's love is greater than the sea. Your smile is more shiny than the morning sky. You are an angel given from God.

Cameron Knollenberg — Grade: 05
Right or wrong, good or bad, my mom will always love me. No matter what my problem is, my mom can always calm me.

Ethan Moos — Grade: 05
Mom deserves a diamond because she is one, gleaming and sparkling in the sunlight. She has always been there for me through better or worse.

Desiree Nettles — Grade: 05
My mom deserves a diamond. She's the best in every way. My mom is just so special. She helps me everyday.

Diana Pajong — Grade: 05
My mom is very giving. She makes me have good feelings. Her love is very kind. She is always in my mind.

Rebecca Romero — Grade: 05
My mom deserves a diamond because of her love. When she has much work to do, she always has time for me too!

* Amethyst winners in bold.

Griffin Thoe   Grade: 05
My mom deserves a diamond. She works at home day and night. She is like the world to me, I love her.

Ashlyn Underwood   Grade: 05
My mom's voice glistens, if you listen you'll find out. My mom deserves a diamond, that's no doubt. A beautiful sunlit garden, that's my mom.

Shelby Winston   Grade: 05
Like a diamond, nothing can break my mom's love for me and my family. Her eyes sparkle like the ocean waves. Love is powerful impact.

Teacher: Lori Montgomery

Avery Brown   Grade: 04
My mom is so cool, she helps me with school. I love her just like she loves me. She's 1, she is so much fun!

Rhett Cook   Grade: 04
My mom is 1 and very fun. She's always by my side and never hides. She will never fade from my heart. She's awesome.

Natalie Curie   Grade: 04
My mom is sweet and kind. She always says to follow your heart. She helps the community. She loves to bake. My mom is incredible!

Jessie DeGraw   Grade: 04
My mom is the best. She is very caring and kind. She has a big heart. She is an angel. She is number ONE!

Mason Genova   Grade: 04
My mother is sweet like sugar. She is nice and joyful. That's why mom deserves a diamond.

Abby Goedecke   Grade: 04
My mom is the best, but she cares about the rest. She always will be number one in my heart.

Nicholas James   Grade: 04
My mom is the great and the best. I love her lots and she is very nice and she is very kind.

Noah Kalkanian   Grade: 04
My mom is loving. She should be hovering like an angel that she is. In Heaven like a diamond in the dark night sky.

Makenna Lee   Grade: 04
My mom's smile shines like the sun. She's the best and better than the rest. My mom is very special and I love her.

Royce Lewis   Grade: 04
My mom deserves a diamond because she helps me when I am sick. She also helps me when I am feeling bad.

Cassie Morrison   Grade: 04
My mom's the best, she'll do the rest just to help us all. She will not quit when we throw a fit!

Anthony Pastrana   Grade: 04
My mom is the best. She is better than the rest. She makes use, all the best. She makes me smile.

Nolan Robbins   Grade: 04
My mom is great, she lets me skate. She's an awesome teacher and nobody can beat her. She is great and never takes a break.

Ethan Steele   Grade: 04
My mom is charming and sweet. She is sympathetic, helpful, and forgiving when I am bad. I will love her forever and ever.

Vincent Tapia   Grade: 04
My mom is great and is fun. I love her from the bottom of my heart. My mom is 1 in the world.

Ruby Tincup   Grade: 04
My mom is extraordinary. She doesn't come out of the ordinary. She is special in my heart. That's why I've loved her from the start.

Teacher: Greg Togawa

Bayley Bachiero   Grade: 05
My mom deserves a diamond because she is the greatest mother in the world and she cares and loves me like no other mother.

Tanner Clarke   Grade: 05
My mom shines in the sunlight. She is the only one that will make me smile. I will always love my mom.

Nick Curie   Grade: 05
My mom deserves a diamond because she is very helpful, kind and joyful. She helps me with my homework and teaches me to be delightful.

Eleanor Ekstrom   Grade: 05
My mom deserves a diamond because she is like the cool breeze of Fall warming my heart and mind, taking care of me with care.

Joelle Engler   Grade: 05
My mom deserves a diamond because she cooks, cleans and always takes great care of my brother and me.

Makenzie Kamai   Grade: 05
Mom's the best in the world. She's more than just a beautiful girl. She's caring, respectful, fair and fun. There's no doubt, she's number one!

Christie Lee   Grade: 05
My mom deserves a diamond because her eyes shine as bright as the sun. Her heart is overflowing with love. I love my beautiful mom!

Melanie Miller   Grade: 05
A whole lot of love for me, looking the best on the family tree, beautiful, wonderful, smart, nice, think twice about a diamond for her.

Nicolas Padilla   Grade: 05
She is a gemstone, her eyes, opals bright and red. Her mind is a jet deep and intellectual. Her heart, a ruby open for all.

William Quinn   Grade: 05
My mom deserves a diamond because she always helps and loves and enjoys all of my qualities. She is the best I could ask for.

Katrina Ramos   Grade: 05
My mom is special and wonderful. She is very hardworking and loving. Whenever I see her, her smile makes my day perfect.. She's great.

Kinsey Tarplee   Grade: 05
My mother deserves a diamond because she is a loving, kind soul that will forgive me for whatever I do wrong. She will love me.

Capistrano Valley High
Mission Viejo

Teacher: Nancy French

Krystal Canning   Grade: 10
Mother of five, lunch packer, taxi driver, motivator, PTA, adored, role model, precious, generous, joyous, loved by many, gift from God deserves way more than a diamond.

Nathan Hunnicutt   Grade: 10
Twenty five words, nothing for a mother. One who cares and sacrifices like no other. Who's loved and lost. A diamond, well worth the cost.

Alex Santo   Grade: 10
A beautiful diamond has the 4 C's; Clarity, Cut, Color and Carat weight. A beautiful mother has the following C's; Caring, Courageous, Confident and Consistent.

IN THE NEWS!

Kids say their moms are real gems

Poetry-contest winners are awarded jewels from a Costa Mesa jeweler who started the event after a fruitless search for his mom. Lori Basheda. Orange County Register. 3-8-2004.

Michael Watson searched 20 years for his mother. By the time he found her, she was dead.

But the journey - which began in earnest on the night the country learned "Who Shot J.R.?" and ended on a telephone in a Costa Mesa jewelry shop - wasn't for naught.

Watson's search inspired him to start a contest, called WHY MOM DESERVES A DIAMOND®, that each year encourages thousands of children to pen their love for their moms.

Beginning Saturday and for the next three months, a parade of Orange County kids whose poems have been selected as winners will go to Watson's jewelry store to collect a gem.

But the real gems are the poems themselves. In 1993, the year Watson started the contest, he received 200 poems from local schools. Now the contest is on the Web and practically part of the spring curriculum in many local schools. This year, some 21,000 poems from every state in the country landed on Watson's doorstep.

It was 1958 when Watson was put up for adoption. As long as he can remember, the woman he calls "Mom," Martha Watson, called him her "little adopted angel."

His dad, Stoy, told him they went to the hospital one day and, standing before a room full of cribs, he shouted "I'll take that curly-headed one!"

As Watson grew up, he needed to hear more. "I needed a past," he said.

His parents finally told him a woman named Betty Price gave him up and that she lived at 2115 N. Delaware St. in Indianapolis, a few hours away. He made up his mind right there to find her someday. He never would have asked why she gave him up, he says. He just wanted to see her.

When Watson got his first car, he drove to the courthouse in Indianapolis to ask for his adoption records. Just as his mom warned, the judge wouldn't hand them over. So he drove to 2115 N. Delaware St. The lot was empty, the house torn down.

A few years later Watson went back to the judge. Again he was turned away. Again he went to Delaware Street. This time he knocked on doors to see if anyone remembered Betty Price. A trusting elderly couple listened to his story. They invited him in to use their phone book. Then they headed off to find out who shot J.R. on the TV show "Dallas" at a neighbor's house.

"Price was like Smith," Watson said. "There were millions." Not to mention it was a rotary-dial phone. Michael locked the door behind him when he left.

Finally, on a third visit to the courthouse, for whatever reason, the judge handed him his folder.

"My heart is pounding; this is something about me!" he recalls thinking. It was an interview Betty Price gave to the court after she handed her baby over. It was full of clues.

She quit school and married Carl Price when she was 16. They had a child. But she divorced her husband because he was "never true to her." She didn't know who the father of this baby was. It was "like a bad dream."

In the interview Betty also says she was from Plymouth, Ind. "It's a lie I followed for many years," Watson says. The search went on for 13 more years.

"It's not an everyday thing," he said. "You forget about it for a year, until Mother's Day. Or you go to a doctor and they ask you to write your history of diabetes and heart disease and you say, 'I don't know.'"

One day, after marrying a woman named Carmen and becoming the father of a stepdaughter, he got that feeling again. This time he sent letters to every courthouse in Indiana looking for a marriage license.

One day he got an envelope from Coatesville, Ind. Inside was the marriage license of Carl Price and Betty Stewart, daughter of Hattie Stewart.

Watson dialed directory assistance and asked for Hattie Stewart.

"Oh, when she said hold for the number I almost hung up," he said. "This is the moment. What do I say? 'Hi, my name is Michael. I live in California. I think your daughter is my mother.' See how stupid that sounds?"

It took him 24 hours to dial. When he did, Hattie Stewart told him he had the wrong number. Michael persisted. Stewart paused.

She told him that her daughter did have a child in 1958, but he was stillborn.

"I said, 'Ma'am, that is me. And I'm very much alive. And you are my grandmother.' There was total silence."

Finally she said, "You know, we always wondered if you were alive."

Sometimes when her daughter was drunk, she would ramble that she had to find Jonathan, the name she gave to her "stillborn" baby.

"Can I talk to her?"

Michael was ready. He had steeled himself for rejection. But death? It never even crossed his mind.

Betty Price, it turns out, died thirteen years before at age 46. Cirrhosis of the liver killed her.

Within a few weeks Michael was on a plane to New Albany. His grandmother drove two hours from Coatesville to meet him at his childhood home. She gave him a picture of his mother when she was pregnant with him. It is the only picture he has of them together.

Brittany Abraham   Grade: 12
More than a heroine, more than a friend. Blessed I am through thick and thin because my mom's love will never end.

Kevin Chambers   Grade: 12
A diamond, like a mother's love, can withstand any hardship, persevere any tragedy, and bless those who receive it.

Christian Cortes   Grade: 12
Her unforgettable smile. Her unconditional love have taught me to appreciate every moment in life, sacrificed it all, she is not superhero, she's a mom.

Jacquelyn Jung   Grade: 12
Despite how long I'm out and how loud "turn down the music" is yelled. She always loves me just a little louder, a little longer.

Lindsey Knittle   Grade: 12
My mom's hands gently pushed me in the right direction, clapped as she encouraged me to persist and molded me into the person I am today.

Theresa Nguyen   Grade: 12
My mother: Too impeccable for make-up, radiant in anything she wears, shines in every step she takes, has a never-ending characteristic of being helpful.

Arya Omshehe   Grade: 12
She's wonderful, beautiful, helpful, and smart. She shows it all from the bottom of her heart. My loving mother, she's the very best thing I got!

Nick Powers   Grade: 12
Like a diamond, my mom has many facets. She is beautiful, brilliant, and flawless. She gives me love, comfort and support. My mom is priceless.

Carden Academy
Huntington Beach

Teacher: Debra Hashin

Noelle Dahl   Grade: 04
My mom is a loving mother and a kind person. She helps my family in every way. She is everything to me.

Robilee Fredericks   Grade: 04
Mother, you work all day to make us happy. You love us with all of your heart. A diamond for you, how can I say no?

Leslie Ha   Grade: 04
Roses are red, violets are blue. You are as beautiful as the sun, loving as the moon. You are everything to me. I'll always love you.

Spencer Hagaman   Grade: 04
My mother spoils me to death. My mother helps me with my troubles. My mother is super-woman and is the goddess of my heart.

Ciarra Nean- Marzella   Grade: 04
Your eyes are like the stars above watching over me. You are Mother Nature being loving to all mankind. Your smile brightens my heart.

Daryn Nguyen   Grade: 04
A diamond shines like moonlight sky, just like my mother's eyes. She'll be the envy of her friends. Her love and care will never end.

Antoinette Nguyen   Grade: 04
My mother is the light in my heart and brings sparkle to life in me.

Emma Rutkowski   Grade: 04
My mom means the world to me. No one could replace her. She is the best mom in the world. I love my mom.

Ashley Sabers   Grade: 04
My mother is my role model. She is sweet, loving, caring, funny, kind, never gives up, terrific, and helpful. I love my mom.

Stephanie Slates   Grade: 04
My mother has eyes that sparkle like a diamond. She is funny, sweet, never gives up and is helpful.

Tiffany Tran   Grade: 04
Jewelry is nice, crystals are shiny, but you're the most precious gem in my life.

Teacher: Colleen Hazard

Janine Abdelmuti   Grade: 06
My mom is a diamond. She sparkles in the sun. My mom is loving, caring and heartwarming. She is the biggest diamond of all.

Caitlin Abrahams   Grade: 06
A rising sun is she, who wonders what I will bloom to be. She gives me energy to grow and that I will always know.

Ricardo Bautista   Grade: 06
My mom has always taken care of me since I was a little baby and she will always be my best friend.

Devin Broderick   Grade: 06
My mom is there for me all day and night, she appreciates me for who I am and loves me and I love her.

Jack Brooks   Grade: 06
My mom cares for me the best she can. She never falls, she always stands. She never doubts. As her son, I am proud.

Noelle Cortese   Grade: 06
She is as beautiful as a flower; comforts me for hours. She's a gift from heaven to a girl at the age of eleven.

Xena Cox   Grade: 06
Until the stars have shown their last. Wherever on this earth I walk, she is there, to excite and inspire. My mom, my dark fire.

Kayla Jett   Grade: 06
My mother deserves a diamond because she is pretty, intelligent, and just like a diamond, anyone instantly falls in love with her.

Christine Keough   Grade: 06
My mom is a helping hand, who is always there for me. She helps me when things are bad and fills me up with glee.

Audrey Nguyen   Grade: 06
My mom is very special. She has helped me to succeed. She has a wonderful smile. There is nothing she can't achieve.

KelleyAnn Thai   Grade: 06
A person sent to me from above, someone to care for me and someone to love. My mother is a gift that I'll treasure forever.

Pauline Tran   Grade: 06
My mom is the light that shines so bright. So I will be able to find my way in the world of never-ending darkness.

Teacher: Kitri Lint

Alicia Antonopoulos   Grade: 05
My mom is a rare beauty. She has a big heart. We shall never part. Her warming hugs never stop loving. I love my mom.

Kylie Antonopoulos   Grade: 05
My mom is amazing. She tries to teach us to become better people, and does everything. She makes it look easy. I love my mom.

Joshua Awad   Grade: 05
She always loves and cares for me. She makes every second of my life beautiful. She has the heart of an angel. My flawless mom.

Lutfil Hardy   Grade: 05
My mom deserves a diamond because she takes care of the house. She cooks for me and takes care of me. Thanks for everything, mom.

Devon Hirezi   Grade: 05
My mom deserves a diamond because she takes good care of me. Her soul is like a gem, and she is special like a diamond.

Jesse Nash   Grade: 05
She works full time to support me. She encourages me in sports. She makes sure there is food on my plate.

Whitley Rudolph   Grade: 05
My mother deserves a diamond because she works very hard, pays for food and rent. She's prettier inside and out than any diamond!

Gizzelle Velazquez   Grade: 05
My mother deserves a diamond because she always puts me in first place. My mom deserves a diamond because she is a gem herself.

Nathan Vo   Grade: 05
My mom deserves a diamond because she is a helpful mom. She is a hard worker and she makes sure I get a good education.

Sabrina Way   Grade: 05
My mom deserves a diamond because she works very hard and helps to support me, my sister and her parents. My mom is very loving.

Teacher: Miller

Cassidy Balloch   Grade: 01
My mom deserves a diamond because she takes good care of us and we are special to her. She gives us lots of love.

Megan Bideau   Grade: 01
My mom deserves a diamond because she is special to me. She reads to me, takes care of me, and folds my clothes.

Sean Flanders   Grade: 01
My mom deserves a diamond because she loves and protects me. She helps me do my math and helps my family.

Johnny Ray Flores   Grade: 01
My mom deserves a diamond because she reads the bible to me. She makes my lunch everyday and she tucks me in bed.

Noah Perelman   Grade: 01
My mom deserves a diamond because she loves me no matter what and she reads me a bedtime story.

Teacher: PJ Stanley

Janan Abdelmuti   Grade: 08
My mother is an intelligent lovely lady, nothing compares to how much she means to me. She provides shelter and warmth for our family.

Cheyenne Arcuri   Grade: 08
My mom deserves the prize because I have a feeling it will be just her size. She's a great mother and I wouldn't want another.

Alec Dahl   Grade: 08
My loving mother is certainly so dazzling in the gorgeous night sky, but during the brilliant light, her love burns like a million spicy jalapenos.

Celina Huynh   Grade: 08
My mother is like a diamond. She is as necessary as the sun. She is unique and irreplaceable. Her radiant aura is incredible.

Jill Nakaso   Grade: 08
My mom cares for me everyday without any yearly pay. Because for me, her love she reserves. A diamond is what she truly deserves.

Austin Nguyen   Grade: 08
Who hath protected and nurtured me with all her might? Who hath loved me dearly for my entire life? This intelligent, beautiful lady, my mother!

Jennifer Nguyen   Grade: 08
My mom gives me tons of hugs along with endless love. She'll love me until the end of time. That's why I wrote this diamond rhyme.

Troy Nguyen   Grade: 08
Since birth, I've been granted the honor of my mother's presence. She's the godsend angel that nurtures my being, that is indescribable by 25 words.

Diana Schwene   Grade: 08
She hugs like a teddy bear. She kisses like a bee. She is beautiful like a fleur de lys and she loves me.

William Sprowls   Grade: 08
Nothing compares to the love she's greatly shared. Her beauty is there for all to see. A diamond would show what she means to me.

Teacher: Dale Vardeman

Camille Carter   Grade: 02
You snug me, you hug me. Your eyes twinkle when you smile. That is why you deserve a diamond from your child.

AraBella Cary   Grade: 02
My mother is very good. Her eyes are as bright as the stars. Her heart will shine like the diamond. I love her.

Kyle Christy   Grade: 02
My mom is loving, caring, joyful and has a beautiful smile. She is a perfect mom for me. A mom like that should have a diamond.

Ashley Hazard   Grade: 02
My mom is so joyful. She is so sweet and kind. She deserves a diamond to wear all the time.

Kathy Nguyen   Grade: 02
My mother is a jewel of my heart, all that I can say is that the diamond in her heart is always there to stay.

Aiden Nguyen   Grade: 02
Why she deserves a diamond. My mom is the greatest. She is the beat in my heart. She is the most precious to me.

Jessica Nguyen   Grade: 02
My mom deserves a diamond. She is sweet as a flower. She is the one in my dreams. Your loving child.

Bryan Perez   Grade: 02
My mother deserves a diamond that sparkles and shines. It would sparkle day and night. But my mother out glows the light.

Amanda Sprowls   Grade: 02
Your smile is as sweet as can be. In my heart, you're just the right diamond for me.

Bashir Sultan   Grade: 02
My mother is loving, caring and sweet. She would sparkle in the light with her diamond so bright. It would be a delight.

Isabella Tran   Grade: 02
My mom deserves a diamond to shine in the night. I can see her smiling at the sight. She cares for me from day to night.

Teacher: Maryann Vasquez

Danielle DeVinney   Grade: 07
My mom deserves a diamond because she's always taking care of me before herself and making me feel better when I'm sad or in pain.

* Amethyst winners in bold.

Jeremy Dreyer　　　　　Grade: 07
Many ways she is really kind. Obviously nice to everyone. Way too many reasons to count on my fingers why she deserves a diamond.

Natalie Flores　　　　　Grade: 07
She is beautiful and dazzling, made just perfect, glistening and shining, graceful in everything she does, just like a diamond.

Raela Frazier　　　　　Grade: 07
My mom deserves a diamond for the grace in her heart. For loving my family each moment we're apart. Blessings she gives to every heart.

Kelly Furuya　　　　　Grade: 07
She has a heart like no other. Is as smart as can be. Always has an answer for me. That can only be my mother!

Dustin Huynh　　　　　Grade: 07
Everyday I see my dream and just what do I see? My mother, heaven's light gleam. A magical entity. That's what appears to me.

Nina Kar　　　　　Grade: 07
My mother, she who cooks and cleans… does most anything. She who's brave enough to stand and fight for me…My savior and my mother…

Ashley Rhyne　　　　　Grade: 07
She's always there for me. She works so hard and so artistically. Moms are like cups of tea; so wonderful, so nice. A pure necessity.

Katherine Rives　　　　　Grade: 07
She gives love like a dove. She shines bright like stars in the night. She shares as she cares. A mother she is to me.

Trevor Sabers　　　　　Grade: 07
She loves me. She cares for ne. She is my role model. She is my star. She's my mom and I think she deserves a diamond.

Emma Silvestri　　　　　Grade: 07
An A+ for love; a star for her. All that my mom has preserved. Because her heart not lacking, her selfless way of acting.

Wesley Slates　　　　　Grade: 07
She's smart, she has a large heart, always finding deals. She cooks tasty meals. Sometimes she throws curves, a diamond is what my mother deserves.

Teacher: Mikelyn Weber

Ruby Anbari　　　　　Grade: 03
My mom shines like gold. She takes special care of me. I love her so much. She is like a diamond to me.

Ryan Bala　　　　　Grade: 03
My mom with such a fine heart is like a diamond. Her precious soul lights up my life.

Timmy Benson　　　　　Grade: 03
My mom's eyes melt into crystals when I see her look at me. When my mom looks at me, I see diamonds shine all over.

Maxx Clemente　　　　　Grade: 03
Her eyes shine brightly with the love she gives me. Her eyes glows with the care she gives me. I love my mom.

Chelsea Huynh　　　　　Grade: 03
My mom is like a beautiful sunny day. She is warm and shiny like the sun. She always loves me.

Alyssa Lambert　　　　　Grade: 03
The crystals in her eyes, the softness of her voice from dawn to dusk gives me warmth.

Nisha Lu　　　　　Grade: 03
My mom takes good care of me. She loves me and shows me that every night when she tucks me into bed.

Abigail Simington　　　　　Grade: 03
She held my hand and touched my heart. Thank you mom for all the things you gave me. I love you so much!

Quinn Simpson　　　　　Grade: 03
Your eyes glitter in the sunlight. The words you say fill my heart with love. You, my mother are a diamond.

Dakota Sumner　　　　　Grade: 03
I love my mom very much. She shines like the sun and her eyes are like diamonds. She is the most wonderful mom ever.

Carrillo (Leo) Elementary
Westminster

Teacher: Linh Tran

Maria Bautista　　　　　Grade: 06
My mom deserves a diamond because she's been supporting in difficult moments and she's also been loving. She's mostly been like my best friend.

Kyle Pham　　　　　Grade: 06
My mom is like the three seasons, hot like the summer, cool like the winter, and pretty as spring flowers.

Donna Tran　　　　　Grade: 06
A smile to see…A voice to hear equals a mom who cares.

Teacher: Cheryl Williams

Mai Nguyen　　　　　Grade: 06
My mom deserves a diamond because without her inspiration and dedication, I won't have the courage to work my way all these eleven years successfully.

Duyen Nguyen　　　　　Grade: 06
Her voice, like nightingales. Her touches, like rose pedals. Her heart, full of love. Her kisses, comforting. Mom, a perfect jewel…a gift of life.

Castille Elementary
Mission Viejo

Teacher: Stuart Evans

Kyla Anderson- clausen　　　　　Grade: 04
My mom's smile shines like a diamond. Her eyes glimmer like a quartz. I love her a lot. That's why she should have a diamond.

Valeria Bianco　　　　　Grade: 05
My mom deserves a diamond because she cleans and cooks all day. She is kind and beautiful and she's loves to help me whenever.

Elisabeth Holder　　　　　Grade: 05
My mom deserves this diamond because she works so hard and always gets the most beautiful things for me. She (in my mind) already won.

Jessica Olson　　　　　Grade: 05
My mom deserves a diamond because she has done so many things for me and I think I should give her something to thank her.

Kiana Reedy　　　　　Grade: 05
My mom should win a diamond because she is a great role model in different kinds of ways to other people; nice and very gentle.

Matthew Stigna　　　　　Grade: 05
"A diamond is forever". So too is a son's love for his mother. A perfect way to tell my mother what she means to me.

Teacher: Shonna Josepson

Marissa Bass   Grade: 05
She works so hard. Nobody could keep up with her work. My mother is so nice. I would have expected her to win an award for "best mom."

Jaime DelBarrio   **Grade: 05**
My mom loves me no matter what. She comforts me and makes me laugh when I'm feeling down. That's why my mom deserves a diamond.

Amy Giacchino   Grade: 05
My mom deserves a diamond because she works hard to teach her fourth Grade class and loves a family of four. I love my mom!

Nicholas Penrose   Grade: 05
My mom deserves a diamond because she works so hard to keep me fed and gives up her time to get me to sports.

Yasmine Tabdili   **Grade: 05**
My mother is a heart-warming, sweet, and kind parent. She works day and night for my brother and I to be happy.

Traci Trojan   Grade: 05
My mom deserves a diamond because she is very nice and loves others. She is a P.E. teacher and very fun to be with.

Teacher: Susie Mc Michael

Lupe Contreras   Grade: 05
My mom deserves a diamond because she's caring for animals and kids. I love her not just because she's my mom, but because she's caring.

Stephanie Kusto   Grade: 05
My mom always buys things for me and my brother. She always thinks of others before herself. She is a kind and loving person.

Maily Wang   Grade: 05
Many moms can't handle two children, mine can. My mom has four children. She takes care of all of us, cooks, loves us and cleans.

Teacher: Donna Smiggs

Alaina Ayres   **Grade: 05**
My mom deserves a diamond because she is like a diamond to me. Her love is beautiful, her personality sparkles.

Ryan Bennett   **Grade: 05**
I have the most caring, loving mother in the world. She slaves day after day keeping our lives in order. Nobody is more deserving.

Kirby Black   Grade: 05
My mom deserves a diamond because she never stops to think about herself. She always does things for other people.

Monica Geiger   Grade: 05
My mom deserves a diamond because she is special and will always have a place in my heart. She is also my hero!

Amanda Gjertsen   **Grade: 05**
My mom deserves a diamond because she is always doing amazing things for everyone. My mom really deserves something as great as her.

Annie Hatton   Grade: 05
My mom deserves a diamond because she never thinks of herself, only others. She does anything for her children and fosters dogs who are homeless.

Nicki Ravari   Grade: 05
My mom deserves a diamond because she is always willing to give up any plans she has to help or comfort someone. She is awesome!

Austin Sechrest   Grade: 05
My mom deserves a diamond because she is pleasant to be around, she is very hardworking and she is always in a happy mood.

Kimberly Shollenberger   Grade: 05
My mom deserves a diamond because she always puts others first and takes care of me and my brother everyday. She also loves me.

Chapman Hills Elementary
Orange

Teacher: Susan Church

Alyssa Barraza   Grade: 03
My mommy deserves a diamond because she skips work to take care of me when I am sick. Last, my mommy completes my heart.

Paige Baskovich   **Grade: 03**
My mom deserves a diamond because her eyes sparkle like gems. Her hugs comfort me. I am proud that she is my mom.

Roger Bejoch   Grade: 03
My mom is as gorgeous as a gem and she has sparkling eyes of beauty. She's always been there for me.

Justin Camba   Grade: 03
My mom deserves a diamond because her eyes glisten in the day and sparkle at night. And with her warm hug, I feel protected.

Rafael Carrete   **Grade: 03**
My mom takes me to soccer practices. And her eyes are the butterflies in the morning. I'm glad that she made me. I love you.

Johnny Choi   Grade: 03
My mom deserves a diamond because my mom is sweet and beautiful. She makes food like food at a really fancy restaurant.

Makaila Croissant   Grade: 03
My mom deserves a diamond because she is caring. She is as shiny as a diamond. She has beautiful sparkling eyes. She is so gorgeous.

Alexa Faber   **Grade: 03**
My mom deserves a diamond because she is a rose in the morning. Her hair is as shiny as a sparkling gem.

Krista Faber   Grade: 03
My mom deserves a diamond because she is just like a diamond. She sparkles everyday. She is very helpful and full of heart.

Julianna Jones   Grade: 03
My mom deserves a diamond. Whenever I look at her sparkling eyes and her shiny hair, it makes me smile, feeling glad she's my mom.

Junee Kim   **Grade: 03**
My mother deserves a diamond because she is beautiful, sweeter than honey and her love endures forever. She is shining through the way.

Cole Nehrir   **Grade: 03**
My mom deserves a diamond because I always see a smile on her face. She's the only heart shaped cloud spotted in the sky. XO

Scout Prosser   Grade: 03
My mom is the greatest person in the world and she kisses me everyday. My mom is gorgeous like a sparkling gem.

Nick Real   Grade: 03
I think my mom deserves a shiny diamond because she cares for us. She support us and she loves us more than anything.

Kyle Shintani   Grade: 03
Mom deserves a diamond because her eyes sparkle like the stars in the sky and her tear drops are like the rain in the sky.

* Amethyst winners in bold.

Hannah Tjoa   Grade: 03
My mom deserves a diamond because she is a beautiful, lovely, and caring woman. She cares for all of us. I love her very much.

Jason Ward   Grade: 03
My mom deserves a diamond because she is always so kind and thoughtful and understanding. She is willing to do something for me.

J P Wright   Grade: 03
My mom's hair is a river of shine. A diamond would match her eyes. I love you, Mom!

Rachel Yates   Grade: 03
My mom deserves a diamond because she rocks the world and the universe. Her eyes sparkle in the sun and she makes me laugh.

Teacher: Susie Spargur

Grant Anderson   Grade: 04
My mom is caring, laughing and friendly. She helps me with my homework. She helps me study for a test. That's why my mom deserves a diamond.

Jenna Angier   Grade: 04
Mom deserves a diamond because of her kindness and love for me and my brother. The diamond will make her shine like the sun.

Nojan Azim   Grade: 04
My mom has beautiful cloudy eyes. She does everything for me like a genie who loves me, cooks for me, and loves me.

Rachel Baxter   Grade: 04
Mom is the best! She drives me to all my activities. She is unique. She is very beautiful, joyful, and playful. She is awesome!

Sarah Bennett   Grade: 04
My mom is a kind, loving person who loves to play with her children. She is funny and always helps me. She is the best!

Corrin Blanchard   Grade: 04
My mom is unique, special and caring. She laughs at almost all of my jokes and she is very enjoyable.

Brandon Carter   Grade: 04
I think she is pretty and she is so nice. When you get something wrong, she will get through it with you. She is helpful.

Brooke Delligatta   Grade: 04
My mom is laughing and caring. When she looks at you, she has a sparkle in her eyes. My mom is loving and thoughtful too.

Caitlin Lim   Grade: 04
My mom is a hard worker and she is the GREATEST mom. She takes care of me and she has long patience, I love mom.

Amelia Pham   Grade: 04
My mom cares for everyone. She even gives people food. She helps everyone we know and she still loves me the most.

Carson Shurtz   Grade: 04
Mom helps me with homework, makes me lunch, dinner and breakfast. She is loving, caring and enjoyable. She is the best mom in the world!

Elena Sternlicht   Grade: 04
Mom, Mother, Madre, Mere, Me. It doesn't matter how you put it, it means the very same thing. A caring woman who loves me.

Payton Thomas   Grade: 04
My mom is beautiful just the way she is. I couldn't ask for more. I love her more everyday. She is a super mom.

Christ Lutheran School
Costa Mesa

Teacher: Jenny Jordan

Gianna Jason   Grade: 08
Love pours from her like a fountain. Her encouragement fills my heart. No words can portray her beauty inside and out.

Branden Paz   Grade: 08
My mom's eyes twinkle like diamonds. Her heart as pure as gold. Her life is worth more than silver. She loves me with her life!

Taylor Spies   Grade: 08
Mom is always there for me; she never lets me down. Her love is everlasting. She makes me smile when I frown. I love her.

Teacher: Susan Vescera

Alyssa Oliver   Grade: 06
My mom loves me so much. I'm her first priority and she always wants me to be happy. That's why my mom deserves a diamond.

Mikey Anderson   Grade: 07
My mom deserves a diamond because she is my hero. When I am sad, she is my rock. Most of all, she is my chauffeur.

Amanda Buhl   Grade: 07
My mom deserves a diamond because she is kind and good-hearted. She is always trying to help me. My mom is a wonderful person.

Peyton Carte   Grade: 07
My mom deserves a diamond because she loves and cares for me. She deserves a diamond because she deserves something as wonderful as her.

Kellie Cavanaugh   Grade: 07
Her love is like the sun, warm and glowing. Her smile is like the moon, bright and inviting. Her generosity makes the world go round.

Noah Collard   Grade: 07
My mom deserves a diamond because she's there for me. Her eyes are like a sea. She's as strong as a brick wall. I love her!

Adam Ditt   Grade: 07
My mom is like a diamond, she twinkles in everyone's eyes. My mom deserves a diamond because she needs something as charming as her.

Abby Griffith   Grade: 07
My mom's eyes as beautiful as the moon. Her heart as bright as the sun. Her love as deep as the sea, she loves me.

Emma Griffith   Grade: 07
I believe that my mom deserves a diamond because she works hard and she has taught me and my family to walk and talk with Christ.

Carl Johansson   Grade: 07
My mom deserves a diamond for all she does for my family. Without her, my life would be incomplete.

Chloe Kuhen   Grade: 07
My mom deserves a diamond because she's ALWAYS there for me. She loves everyone with all her heart. She is my diamond and my life.

Hayleigh Perry   Grade: 07
Her eyes like sparkling diamonds. Her heart like pure gold. Her soul so endearing. The love that she holds.

Elijah Reiland   Grade: 07
My mom deserves a diamond because she's been a wonderful influence on me. She's always been there for me, and I know she always will.

Kristin Snapper   Grade: 07
My mom is like a diamond because she is beautiful on the inside and out. She's strong and brings joy to everyone around her.

Lauren Steinke   Grade: 07
So funny and bright, I'd like her to have that diamond tonight. I love my mom so much. I'd like her to have that diamond to touch.

Cedric Thomas   Grade: 07
My mom deserves a diamond because she does almost everything around the house and doesn't get thanked every day. So thank you, mom.

Analysa Vivanco   Grade: 07
I love my mom. She is loving, pretty, she cooks and she cleans. Mom does everything. My mom deserves a diamond and much more!

Tayler Young   Grade: 07
Her eyes are like stars in the night. Her smile gleams in the moonlight. When she talks, it's like music and I love her.

Madison Zirneklis   Grade: 07
My mom deserves a diamond because her eyes sparkle like diamonds, her smile shines like diamonds, and she is as precious as a diamond.

Olivia Zollman   Grade: 07
My mom deserves a diamond because she loves me and cares about me. Another reason is because she is a great wife to my dad.

Cielo Vista Elementary
Rancho Santa Margarita

Teacher: Michelle Cheon

Joshua Andrade   Grade: 06
My mom is a gorgeous angel floating from the heavens filling my heart with never ending love to savor forever. I'll cherish you always mom.

Micaela Balcaza   Grade: 06
The shining star in my heart, the hero of my life, the one who gave me birth, the apple of my eye. Who? My mom.

Isaiah Bridges   Grade: 06
My mom is a flower ready to bloom. A diamond that lights up the night with beauty. A sea of love that never ends. Mom.

Brianna Brito   Grade: 06
The warmth in my heart comes from her eyes. As beautiful as the sea. She is an angel to me. I love you, mom.

Shelly Ferrer   Grade: 06
My mom 's love is like a flower, forever in bloom. Her beauty is like a star, brilliant, shining high in the sky.

Mikala Johnson   Grade: 06
An everlasting light that shines to the heavens above. An angel that glows in the darkness and a flower blooming forever, my mom.

Jenna Johnston   Grade: 06
My mom is like a shooting star, dancing across the big wondrous sky, lighting up cold dark nights, my mom's love is my everlasting wish.

Shawn Lam   Grade: 06
My mother is my guardian, whether she's working in the garden or in the kitchen. When I'm gone, she misses. When I'm hurt, she kisses.

Marissa Mortenson   Grade: 06
My mom is a book that never ends. A tree that keeps on growing. A heart as big as the world. Always watching over me.

Mitchell Timken   Grade: 06
My mom is as beautiful as the night sky. She shines like a brilliant, gleaming star tucking herself behind the moon. She is elegant tonight.

Madison Upchurch   Grade: 06
Gentle as a wave, kisses that are soft, pretty as a porcelain doll, a voice warm as a the blazing sun, my Mother.

Teacher: Doreen Costa

Erin Beall   Grade: 05
Whenever my mom smiles at me with her breath taking marvelous smile, it gives me reassurance that for all eternity she will love me unconditionally.

Cooper Blythe   Grade: 05
My mom guides me like the moon on a dark night. Her smiles are full of joy. She is like an angel, filled with love.

Shane Brudner   Grade: 05
What do I see when my mom is gazing at the night? I see a bright Holy light shining on my radiant mom till dawn.

Kendall Derbyshire   Grade: 05
Eyes dazzle like a shooting star. Heart is filled with gentleness like a guardian angel. Smile is like all the diamonds in the world.

Nayeli Duarte   Grade: 05
My mom's eyes glisten like a diamond. My heart is filled with her love. She gave me a path to life. "Mama", I love you!

Austin Fine   Grade: 05
Her face is a beautiful sight. Her eyes are brown and bright. She loves with great might, and her hugs are very tight.

Victoria Gonzalez   Grade: 05
My mother has eyes of endless love and a smile more luminous than light. Her hugs are warm and tight. Her love always takes flight.

Jaclyn Holding   Grade: 05
I'm never astray; my mother's definite hands guide me. My mother is unlike any other; acting as my guardian angel. Her affection will always last.

Savannah Jones   Grade: 05
The glimmer in her eyes. The warmth of her heart. The spark in her kisses. Her smile like pure art, my caregiver, love, my mother.

Tiffani Lamas   Grade: 05
Her eyes glisten like a shimmering star. Her heart is a fragile blanket wrapped around me. Her soul is like an angel from Heaven above.

Mia Marcotrigiano   Grade: 05
Her unique eyes sparkle in the moonlight. Her kiss sparks with love. She's a queen in my heart forever and without her, I'm in complete.

Tiana Merk   Grade: 05
Thoughtful, devoted and unique. That's my mom. She loves me through the ups and downs. Warming smile assures me that I'm safe. My mom!

Huntyr Mina   Grade: 05
Loving and kind, I call her mine. She gave me life and devoted the rest of hers to me. So she deserves this diamond, see?

Clara Nguyen   Grade: 05
With the slightest touch of her fingertips, she can fill that empty hole in my heart with happiness and joy to make my life complete.

Vincent Nicandro   Grade: 05
A guardian angel of the stars of night. Beholding eternal comfort and light. She soars gracefully like a dove. My mom...a gift from above.

John Ortega   Grade: 05
My mom is special to me in every way. She comforts me when I'm sad. She's what a true mother could be. I love Mom.

* Amethyst winners in bold.

Jake Reitan   Grade: 05
She is the star in the dark night sky. Her smile is as dazzling as the sun. She is the keeper of my life.

Jake Stringer   Grade: 05
Eyes twinkling like a thousand sapphires. Her kindness fulfills anyone's desires. Her lips as red as a cherry. Mom's heart is so loving to make anyone merry.

Hector Valerio   Grade: 05
Her eyes are luminous like the stars up high in the sky. She is very compassionate and considerate. She deserves a diamond.

Liberty Worapot   Grade: 05
It is she whom gave live to me. A wonderful person who gave me a heart. Her eyes are like diamonds, glistening forever inside me.

Niguel Ziegler   Grade: 05
Her love, compassion and hospitality all rest in her gorgeous eyes. She's there through good times and bad. She's Mommy and I'll always love her.

Teacher: Mary Duffy

Ryan Krajec   Grade: 05
My mom is as sweet as a strawberry, green as a watermelon, purple as a grape and smells like a candy cane. She is my life.

Thomas Mayes   Grade: 05
My mom deserves a diamond because she spends time with me. We enjoy walks around the pond. I love her because she is my Mom!

Jose Diaz   Grade: 06
My mom deserves a diamond because she is there for the good and bad days. I want to show her I appreciate everything she does.

Connor Meehan   Grade: 06
My mom deserves a diamond because she is a loving, caring individual. The room lights up when she smiles. My mom is awesome. Love you!

Teacher: Leslie Finch

Charles Alatorre   Grade: 05
Who's the person who gives me love? Without her, I would still be a thought above. She's supportive in all I do. She's my mom.

Sara Allen   Grade: 05
My gorgeous mother's eyes glisten in the sunlight. Her smile gleams with compassion. Her facial features sparkle with love. I love her always, my Mother.

Brittany Beard   Grade: 05
A dove, a rose, an angel. Eyes like diamonds, sweetness in her voice. Flawless in every way, my mother.

Rosa Collazo   Grade: 05
When I gaze in her eyes, I see my life. Her smile glistens like sun that keeps me alive. Her hair reflects the gorgeous ocean.

Nathan Dacoear   Grade: 05
My mom is as beautiful as a dove. Everlasting is her love. More graceful than a gazelle. Believe me you can tell. I love my mom.

Wade Dungan   Grade: 05
She is the one who gets me out of pain and trouble. That flowing hair, those diamond eyes, that surely is my mother.

Mila Fernandez   Grade: 05
The moon reflects off my mom's eyes. Her blond, soft, silky hair waves like wind. Her warm arms wrap around me. Her voice sings lullabies.

Devon Ingram   Grade: 05
She's beautiful, she's delightful. Her eyes sparkle. Her hugs make me happy. She is special. Who is she? She's my mother and I love her.

Marc Lafyente   Grade: 05
She loves me, caring for me always, she is flawless. Having a heart as perfect as a diamond. My mom.

Circe Lopez   Grade: 05
The night sky sparkles in her eyes. The warmness in her hugs. Kisses on my cheek warms my heart. Always there for me. MOM.

Kristina Norton   Grade: 05
My mom is gorgeous, loving, an angel. Her eyes sparkle like diamonds. Her smile takes my breath away. I will love her always. Mom.

Antonino Panzarella   Grade: 05
When I'm held, she penetrates pains and fears that disappear with her loving touch. My mom is the apple of God's eye.

Kara Peak   Grade: 05
Holds me tight, like a soft bear. Smells like blooming roses. Eyes glisten like the shining sun. Her words are as sweet as candy. Mom.

Kyle Weyman   Grade: 05
My mom deserves the diamond for what she does for me. Her eyes shine brighter than the sun and she's always there for me.

Teacher: Kathy Kido

Lupita Bello   Grade: 04
My mother warms my heart with joy. She is like a beautiful pearl. Her eyes are like a crystal clear diamond.

Gavin Bergini   Grade: 04
My mom's hair blows like sunflowers on a summer breeze. Her heart is my shield of love. She fills me up with love and compassion.

Jordan Block   Grade: 04
Eyes that sparkle like diamonds. Smiles that are positive. Hugs that make me feel safe. I love my mother.

Jonathon Cardenas   Grade: 04
My mom's eyes are like a glittering sapphire of beauty. Her heart gives a spark that gives a flame of sweetness. She deserves a diamond.

Adam Farrell   Grade: 04
My mom's kisses are as bright as a rose. Her eyes glisten through the night sky. Her loves is as big as the universe.

Kimberly Jones   Grade: 04
Eyes gleaming like moonlight. Laughter like a bird chirping a song. My mother deserves a diamond for her loving, caring, special, and gifted ways.

Olivia Land   Grade: 04
When I hear my mom singing. I feel like I'm safe and sound. When I hug her, I feel like I'm hugging a bright star.

Berkiel Molinard   Grade: 04
Beautiful hair, helping hand, special cook. Hugs that calm me. Heart that will always be with me. Love that lasts forever. My mom I will love.

Cristal Ocampo   Grade: 04
My mother is the key to my love. My mother is the key to my happiness. My mother, the rose of my heart.

Katrina Parran   Grade: 04
Her eyes sparkle like the sunset. Her hair glows like a star. Her heart is like the ocean water splashing. She takes away my pain.

Kevin Quredo   Grade: 04
Her eyes are brown as chocolate. The birds wake up to see her. She protects me from bad dreams. I love her with all my heart.

Michael Seitz   Grade: 04
Her eyes sparkle like glass on a sunny day. Her blond hair waves in the wind like a flag. Her lips are like a rose.

Savannah Valdez   Grade: 04
My mom is like a diamond. She dazzles and glows in her soul. She is like an angel in my heart. I love you, mom!

Teacher: Ann Larson

Armando Araujo   Grade: 04
Hard worker, cleans houses. Buys me clothes, cooks my meals, gives me hugs, says, "I will love you forever". She is my very special mom.

Skylar Jones   Grade: 04
Her eyes sparkle like emeralds. My heart beats with joy when she is around. When we are apart, I am homesick. I love you mom.

Alexandra Sotomayor   Grade: 04
Eyes twinkling in the light. Hair flowing like a river. A voice sweet sounding as a bird. Warming me with hugs when I'm sad. Mom.

Eliza Bulanadi   Grade: 05
My mom's eyes shine like the sun. Her beauty is everlasting. Her smile makes me happy. Her soft words make me feel safe and loved.

Rae Duarte   Grade: 05
My mom's eyes glisten in the sun. When I am sad, she is my shoulder to cry on. I wouldn't ask for a better mom.

Natalie Kelly   Grade: 05
Her eyes twinkle in the light. Her hugs keep me warm. Her love will never end. My mom. I will treasure forever more.

Brian Seymour   Grade: 05
My mom's kindness is endless. She has eyes of sapphires. Her lips are red rubies of beauty. My love for her is everlasting.

Tyler Canzoneri   Grade: 06
My mom is like a shining sea. Vast waves for me to see. Her smile is like a rainbow watching over me. I love mom.

Allison Copeland   Grade: 06
Looks like an angel from heaven. Eyes sparkle like shining stars. Heart beats with love and compassion for me. Gives me hugs and kisses. Mom.

Rachel Fontes   Grade: 06
My mom is as gorgeous as the sea. Her eyes sparkle like the moon. When she hugs me, I can never let go. Mom.

Conner Haynes   Grade: 06
My mom is the light from glistening stars. She is the sea where the seagulls sing. My mom is forever in my heart.

Alyssa Miller   Grade: 06
She is like a spectacular waterfall pouring her love all around me. Her eyes sparkle like diamonds when she is with me. My mom.

Kaitlin Ong   Grade: 07
My diamond, sparkling and brilliant. Oodles of fun to be around. My mentor; always there for me.

Teacher: Shannon Schlict

Luis Garcia   Grade: 04
Sweet as a flower, bright as a star, blue like the ocean, bright like a diamond, warm like a blanket, and always sweet mom.

Brendon Nikalus   Grade: 04
My mother is great and takes care of me and my sister. She cooks dinner and works at a doctor's office and donates to kids in need.

Teacher: Sharon Smith

Bailey Boyster   Grade: 01
I love how your eyes twinkle very, very much. I love the way you grin at me. Your smile is very pretty. I love you.

Valentina Perla   Grade: 01
To my diamond Princess, I will give you my love to my Princess lady, you are pretty like the stars in the sky.

Cole Stebbins   Grade: 01
I love you mom. Your eyes look like golden crystals. The way you look at me, I see my reflection in your eyes.

Aryan Talle   Grade: 01
When I wake up from sleeping, you eyes shine. Your eyes are like the sun. I would give you my heart.

Circle View Elementary
Huntington Beach

Teacher: Katie Andruss

Makena Booher   Grade: 05
My mom's my idol. She's special in every way. Whenever I'm sick, she nurses me back to health. She deserves a diamond, not an almond.

Tyler Fewell   Grade: 05
My mom deserves a diamond. It would be a mere piece of quartz compared to all the nice things she does for me. She rocks.

Victoria Jones   Grade: 05
Mom's so amazing, opens her heart. Mom deserves a diamond from the start. Mom's pretty eyes and silky hair. Mom's the one who's always there.

Cami Kelley- Hickman   Grade: 05
My mom's a pearl, a diamond indeed. Without her, I'm incomplete. She makes my earth spin. She is my life. I couldn't ask for more.

Daniel Klemm   Grade: 05
I know my mom deserves a diamond with the fullness of my heart. It's really hard to bear sometimes when we're so far apart.

Joshua Kurtz   Grade: 05
My mom is the best. My mom deserves a diamond because she will pass the test. Mom's a strong willed person, who's cuter than the rest.

Grant Kuster   Grade: 05
My mom deserves a diamond because she's best. She's better than all the rest. My mom is treated with respect because she's perfect.

Makena Low   Grade: 05
Skin so soft. Love so kind. Her name is mom. I'm glad she's mine.

Andrew Schiffer   Grade: 05
My mom is an angel from above. Her heart beats like a morning dove. She is my very favorite person. She deserves the biggest diamond.

Mark Schneider   Grade: 05
Her face sparkles like diamonds she should get. Her body is so amazing that you can't forget. There's no competition, the diamond will be hers.

Michael Todd   Grade: 05
My mom deserves a diamond because she is awesome and so incredibly nice. Her heart is a blossom!

* Amethyst winners in bold.

Mitzi Williams Grade: 05
My mom deserves a diamond because her eyes are like two. Her hugs so warm and tender, her love is always true.

Matthew Williams Grade: 05
My mom is great. Her eyes sparkle like the sun. She makes me have lots of fun.

Teacher: Ashley Bowen

Maxwell Cancilla Grade: 05
Mother is the most caring, loving mother in the world. She takes care of me even when she's sick. Mother is always there for me.

Robert Changkoepp Grade: 05
My mother's a charm to be around all day, no matter how you feel she'll brighten your day, when you need her, she'll find a way.

Brandon Doan Grade: 05
My mom is like a dove flying high. At night she is like a twinkling star in the sky. That's why she deserves a diamond.

Erin Gates Grade: 05
My mom's so beautiful like a pearl. She's better than a superhero. If she wins a diamond, she'll be two moms. She's already a diamond.

Zachary Goodale Grade: 05
My mother supplies love, as though a flood. Her smile of gold, never grows old. She never ignores me, she simply adores me.

Viva Henny Grade: 05
My mother has a crystal in her eye. Her silk heart touches my helpless soul that pleads her strength so I'll have a vibrant heart.

Jessica Kent Grade: 05
My brilliant Mother once besought, daughters will make you shine like the sun, sparkle like the moon. You shall be very blessed to behold someone special.

Cole Kuster Grade: 05
Wind coos her name. Her heart is like a ruby on a plain. Her kind ways are hard to find. She's always on my mind.

Jasmine Le Grade: 05
My mom is an angel, her wings soar above me. She cries pure tears with love in them. She's magnificent, a one of a kind.

Taylor Marosek Grade: 05
My mom is the light that guides me through the dark and dreary sea. My mom deserves a diamond as big as her heart.

Kim Nguyen Grade: 05
While we watch the sunset, her heart gleams with pleasure and pride. Her eyes sparkle with care. She has raised me through all years.

Sarah O' Brien Grade: 05
The wind sings her name. Her heart is a rose in an open plain. My mother's eyes heal my heart. We shall never depart.

Brenden Sallstrom Grade: 05
My mom's s nice, she's very bright. My mom's a great role model for everyone I know.

Alejandro Valdez Grade: 05
Through the good, through the bad. My mom gave me what she had when she puts me to bed she said, "I try and try."

Erik Vick Grade: 05
Her eyes like glittering diamonds and her smile lights the way, she is loving and kind. I love her. She is my mom.

Teacher: Stan Carroll

Sumaya Awan Grade: 05
My mom is great. She gave me life and now she deserves a mighty gift because she opened my eyes and heart.

Cole Hendzel Grade: 05
My mom's prettier than the diamond itself. Her eyes sparkle like stars! Whatever I do and go, she'll love me and I'll love her.

Sean Reed Grade: 05
My mom deserves a diamond because she has a heart of gold and she gives me hugs when I am sad.

Taitana Sanden Grade: 05
My mom's the love of my life, the world's most wonderful person. She'll give me everything from her soft hugs to her wonderful sweet love.

Ryan Southerland Grade: 05
My mom's sweet and full of love. She shows me that with gentle hugs. That's why I truly love her and hope she lives forever.

Teacher: Emily Domenici

Abby Jones Grade: 04
My mom deserves a diamond because she is very sweet and kind. She helps me in school from math to science. I love my mom!

Aaron Karehl Grade: 04
My mom is the best mom ever. She always helps me with my homework so I can finish the page. I love my mom.

Mallory Matsumae Grade: 04
Kind, nice, polite, mom. Always a solution. Mom is my sunny day. Not just an average, mom, so special to me. Mother.

Joshua Nacino Grade: 04
She is kind, nice, loving, awesome, protective, helpful. She makes good eggrolls and tuna burgers. She helps me with homework and games. She likes diamonds.

Casey Primich Grade: 04
I say my mom deserves a diamond because she helps us so much with our lives. My mom is loving, caring, and is most wonderful.

Julie Vargas Grade: 04
I think that she deserves a diamond because she is the best, most spectacular mom ever. She cuddles me and supports me. I love you.

Arianna Brack Grade: 05
Everyday you look at me with your mother eyes and make my day special just by that surprise and they twinkle just like diamonds.

Teacher: Jennifer Fisler

Gabriel Abrams Grade: 04
My mom deserves a diamond because she means everything to me. To me, she makes the world go round. She loves me.

Tyler Bigelow Grade: 04
My mom deserves a diamond because she is an incredible mom. She gives my sister and I the best life she can provide. I love her.

Lauren Colodny Grade: 04
My mom is an amazing woman. She is as beautiful as a swan. A soul warm as fleece and she has nothing but sweet intentions.

Thea Elkhouri Grade: 04
Flowers bloom in my mom's eyes, things seem brighter around her. Her smile is brighter than the sun. Her heart gleams brighter than a diamond.

Renee Hsu Grade: 04
Passionate, loving, truthful, and caring. Hugs of warmth, kisses of love. Just a few phrases about my mom.

Ethan Knox   Grade: 04
My mom is caring, funny and sweet. She deserves a diamond because she has a diamond heart that never breaks. She is a fabulous mom.

Jennifer Le   Grade: 04
My mother deserves a diamond. She's filled with love and care. With eyes that twinkle in the light. She will always be in my sight.

Makenzie Lilly   Grade: 04
My mother's heart shines like a diamond. Her smile is bright like the sun. She inspires me and makes me happy. I love my mom.

Lance Mashita   Grade: 04
My mom deserves a diamond because she always takes care of me and my three brothers. She is very calm and has a loving heart.

Jessie Patzlaff   Grade: 04
My mom deserves a diamond because she is nice and caring. Her eyes shine bright like beautiful rubies. She inspires me, she makes me happy.

Stephanie Tran   Grade: 04
My mom spends all her time with her family even though she works all day. She's like a flower that shines out among others.

Douglas Truong   Grade: 04
My mom is a Phoenix soaring here and there. Showing off her beauty, whenever she is near. Singing her song softly in my ear.

Teacher: Jessica Haag

Jeremy Anderson   Grade: 04
Dear Mother, or should I say the kindest person in all the world. You are like an angel. Who flies above all clouds.

Chance Burden   Grade: 04
Her glowing face. Her sparkling eyes. Her loving soul deserves a diamond. I love her a lot. She's different from the rest. She's the best!

Anna Carroll   Grade: 04
No gem as sparkly as her heart. The one that gave me life. The one I go for when I need help. My awesome mom.

Dylan Chennault   Grade: 04
My mom deserves a diamond, to match her constant cheer. My mom deserves a diamond, without her I wouldn't be here.

Daniela Falagan   Grade: 04
Her rosy cheeks, sparkling eyes, makes my mother look like a young schoolgirl again. She makes me feel special and like my soul is gold.

Fiona Fisher   Grade: 04
Beautiful, flawless, she's the best, kind, loving, unlike the rest. Her heart of gold, she works so hard. Just to keep me happy, that's mom.

Teresa Guerre   Grade: 04
My mom is gold. She'll take care of me. She is like a crystal that shines with glee. She's caring, I'm sure you will see.

Michael Justin   Grade: 04
Mother, mother is a great lover, as beautiful as can be. Eyes twinkling like stars in the sky. Mother deserves a diamond, you know why.

Noah Liss   Grade: 04
Angelic and caring, super sweet, extremely nice and amazingly neat. To sum these up I think of mom, on her finger, she deserves a diamond.

Megan Mulholland   Grade: 04
My mom gave me life. Her warm hugs heal my sadness. I am proud that I can call her mine. She deserves a diamond.

Nathan Nguyen   Grade: 04
As graceful as can be, a shining light showing the difference from day and night. A hero, a friend, a loved one indeed. My mother.

Nathan Robledo   Grade: 04
Mom is the best on Earth. She gave me birth. As beautiful as a dove. So full of such love.

Madison Stites   Grade: 04
Beautiful, kind just like a dove. Sent from heaven straight above. Precious and special like a pot of gold. My mommy's love never gets old.

Antalique Tran   Grade: 04
She's very bright, like a little light. She's the one I love, just like a snowy, white dove. A diamond for her she's my mom.

Jenna Turner   Grade: 04
Mom is an ice cream with a special cherry on top. She gets a diamond, her mouth will drop. She's flawless like a crystal heart.

Chelsey Wang   Grade: 04
Loving, caring, quite beautiful inside. She'd spare her life for me. Without her on Earth, my life would be incomplete.

Teacher: Joannah Labrador

Malikah Awan   Grade: 03
My mom is very special because she makes me feel better when I'm sad. She also checks if I'm feeling well and she's my mom.

Kaitlin Conroy   Grade: 03
My mom deserves a diamond because she works hard at everything she does and is very nice. My mom is awesome! She deserves a diamond.

Catly Do   Grade: 03
My mom deserves a diamond because she is a great mom and is so loving to me. She is the best mom in the world.

Matthew Karnowski   Grade: 03
My mom deserves a diamond because she always is helping my class and my school. She gives me healthy foods and watches out for me.

Teacher: Meredith Phillips

Ryan Gueon   Grade: 04
My lovely mom who wants the jewel, if she gets it, she can be cool. My mom works hard, she does not need a bodyguard.

Michael Magula   Grade: 04
I think my mom deserves a diamond because her eyes sparkle like one. My mom is a 50 carat diamond to me.

Chad Phillips   Grade: 04
My mom deserves a diamond because she is always nice to me. She is the greatest mom anybody can ever get. I love my mom.

Eric Rymer   Grade: 04
My mom deserves a diamond because she's been a great mom. I think she deserves this diamond more than any other mom.

Zachary Torres   Grade: 04
My mom is a very find mom. She does whatever she can to help me. She always takes me to sports. She is awesome.

Valerie Yamasaki   Grade: 04
My mom would like to have a diamond because her smile is like a rose and there is why I would like her to win this.

* Amethyst winners in bold.

Teacher: Joyce Stalcup

Maddie Baker   Grade: 04
My mom deserves a diamond because she helps when I get hurt. She teaches me a lot of things and cares for me.

Haleigh Cardwell   **Grade: 04**
My grandma deserves a diamond because she is everything that I can ask for. She's my life. I love her. She's the best.

Peyton Coutts   Grade: 04
My mom is really nice, kind and beautiful. She helps me with my homework. She takes me places where I want to go.

Nelson Dowell   Grade: 04
My mom deserves a diamond because she's the one who does the work around the house. She is very thoughtful and she deserves a gift.

Tyler Frydman   Grade: 04
My mother is as loving as can be. The wonderful thing about her is she never stops loving me. She deserves it you see.

Cade Smith   Grade: 04
My mom deserves a diamond because she does a lot of work. I love her so much and she loves me a lot too.

Megan Tan   **Grade: 04**
My mom's heart is bigger than you think. Her heart always has love and kindness. She'll work me through my troubles and keep me safe!

Teacher: Gary Turner

Angelina Bissin   **Grade: 05**
She's the light in my life. That I hold so very close to my heart. The one I loved from the very start. My mom!

Brittney Mohl   Grade: 05
Your hair is so beautiful in the wind and your smile is so big. There are so many reasons why you deserve a diamond.

Clegg School
Huntington Beach

Teacher: Michelle Sale

Takia Allen   **Grade: 08**
My mom, she's the bomb, her sweet chocolate kisses are so sweet. She's an angel flying so high. I'll always love her until I die.

Eliza Ana Batac   Grade: 08
My mom's caring and loving. She picks me up when I'm down. She's my guardian angel. She deserves everything, not just a diamond.

Nicholas Bradshaw   Grade: 08
I will love my mom forever, we are always together in the heart. She is always there when I need her. I love my mom.'

Angie Cardenas   Grade: 08
To describe her would take up more than a million words. Love her forever, so special, nice and with her uniqueness. Yes, that's my mom.

Kevin Dam   Grade: 08
My mom loves my family, cares about everyone, can't stop loving my mom.

Jessica Edward   Grade: 08
My mom deserves a diamond because she is always ready to help me no matter what. She is very patient and loving.

Katarina Gott   Grade: 08
She adopted me when I was young, smiled at me when I was down, loved me when love was lost. I'll love you forever, mom.

Nano Haddad   Grade: 08
I love my mom. I love her forever. I hope we'll always be together forever through eternity, we go through the bad and the good.

Lucia Hinogo   Grade: 08
My mom is really kind. She cares for me. She is strong and she is with me through the bad and good days.

Crystal Hoang   Grade: 08
My mom is perfect in every way to me. She loves me and I love her too. She deserves a diamond because she is a diamond.

Joe Jones   Grade: 08
There are no words in the English language to describe my grandmother. All I can say is, my grandmother ages like fine wine.

Hana Kurihara   Grade: 08
Like a ray of sunshine, she brightens up my day. Like an unwavering candle, she chases dark fears away.

Charles Laitipaya   Grade: 08
My mom is with me the best of days and the worst of days but she loves me every day.

Kiana Mey   **Grade: 08**
When you look into a diamond, you see multiple reflections. When you look at my mom, you see everything that makes up "Mom".

Paul Nguyen   Grade: 08
My mom deserves a diamond because she is the definition of a mom. To me, a mom is loving and that is what she is.

Nhu Nguyen   **Grade: 08**
She is my mom, who shines my hopes, the one who gives me the world, and the brightest diamond in my heart.

Lincoln Nguyen   **Grade: 08**
My mom deserves a diamond because her extraordinary love towards others and her will to sacrifice in order to help those in need is undeniable.

Trent Ohishi   **Grade: 08**
She is assertive, yet elegant. Thoughtful, yet selfless. Cool, yet she can keep me safe. My mom, yet my best friend and I love her.

Dan Pham   Grade: 08
Cooking, cleaning, giving it all, out to be the best mother she can be. Makes her deserve something like a diamond.

Alexandria Pilatos   Grade: 08
My mom deserves a diamond because she is my best friend and I know that she will always love me no matter what happens.

Trevor Poteet   **Grade: 08**
She is smart, caring for me as if she did not, she would die. Without her, my life would be a dark and empty void.

Jacob Ramirez   Grade: 08
I love my mom. She is the bomb. I would scream it on the intercom. That's how much I love my mom.

Viridiana Segura   **Grade: 08**
This person is my soul. This person is my life. But the best part of all, this person is my Mom.

Leyla Szilagyi   Grade: 08
My mom deserves a diamond because even though she's not perfect, she's pretty close. She accepts her very few flaws and she supports my family.

Theresa Tran   Grade: 08
My mom may not be everything I want, but she is everything I need. She is like a diamond, she will always be priceless.

Stuart Urbano   Grade: 08
My mom deserves a diamond because she loves me and cares for me even on the best and worst of days.

Demi Zamora   Grade: 08
My mom is my best friend. She's here until the end. She's funny, sweet and kind. She has a beautiful mind. Forever lasts her love.

College Park Elementary
Irvine

Teacher: Johnnie Hunt

Shreshta Aiyar   Grade: 06
My mom deserves a diamond because she is kind, caring, honest, smart, and hard working.

Nathan Brown   Grade: 06
My mom deserves a diamond because she only wants what's best for my sister and me. She has and always will be great to us.

Armon Fayyazi   Grade: 06
My mom deserves a diamond because she always helps people. She helps me around the house and homework. Plus she would do anything to help.

Dana Lansigan   Grade: 06
My mom's always there for me without expecting anything in return. She's my guardian angel. She really deserves something as precious as a diamond.

Grant Tingirides   Grade: 06
My mother deserves a diamond because she juggles her job, being home in time to help all three kids with homework, and I love her.

Anthony Xu   Grade: 06
My mom deserves a diamond because she needs a reward for bringing me this far into life. She has tended me so I could have a future.

Teacher: Michelle Patterson

Tom Aizenberg   Grade: 04
Mom's cuter than a bunny and is really, really funny. She says I love you, I say that back and her heart's bigger than Jupiter.

Kellie Crouch   Grade: 04
Your eyes are green as lily pads. Your hair is like a blossom. My mom, she loves me dearly, as much as I love her.

Trang Hoang   Grade: 04
My mom deserves a diamond for she always cares for me, work and work, that's all she does. To make me happy, to me pleased.

Ah-Young Ko   Grade: 04
My mom is sweet like candy hearts and pretty as a sun setting at night. Her eyes sparkle like the diamond earrings on her ears.

Andrea Lee   Grade: 04
My mom's eyes are filled with love. She's kind and gentle like a dove. She's very, very nice. But, she's never cold like ice.

Hanna Leka   Grade: 04
My mom is like a diamond. Her heart is filled with joy. Her lips are red as roses and eyes like the stars.

Eric Matthey   Grade: 04
Like a diamond, valuable as can be, helps with everything, always there for me. Even if I'm bouncing off the walls, my mom sits calmly.

Katie Minerman   Grade: 04
You are as pretty as a diamond with eyes that shine like an emerald and your heart is filled with love, courage, honesty and faith.

Sarah Morgan   Grade: 04
Mom, your heart is gold, when you shine you feel like a golden sun. The things you do are crystal blue, so I love you.

Kyle Myers   Grade: 04
My mom is worth more than a million diamonds. She looks prettier than a rose. She is a rare sight. I love her the most.

David Nacario   Grade: 04
My mom is a loveable person. Everyday she makes me smile. Her heart shines like a sun. My mom deserves a diamond.

Brenda Nguyen   Grade: 04
My mom deserves a diamond, she works hard everyday from morning to night helping me and always making me very happy.

Daniel Olivares   Grade: 04
Her hair is black as night time. Her teeth as white as clouds. Her skin is tan as sand. She is my mom.

Andrew Xiao   Grade: 04
I smile everyday. Everyday I laugh. Everyday of my life I get love and all that comes from my mom. Thank you very much.

Teacher: Kelly Tyndal

Joshua Hall   Grade: 03
My mom deserves a diamond because she has worked hard and helps the whole family. She is also loving and kind.

Jacob Huynh   Grade: 03
She is a very nice person. She takes care of me. She always makes me dinner and she always buys me stuff. She is nice.

Brayden Kamai   Grade: 03
I think my mom deserves a diamond because she is selfless. She does nothing for herself. She cleans the house. I can now repay her.

Kayanna Klein   Grade: 03
Mom deserves a diamond because she is nice, careful, kind, pretty, fun, loveable, and huggable. It would be the best present my mom ever got.

Reah Mehta   Grade: 03
My mom works hard. She buys food to eat. She works very hard to let us sleep somewhere. She works hard for a home.

Samantha Ree   Grade: 03
My mom does all the dishes, cleans up, she cooks. She helps me with my homework whenever I need help.

College View Elementary
Huntington Beach

Teacher: Jan Richards

Daniel Hencke   Grade: 04
In the morning, her smile fills me with joy. Her love is the best thing. She is all I can wish for. I love her!

Holly Hennessy   Grade: 04
She is the twinkle in my eye, the moon in mind, the love of my heart, the peace of my life, the love everyday.

Jason Roe   Grade: 04
My mom is so nice and pretty. She has a beautiful twinkle in her eyes. She is a great cook too. I love my mom.

Ricardo Talavera   Grade: 04
Sweet, nice, cute, beautiful, playful, shy, good, funny, brave, cool, respectful, special, awesome, happy, responsive, peaceful, careful, great, perfect, neat, gorgeous, gentle, and intelligent!

Jacklyn Zalpa   Grade: 04
My mom is the only thing in my heart that never stops beating. My mom is my hero, she is my best friend and my everything.

* Amethyst winners in bold.

Concordia Elementary
San Clemente

Teacher: Barbara Keim

Lauren Adolph   Grade: 03
My mom's eyes sparkle like the sun. She's my diamond. My mom is a gift from God. She takes care of me when I'm sick.

Jack Boatman   Grade: 03
My mom's eyes are like the sun when it sets over the ocean. I couldn't have someone better than her.

Kyle Burick   Grade: 03
She's my sunshine on a cloudy day, she's the rain that washes my blues away, I can always count on her. She's my creator.

Alexxa Elseewi   Grade: 03
She shines just like a diamond, she lights up the sky too. I think she should get a diamond just from you.

Olivia French   Grade: 03
My mom's heart and eyes shine like the light, the way a diamond is because she is a beautiful, loving gift from God.

Roxanne Gillotte   Grade: 03
My mom is the apple of my eyes, the key to my heart. My mom is the best mom I could ever ask for.

Marissa Gomez   Grade: 03
My mom deserves a diamond. Her eyes sparkle like the beautiful ocean. Her laugh makes me smile. Her heart is big like the earth.

Delanie Kahn   Grade: 03
My mom means everything to me. She is the one who takes care of me if I'm sick or hurt. I love her.

Hailey Reed   Grade: 03
My mom's as sweet as a peach. She takes me to the beach, she shines brighter than the sun. I couldn't have a better mom.

Louis Spinelli   Grade: 03
My mom's eyes shine like stars in the sky. Her heart is as big as the galaxy.

Finn Swartz   Grade: 03
My mom deserves a diamond because she is my heart and I could not live without her.

Teacher: Cathy Ramirez

Kai Castro   Grade: 03
Her eyes sparkle like a diamond. She is the key to my heart. She is the best mom in the world. She is special to my family.

Emily Grothjan   Grade: 03
She is beautiful in many ways and she is nice and pretty. Her eyes shine like the stars in the sky. I love my mom!

Anna Sanchez   Grade: 03
My mom is so sweet, she shines in the light and twinkles in the dark.

Cook (A. J.) Elementary
Garden Grove

Teacher: Kelly Ebright

GiaHuy Bui   Grade: 06
My mom deserves the diamond because she left everything in Viet Nam and came here for me and my sister to have a better future.

Alondra Burgos   Grade: 06
My mom deserves a diamond because she works all her life for me. This diamond will thank my mom for all the hard work.

Kathleen Dang   Grade: 06
Sunset. Moonshine. Thousands of words can describe how wonderful she is. My beloved mom, she's all I can ask for in a mother.

Tiffany Do   Grade: 06
The reason why my mom deserves a diamond. My mom is nice and caring and she protects me all the time, and she's my hero.

Henry Hoang   Grade: 06
My mom deserves a diamond because when I have a problem, she gives me the best advice out of all of my choices.

Simon Nguyen   Grade: 06
I think my mom deserves a diamond is because she is always hardworking even when she is exhausted, she keeps working.

Trinh Nguyen   Grade: 06
My mom is the perfect mom! She cooks, cleans and when we do something wrong, she corrects us. I think she deserves that pretty diamond!

Kamalii Nihipali   Grade: 06
I think my mom should get the diamond because she's caring. She's always there when you need her, loving and she's so fun!

Michelle Phan   Grade: 06
If there are no moms, the sun will melt, the flowers will die. That is why a diamond goes to this heavenly mother of mine.

Carissa Stevens   Grade: 06
My mom deserves a diamond because she is always giving towards others. Every time she wants something, the money is spent on other people.

Brian Strahan   Grade: 06
I have a special mom that plans fun things for school, and helps me at home. This is why she deserves to win this diamond.

Tina Tran   Grade: 06
My mom loves me very much. She's very nice. My mom spoils me, but now it's time for her.

Nathaly Uribe   Grade: 06
My mom is caring and sweet. She tries her best to be a hard worker at her work and at home. She also helps others.

Tommy Vu   Grade: 06
When I wake up bright and early, she is busy and always hurrying. I wish I can repay, so please hand me your diamond today!

Teacher: Shannon Kosai

Tony Arreola   Grade: 06
My mom gives up material items that she desires so that she can stay home and take care of her six kids, including me.

Jacquelyn Do   Grade: 06
Your eyes are winter snowflakes. Your hugs are warm jackets in fall. Your words are spring flowers. Your beautiful smile is warm sunshine in summer.

Christian Garcia   Grade: 06
My mom loves me unconditionally and teaches me how to be responsible and a good citizen. She never yells and works hard without complaining.

Centi Le   Grade: 06
My mom is very special to me because she sold her whole house to feed me and takes care of me since I was little.

Michelle Pham   Grade: 06
Mom loves us all from big to small. She's nice and very bright. Her love's great, she cares a lot. I'll love you forever mom.

Amy Ta   Grade: 06
I think my mom deserves a diamond because she works very hard to take care of me and the family. I owe her a lot.

Linn Tran   Grade: 06
If I won a diamond, I will give to my mom on Mother's Day to remind her that her lovely daughter will love her forever.

Teacher: Leah Nazaroff

Lisa Bang   Grade: 04
Why my mom deserves a diamond? She is extremely helpful. My mom deserves a diamond because she always cares about me and works very hard.

Julissa Casas   Grade: 04
My mom deserves a diamond because she's a bright person in my life. I am a miracle from heaven to her.

Jesus Gonzalez   Grade: 04
Why mom deserves a diamond? Well, my mom is loving and sweet like candy. She is hardworking. She is neat and funny. She is caring.

Valarie Ho   Grade: 04
The reason that my mom deserves a diamond is that she cares for my sister and me a lot. She is also very kind and loving.

Mohammed Mc Carfy   Grade: 04
The reason that my mom deserves a diamond is because she is very polite and very kind. She also has a way with people. She loves me.

Anna Pham   Grade: 04
My mom deserves a diamond because she pays for my educations. She buys me good food to eat. She is the best.

Dylan Rodriguez   Grade: 04
My mom deserves a diamond because she's hardworking. She always does something special for me. Now I want to do something special for her.

Jenny Vu   Grade: 04
My mom deserves a diamond because she takes care of us. She cooks and buys clothes for us. My mom is the best mom ever!

Tuan Tran   Grade: 05
Why my mom deserves a diamond? My mom deserves a diamond because she works hard, careful, and responsible for me and she cares for us.

Corey (Arthur F.) Elem.
Buena Park

Teacher: Shelli Abbott

Hailey Arreola   Grade: 05
My mom deserves a diamond because of all her hard work she has gone through helping me with my   Grades.

Anthony Castillo   Grade: 05
My mom deserves a diamond because she works hard and I wish to repay her with something special.

Gabrielle De La Merced   Grade: 05
She feeds, clothes, and takes care of me. She spends money on me instead of herself so I'll be happy. She's the best mom ever!

Cerrone Fields   Grade: 05
My mom deserves to have a diamond because she helps people when they need it. She helps the homeless and my family.

Jun Kim   Grade: 05
My mom deserves a diamond because she has been working really hard, kept me safe for more than eleven years and loves shiny, white diamonds.

Maurice Morrell   Grade: 05
I think my mom deserves a diamond because she raised good children. She is such a great mom. She works hard for her family.

Mark Perea   Grade: 05
I think my mom deserves a diamond because she does the laundry, washes the dishes, takes out the trash, makes the beds, and cooks dinner.

Carolina Perez   Grade: 05
My mom deserves this diamond because she cleans the house, cleans my room, works very hard, and never gives up on her own homework.

Erick Ramirez   Grade: 05
I think my mom deserves a diamond because she is funny, silly, nice, cool, awesome, incredible, and good. I think she deserves it very much.

Priscilla Robles   Grade: 05
One reason why my mom deserves a diamond is because she works hard all day and barely rests. She deserves a present like a diamond.

Sergio Rodriguez   Grade: 05
My mom deserves a diamond because she is sweet, careful, caring, and loving. She takes great care of me and my brothers.

Teacher: Eva Araujo

Taylor Blevins   Grade: 04
Her eyes twinkle like the diamond beyond the stars, her heart is made of dazzling crystals beyond the ocean.

Silvia Chen   Grade: 04
Her heart is made of pure gold. Her smile makes blossoms bloom. She is sweeter than any honey. My mother she will be.

Andrea Estrada   Grade: 04
Your eyes are like crystals and your face is as smooth as a bear. Also, your smile is as wonderful as your pretty little heart.

Sarah Hultman   Grade: 04
Her eyes are dazzling like diamonds. Her cheeks like roses. Her voice beautiful like the song of birds. Her face just like the sparkling sun.

Brandon Jensen   Grade: 04
I think my mom deserves a diamond is because she is the most loving one. Her love is so strong, it won't come apart.

Carolina Lopez   Grade: 04
My mom deserves a diamond because her eyes sparkle like shining stars in the night. Your skin is white like the clouds in the sky.

Hugo Lopez   Grade: 04
Your eyes are brown and your skin is peach. Your hair is black, a little brown and your heart is gold. Your eyebrows are brown.

David Mireles   Grade: 04
When I look in my mother's eyes, I see a twinkle. Her eyes look like big emeralds. She makes sacrifices for me everyday.

Vianney Rivero   Grade: 04
The stars twinkle when my mom smiles. Her eyes shine like the beautiful golden sun. The trees dance to her beautiful singing with wonderful joy.

Renee Rodriguez   Grade: 04
Her eyes are dazzling as crystals. She has hair that twinkle as a pearl because she's a gemstone and she's the only mom I chose.

Christian Rodriguez   Grade: 04
Mom, very special indeed. Her eyes dazzle like diamonds. Her hair shines like rubies and the last part of my heart.

Marisol Sanchez   Grade: 04
Her eyes shine like jewels, her hair shiny like a brass whistle, her voice like a bird's song and the kindness of a dream.

* Amethyst Winners in bold.

Alexandra Tageloo — Grade: 04
Dance, B.M.X., Wrestling and three children makes my mom deserve a diamond. She takes all the children to competitions. The sunshine in my mom!

Alex Vazquez — Grade: 04
Mom, in your special way, you're there for me everyday. How can I thank you for all you do? Nobody loves me like you.

Danyel Wickoff — Grade: 04
My mom is a dazzling ruby who completes me, and has a beautiful sparkle in her eye and would compete for me.

Teacher: Wendy Roxas

Claudia Brewer — Grade: 04
You shine like the night sky moon. You sing like the flowers in the morning dew. You are as beautiful as sunlight in the morning.

Irene Choi — Grade: 04
she is the beautiful jewel in my ring. For loving me forever. I'll love you put a diamond in my ring.

Anthony Colbert — Grade: 04
My mom is like the sun, she shines in the sky and you can't miss those beautiful eyes and she's the best thing in life.

Raymond Durazo — Grade: 04
As beautiful as a jewel, eyes glisten like a waterfall, hair like a horse's mane, teeth like a pearl. My mom, a sweet flower.

Elena Felix — Grade: 04
Pure diamonds are her eyes gazing into mine. Her voice as smooth as sapphires, as her smile lights up the sky.

Brandon Garnica — Grade: 04
My mom deserves a diamond because my mom's hair sparkles like the Nile. Her eyes are like the starlit sky or soon like HER diamond.

Eunice Kim — Grade: 04
Her smile and face shines like gold. She calls me diamond everyday. She keeps me safe and clean like a piece of gold.

Savanna Nugent — Grade: 04
Her eyes are like a crystal, her heart is like a rose, but in my mind, she's a shining star.

Reymond Rubio — Grade: 04
Her heart beeps like a lion, her love goes higher than a million. My mom is full of love.

Andrew Vuong — Grade: 04
A woman of compassion, beauty and love. She has glowing eyes. Deserving a miracle, a mystic heart shines beside her angelic soul of wonder.

Courreges (Roch) Eleme.
Fountain Valley

Teacher: Jennifer Blake

Ian Bast — Grade: 05
My mom deserves this diamond because I love her and my family wouldn't keep going if she wasn't there. That's why she deserves this diamond.

Tara Beckman — Grade: 05
The twinkle in my eye. A friend to me. Comforts me if I cry. This is really my mom, true as can be!

Tram Dang — Grade: 05
My mother's heart, a precious gem, made of gold and when I see her sparkling eyes, it's like the glittering diamond of life.

Hunter Kennedy — Grade: 05
My mom, she is as beautiful as the ocean. She stands out to me like the sun. She will be in my heart forever.

Darren Rolfe — Grade: 05
Marvelous, Magnificent, and Momish. Outstanding and Optimistic. Merry and Magical. I love my mom most.

Ashley Schoon — Grade: 05
Her love is guidance, her love is care, her voice is sacrifice and wisdom every moment we share. Love is my mother.

Kervin Tomblin — Grade: 05
My mom always helps with homework, keeps the house clean, cooks good food, and works hard. Win or lose, mom's precious and flawless.

Leigha Williams — Grade: 05
Roses are red, violets are blue, I love my mom more than anyone I knew. She brings me love and hope to my life daily.

Lauren Wong — Grade: 05
My mom is a star in my life. She guides me through the dark night. And without her wisdom and caring, I am nothing.

Teacher: Jennifer Hisgen

Allison Bebout — Grade: 03
Her eyes sparkle like a diamond in the sky. I love you mommy. Your heart is like red, shiny pearls. Your smile shines through mountains.

Ziv Bernard — Grade: 03
The sun is yellow. The moon is white, but my mom's eyes shine out so bright.

Sierra Browne — Grade: 03
I need some sparkle, glitter, and shimmer to make your beautiful soul. Nothing can be made better than you!

Olivia Espinoza — Grade: 03
My mom's twinkling eyes. Her glimmering face, just like a diamond. All sparkly and bright.

Amelia Fee — Grade: 03
Her eyes glitter just like an emerald. Her lips as pink as a diamond. Her hair as brown as a crystal. I love her, Mom.

Alexa Martinez — Grade: 03
My mom is as pretty as can be. She deserves a diamond as pretty as her. Her eyes sparkle in the light of the sun.

Kasey Tran — Grade: 03
A drip of love from her emerald. The shimmering light gives hope in her.

Zachary Vannah — Grade: 03
A sparkling jewel shines and loves, your precious heart above the clouds. That's coming in for flower's pollen, and our world to meet you.

Teacher: Kelly Marin

Sofia Flores — Grade: 05
My mother deserves a diamond because she gives my two sisters, my two dogs and my dad food, clothes, shelter, and toys. I love her.

Katelyn Huffmire — Grade: 05
My mom is very passionate. When I need help, she's always there. I see twinkles sparkling in her eyes. She hugs me with great care.

Kassandra Pop — Grade: 05
My mom deserves a diamond because she cooks and cleans. She works twelve hours a day to save other lives, and it might be yours.

Simon Tanvilai   Grade: 05
My mom gives life, happiness, love. She comforts me when I'm sad. Takes ares of me when I'm sick, and teaches me right and wrong.

Anelysse Waters   Grade: 05
I want my mom to have a diamond because she is hardworking and she cares a lot about my family.

Teacher: Valerie Ruig

Cameron Bald   Grade: 05
My mom is like a diamond so caring and rare. Giving me love and hope, like angels way up there. This is my mom.

Justin Bebout   Grade: 05
Mom, I appreciate everything you do. You are as sweet as honeycomb. But, nothing compares to the warmth you put in my heart.

Ritesh Bhatt   Grade: 05
As gorgeous as a rose, as spectacular as a sunset. A shining diamond, precious and distinctive and priceless, and so affectionate because she is my mom.

Maggie Bui   Grade: 05
My lake of tears, a black cloud is surrounding, trapped in a tower of endless fear. Thought I need not despair, mom is here!

Julienne Chiang   Grade: 05
My mom is precious. A smile greater than the sun. More kindness than the stars. Comfort like nature's music and those things bring me joy.

Michelle Doan   Grade: 05
My mom is a guiding light in the sky. Shining to give me hope, love, and courage. Showing me the right direction to go.

Tracy Keller   Grade: 05
My mom is a jewel, delicate and charming. She is precious, yet priceless. Loving and kind. Her heart is like gold. She is my mom.

Rachel Klotz   Grade: 05
My love for her is priceless. Her beauty is a fresh cut rose. No diamond can describe her. My mom is loved, that's for sure.

Calvin Le   Grade: 05
My mom is like a star shooting to bring me cheer. She is like a fire inside of me, burning away all of my fear.

Alice Lee   Grade: 05
A spectacular diamond shining brightly to give me hope. A devoted candle that burns to give time for me. My miraculous mom.

Joey Lesnick   Grade: 05
My mom is everything to me, my hope, courage, strength, love. I couldn't live without her. She has more value than the universe for me.

Katie Mc Cutcheon   Grade: 05
My mom gives me hope and love like an angel above, like a star. She guides me, always there for me. I'm glad she's mine.

Neil Mc Henry   Grade: 05
Like a diamond in the sunlight, my mom is so very precious and valuable. She is so unique and rare, I just have to care.

Sahil Sharma   Grade: 05
My mother is like an angel. Her wings surround me in love. God's grace granted me a wonderful mother. She is heaven sent!

Sean Strom   Grade: 05
Mom, your marvelous and priceless like an angel from the blue. Your beauty means more to me than the world. You are my mom, "loveable".

Kevin Takeda   Grade: 05
So watchful and warm. Mom shines like the brightest gem. Soothing me when sad and make me glad. Loving me, like the angel she is.

Covenant Christian School
Orange

Teacher: Monica Dorame

Alissa Macdonald   Grade: 03
My mom deserves a diamond because she's elegant and bold and when I look into her eyes, I see her heart of gold. Thanks mom.

Emma Rowe   Grade: 03
My mom deserves a diamond because she is the light of my world and the light of my soul. Her eyes twinkle like bright stars!

Breana Yip   Grade: 03
My mom deserves a diamond because she works hard to take care of me and takes me fun places like Disneyland and roller-skating.

Teacher: Michael Hubbard

Sandra Castaneda   Grade: 07
Moms care, moms are loving, moms put food on your plate, a roof over your head. That's the mom I have, and she deserves the best!

Bridget Hards   Grade: 07
My mom is thoughtful. She is beautiful, she loves me. She also protects, gives me shelter and makes sure I don't get hurt.

Raeann Jones   Grade: 07
My mom works all day. She is a true servant of God. I love my mom a lot! She always works to provide for us.

Belem Montiel   Grade: 07
My mom cares about me and my brother. She loves us both very much, but she loves God mostly. She's awesome and the best mom.

Cayla Paretti   Grade: 07
My mom works really hard. She feeds me, shelters me and keeps me from getting sick. The best thing is that she loves me.

David Pickering   Grade: 07
She has a twinkle in her eye that controls the night sky. She is as beautiful as Mother Nature and beauty itself.

Teacher: David King

Nick Avellino   Grade: 05
Her eyes shine bright through dark night. What beautiful eyes like sparkling stars at night even when she's sad, they never seem to fade.

Michael DeVries   Grade: 05
Star bright starlight, my mom's eyes are so bright. She helps me even when she's busy. I love my mom so much.

William Meissner   Grade: 05
My mother and her eyes sparkle like diamonds in the sky. Her heart shines like gold and her soul soars like an eagle.

John Youngman   Grade: 05
My mom is beautiful in my sight in the night. She is so bright. I hug her tight before I go to bed at night.

Teacher: April Matthews

Charles Battaglia   Grade: 04
My mom's the best! She deserves this diamond because she bakes and she makes me feel safe. She's very pretty and busy like a bee!

* Amethyst winners in bold.

Brayden Jones   Grade: 04
My mom deserves a diamond because she's flawless and brave. She does everything for us. She's awesome and caring, so she deserves a diamond.

Jaylee McClain   Grade: 04
My mother is sweet, very neat, and beautiful. She helps me when I'm hurt. She cleans off the dirt. She cooks and cleans with me.

Imani Moreen   Grade: 04
My mom is an angel sent from Heaven and she is the best mom a child could ever have and she always thinks about me.

Keaven Saucerman   Grade: 04
I have the best mom in the whole world because she loves me no matter what. She's fun, playful and she comforts me.

Teacher: Sash Salzer

Justine Hawelu   Grade: 06
My mom deserves a diamond because she is unique and special to me. She is sweet and helps my family. She is number one mom.

Brittany Miller   Grade: 06
She is so loving, so sweet. Whenever I see the night sky, I think of her as a star that shines.

Frankie Rangel   Grade: 06
She works very hard to keep me in a great school. She is fun and she is loving. She likes to make people happy.

Kyle Valverde   Grade: 06
My mom is funny. She is a good cook. When I am sad, she cheers up when I am bored. She always has something fun to do.

Madison Wells   Grade: 06
She is the best. She is fantastic and she helps me a lot. My mom is magnificent and a lot of fun. My mom is like a friend.

Austin Flores   Grade: 08
My mom is a very caring person and is a really nice person. My mom takes good are of me when I am sad.

Jennifer Henderson   Grade: 08
My mom shines a light in my path. She is kind and caring. She is beautiful in so many ways. My mother sparkles as a diamond.

Jocelyn Ocampo   Grade: 08
My mom is a beautiful as a cherry blossom and gentle as a swan. As sweet as truffle on Christmas Day. She's super mom.

MollyKate Smith   Grade: 08
My mom is the most generous person in the world. She constantly puts people before her, and loves me with all her heart.

Hannah Van Den Berg   Grade: 08
I do not know what Cinderella was saying about stepmothers being evil. My stepmother is beautiful on the inside and outside.

Cox (James H.) Elementary
Fountain Valley

Teacher: Christine Carrasco

Joshua Kline   Grade: 02
My mom deserves a diamond because she is graceful, lovely, talented, and most of all loved very much.

Desiree Le   Grade: 02
My mom deserves a diamond because her heart always thinks of me. She cares and loves me very much. She loves me with her soul.

Evangelena Mata   Grade: 02
My mom deserves a diamond because she takes care of me when I'm sick. She gives me medicine or a band-aid when I have cuts.

Whitney Sargis   Grade: 02
My mom deserves a diamond because her heart is as sweet as a cupcake. She helps me when I am hurt.

Britney Tran   Grade: 02
My mom deserves a diamond because she helps me with homework, makes food for me, and when I do something bad, she still loves me.

Teacher: Sherri Foulke

Daniel Ahn   Grade: 05
Mom deserves a diamond because it sparkles like her eyes. Nothing can compare to her beauty, but a diamond made for will.

Liana Castro   Grade: 05
Mom's raised kids and grandkids. She's fought for better, healthier grandkids. Mom's a hero! She's one of a kind, once in a lifetime.

Jacquelyn Freeman   Grade: 05
My mom deserves a diamond because she is the most encouraging person I know. She always tells me she loves me. She really means it!

Carolyn Koo   Grade: 05
Mom deserves a diamond because she helps me everyday. She is always there when I need her. She helps everyone around and spread joy slowly.

Michelle Lee   Grade: 05
My mommy deserves a diamond because she is caring. She is beautiful and she works hard just to take care of me and my brother.

Jessica Robinson   Grade: 05
My mom is strong like a diamond, genuine like a diamond, and beautiful like a diamond. My mom deserves a diamond. She is a diamond.

Stephanie Sun   Grade: 05
My mom deserves a diamond because she cares and works to make my family happy. She spends more money on us than on herself.

Teacher: Teri Langston

Brandon Fischer   Grade: 01
My mom is the loving mom. I love her so. Her dazzling eyes shine in the sunlight. My mom is the coolest mom.

Katelyn Flores   Grade: 01
My mom's eyes are shiny like a diamond in the sun. I see her looking at me.

Amelie Nguyen   Grade: 01
Roses are beautiful like your eyes. Your golden heart goes in my soul and my love spreads.

Maria Ramirez Meja   Grade: 01
My mom is the best mom ever. Her eyes shine in the light. My mom is nice.

Caitlyn Tran   Grade: 01
I love my mom. She's really cool. She is as pretty as a flower.

Ryan Trinh   Grade: 01
My mom is very nice. She always takes care of me. My mom loves me so much that it fills up her whole heart.

Teacher: Kathi Manuel

Joshua Bailon   Grade: 02
My mom is sweet. Her eyes shine like stars in space. She is my angel and teddy bear. She loves me very much.

Audrey Carr   Grade: 02
Mom is as sweet as arose. Her eyes sparkle like diamonds. She helps me with my homework. That's why my mom deserves a diamond.

Cassie Chawke — Grade: 02
My mom is as sweet as a cherry. She plays the flute. Her eyes twinkle like diamonds. She loves me from deep in her heart.

Elizabeth Luna — Grade: 02
My mom takes care of me and holds me tight. Then she kisses me goodnight. She loves me so I love her…I do!

Jemma Paradise — Grade: 02
Mom's heart is filled with kisses, her hugs filled with love. She reads stories when she tucks me in at night. I love her tremendously.

Joseph Tran — Grade: 02
Mom's sweet as a heart. She loves me a lot. She cares for me like a bird who protects my heart. Her eyes sparkle a lot.

Taylor Waldschmidt — Grade: 02
Mom's as sweet as candy, as beautiful as a rose. She loves me so much. I love her as well. She is the best ever!

Justin William — Grade: 02
Mom is sweet as chocolate. She thinks I am her diamond. I love her so much. She kisses me goodnight. I love her.

Crescent Ave Christian
Buena Park

Teacher: Kristen Torres

Sydney Bostrom — Grade: 05
My mom so sweet like an angel guiding the way. I admire her so much as she is my friend, guardian angel, and mom.

Logan Eaton — Grade: 05
Her eyes twinkle. Her smile brightens the world. Her heart like the forest diamond. Her voice like a running river. Her scent Heavenly. Mom.

Olivia Jones — Grade: 05
My mom is like a beach. She gives me waves of laughter. Her eyes are bright like the sun. She has freckles like the sand.

Summer Kusik — Grade: 05
Her eyes sparkle like the diamonds of my heart. Her hair has waves of gold. Her love is like a rainbow. I love you, mom.

Lydia Law — Grade: 05
Mom is patient, mom is kind, her smile is one can find. Eyes of pearls which shimmer and glow. Love you, mom. Hope you know.

Victoria Okada — Grade: 05
My mother is unforgettable just like the first shooting star you ever saw. She is like a treasure just like a box of jewels.

Monica Overton — Grade: 05
Like the sun, she shines bright. When it comes to stars, she shows more light. She's the brightest one. She's the light of my life.

Elissa Vong — Grade: 05
My mom offers me wings to fly high, fly inside the bright-blue sky. She has a warm heart; that we cannot be apart.

Crescent Elementary
Anaheim

Teacher: Sharon Cecchi

Christian Araiza — Grade: 05
My mom deserves a diamond because she is the sweetest woman in the world. She would die to save my life, I really love her.

Neela Chakraborty — Grade: 05
My special mom deserves a diamond because she sacrifices so much for me. She never buys anything for herself but always gets stuff for me.

Gianna Furumoto — Grade: 05
My mom deserves a diamond because she is one. She is a golden lotus, popping up in pure beauty amidst all the mud.

Quin Garant — Grade: 05
My mom is my diamond because she always comforts me when I'm afraid. She loves and kisses me. Mom is the jewel in my life.

Catherine Han — Grade: 05
I believe my mom deserves a diamond because she's the most loving mother and cannot compare to the most costly gem. A jewel would remind her that.

Janelle Obligacion — Grade: 05
My mom deserves a diamond because she preserves us in our warm home with every breath she takes. Mommy, I truly love you

Malakai Panochit — Grade: 05
My mom deserves a diamond because she cares, loves, and helps me. When I'm hurt, or sad she stops doing anything and helps with care.

Laura Smith — Grade: 05
My mom deserves a diamond because she is a diamond in my life more precious than any jewel. She's priceless to me. Glimmering so bright.

Jake Song — Grade: 05
My mom deserves a diamond because she is so loving, compassionate, and hardworking. She is also the most caring person I know.

Justin Venckus — Grade: 05
My mom deserves a diamond because she helps people with anything they need. She is also generous, kind, sharing, and raises three kids with care.

Gelek Wangyal — Grade: 05
My mom deserves a diamond because she is the most loving, helpful mom out there. She's always willing to give her time to others.

Teacher: Michael Cretney

Michele Ballestero — Grade: 06
My mom has eight kids and works as a full time nurse. She also finds time to take us to our sports. She loves us!

Oscar Flores — Grade: 06
My mom deserves a diamond because all these years she has been a wonderful, caring, and loving mother to me and the whole family.

Samantha Gentile — Grade: 06
My mom deserves a diamond because she is nice. Works three jobs. Also works hard. She also is there for me and my brother.

Erica Guerena — Grade: 06
My mom deserves a this because she has been through thick and thin, but she has always been there for me. I really, truly love my mom!

Dylan Higelmire — Grade: 06
My mom has a wonderful personality and she is a loving person who takes valuable time out of her life for the poor. She's great!

Austin Hubbard — Grade: 06
My mom deserves a diamond because she works hard all year. I can't repay so I hope this might show how I appreciate her.

Andrea Kim — Grade: 06
She deserves a diamond because she is the best mom you could have! She cares for me and cheers me up every time I'm down.

* Amethyst winners in bold.

Kailey Merino   **Grade: 06**
My mom deserves a diamond because she works very hard to keep the family functioning. She also has a job. She loves me every second.

Fawzia Rab   Grade: 06
My mom deserves a diamond because she always compliments me, helps me with homework, and exercises with me. Clearly my mom deserves a diamond.

Cole Ruggles   Grade: 06
My mom deserves a diamond because my mom is the best and she always helps me with my homework and takes care of me.

Teacher: Natalie Depalma

Timothy Cunningham   **Grade: 03**
My mother's face is crystal gold, her body is a gem. Her heart is a diamond, filled with all love and joy.

Nicola Furumoto   **Grade: 03**
My mother, better than a diamond, brightly shines in sunlight and in moonlight. She shines like a crystal of love and kindness.

Kira Kawano   Grade: 03
Her eyes shine like diamonds. Her heart's made of gold. Her smile's like a crystal. Her life is like gold.

Ida Kazerani   Grade: 03
Gleaming like moonlight, shimmering like a candle, twinkling like her eyes. She stares into me, protecting my body. Mom.

Spencer Leonardi   Grade: 03
My mom has a gem within her reach. Our souls join together. Her beautiful eyes reflect off of me. My mom deserves a gem.

Jessica Octavio   Grade: 03
Her eyes glisten like crystals that outshine the moon and the stars, with a heart out of pure gold.

Thomas Ota   Grade: 03
With a bit of stars and moon, my mom's eyes will sparkle like a blue diamond brighter than the sun.

Gracie Tellers   Grade: 03
Her eyes twinkle like crystal stars in the indigo sky. Her diamond heart is so sweet. My mother is the gem in me.

Madelene Thomas   Grade: 03
My mom is like a gem twinkling in the light, her everlasting beauty, her everlasting shine. It will be there for all eternity.

Jacqueline Venckus   Grade: 03
My mom is so sweet, her heart made of gold is brighter than anyone the world knows.

Jacqueline Venckus   **Grade: 03**
Look at my mom's eyes when the moon glares so bright looks like a gem like the shimmering water at night.

Zachary Yuan   Grade: 03
Her voice echoes in my soul. Her eyes glitter like two sparkling onyx gems. My mom is my diamond.

Teacher: Amie Shields

Natalie Bishay   **Grade: 05**
Mom's great in every way. She's the encouraging start of a wonderful day with big smiles and a big heart. Everyday's worth a start!

McKenna Branham   Grade: 05
My very own mom deserves a diamond because she is pretty, caring, helpful, giving, kind, smart, loving, happy, special, fair, brave and she loves me!

Christian Chae   **Grade: 05**
My mom deserves a diamond because she is the most loving, compassionate, affectionate, genial, affable, amiable, gregarious, sociable, and convivial mom in the world.

Ahnna Chu   Grade: 05
My mom deserves a diamond because she is very supportive toward my school and ice skating. She's caring, kind and gentle.

Samantha Claproth   Grade: 05
My mom deserves a diamond because her beautiful brown eyes sparkle and all of her comforting hugs are as sweet cupcakes. I love mom!

Cienna Eltiste   Grade: 05
My mom deserves a diamond because she is spectacular like a diamond. Also because she is a phenomenal mom while taking care of three kids.

Sadaf Esteaneh   Grade: 05
My mom deserves a diamond because she is as sweet as a cookie, loving, and caring. She's beautiful and always there for ne!

Jason Huynh   Grade: 05
A twinkle of love that shines bright. A glitter of care in her eyes. My mom sparkles unlike any other. She is my gorgeous diamond.

Samuel Marquez   Grade: 05
My mom deserves a diamond because she is kind, a forgiver, trustworthy, smart and hardworking, thoughtful, always happy and she takes care of other people.

Kamyar Mivehchi   Grade: 05
My mom deserves a diamond because she drives me to sports. She keeps food in my mouth and clothes on my back.

Samar Nasser   Grade: 05
My mom deserves a diamond because sometimes she can be mean but I know she loves me a lot and she'll be there for me forever.

Kimberly Nguyen   **Grade: 05**
My extraordinary mom deserves a flawless diamond because she's the key to my success in academics and social life. She's the jewel of my life.

Anoushka Patel   Grade: 05
My mom deserves a diamond because she is amazing. She is always kind and caring to others. If she won she'd treat it like children.

Megan Snader   Grade: 05
Mama deserves a diamond because she is caring in every way. She works arduously as I go play. Mommy so sweet deserves a diamond everyday.

Jashanna Walia   Grade: 05
I want my mom to win because she is the funniest mom ever! She's pretty and very loving. Mom is always there for me.

Alannah Woodward   Grade: 05
My mom deserves a diamond because she's pretty and talented. She's a great cook and worth a 5,000 carat diamond. Mom will always be mine.

Teacher: Michelle Venckus

Danielle Garcia   Grade: 06
Mom deserves a diamond to put on her warm, soft hand that she always hugs me with and for the hard work that she does.

Alejandra Gomez   Grade: 06
Mom deserves a diamond because with the diamond she'll keep a special memory of me and it will express how much I care about her.

Loralynn Ingreso   **Grade: 06**
My mom deserves a diamond because she glows with her inner and outer beauty, and she is the best mom in the world.

Shylah Jones   Grade: 06
My mom deserves a diamond because she always works to feed, clothe, and love us. She helps us all and always grants our wishes.

Meagan McNeff   Grade: 06
My mom deserves a diamond because she is understanding, forgiving, caring, giving, loving, sharing. She's patient and happy. She is the best mom ever.

Trisha Nguyen   Grade: 06
My mom deserves this diamond because of her effort, care, and support. These things that she has accomplished in the past mean everything to me.

Dominique Parker   Grade: 06
My mom deserves a diamond because she loves me unconditionally despite my flaws. She is a strong, independent woman, and she works hard for me.

Shiyani Patel   Grade: 06
My mom deserves a diamond because she is loving, caring, supporting, and very hardworking. My mom deserves a diamond because she always encourages me.

Paige Petrus   Grade: 06
My mom deserves a diamond because she is beautiful, caring, priceless, and works so hard to help out our family.

Haley Porter   Grade: 06
My mom deserves a diamond because she loves me. She cares for me even when times are rough. She is kind and wonderful and beautiful.

Sheridan Stark   Grade: 06
My mother deserves a diamond because she is nice to everybody, caring, loving to everything and everybody. My mom means one million worlds to me.

Paige Vitolo-Howard   Grade: 06
My mom deserves a diamond because she loves me, she's hardworking and outgoing, puts others first and helps all sorts of people. BEST MOM!!!

Teacher: Michelle Ward

Justin Arevalos   Grade: 06
My mom is sweet. My mom is giving. Whenever I see her, I start grinning. So now, she is my heart so I am winning.

Cameron Crippen   Grade: 06
I love my mom with my heart. I've always loved her from start. She's like a crystal ball inside. In her I can confide.

Ryan Disciullo   Grade: 06
The heart and soul of my house, sparkling image in my mind. The one who brightens everyone's day, and time without her unimaginable. My mom.

Lacie Gamell   Grade: 06
Her eyes sparkle like the moonlit sky. Her spirit as pure as gold. My mother, the gem of my life.

Takumi Iwasaki   Grade: 06
Your eyes shine like the sun. Your smile is the moon. And I am the land below you.

Jena Jekums   Grade: 06
My love for my mom is as deep as Earth's core. In its fiery heart, my devotion is stored.

Renee Lee   Grade: 06
Her eyes glisten like stars above, her soul is bright as the sun. Her heart beats like canaries chirping, my mom is no ordinary mom.

Adlih Loetz   Grade: 06
My mom is my best friend. Our love for each other will never end. She may be older than me, but in her I believe.

Kevyn Lofink   Grade: 06
My mom is the best mom you will ever meet. She shines just like a star and her eyes are as pure as a rainbow.

Emily Majer   Grade: 06
My mom is my heart. She warms me so dearly. The happiness in her eyes makes me smile so brightly.

Jermaine Permejo   Grade: 06
My mom is the shining light and is very bright. Aren't I right? My affection for her is stronger than anything else.

Rohan Sidhu   Grade: 06
She smiles like a sun. Her eyes like glitter. Her soul like crystal which melts in the sun.

Trevor Smith   Grade: 06
The sweetest mom you ever did see. Would be the one closest to me. She helps anyway she can. I can't live without her.

Abby Tellers   Grade: 06
She opens my soul. Expresses my life. She shines like the bright sun and the glowing moon. She's my mom, the bright shining one.

Rebeca Vargas   Grade: 06
The sparkle in her eyes. The shine in her soul. Her smile like the shining sun above.

Crown Valley Elementary
Laguna Niguel

Teacher: Heidi Albers

Olivia Baer   Grade: 03
Mom is as sparkly as a dark starry night. She is also very bright. When I am right; and is strong when I am wrong.

Nik Gamble   Grade: 03
She reads with me and helps me with my homework and helps everyone in my classroom. She works hard running her own business.

Maximiliano Garcia   Grade: 03
My mom deserves this diamond because she cares about me and my brothers and she buys a lot of stuff for us. She is the best mom.

Nicholas Hardiman   Grade: 03
My mom is the best. She is nice. It is my mom's anniversary on Valentine's Day. That is why mom deserves a diamond. Mom is awesome.

Kylie Schmiedeke   Grade: 03
My mommy deserves a diamond because not only does she care for me, but other people in my family. That's why my mom deserves diamonds.

Teacher: Jane Freet

Dylan Baer   Grade: 05
My mom deserves a diamond because she is very thoughtful and cares and thinks about everyone else before herself and is a very generous person.

Chad Breece   Grade: 05
My mom takes care of me and helps me but she loves me and that's why she deserves a diamond.

Jack Galloway   Grade: 05
Wow! My mom cooks extraordinary food especially bacon sandwiches. She's kind and loves to play Wii with me. That's why my mom deserves a diamond.

Iris Hou   Grade: 05
Her eyes are like gems. Her smile is warm. She's one of a kind. I'm lucky she's my mom.

Justin Kuhn   Grade: 05
My mom deserves a diamond for all the hard work she does in the house. She always cooks our family good tasting dinner.

* Amethyst winners in bold.

Makenzie Lynch   Grade: 05
My mom deserves a diamond because no matter how sick I can get, she stays up all night with me.

Amanda Nedula   Grade: 05
My mom sparkles, she's as bright as the sea. She works hard and loves me. She's a star that's tranquil. My mom deserves a diamond.

Chad Oldenburg   Grade: 05
I love my mom. She is fine. She is the one of God's designs. She dusts, sweeps, keeps everything clean. And, she loves me!

Amanda Reider   Grade: 05
She cooks, she helps with homework, she drives to school, she picks up from school, and she shops. Who is this? The World's 1 Mom; mine.

Tori Reinhart   Grade: 05
My mother, the one who gave me life, deserves a diamond because she does everything possible for my sisters and I. She truly is wonderful!

Maddy Tompkins   Grade: 05
My mom deserves a diamond because she works hard, is always relaxed, helps us when we need it, and is an awesome person.

Thomas Wick   Grade: 05
My mom does so much stuff around the house like cleaning all of the rooms and that's why my mom deserves a diamond.

Nathan Zwieg   Grade: 05
I think my mom should deserve the diamond because she helps other classes with there work. And she is nice, and generous, sweet and loving.

Teacher: Mary Maggay

Sydney Allison   Grade: 04
The sun shines on the sea, sparkles like my mother. My mother is the best mom in the world! I appreciate my mother a lot!

Olivia Binkowska   Grade: 04
My mom deserves a diamond because she's like a star in the sky. My mom deserves a diamond because her words are like gold.

Emma Bray   Grade: 04
I love her close. I love her dearly. She has helped me always. Mom, an angel from above, a diamond is something she deserves.

Jasmine Brewster   Grade: 04
My mother is a blessing of gold. She is like sapphire, topaz and a diamond. That is what my mother deserves, a diamond.

Eddie Carney   Grade: 04
A gaze into my soul, almost as sweet as the sunset, and a voice as the morning dew to come…

Kendall Clothier   Grade: 04
My mom is an angel. My mom is a bird, her wings spread out as far as her heart, full of love and passion.

Koakupa'a Flores   Grade: 04
Rubies are red, sapphire is blue. My mom is beautiful and that's why she deserves a diamond from you.

Griffin Garrett   Grade: 04
My mom helps me with my homework and she is responsible and she's pretty.

Gabriella Gray   Grade: 04
My mom's my angel, my flower, my doctor when I'm sick. She's as beautiful as sunlight, she's my hope, my life.

Katie Hawton   Grade: 04
She has golden eyes, and very beautiful eyes too. She cared me so much and loving too. I love her too. I play with my mom.

Baylor Jones   Grade: 04
My mom deserves a diamond because she helped me get rid of my fears in pitching for my baseball team for travel ball for me.

Stephanie Magnelli   Grade: 04
My mom is very caring, she is also very loving for my sister and I. God made my mom a good person. I love her.

Jordan Matthews   Grade: 04
I think my mom deserves a diamond because she works hard to help me. She is my nurse when I am sick.

Wyatt Mc Kinney   Grade: 04
My mom is an angel in my eye. I love my mom. Her heart is as big as a diamond.

Konrad McKeague   Grade: 04
Her eyes are as wonderful as possible. She can help me do my homework without cheating. Her brain is super smart. And, she loves me!

D.J. Moynahan   Grade: 04
My mom deserves a diamond because she is the most beautiful, caring, nice mom in the whole universe. She would be the diamond I would pick.

Alex Murrillo   Grade: 04
My mom deserves a diamond because she is a hard working woman, she cares for people. I will always know she'll be there by my side.

Adam Naami   Grade: 04
She is an angel that came from heaven and is also my heaven and my life.

Nicolette Notti   Grade: 04
She is overflowing with love, care and kindness like our majestic waterfalls. She loves and cares for me like Mother Earth does for us.

Kristen Ostendorf   Grade: 04
When my mom adopted me, she knew I needed a family. I looked at her and her eyes sparkled. That's why I love her.

Kimia Parvizi   Grade: 04
My mom deserves a diamond because she helps with my homework. My mom is wonderful and beautiful. My mom is loves me and I love her too.

Taylor Rake   Grade: 04
My mom is an angel that has dropped down from above, she's as beautiful as a flower, and as nice as a dove.

Sommy Sadeghi   Grade: 04
You've always took care of me when I was sick. Whenever I'm sad you make me happy. You're the best mom.

Anastasia Soterapoulos   Grade: 04
Your eyes are green like the grassy field. You are the flower that stands out of them all because you are the prettiest of all.

Abby Wagner   Grade: 04
My mom helps me with my homework. She cleans my room. She is like my pot of gold that glimmers like a diamond.

Teacher: Patty Mc Mahon

Molly Brennan   Grade: 04
My mom deserves a diamond because she is thoughtful, loving, pretty, and much more. My mom would deserve something beautiful because I love her a lot.

Allison Cease   Grade: 04
My mom deserves a diamond because she is beautiful and smart and many, many more. She is kind to everyone around her. She rocks.

Cody Curtis   Grade: 04
My mom deserves a diamond because she will help me with homework and is helpful, hardworking and does not even have one gem right now.

Jamie Dietz   Grade: 04
My mom deserves a diamond because she is very hardworking and outgoing, she always makes me laugh. I really think she deserves a diamond.

James Doyle   Grade: 04
My mom deserves a diamond because she is happy, loving, and full of care, and I love her very much and she is special.

Kalani Fajardo   Grade: 04
My mom deserves a diamond because she is loving, caring, funny and nice. She works so hard to make us dinner! She is the best.

Courtney Frickman   Grade: 04
My mom deserves a diamond because she puts me to bed at night and we read together. My mom could not be any better.

Maya Haider   Grade: 04
My mom deserves a diamond because she is special to me. When I'm lonely, she comes and makes me feel special. I love my mom.

Hiromi Lee   Grade: 04
My mom deserves a diamond because she is very patient. When she smiles, I feel good. My mom deserves a diamond as beautiful as her.

Ryder Lynch   Grade: 04
My mom deserves a diamond because she's smart, funny, cute, and helps you if you need it and that's why my mom deserves a diamond.

Luke Myer   Grade: 04
My mom deserves a diamond because she is a spectacular mom and she works so hard to put food around the table, she's the BEST!

Meryl Reinhart   Grade: 04
My mom deserves a diamond because she has gone through so much for me and I love her very much. She's the best mom ever.

Amber Sislin   Grade: 04
My mom deserves a diamond because she is always there for me when I need her. Her eyes always sparkle just like a diamond.

Justin Wolcott   Grade: 04
I've always wanted something that sparkles like my mom. She gets us out of bad situations. That's why my mom deserves a diamond.

Teacher: Diana Stratford

Colton Brown   Grade: 05
My mom deserves a diamond because she is always there when I'm sick. She does a lot of stuff that's fun with me.

Brian Clinkenbeard   Grade: 05
My mom deserves a diamond because she is caring for others and she helps our family by making dinner, drives us places, and works hard.

Aiden Gerard   Grade: 05
My mom is the coolest, hardest working mom there ever was, takes care of me no matter what. That is why she deserves a diamond.

Kaylee Hepburn   Grade: 05
My mom deserves a diamond because she always gives me a shoulder to cry on when I need her most.

Chloe Hopper   Grade: 05
My mom deserves a diamond because she is brave when times are hard, like they are in our lives. Right now, I love her.

Dominick Mesinas   Grade: 05
My mom deserves a diamond because she is always there for me. She also packs my lunch. That's why she deserves a diamond.

Nathaniel Stombaugh   Grade: 05
My mom deserves a diamond because she was nice enough to raise my brother, sister and I, and she never has gotten rewarded good enough.

Teacher: Kathleen Tierney

Ryann Beveridge   Grade: 03
My mom deserves a diamond because she protects us, is kind, is unique, special, and has a golden, silver heart; and is the best mom.

Tommy Maroon   Grade: 03
My mom deserves a diamond because she is selfless, patient, kind, loving, gentle, and she loves me and my family. She is great!

Venessa Pizano   Grade: 03
Mom deserves a diamond because she is our special mom that we love, respect and care for and we'll always be grateful for being mom.

Teacher: Carrie Wulf

Madison Brown   Grade: 03
My mom wakes each morning sparkling with beauty. She has many roles; a cook, driver, teacher and friend. She is the perfect mom - absolutely flawless.

Alex Downhower   Grade: 03
My mom deserves a diamond because she cleans my room. She also makes me breakfast. She helps me when I need it.

Nicky Gomez   Grade: 03
My mom is special. My mom is good. She's like my angel, so clever and fun. I'll always love her forever and forever.

Colin Reider   Grade: 03
My mom deserves a diamond because she always helps me with my homework no matter what she is doing. She is very special and unique.

Garrett Simco   Grade: 03
My mom's the best because she makes breakfast for dinner. Some nights she lets Reagan look at the moon. She's the best mom ever!

Brennan Zoerb   Grade: 03
My mom is the best because whenever things got hard, she was always there.

Michaela Zwieg   Grade: 03
Every night my mommy sings to me. Before I go to bed, she tucks me in. She always kisses me on my forehead at night.

Culverdale Elementary
Irvine

Teacher: Sally Frueh

Mohamed Ali   Grade: 05
My mom deserves a diamond because she cooks, cleans and never says a thing. Her eyes twinkle. She helps disabled people all the time.

Kieran Colvin   Grade: 05
She is very beautiful and kind. I like to be by her side. She is very funny and sweet. I love my mom.

Demi Dang   Grade: 05
Every time I look at my mom, her eyes light up like a shining star at the night. Her hair sparkles and her lips gleam.

Jason Eaves   Grade: 05
My mom deserves a diamond because her eyes sparkle like the sea, her hair blows like the wind. Her smile shines like a diamond.

* Amethyst winners in bold.

Spencer Fertig   Grade: 05
My mother deserves a diamond because her heart is like an enormous gem of passion. Her soul is as pure as gold. That...why.

Elizabeth Georgio   **Grade: 05**
My mom loves me so much. I love her gentle touch. She always makes me laugh and smile, even if I'm not happy for awhile.

Ji-Yun Han   **Grade: 05**
Mom is something everyone has, but mom like mine is very rare. Her eyes are full of love and care. Looks at everyone with compassion.

Junya Honda   Grade: 05
My mom shines like a diamond and she's cool like a ruby and that's because she's nice to me.

Michelle Jenei   **Grade: 05**
My mom is a star in space that shines the brightest and wins every race.

Basel Khartabil   Grade: 05
I think my mom deserves a diamond because she doesn't have enough jewelry and a diamond is just enough for my mom.

Sydney Le   Grade: 05
As I look at her, she gives me a warming smile. She says she's not perfect, but to me it's enough. I love my mommy.

Nellie Paing   Grade: 05
My mom deserves a diamond because she is the nicest person I know. She loves to help me with school. That's why my mom's great.

Tiffany Pettit   Grade: 05
My mom's smile is like a hot muffin. My mom's tears are like cries of thunder. I would give up anything just for her...

De Portola Elementary
Mission Viejo

Teacher: Dorothy George

Sydney Atwood   **Grade: 05**
Graceful, honest, goes with the flow. Her eyes glitter like winter snow - crafty, loving and quite kind and she's smart as Albert Einstein. My mom.

Nikola Drobnjak   Grade: 05
Scent as sweet as roses. Eyes sparkling like stars. She will amaze you with her knowledge. When she smiles, she breaks my heart. My mom!

Bailey Gwartney   **Grade: 05**
My mom is the best, she's warm as a nest, takes care of me alone, hardly talks on the phone, and never gets any rest!

Chloe Hansen   Grade: 05
She looks like shining stars on a dark winter night. Her eyes sparkle like fairy dust. My mom is the shining star of my life!

Matthew Lucero   Grade: 05
My mom is nice. My mom is full of spice. With every child comes only one mom and I know she's the one for me.

Elise Martinez   **Grade: 05**
My mother: More beautiful than a spider web sparkling with diamond dew drops. More calm and elegant than an ocean sunset. Sweeter than the ripest cherries.

Jocelyn McLean   **Grade: 05**
Her firm hugs making me feel warm. Her loving heart shining like diamonds. She never gives up. She keeps going and going. My mom.

Jake Newman   Grade: 05
As enchanting as a rainbow - her eyes sparkle like a star. She's as charming as a sunset about to go down - sweet as Hershey's chocolate!

Julianne Pellizzon   Grade: 05
Hugs hot like a fire, heart as big as a sun, eyes like twinkling stars, as gorgeous as a million flowers - Mom's love for me!

Douglas Simsarian   Grade: 05
The mom I love is like a glowing star lighting up the deserted skies. She's a genius all night, and more giving than anything living.

Dominic Slezacek   **Grade: 05**
Your love makes my day bright. You're beautiful like butterflies. Your silly smile creates happiness. Your beautiful face shines like a diamond. Mom, you're great!

Yasmeen Sobaih   Grade: 05
Cheeks as smooth as velvet. Heart as noble as a queen. Eyes sparkling like golden sapphires. Her love as precious as pirate treasure to me!

Calen Torres   Grade: 05
You should see my mom, she's great. She is always on time, she's never late. Her smile's bright like a shining light. That's my mom!

Connor Wilde   Grade: 05
Has eyes that sparkle and lighten up my heart. Hugs are as warm as sun-soaked sand. Lips are as red as blooming beautiful roses.

Giselle Aldana   Grade: 06
My mom 's eyes are like two delicious chocolate mud pies. Hearing her laugh is as joyful as watching a sunset. My mom's hugs are long-lasting!

Landon Ballard   **Grade: 06**
Mom is loveable like a brand new teddy bear. She is a priceless antique. Glistening eyes like the sea and enchanting like the Northern Lights!

Cheyenne Berbey   **Grade: 06**
Vivid and beautiful, always there! Can't stop loving; her heart is never bare! She has good companions because her attitude's like a champion. My mom!

Kristen Cecil   Grade: 06
The sound of her voice, like thousands of angels singing. Her eyes, like two crystal clear pools of water. Her skin, as soft as velvet!

Kevin McKinney   Grade: 06
Mom is filled with love like a teddy bear. Lips are like red roses. Her eyes are like emeralds. Her warm heart is like cocoa!

Anthony Miller   Grade: 06
The one who blooms like a rose, who shines like a sunrise. Who is generous to others, is caring and wonderful. One and only mom!

Teacher: Donna Hyde

Dillon Card   Grade: 06
My mom deserves a diamond for her compassion and her love. Her kindness always sings to me as if she was a dove.

Brett Guerrero   Grade: 06
My mom deserves a diamond because she's always there for me. She is a dedicated parent and supports me in everything I do.

Tyler Lloyd   Grade: 06
My mom, she's so very sweet. She's cool. She's also very neat. She always says, "I love you"! It's very true, "I love you too!"

Sunrae Taloma   Grade: 06
Eyes like emeralds, hair like gold, laughter like bells, skin like rose petals, everlasting love, no diamond needed when my mom is near.

Marina Weinberger   **Grade: 06**
Mom lives the sadness out of people with a warmhearted smile. With an embrace, she pours love over me. She's the diamond in my heart.

Teacher: Kathy Moon

Romy Abboud   **Grade: 02**
Mom, you are the beautiful glue that holds our loving family together. Beautiful as a full moon shining on a sparkling lake. I love you.

Keemia Beizai   Grade: 02
My mom's heart and soul are like a lovely rose. She blooms and smiles and fills our hearts with love. She is my perfect mom.

Kyle Cota   **Grade: 02**
Her eyes shine in the brightness of the shining, sparkling hot sun. Her love holds me together. Her heart fills me with love and warmth.

Jackson Emmett   Grade: 02
Mom's gentle touch relieves my pain. Her hair is as soft as silk. Mom is a beautiful goddess and the sun of my world.

Amber Saxon   **Grade: 02**
Mom, your gentle touch relieves my pain. You are a never-ending song in my heart of comfort, happiness, and being. You are mine. Thank you.

Tyler Shamas   **Grade: 02**
Mom's eyes sparkle like the blue never-ending ocean at sunset. Her love is like refreshing water on a hot summer day, she's my world.

Simar Singh   Grade: 02
My mom's voice is soothing. She is beautiful like a royal princess. She fills her family's hearts with love and happiness like a rainbow sunset.

Emily Stevens   Grade: 02
Mom is the warmth that keeps our family blanketed with love. She is like an angel sent down from heaven. I will always love her.

Nathan Thompson   Grade: 02
Mom fills my heart with love and care. Her gentle touch heals my pain with joy. Mom will be my life forever. I love her.

Carson Totty   Grade: 02
Her eyes sparkle like the ocean. Her loving touch is like a gentle feather. Her scent of love is tremendous. She is my best prize!

Teacher: Mike Ravetti

Katie Cao   Grade: 06
Diamonds and gems in all of its kind, but no other can compare to my mother's beautiful crystal eyes.

Medina Islami   Grade: 06
The sunlight passes like the wind everyday. Her eyes shine like stars with the moon. She has great etiquette. My mom is a beautiful diamond!

Edmond Rhew   **Grade: 06**
My mom is a diamond that leads my way like a bright torch. Her eyes are shining like a ruby that gleams through my heart.

Deanna Tommarello   Grade: 06
My mom sparkles in the glorious sunlight and glows in the amazing moonlight. Her eyes shimmer like the beautiful diamond she deserves.

Teacher: Kelly Wheeler

Morgan Barraza   **Grade: 05**
You guide me through life. During bad times you gave advice. Your laughter and voice are lullabies. I don't want there to be any goodbyes.

Jake Brady   **Grade: 05**
My mom has the warmth of a dragon's fiery heart, the love of a mother of no other kind. She is special because she's mine.

Leah Cernicky   **Grade: 05**
Her countenance shines like sunlight on the ocean. Her harmonic laughter floats in the air. She always smells like lotion on her bouncy golden hair.

Christian Connella   Grade: 05
My mom's always there for me. The laughter, the smiles, the tears. No matter how far apart we are, our friendship and love is forever.

Danielle Jelden   Grade: 05
Hair red as the darkest rose, eyes brown as the darkest chocolate. She's the one you can count on and loves English - Mom.

Courtney Kim   **Grade: 05**
She wipes away my tears. I know she always hears what I have to say. And at the end of the day, she loves me.

Scott Kruger   Grade: 05
My mom has sparkling eyes even though she's over worked for me and my brother. Her heart is full of love. I love you, mom!

Keely Mc Laughlin   Grade: 05
Everyday there is a blanket of love. I feel as if I'm in a daydream. No one can harm me because my mom is there.

Adam Palmer   Grade: 05
My mom's eyes twinkle like a shooting star. If I am sad, she's always by my side. Her heart is always open for loving me.

Marisa Rigel   **Grade: 05**
My mom deserves a diamond because she's as brave as a lion but as loving as a lamb. She's full of kisses and never hisses.

Taylor Rivera   Grade: 05
My mom is like a shining star. I feel her love near and far. She cares so much about me. Her love never ends.

Sean Rochford   Grade: 05
My mom deserves a diamond because of her bright blue eyes. When we hug, my heart just flies. I love my mom. She's the best.

Ilana Roth   Grade: 05
My mom has emerald eyes of green. She's awesome and unseen. It's hard to tell who loves more. Her to me, or me to her.

Miles Toma   Grade: 05
Eyes like the sunshine. Mind, grand and divine. Hands as soft as moss. Not strict, but still the boss. All beauty and brilliance is hers.

Shaina White   Grade: 05
A superhero for me, weeks work with no sweat to see, dark brown meadow eyes comfort me, the lovely woman you see is she, Mommy.

Deerfield Elementary
Irvine

Teacher: Carmen Conferti

Zaned Abassi   Grade: 06
My mom deserves a diamond because she was the one that brought me to planet earth and has took care of me when I was sick.

Tamilia Adhiningrat   Grade: 06
My mom deserves a diamond because she has battled breast cancer and can still put on a happy face after all she has overcome.

Dominique Arends   Grade: 06
I think my mom should win a diamond because of how nice she is and takes good care of everybody in my family.

* Amethyst winners in bold.

Daniel Bailey   Grade: 06
She is like a majestic eagle, teaching her young in the right path so that they can one day spread their wings into the world!

Michael Delgado   Grade: 06
I think my mom deserves a diamond because she has done everything for me and she's sacrificed a lot for me.

Sarah Kessler   Grade: 06
Mom deserves a diamond. Three kids, full time job, she is tolerant; I love her so much. She is my favorite person; she is my role model.

Noah Miller   Grade: 06
My mom deserves a diamond because she always cleans my room, does chores and makes dinner. I'm in debt for paying her back!

Michelle Morgan   Grade: 06
Karen is my mom and deserves a diamond because she is flawless! Mom always puts others first and herself last. I love her very much!

Cynthia Tang   Grade: 06
My mom, a great one, she is loving, caring, kindhearted. Though words cannot truly describe her. I'll always love her forever.

Manar Totonji   Grade: 06
I think my mom deserves a diamond because she cleans the house, helps me in math, and teaches my two home-schooled brothers.

Nicklaus Yu   Grade: 06
I think my mom deserves a diamond because she always helps me with my homework. She also takes me to my basketball games and watches.

Teacher: Cathy Heller

Ethan Agapito   Grade: 06
I think my mom deserves a diamond because she cares a lot about our family. She's funny, smart, and she's always fun.

Ben Caterinicchio   Grade: 06
My mom is the most inspiring person I have ever met. That's why she deserves a diamond.

Brittany Cooper   Grade: 06
My mom deserves a diamond because she does everything for me, and I want to give something back. I love you mommy.

Connor Dolin   Grade: 06
My mom deserves a diamond because she is a wonderful woman, who does so much for her family and never gets anything in return.

Sara Imson   Grade: 06
Most people say that they think their mom's are pretty, hardworking, well I think so. I think my mom deserves it because I Love her.

Kendra Kelly   Grade: 06
My mom deserves a diamond because I think she works too hard. I love her with all my heart, and I want to show it!

Jeffrey Moreno   Grade: 06
I think my mother deserves a diamond because she is very loving and cares for my family very much,.

Melanie Nguyen   Grade: 06
My mom deserves a diamond because she protects me. I believe she needs a diamond to protect her. My mom deserves that diamond!

Leilah Sarpas   Grade: 06
My mom is really loving and loyal, and I know she will be there for me and other people too. She takes me anywhere.

Yoseph Sarwary   Grade: 06
If I had enough money I would buy my mom a diamond. Because she's supportive, caring, loving, and she deserves a diamond.

Alohyu Vatsavai   Grade: 06
I think my mom deserves a diamond because she is caring and helps me when I need it. That's why my mom deserves a diamond.

Teacher: Kathy Larson

Ashley Choi   Grade: 04
When I'm scared, she comforts me with her soothing smile. Her love for me compares to nothing. For she's the diamond of my life.

Oyshi Dey   Grade: 04
My mom is a tree that nurtures, shelters, and cares for me. Her soft branches and her ebony black leaves hug and protect me.

Pranav Ganeshan   Grade: 04
Mom has diamonds glistening in her eyes as a star glistens in the sky. She shines like gems twinkling in the light.

Andrew Liao   Grade: 04
I want my mom to have it, for being a really good mother. She's given me so much. So the diamond should be hers.

Grace Liu   Grade: 04
My mother is the God of fire, ice, and lightening. She rules the land and sky. Her wisdom tells right from wrong. My mother is "LIFE".

Deeksha Panuganti   Grade: 04
My mom is the sun, the sun is a diamond. That's why my mom deserves a diamond. She is a beautiful, wonderful mom.

Phillip Seo   Grade: 04
The sunset rises over the oasis. It's beautiful and great. Just like my mom, she deserves a diamond, it's fate.

Alexandria Wall   Grade: 04
Mom's heart is made of gold. Her lips are two rubies and her eyes are sparkling jewels. My mom is the diamond of my life!

Natalie Wang   Grade: 04
I think mom deserves a diamond because she is an angel, helping and protecting. She is kind, understanding, and loving. She is my shining beauty.

Mingjie Zhong   Grade: 04
My mom has given me lots of love. If I gave her a jewel, she will be rewarded with love.

Del Cerro Elementary
Mission Viejo

Teacher: Darlette Dexter

Andrew Damon   Grade: 04
The only star in the sky tonight, twinkle bright, but not as bright then my mom's glittery eyes.

Lauren Desloge   Grade: 04
My ,mom is the sun, the moon and the stars. She helps me when days are hard. I love my mom and she loves me.

McKenna Etheridge   Grade: 04
My life is like a cave with no light, but her soothing voice brightens the path to light days. I love her!

Sarah Felt   Grade: 04
Her eyes sparkle like the light of a diamond. She shines like the twinkle of a star. Her heart is as bright as the sunlight.

Anthony Marin   Grade: 04
In the night, my mom's eyes twinkle like the stars. In the day, her eyes shine like the sun.

Jessica Trow   Grade: 04
Glittering, twinkling, bright eyes shining in the light, cannot wait until she tucks me in and says to me good night.

Bethany Widen   Grade: 04
Sparkle, glimmer, bright and brilliant. These words describe my mom's eyes. They glisten in my heart. She's my inspiration, the gem of my life.

Teacher: Alice Donawerth

Paige Hughes   Grade: 06
My mom is like a bird soaring. When I see her, my heart pounds with love. That is why my mom deserves a diamond.

Braden McPherson   Grade: 06
I love my mom and I think she's the best mom in the world. She's nice, loving and caring, best part she loves me back.

Sarah Mehta   Grade: 06
My mother is perfect like the stars in the sky. For she gave me my wings that I spread to fly.

Teacher: Barbara Hoefer

Patrick Cespedes   Grade: 05
Her face is exquisite and shines like a radiant star on a unilluminated night. Her heart is immense. She loves me excessively. I'm greatly appreciative.

Lucas Crandall   Grade: 05
Love is being adopted. My mom deserves a diamond because she really loves me. My mom deserves a diamond because love is her specialty.

Nicole Griffith   Grade: 05
Mom, busy, helpful, sharing, loving, giving. Makes me feel special. My mother.

Jorgina Gruenbeck   Grade: 05
Her voice is a symphony of safety and love. She's a shimmering star of hope, a treasure in the ocean, a diamond shining brightly.

Emily Ho   Grade: 05
My mom's smile is as bright as the sun. She lights my heart with rainbows of joy. She's my voice's joy. I adore my mom.

Emily Johnson   Grade: 05
Mom - sweet, strong, caring, loving, helpful. Her eyes, diamonds sparkling like ocean waves. Her smile warms my heart. What would I do without her?

Hayden Lyskoski   Grade: 05
Mom, caring, beautiful, living, laughing, loving. Who's masterful green eyes sparkle like daylight.

Katie Negrete   Grade: 05
Mom works everyday without shopping for my family. She's the shining light that glows to let me find my way out. Her smile glows forever.

Divya Prem   Grade: 05
My mom deserves a diamond, she's everything to me. She won my heart and I won hers. It's how it was meant to be.

Jillian Stoewer   Grade: 05
Mom, she is the moon that lights up the darkest times. She is the love in my heart. She is my one and only diamond.

Gordon Wong   Grade: 05
Like diamonds in the light, dragonflies at night. Both shine true like Mother who can make bad days good as new.

Del Obispo Elementary
San Juan Capistrano

Teacher: Kelli Groves

Calista Henson   Grade: 03
I love my mom. My mom is sweet. She deserves a special kind of treat. She is kind and knows me best. I love her!

Gate Hill   Grade: 03
My mom deserves a diamond because she feeds me every night. She takes care of me and doesn't yell at me. She plays a lot.

Oceana Mc Coy   Grade: 03
My mom deserves a diamond because she is helpful to everyone. She is very nice and makes the most wonderful dinners of all.

Chris Weber   Grade: 03
My mom deserves a diamond because she cooks really well. She cleans like a professional cleaner. She gives me so many wonderful things.

Dylan White   Grade: 03
My mom deserves a special treat because she is beautiful, nice, and a loving mom.

Shane White   Grade: 03
My mom deserves a diamond because she has been taking care of me for my life. She is as nice as a diamond.

Justine Yslas   Grade: 03
My mom is very lovely and sweet. She sparkles like a diamond in the sky. She's wonderful and kind. She smells like a beautiful rose.

Teacher: Cynthia Lukens

Dianne Castellon   Grade: 01
My mom deserves the diamond because she is nice and my mom is smart. My mom is good at math and my mom is fun.

Noah Cuevas   Grade: 01
My mom deserves a diamond because she feeds me. She loves me. She takes me to school. She helps me. She takes care of me.

Kristina Giles   Grade: 01
My grandma deserves a diamond because she helps me clean my bedroom. She takes good care of me.

Natalie Lopez   Grade: 01
My mom deserves a diamond because she is nice. She works hard and she is smart and she is good at math.

Danielle Rathbun   Grade: 01
My mom deserves a diamond because she helps me, and she cooks dinner for me. She knows good answers and she loves me.

Sage Rollins   Grade: 01
My mom deserves a diamond because she does whatever I say and hugs me.

Zoe Schmitzer   Grade: 01
My mom helps me and she is kind and nice. She comes and helps my friends and me at school.

Liam Short   Grade: 01
My mom deserves a diamond because she is pretty. She works very hard and loves me.

Eader (John H.) Elementary
Huntington Beach

Teacher: Lisa Viger

Elizabeth Brisky   Grade: 02
My mom's eyes twinkle like stars in the sky. No matter how far, she'll be in my heart. Mom reminds me of crystals that shine.

***** Amethyst winners in bold.**

Christine Brown   Grade: 02
My mother is shining love, when I hug her, her love goes through my soul. My mother is a shining diamond, that I really love.

Camryn Curren   Grade: 02
When I look at the stars at night. I see the sparkle of the stars that I see in my mom's eyes. She is love.

Cameron Eden   Grade: 02
My mom is so beautiful. When I look at her, there is a twinkle in my eye. I make her gold, she makes me silver.

Craig Erickson   Grade: 02
My mom is beautiful. She is the nicest mom ever. My mom has a heart of gold. She is full of love and sunshine.

Ryan Haley   Grade: 02
Her eyes bloom like roses in the meadow. Her heart is as red as an apple. She is as beautiful as mist from the ocean.

Lexie Perry   Grade: 02
My mom has the eye of the diamond. The eye of the diamond is the eye of the tiger. My mom has diamond tiger eyes!

Donovan Phillips   Grade: 02
My mom has eyes like diamonds. She has hair as mountains. She is so beautiful. She is as beautiful as the ocean.

Samantha Schofield   Grade: 02
She shines like stars in the sky. She is brighter than the sun. My mom is my life. My mom is my heart.

Elaina Siegel   Grade: 02
I love my mommy. She shines like the sun and the stars. When I look at her, my heart is filled with love and excitement.

Greg Suhr   Grade: 02
When I gaze into my mom's eyes, I just see pure gold. I see a diamond too. I love her more than anything.

Eastbluff Elementary
Newport Beach

Teacher: June Elsten

Aubrey Burger   Grade: 06
My mom deserves a diamond because she sparkles like the star and shines in the moonlight.

Lauren Burger   Grade: 06
My heart is filled with love, for the one who's been with me through the years. Mom deserves a diamond as flawless as herself.

Marina Cahill   Grade: 06
My mom is the best thin in the world. She keeps me warm when it is cold. My mom's heart is filled with good.

Matt Daruty   Grade: 06
My mom is made up of 50% caring for me, 25% laundry, 10% herself, 15% lunches, and 100% love.

Sally Debbas   Grade: 06
When mom's with me, life's brightening. Without her, it's frightening. My mom's the best, never gets a rest. I hope she'll have an everlasting zest.

Avalon Dressler   Grade: 06
You know my mom is very uplifting. She makes the sun shine so bright. If I didn't have her, my life would be dark.

Cameron Kelley   Grade: 06
Beauty with strength, like no other. Diamonds, gems like a mother. Strengthened and clear. Diamonds, for mother we hold so dear.

Sydney McKeown   Grade: 06
When I think of my mom, I think of beauty and love. Her eyes are like light blue waterfalls falling from a cliff.

Kayleen Nguyen   Grade: 06
My mom is really sweet and caring. She brings her heart out to anything. My mom is an everything to me. I love my mom.

Caroline Quigg   Grade: 06
One small candle flickering, the gloom consumes. She smiles one smile, the flickering resumes. When she smiles, it's seen for miles. I love my mom.

Ashley Reynolds   Grade: 06
Diamonds shine amongst rocks, it reminds me of my shining diamond, my mom. She is the sun in the horizon, she is my shining star.

Cleo Seger   Grade: 06
She may not be perfect, but she tries. Whenever she walks by, she whisks away my troubles, leaving behind wonderful feelings. She is my mom.

Jack Shields   Grade: 06
As cupids final arrow is shot, a poor boy feels love. His final words, "I love mom".

JJ Vogel   Grade: 06
Wonderful, cool, colorful describes my mom. She is one hard worker. In my mind, my mom is a sparkling shining diamond.

Giorgio Weismann   Grade: 06
My mom is the limestone. Cosmos in the flower bed of opal poppies. She is a torch light blazing in the dark giving me life.

Alexander Wendland   Grade: 06
As the sun sets on the edge of the Earth, it reminds me of my mom. Her love radiating from her heart towards me.

Andrew Wysopal   Grade: 06
A beautiful gift, made perfect for me, constantly caring for all she sees. Taking everything that needs a home.

Martina Zaki   Grade: 06
My mom is as graceful as a swan, as beautiful as a sunset and the most precious gem to my heart.

Teacher: Maggie Kirk

Sarah Bauerlein   Grade: 05
As my mom stares down at me, with her eyes sparkling with much glee. It makes me feel very happy to see her love me.

Nikki Daoust   Grade: 05
My mom created little old me. She makes my day full of glee. My mom's got nerves. A diamond's what she deserves.

Georgia Muller   Grade: 05
Even on the darkest night when the moon doesn't show. I have the brightest light which is my mother's glow.

Natalie Zahabi   Grade: 05
My mom is special to me. Yes, she truly is. Every morning, she wakes me up. At night, she gives me a kiss.

Teacher: Candice Lighter

Ally Doherty   Grade: 05
My mom is sweet like candy, intelligent like a scholar, funny like a clown, outstanding like a star AND, as beautiful as a rose.

Nicolas Guizan   Grade: 05
Beautiful, stylish, sassy and has personality. Those are the qualities my mom has, and those are the qualities a diamond has. It's a perfect match!

Brenden Hueston   Grade: 05
Mom's my motivator. She's always there helping with homework, cheering me on in sports and tips on everyday life. It's time to give back.

Nadia Kim   **Grade: 05**
My mom deserves a diamond because she is like a glowing bright star who lights my paths in my life. She shines in my heart.

Alex Metherate   Grade: 05
My mom is like the first sparkling diamond in time. When I'm sad, mom comforts me. She helps me with school work. She's the best.

Aimee Nguyen   **Grade: 05**
My mom struggles between career and motherhood, teaches me compassion by leading example and gives unconditional love. But most importantly, she believes in me.

Camila Vincent   Grade: 05
My mom deserves a diamond because she is a beautiful as a swan, sweet like strawberries and as cuddly as your favorite teddy bear.

Teacher: Lacey Rellaford

Amanda Calhoun   Grade: 02
My mom deserves a diamond because she is thoughtful, she helps you when you're sick and hurt. My mom is the sparkle in my eye.

Kristina Narinyan   Grade: 02
My mom deserves a diamond, my mom is a glimmer in my eye. She's my heart, she's mine, and she shines as a star.

Aleia Panes   Grade: 02
She takes care of me when I am sick, she is sparkles to my eyes. She smiles like rose, she loves me more than anyone!

Teacher: Karen Selby

Spencer Bentley   Grade: 04
My mom's voice is like an angel in the trees that are blooming the prettiest flowers in the world, and the talent of twenty operas.

Tyler Flood   Grade: 04
My mom has the best soul, she is caring, helpful and very nice. Her eyes sparkle in the morning sun. She is the best mom.

Sam Haase   Grade: 04
As my mom looks into my eyes. As the sun shines into her sparkling pupils, she begs for a diamond ring.

Anna Hartog   Grade: 04
I think my mom deserves a diamond because she is loving and kind. When she smiles, I feel warm inside, and I love my mom.

Christy Huebner   Grade: 04
Not crusty on the outside, but so flawless like the sauce topped with love-mushrooms, cheese, not peas. I love my yummy pizza pie mom.

Emma Lambert   Grade: 04
My mom's an angel. She's an angel because she loves me and takes care of me. I hope she spreads the love to you.

Charlotte Lynskey   Grade: 04
My mom deserves a diamond because she brings so much joy to my life. She takes wonderful care of me and will love me forever.

Kennedy Mulvaney   Grade: 04
She's an angel from Heaven, a pearl from the sea and nothing can break my love for my mommy!

Jessica Narinyan   Grade: 04
My mom has a sweet soul and a brilliant mind. When I see her eyes that sparkle like the millions of diamonds in the moonlight.

Neela Nassiri   Grade: 04
My mom has rubies for kidneys, an emerald for a spleen, a diamond for her heart, and a mind full of me.

Griffin Peters   Grade: 04
Amazing, loving, incredible, those are the words that describe my gold hearted mom. She is not just my mom, but she's my friend.

Jasmine Prow   Grade: 04
My mom deserves a diamond because her love and care for me is as bright as the sunset reflecting on the beautiful blue ocean.

Sina Schwenk-Mueller   **Grade: 04**
Filled with love and tenderness, her beauty glowing. Her gentle touch. She is my mother, my glowing sun. She is my sparkling diamond.

Ava Shields   Grade: 04
Delicate, yet strong. Elegant and graceful, courteous, yet playful. My mother's love for me is nonstop and unchanging, my love for her is forever.

Kami Wilkins   Grade: 04
My mom's personality is bright and warm like the sun. You could swim in her chocolate brown eyes as you could the shimmering ocean.

Caroline Wood   **Grade: 04**
The moon can light the midnight sky. The sun can light in the day, but my mom shines all my life.

Teacher: Kathy Smith

Alessandra Allen   Grade: 06
My mother is amazing; always cooking. Smiling; laughing. Doing things for me all the time. Raising me, teaching me; all the while loving me.

Raymond Andrade   Grade: 06
I love my mom, I love her so, I want the whole wide world to know. She's so sweet, I now know my life's complete.

Phoebe Andujar   Grade: 06
My mother is not a precious gem, nor an ordinary rock. She is unique in every way. He is a strong rock with same beautiful sparkle.

Madison Blaylock   Grade: 06
Her smile's bright. It lights the room. If my love was sound it would BOOM! My mom's the bomb for me. I love her dearly.

Kendall Corwin   **Grade: 06**
My mom is as tough as a diamond. My mom is as gentle as a rose. My mom is a gem that nobody can oppose.

Ethan Hasan   Grade: 06
My mother, she is very nice and loyal. My mom takes care of me and encourages me. She will always be there for me.

Alexa Luckow   Grade: 06
Love is endless, love is always. Love never hates, love never tries. If I had to choose one loving person. My mom would be mine.

Brianna Mahaney   Grade: 06
My mother warrior comes home every night, does so much, almost faints. The ground shakes when she is near. My mother warrior has no fear.

Brittany Nielsen   Grade: 06
My mom holding me with optimal comfort. Flawless kisses hit me with great force. My mom, my idol.

Niki Nourmohammadi   Grade: 06
Mother, my person just for me, deserves this diamond you can see. I give the Queen of Royalty a reward living eleven years with me.

Hadley Piper   **Grade: 06**
Mom, like a dove in the sky flying so high. Reaching her levels in her daily life. Mom, also so graceful in her life.

Wesley Robins   Grade: 06
Brilliant, shining, gleams like a star. These are only a few words that describe my amazing mom.

* Amethyst winners in bold.

Emily Schwartz   Grade: 06
Sparkle, sparkle. I am not talking about a diamond. I am talking about my MOM! She is as beautiful as a diamond.

Katie Toda   Grade: 06
Diamond is a perfect gift for her, for being a funny mom. She makes the house full with laughter, and keeps my body warm.

Eastside Christian School
Fullerton

Teacher: Joann Kurumada

Laura Bayeh   Grade: 05
My mom is wonderful. She shines in the light of the sun and whispers, "I love you" in the night. I love my mom.

Kyle Dudevoir   **Grade: 05**
My mom's heart is a diamond. She is tender, loving and kind. It's never dark in my house because she's always there to shine.

Cambria Jones   **Grade: 05**
There is no other mother like mine in the world. She shines like the sun every year, every month. My mother, no other!

Julie Lee   Grade: 05
My mom is a diamond of my life. Her eyes are stars twinkling on a cool winter night. She shines in my heart. I love her.

Morgan McCool   Grade: 05
My mother is a gem in my heart. She shines in my soul like a diamond. She is loving and amazing. She is my diamond.

Sarah Ritter   Grade: 05
Mom is the best mom ever! Her eyes shine with the golden light of God. There isn't one doubt that God sent her. Amen!

Madison Bock   **Grade: 06**
My mom is love. Warm cuddles and smiles. My mom is there when I feel so helpless and alone. Mom, the warmth of my world.

Delton Crandell   **Grade: 06**
My mom is like the sun, when it's day. She shines at night, she glows in the dark. She never stops glowing like the moon!

Teagan Frakes   Grade: 06
Her heart is full of inner beauty. Her eyes glow like shining, twinkling stars, her hugs are ones of love. Her smile shines like the sun.

Tia Hatch   Grade: 06
My mom is always there to listen. She never ignores me. My mom is sweet like honey, all the bees want to go to her.

Andrew Hatfield   Grade: 06
Mom, a divine soul who cares and loves all she knows. Mom, a diamond in the rough who sparkles like a star in night sky.

Lauren Huntly   Grade: 06
My mom's the best. She is beautiful, loving, helpful and thoughtful beyond words. My mom is so special to me and nobody can ever replace her.

Steven Shin   Grade: 06
When I go the wrong way, my mom is there for me. She waits for me always. Mom shows love and kindness to all children.

SaraJane Steele   Grade: 06
My mom is bright, so pretty and light. My mom tells me which way to go everyday. She is a bright light that shines over me.

Kimberly Stratton   Grade: 06
My mom is an angel sent from heaven above. She loves me all the time no matter what, with unconditional love.

Autumn Sylve   **Grade: 06**
When my soul is mourning and my day is rainy, her bright spirit lifts me off the clouds. She brings me a waterfall of confidence.

William Tse   **Grade: 06**
A diamond sparkles in shining hue, it takes someone great to rival its beauty. That person is my mom. That's why my mom deserves a diamond.

Alicia Vasquez   Grade: 06
Moms will care for you from the beginning to the end. She will spread her love around the room as she hugs you with love.

Eastwood Elementary
Westminster

Teacher: Kym Slingerland

Danielle Downing   **Grade: 05**
Laughing, spending time together, sharing, funny stories, holding me when I cry, and loving me. Always encouraging me to be my best. That's my mommy!

Nikoli Spry   Grade: 05
My mom's eyes are like blue diamonds in the moonlight. Her beautiful eyes calm me down all the time and everywhere.

Dalyn Stradtmann   Grade: 05
The twinkling in my grandma's heart. Shining just like my grandma's eyes. I will love her forever. That's why my grandma deserves a diamond.

Hannah Tischler   Grade: 05
Her eye's sparkle like gold. Her heart fills with love and joy. Her smile brightens the whole world.

Daniel Tran   Grade: 05
I want to win my mom a diamond because we share a magnificent bond. She has strong benevolence and I look up to her perseverance.

El Dorado High
Placentia

Teacher: Amanda Wolf

Veronica Kim   **Grade: 10**
They say diamonds last forever, but I found something better. With the patience of a saint, my mom's unfailing love will outlast any diamond.

Jasmine Miller   Grade: 11
Haiku for Mom - Patience is key when raising an autistic child. Mom goes beyond that.

El Rancho Charter
Anaheim

Teacher: Latisha Lorenz

Katrina Bessem   Grade: 08
The one who glistens in the warm summer sun. Courage, trust, hope is what she gives me. Most of all, love. The gift received everyday.

Tracy Chu   **Grade: 08**
My mom deserves a diamond because she's an angel from above, as peaceful as a beautiful dove, a diamond-worth angel who's full of love.

Natasha Co   **Grade: 08**
Like a star in heaven, she shimmers in my eyes. Like an elegant bird singing, her voice is music to my ears. My treasured mother.

Remi Cruz   Grade: 08
She's as flawless as a diamond, but as delicate as a rose. She always keeps me smiling, especially when it matters most.

Alexis Emeterio   Grade: 08
My mother's smile glows like a sunset. Her
eyes are blue as the shining sea. She is the
most caring person you'll ever meet.

Jane Lu   Grade: 08
My mom resembles a flawless diamond
in many ways - beautiful, shining,
radiant, motivational, and perfect.
However, a diamond holds a price; my
mom is priceless.

Sanam Vonkaenel   Grade: 08
My mom doesn't deserve a diamond, she
deserves a million or more. I'm sorry
that I can't afford all that's in the store!

Eldorado School/ Emerson Honors
Orange

Teacher: Heather Krstich

Zoe Bentley   Grade: 01
She is very nice. She is flawless. She is
very fine. I love her so, so much. She is
very nice.

Olivia Thompson   Grade: 01
My mom deserves a diamond because she
is magnificent, beautiful, lovable, huggable
like a stuffed animal. That is why!

Teacher: Elizabeth Merket

Guillaume Banales   Grade: 03
My mother. She shines like a butterfly.
She has eyes like a diamond. She has
gold in her soul.

Netra Chakravarthy   Grade: 03
My mom gives love to everyone. She gives
me cookies one by one. She brings me toys
that are full of joy. She's always nice.

Skyler Grigg   Grade: 03
My mom is beautiful like a gem. I wish I
could see her more. I love her.

Margaret Laton   Grade: 03
Starlight, star bright, I think that she's bright.
I love her so, she's the best I know. I think
she deserves a diamond.

Yoori Lee   Grade: 03
My mom should get a diamond because my
mom loves me everyday and I love mom
too.

Matthew Mead   Grade: 03
My mom deserves a diamond because she
is loving and beautiful. She has eyes like
diamonds. She's my mom, and she is a
loving angel.

Teacher: Cathy Merket B.

Mikayla Brownell   Grade: 02
I love my mom. Her eyes sparkle. Her hair,
it smells good. I love my mom!

Noah Cohen- Wanis   Grade: 02
My mom should get a diamond because it's
so hard to take care of us three boys.

Anna Spence   Grade: 02
I love my mom. She works very hard. My
mom loves me. She gives good hugs. She
is very nice, very beautiful and loving.

Emery(Charles G.) Elem.
Buena Park

Teacher: Becky August

Vanessa Ayala   Grade: 04
My mom deserves a diamond because she
shines like the sun. She smells pretty like
rosy rose. She tries to spend time with us.

Miranda Diaz   Grade: 04
My mom sparkles like a star, her eyes
twinkle like she was just born. When I look
up, I see a rainbow because of my mom.

Jasmine Esparza   Grade: 04
My mom is like an angel, she's as nice as
can be. Everyday I wake up and think of
her with me.
Lana Fruto   Grade: 04

My guardian angel speaks to me with
words like a Bible Psalm. Her presence
means the world to me. My angel's
precious name is; Mom.

Alexis Mc Dannel   Grade: 04
My mom is an angel, I will love her forever
and ever. Her hair is like chocolate Hershey's.
She shines like my diamond angel.

Kelsey Miche   Grade: 04
She's a heavenly angel. She's indeed, a
true friend. She will never let you down.
She glows from the inside. She has a true
heart.

Teacher: Karen Chalmers

Jezinya Chavira   Grade: 03
My mom deserves a diamond because she
looks beautiful as a rose. My mom is like a
movie star in my heart.

Rebeca Paredes   Grade: 03
My mom deserves a diamond because she
is nice and she helps me out. She also
helps people so they can learn about God.

Anthony Sam   Grade: 03
My mom deserves a diamond because
she's like a treasure to me. She is like the
god of love and beauty. She deserves a
diamond.

Teacher: Jon Christensen

Mitchell Fruto   Grade: 06
You lift me to the heavens, up to the
stars of the darkest hour. Without you,
I'll be relentless upon sight. To me,
you're exquisite.

Rachel Kim   Grade: 06
My mom is a sparkling star. Divine and
exquisite is she. Shimmering through the
dark. She is my guide through everything
I do.

Joshua Lee   Grade: 06
To some people, "Mother" is a simple
word. But to me, there's meaning to
it. Intelligent, extravagant, gently and
compassionate. That's my way, saying
"Mother".

Scarlett Perez   Grade: 06
Diamonds my mom deserves for her
angelic laughter beats any curse. Her inner
and outer elegance impresses all. Her
extravagant soul, the best of all.

Veronica Sanchez   Grade: 06
Her smile shines like a golden sun. Her
voice soothes me when I'm sad. Her eyes
sparkle like diamonds. She is a wonderful
mom.

James Stirdivant   Grade: 06
My mom is bright, as bright as the sun's
light. Without that light, I am nothing more.
I need my light for comfort.

Sachin Suresh   Grade: 06
My mom is a lantern that will guide me
through my troubles. She will always
stand beside me. Without her, I am a dark
shadow.

Teacher: Leanna Crawford

Jake Ahn   Grade: 04
Her love is brilliant, her presence strong,
and her devotion everlasting. These
characteristics are why my mom is a
treasure to me like a diamond.

Jourdan Cerillo   Grade: 04
My mother is a jewel. She is a gold
crown. She fills me up with joy. She is
my diamond in my heart.

* Amethyst winners in bold.

Brittany Emsais   Grade: 04
Her eyes like the sun. Her heart like the moon. She lights up the way for me. She cares and loves me. That is why.

Andrew Park   Grade: 04
My mom's eyes shine like the golden sun and her heart is always opened for me. When I'm sad and if I am in trouble.

Shawn Park   Grade: 04
My mom deserves a diamond because she has a pure heart and a strong love like a diamond.

Erika Pena   Grade: 04
Her hair as dark as the soothing night. Eyes like two twinkling stars. Her smile as warm as the sun. She is truly beautiful.

Victoria Replogle   **Grade: 04**
My mom's heart is always open. When I am sad, she makes me happy. She is a joy to be around. I love my mom.

Nicole Song   Grade: 04
My mom's voice is like birds singing. My mom's eyes are like stars sparkling. My mom's heart is as warm as the sun.

Heather Sullins   Grade: 04
My mom deserves a diamond because she's a great cook and fun playmate. Best of all she writes me love notes each day.

Chloe Torres   Grade: 04
My mother is the brightest light in my life and gives me warmth from her finger tips. For she is the diamond of my heart.

Teacher: Brian Eldridge

Leslie Escalante   Grade: 05
She keeps me warm when I'm cold. She's the light to my soul. She inspires me. She gives me advice when I need it.

Vanessa Rios   **Grade: 05**
She lights up the room like a glowing star. The star of love, sweetness, friendliness, and happiness. But she's mostly the star of my heart.

Angelica Santos   Grade: 05
My wonderful mom is full of beauty. She cares and loves me with all her heart. I love her and she loves me too.

Teacher: Jennifer Ferrara

Jordan Adamson   **Grade: 06**
Her smile glistens like seashells on the radiant sand. Her love flows continually as does the ocean. Her inspiration shines on me like the sun.

Arturo Avina   **Grade: 06**
Who guards me from misfortune? Whose heart is larger than Jupiter, only more valuable than diamonds? My mom. My love. My irreplaceable treasure.

Tiffany Ayala   **Grade: 06**
Powerful, as a queen at her throne, steady as a jouster, faster than seven swords pulsing through evil, protecting the world, ruler of my family.

Jerry Botello   Grade: 06
My mom is like an angel sent from heaven. She has an immense heart with unconditional love. I love my mom.

Sydney Choi   Grade: 06
Unconditional affection in her heart raising me to become the best I can. Escorting me through the tough times. Always there, my everything, my mom.

Richard Diaz   Grade: 06
My mother is a butterfly twinkling like the sunlight. Eyes glistening in the moonlight, like a sparking diamond. She's heaven on earth. My mom.

Sara Diaz   **Grade: 06**
The star that shines on the darkest night. A candle that gives radiant light. She guides with strength and might. Her love remains forever bright.

Jonathan England   **Grade: 06**
My mother is a diamond, she shines like frosty mornings and her moonlight's reflection twinkling on a motionless lake. Her beauty is priceless. Mom.

Katherine Hernandez   **Grade: 06**
Oh, I do not deserve this angel. Heavenly, sleeping before me. When she wakes, the birds sing along with my beloved and touched soul.

Amy Koo   **Grade: 06**
Mother, a beautiful gem. Set in our family bracelet of gold. Purer than silver, more precious than diamonds. My loving mother...gem of my life.

Sebastian Lazarte   Grade: 06
Her smile glistening like a dandelion, a radiant flower through the path of darkness, her love blossoming every moment.

Chris Lee   **Grade: 06**
My mother's love is deeper than ocean's. Her eyes sparkling like pure water. She quenches my thirst she filleth my cup. My loving pure mother.

Karen Lee   **Grade: 06**
As enduring as a tree. Who knows what's best. Swifter than any river. Who hastens to protect. Better than all someone who cherishes me. Mom.

Anthony Minton   **Grade: 06**
Her touch lifts my essence. Her tremendous desires for me never end. Her alluring words of wisdom fill my heart and somehow touches my soul.

Alice Park   **Grade: 06**
Her eyes scintillating like the celestial stars on a clear summer's night. My mentor, my guardian, her angelic voice. I cherish.

Joshua Parong   Grade: 06
She is a diamond. Strong! Her love never breaks into pieces. She always shows how much she loves and cares for me. Everlasting love, Mom.

Corrinne Santos   Grade: 06
She's like a rose beautiful and sweet smelling. The soft, white moon watching over me when I sleep. She is my whole world. My mother.

Celine Tran   **Grade: 06**
Mother is a cat, I'm her kitten. We struggle and play together. She licks my wounds. Heals my heart. I listen to her purr.

Teacher: Michelle Henderson

Kacy Avena   Grade: 03
She supports me and nurtures me. Her love is forever and pure. My one and only guardian angel, my mom.

Megan Edwards   **Grade: 03**
Her eyes are like the crystals to my heart. Her smile lights my kingdom brighter than the sun. Her laugh makes my garden glow.

Jasmine Grimaud   Grade: 03
My mom deserves a diamond because she brightens my life and has stars in her eyes and lives in my soul and loves me so.

Daniel Hernandez   **Grade: 03**
A diamond is beautiful, rare and everlasting...just like my mom. Neither breaks under pressure and their light always shines brightly.

Sooah Jeong   Grade: 03
Mom, your smile makes my heart shine even on gloomy days. You've taught me what's right for a very long time. You are the best.

Wendy Sol Park   Grade: 03
My mom deserves a diamond because her eyes sparkle like diamonds and her heart is full of love.

Teacher: Steve Little

**Lauren Fruto   Grade: 06
In a crowded garden full of other buds waiting to blossom. Her magnificent color and lovable petals are only one of a kind.**

**Noah Sanders   Grade: 06
Heart as pure as gold but as light as the steady beat of a butterfly's wing. Kisses as gentle like a feather floating up above. My mom.**

Samuel Thomas   Grade: 06
My mother's voice is as soft as a bird cooing in the twilight sky, she is cozy like a cat, warm, snuggly and bright. Mom.

Samantha Tuccio   Grade: 06
She's like a rollercoaster she has her ups and down but over all it is a thrilling ride never knowing what to expect - My mom.

Valerie Williams   Grade: 06
Loving like a puppy protecting like a lion and as graceful as a doe. My mother, a beautiful and generous lady.

Teacher: Scott Magnin

Melissa Sam   Grade: 06
She's like Aphrodite, the Goddess of Love and Beauty. Without her, I'm nothing. Everything reminds me of her. All I think about is you, Mom.

**Megan Tanielo   Grade: 06
Her majestic smile brightens every dark day. She's the guiding star through challenging obstacles. All her warm thoughts and words turn into love.**

Teacher: Cindy Senften

**Teacher: Yenah Kim   Grade: 03
Giving me all her love and care. So special and strong. Easily forgiving. Always in my heart. How can I compare my mom with diamonds!**

Brandon Park   Grade: 03
My mom deserves a diamond because she is sweeter than a peach, prettier than a flower, nicer than any other mom, and she loves me.

Teacher: Laura Stanley

Michael Baik   Grade: 02
My mom deserves a diamond because she loves me and she's kind. She deserves something sparkly that is special and lucky.

Hannah Kim   Grade: 02
My mom deserves a diamond because she is caring and loving. She's neat and very sweet. She gives hugs and kisses with joy.

Midajah Meneses   Grade: 02
My mom deserves a diamond. She is pretty and a jewel. She's an angel from heaven. She is oh so special.

Nathan Wilson   Grade: 02
My mom deserves a diamond. She cares for me wherever I go. She deserves a pretty diamond, that's just as pretty as she is.

Enders Elementary
Garden Grove

Teacher: Cindy Chorpenning

Macy Boyle   Grade: 03
My mom deserves a diamond because she has fed me and helped me stay alive. She's not just a mom, she's a friend to me.

Jasmine Perez   Grade: 03
My mom deserves a diamond because she sacrifices for me, she gave me a house. She gives me all the love and care I need.

Jacob Quezada   Grade: 03
My mom deserves the diamond because she is nice and she is lovable and she is good to kids and to parents.

Destiny Ruvalcaba   Grade: 03
My mom deserves a diamond because she takes care of us, helps us clean, she stays up to do laundry.

**Keri Tate   Grade: 03
My mom deserves a diamond because she works hard, comforts me when I am sad, and she loves me for who I am.**

T. J. Tonkin   Grade: 03
My mom deserves a diamond because she made me and she is the greatest mom in the world. We're one in eyes of Mother Nature.

**Karlie Woirhaye   Grade: 03
My mom sacrifices her life to try to give us a good life. That's why she has way more than a diamond, she has family.**

Teacher: Kendra Hohman

Ryan May   Grade: 03
I think my mom deserves a diamond because she helps and supports me at school, home, and anywhere I go.

Holly Sheffield   Grade: 03
My mom deserves a diamond because she has done so many things for my family since my dad died. She is just so special.

Jacob Thomas   Grade: 03
My mom deserves a diamond because she takes care of me and makes sure I'm safe. She loves me.

Teacher: Hoa Tran

Cheyenne Beasley   Grade: 03
I think my grandma needs a diamond because she always spends money on me, never herself. She needs something to show she's special to me.

**Jessica Morales   Grade: 03
I think my grandma deserves it because she is the best Grandma, because she raised six babies and my dad. She's the super queen!**

Kimberly Rasey   Grade: 03
My mom deserves a diamond because she takes care of me. She takes me to lots of places. She always helps me. I love you mom.

Ethan Ross   Grade: 03
I think my mom deserves a diamond because she did a good job raising me and my sisters. She is the best mom ever!

Tyler Thomas   Grade: 03
My mom deserves a diamond because she can't stop thinking of me. She does so many things for me. She's the nicest mom in the world.

Esperanza
Mission Viejo

Teacher: Pat Haberfield

**Jackson Trujillo   Grade: 10
My mother deserves a diamond because she would keep a diamond safe like me.**

Randall Linares   Grade: 12
My mother deserves a diamond because diamonds are beautiful and she is beautiful both inside and outside.

* Amethyst winners in bold.

Excelsior Elementary
Garden Grove

Teacher: Christine Crandall

Jenny Huynh   **Grade: 06**
Every mom has a heart of gold. In many hearts, she's never old. Gem tears fall when she cries and every mom deserves a diamond!

Angelique Nguyen   Grade: 06
Diamonds and mothers are things that shine brightly. Mothers give life to us kids. They work hard, but yet still smile and dazzle so brightly.

Quinton Ta   Grade: 06
Mom deserves a diamond because she works hard each day. She cleans and works and works and cleans, and teaches us what love really means.

Fairmont Elementary
Yorba Linda

Teacher: Pat Shea

Alyssa Armendariz   **Grade: 04**
My mom is my life. Her voice is like a hummingbird in a beautiful blue sky and her eyes sparkle in the sunlight.

Sarah Barron   Grade: 04
My mom cooks and cleans and does everything in between. She combs my hair and she is always there. My loving mom deserves a diamond.

Eric Bigani   **Grade: 04**
My mom deserves a diamond because her eyes are like aquamarine in a shimmering night with golden shooting and blinking stars with hazel wolves howling.

Justin Conk   **Grade: 04**
Her eyes sparkle as if they're confetti raining down from the sky. She moves gracefully like she were a ballerina dancing in a ballet.

Becky Crandall   Grade: 04
Angel kisses fill my mother's face with love like a swan in the evening sunset sky. Her smile flutters in heaven laughing with joy.

Jennifer Fain   **Grade: 04**
My mom is like a desert sunrise brightening the azure sky every morning. Her sunlight energizes the lives around her and provides steady nourishment.

Hannah Flink   **Grade: 04**
My mom's hands are as soft as a milky white and fluffy sheep. Her hugs fill my heart up to 100% warm and cozy love.

Brooke Fuller   Grade: 04
Who has eyes that twinkle from afar, and a heart that is 10x bigger than a star? Mom, that's you! You really do!

Andrew Hauptmann   **Grade: 04**
My mom is so cute. I love her so much. She puts a sparkle in my eye. She is golden treasure on the beautiful beach.

Jonathan Hood   **Grade: 04**
Quiet and loud, humorous and funny, beautiful as a crimson blossom waving in the breeze, small and wonderful is why Mom deserves a diamond.

Kayla Johnson   Grade: 04
Mom is a joy to me. She is like a kind friend. She is important to me. I love her as big as the earth.

Danielle Lavigne   Grade: 04
You fill my heart with laughter and my mind with precious thought. My love for you is priceless, mom, and never could be bought.

Michael Mantoura   Grade: 04
Mom is there when I need her the most. No amount of money is worth the love she shares. I love you, Mom.

Christopher McKeever   Grade: 04
My mom is the only rose out of my whole rose garden that brightens my day every step I take.

Citlaly Ocampo   Grade: 04
Someone is bright like a star and such a heart. Someone so beautiful like the night in the sky. I know my mom is all.

Jack Rentfro   Grade: 04
My mom says that she does not need a diamond because I am her diamond that shines in her heart.

Anthony Robert   Grade: 04
My mom sparkles and shines. She is oh so fine. Her mouth is sweet. Having her as a mom is a real treat.

Olivia Robert   Grade: 04
My mom's chocolate brown hair shines in the night. Her beautiful hazel eyes warm my heart. Her personality makes me want to sing, she rocks.

Bridgette Roberts   Grade: 04
Mom is a diamond sparkling bright; she is a star gleaming at night. Her thoughts and prayers fill my heart with delight.

Jared Serrao   Grade: 04
My mom's love is like a pot of gold at the end of a rainbow. The colors are her love; the pot is her heart.

Simone Thomas   **Grade: 04**
My mom deserves a diamond because she believes in me. Her happy soul always makes the house and everyone in it feel bright.

Logan Venero   **Grade: 04**
My mom is as bright as a billion suns, her heart sings like hundreds of golden harps in the clouds of heaven.

James Welham   Grade: 04
My mom deserves a diamond because she glitters like the sky when she helps me and people in need so she shines like the sunset.

Jacob Yee   Grade: 04
My mom is like a treasure at the bottom of the ocean. She is sweeter than any piece of candy. My mom is the best!

Fairmont Private School (Edgewood)
Santa Ana

Teacher: Laura Escutia

Halah Biviji   **Grade: 02**
Mom deserves a diamond because she gives hugs and kisses. She loves and cares about me. She never gives up on me. I love mom.

David Gao   Grade: 02
My mom deserves a diamond because she is beautiful as a diamond. My mom shines. She loves me. I love her too.

Amber Reid   Grade: 02
My mom loves me. She cares for me. She buys me toys. She gives me medicine when I am sick. She helps me clean up.

Eunice Rho   **Grade: 02**
My mom deserves a diamond because she is the best. She always cuddles me when I am cold. Mom deserves a diamond with love.

Allyson Rosenblum   **Grade: 02**
My mom deserves a diamond because she loves me. I tell my mom my problems and she fixes them. She takes care of me also.

Ronak Yvas   Grade: 02
My mom is wonderful. She takes me to school. She cleans the house. She makes the best food on Earth. She is the funniest mom.

Xerxes Zangeneh   Grade: 02
My mom deserves a diamond because she works hard. She helps people a lot and she keeps trying.

Teacher: June Huang

Parisa Baher   Grade: 06
My mom, hardworking, caring and loving deserves a diamond because she is the most inspiring person in the world to me. I love her incredibly.

Amanda Cohn   Grade: 06
She is sweet as candy. Beautiful as a rose. Wise as an owl. My mother knows how to care and love anyone, everyone, and everything.

Marc Sayyur   Grade: 06
With Mom so near, I have no fear; it's crystal clear that Mom deserves with no reserves a crystal diamond. Though Mom values much more.

Bradford Lee   Grade: 07
My mom deserves a diamond because she's like a star in the sky. She twinkles every now and then, which fills my heart with love.

Alexandra Mowrey   Grade: 07
My mom is like a diamond, unique in her own brilliance but worth more because she gives me priceless memories lasting forever in my soul.

Christy Park   Grade: 07
My mother's charisma sparkles with the intensity of a million stars and shines through the darkest of nights - just like a twinkling diamond.

Rochelle Rouhani   Grade: 07
My mother shines, smiles every day, and is beautiful; she deserves a diamond because it shines with her, gives her more happiness, and adds beauty.

Jessica Rutten   Grade: 07
My mother is the sun perched on the horizon, the bandage around my heart and without her in my world, my soul would fall apart.

Ellen Kim   Grade: 08
She is my shining beacon in the middle of darkness, evoking hope, love, and smiles. My mentor, my friend, my inspiration, my mom.

Thao-Ann Nguyen   Grade: 08
A gentle breeze in an afflicted world, pacifies my heart as she soothes my woes. She emits a dazzling aura much brighter than any diamond.

Nikita Patel   Grade: 08
The heart of the sea, a gem-like stone, a second beauty of me, dabbing, molding, perfecting my soul, exceeding her incredible limitations as a whole.

Matthew Tatarka Brown   Grade: 08
Dependable when needed most. Intelligence unending. Advises with love. Never at a loss for words. Eager to help me to succeed. This is my mom.

Olivia Walmsley   Grade: 08
When night shines, the sterling stars above makes me think of you. Your pensive soul, your distinguished flairs, and your compassionate cares; I love you.

Kennedy Wells   Grade: 08
She has a golden heart glowing even through the darkest nights, open arms for me. Love flows in where sadness once was.

Teacher: Denise Miller

Nivin Singh   Grade: 06
My mom deserves a diamond because she is a dedicated mother. She works hard to make a flawless family. In return, we love her back.

Chase Walmsley   Grade: 06
My mom deserves a diamond because she is helpful and hardworking to make mine and other people live better. She's like a wonderful summer's day.

Zachary Calilung   Grade: 08
Morning wakes to sunshine, yet, never sets at night. Always bearing merriment, to aid great plight. Better than any other, she is my mother.

Erin Dubreuil   Grade: 08
My mom, my shining star, fills my day with light and joy, cares for me and provides everything for me to succeed and be happy.

Sanjna Ghanskani   Grade: 08
Exults all with her altruistic and benevolent smile. Executes every movement with impeccable alacrity. A paragon to her naïve daughters. A mother beyond perfection.

Fern Drive Elementary
Fullerton

Teacher: Jennifer Ahn

David Choi   Grade: 02
Mom is like a polar bear. She gives me her heart. She is humorous like a clown. She blesses me and sparkles like an angel.

Darby Clement   Grade: 02
My mom cooks and cleans all for me. She is as busy as a bumblebee. My mom deserves a diamond as you can see.

Rebecca Cocis   Grade: 02
My glow, my shine, my radiance, and my sparkle. When I'm sick, she takes care of me. My mom is a shining diamond.

Connor Delgado   Grade: 02
She sparkles so colorfully and glows like a rainbow. So radiant, so terrific, so loving, so marvelous. My mom is so elegant.

Sean Gilberto   Grade: 02
My mom 's eyes are as bright as a star, like a diamond. She tucks me in bed. My mom is very gentle with me.

Abigail Lange   Grade: 02
So elegant. So loving. She sparkles like a diamond with the things she does. But best about her is the love that glows.

Ximena Pacheco   Grade: 02
My mom is a diamond. She will always be in the bottom of my heart. Her cooking is heavenly. She will be a diamond forever.

Mandi Parrott   Grade: 02
Beautiful like a diamond. Sprouts everyday and night. Humorous, loving, and hardworking. I love you, Mom.

Teacher: Joe Conti

Chris Cully   Grade: 06
My mom is like an elegant dove perched in a tree and is as gentle as can be. That is why she deserves a diamond.

Bailey Danford   Grade: 06
My mom deserves a diamond because she sparkles like a star shines like the sun and glows like the moon. I truly love my mom.

Joshua Kang   Grade: 06
My mom deserves a diamond because she is always good, pink hearted and always has her love ready for me. Whenever I come home.

* Amethyst winners in bold.

Dylan McDowell   Grade: 06
My mom deserves a diamond because she is hardworking and always trusts in God. She is also the best mom I have ever known.

Mitch Tongilava   Grade: 06
My mom deserves a diamond because she's a super hero to me. She is a role model. Not only that, she's a hardworking mom.

Vincent Vuong   Grade: 06
My mom is comparable as waterfalls, softly drifting down, like snow falling from the sky to bring heavenly happiness and astounding joy into my life.

Teacher: Patricia Kawaguchi

Lauren Bowlby   Grade: 02
My mom cooks as good as a professional chef. My mom's heart is as a tender as a new baby born on Valentine's Day.

Emma Brown   Grade: 02
My mom's lips are as red as licorice. Her heart is as warm as the sun.

Jessica Calhoun   Grade: 02
My mom's eyes are as colorful as a rainbow. My mom is as cute as a funny, white polar bear cub.

Natalie Goldman   Grade: 02
My mom's eyes sparkle like a yellow, golden star. My mom is as sweet as a Hershey's dark chocolate bar.

Giselle Rodriguez   Grade: 02
My mom is as pretty as a crystal heart. My mom's eyes shimmer as glamorous as the glowing sun.

Karis Ryoo   Grade: 02
My mom's eyes are as glamorous as a crystal star. My mom is as pretty as a beautiful heart.

Teacher: Silva Rivera

Victoria Amador   Grade: 02
My mom shines in the sun with her silky, black hair. She looks like a shining star. I will always love her very much.

Joy Hur   Grade: 02
My mommy's sweet kisses, when I sleep. And when I wake, I still feel the kisses on my cheeks.

Erin Kolb   Grade: 02
My best buddy. Outstanding at tucking me in. Mom, I love you.

Hope Ross   Grade: 02
Magnanimous Mom. Outstanding singer and kisser. Makes me smile when she sings. Magnificent manager. You're number one.

Elaine Vuong   Grade: 02
My mom is as beautiful as a rose, opening her petals as she opens her heart to her family. Giving us great love and care.

Teacher: Angei Wright

Alanis Brittain   Grade: 06
My mom deserves a diamond because she adopted me, my little brother, and my sister. She gave up her entire life and deserves one. Thank you.

Kristina Foley   Grade: 06
My mom sparkles like star in the sky. She shines so greatly that she looks like a moon. A diamond would make her brilliant.

Lindsay Harris   Grade: 06
I know why my grandmother deserves a diamond. She deserves one for taking on the responsibility of adopting my siblings, loving, and caring for us.

Amber McNatt   Grade: 06
Mom is the one I truly believe in. She is a first class supermom. She's all that matters in the world to me. Wow!

Joe Richardson   Grade: 06
My mom is the sunlight of my day. She's the moon I see far away. My mom helps me to a dream. She's my friend!

Gadiel Ticlea   Grade: 06
My mom deserves a diamond because every time I feel sad, my mom cheers me up. My mom shows her love toward me every day.

Fisler (Robert C.) Elem.
Fullerton

Teacher: Sonya Lee

Sonali Bapna   Grade: 06
Sweet as milk chocolate, pretty as a bright red rose , rich as a sparkling diamond, with the warmest heart! She means the world to me.

Jae Jeong   Grade: 06
My mom would have to deserve a diamond because all mothers are special. She means everything to me. A diamond means like my mom.

Rachel Kim   Grade: 06
Crystal clear. I see her beauty, love, compassion. A beautiful soul, sparkles in the eyes. The love of my life. Jewel of my heart.

Ashley Kim   Grade: 06
My mother is precious. Her smile is worth a diamond. Her caring mind is worth a diamond. She is all the diamonds in the world.

Christine Ku   Grade: 06
My mom deserves a diamond because she deserves to shine like a diamond and I want her to know that she glitters like the diamond.

Sierra Scolaro   Grade: 06
Mother. I look at her, seeing compassion, love, and positivity before me. When my heart sinks, she works hard to rebuild it. Mom, representing happiness.

Kyle Shelton   Grade: 06
I would love to see the glow in my moms eyes and for her to know she has a child that appreciates what she does.

Jennifer Shin   Grade: 06
My awesome mom obviously deserves a diamond because she loves everybody for who they are. She's the most unique person who's like no other person.

Kelly Song   Grade: 06
The diamond shining like the stars staring at me like my mother's eyes. Shimmering in the light and giving light in the dark.

Adrien Truong   Grade: 06
Bad or good days, my mom is always there. Whenever I turn around she's there, comforting me wherever I am. My own traveling, sparkling gem.

Michelle Yook   Grade: 06
My mom deserves a diamond because she shines brighter than any star, as bright and shiny as a diamond.

Foothill Ranch Elementary
Foothill Ranch

Teacher: Joyce Rubel

Callie Altman   Grade: 04
Mommy gently wakes me up with a kiss that sparkles. Her radiating glow loves me all day until bedtime. Prayers and dreams are for mom.

Angela Chang   Grade: 04
Busy mornings making three lunches. Busy afternoons picking up three kids. Busy nights tucking them in. Her day's gone caring for me. Thank you mom

Mara Coleman   Grade: 04
My mom is as sparkling and brilliant as a diamond. She glistens in the moonlight. Her heart is as big as a full moon.

Matthew Imler   Grade: 04
When I look into the starry sky, the brightest star reminds me of how bright my heart shines for you.

Celine Keissieh   Grade: 04
Your eyes shine at me, the crystal of your heart glitters with love. You are the diamond of my world. You are my beloved mother.

Ria Vidhate   Grade: 04
My mothers hands work like a charm, anything she does from her heart. Her eyes shine like the sun. Her heart loves me a ton.

Jason Ye   Grade: 04
Her love as precious as a pearl, her eyes as bright as the sun. My mom deserves a diamond, because she is the best one.

Michelle Yeh   Grade: 04
My love for you is within reach. You grasp it never letting go. Our love is strong for 'tis not replaced by dazzling jewels.

Justan Zommers   Grade: 04
She holds her hand out, she holds her hand high. She holds out her heart to me with a twinkle in her eye.

Fountain Valley High
Fountain Valley

Teacher: Patty Munoz

Catherine Do   Grade: 09
Because she does anything for me. Tries to please, never complains, always gives never asks. Because she does so much, gets nothing, and deserves everything.

Anderson Hua   Grade: 09
Mom bakes me fairy tales, stirs in some happiness, sprinkles, some laughter, lots of hugs and kisses, and a happily ever after.

Jennifer Luong   Grade: 09
Morning ray's kindness, her heart a golden sun; glowing moonlight's comfort, sanctuary to my soul. My mother's love, a flower blooming through all life's seasons.

Fullerton Union High
Fullerton

Teacher: Cindy Ortiz

Leticia Aguilar   Grade: 09
She is the sun's bright rays giving light and hugging me warmly. Always there when I am down; my mom, a hidden treasure.

Esmeralda Bautista   Grade: 09
Mother, the beating of my heart calls your name - an elegant melody. The sweet harmony of my life. I hope the music never stops.

Austin Bond   Grade: 09
She is every beat of my heart pushing and pushing me toward my dream. Her hugs make time stop. I savor each moment, never forgetting.

Patricia Coria   Grade: 09
She is the warm coat upon my back, keeping me safe from the cold. Protecting me from the harm and giving me comfort.

Jessica Covarrubias   Grade: 09
My mom is like the sun shining when it's dark. My blanket that comforts me, nothing else can be what you have been to me.

Jeniece Hill   Grade: 09
She is an angel from above. She watches over me and protects me from harm. Her love is like a; fountain, it's constantly overflowing.

Priscilla Lopez   Grade: 09
Mommy, you're the light to my soul filling me with love and joy. When you're with me I'm never in darkness. My Angel from above.

Destinee Martinez   Grade: 09
An angel sent from heaven to guide me through life's journey gave me the strength to face anything. Now I thank you for understanding everything.

Evalize Navarro   Grade: 09
I no longer wonder why, I can't believe I'm here where I am today. You're such a major part in helping me find my way.

Hector Robles   Grade: 09
You're the air I need. You give me strength to keep on going. Helping me face anything in my way. You're the reason I breathe.

Gilbert Sanchez   Grade: 09
A bright light standing out in the darkest night. My mom's love is undefined make me complete.

Katelynn Valencia   Grade: 09
Like a peaceful winter evening, keeping me warm with her blanket of love comforting my needs.

Joseph Zamora   Grade: 09
My mom is like a rose making my garden a brighter place. She comforts me when I'm feeling down. I can't live without her.

Garden Park Elementary
Garden Grove

Teacher: Angela Balius

Kristin Cortines   Grade: 02
My mom's eyes shimmer like a shiny diamond. She nurtures me when I'm sick or sad. She wouldn't trade the world for me!

Connor Fitzgerald   Grade: 02
My mom gives me great, warm, loving hugs and takes great care of me when I'm sick. My mom is beautiful.

Sean Gellerman   Grade: 02
My mom's eyes sparkle like diamonds. My mom is a genius in the kitchen. When she hugs her best hugs they make me feel warm.

Loni Kezeor   Grade: 02
My mom deserves a shining diamond because when I am shivering. Her warm arms squeeze me like an oven.

Caitlin Kheang   Grade: 02
My mom tells me the best stories. She always takes care of me when I am sick. Her smile is as bright as the moon.

Lauren Rasmussen   Grade: 02
My mom is a diamond that is polished with love each and every day. My mom is like a dear friend who loves me.

Jason Vo   Grade: 02
My mom deserves a diamond because she's always there for me. She's always marvelous to me. I like her famous hugs, they warm me up.

Nicholas Whitford   Grade: 02
My mom is good at making my favorite waffles. She's as sweet as a sugar cookie. She makes every food just how I like it.

Shane Wilkinson   Grade: 02
My mom is always there for me when I need her help. Her eyes shimmer like the bright sun when she smiles.

***Amethyst winners in bold.**

Teacher: Lori Wolsky

Dylan Balogh   Grade: 02
My mom is as beautiful as a flower. My mom cares for all of my family. My mom is a peaceful person. I love her!

Ananaiuh Fiaseu   Grade: 02
My mom deserves a diamond because she's perfect and peaceful. She is beautiful and she loves me. I think she is an angel.

Amanda Kovacs   Grade: 02
My mom brightens my day. She is a jewel sparkling in the sun. She is an angel from heaven. I love her!

Mateo Leon   Grade: 02
Mom, you are a beautiful angel sent from above. Your eyes sparkle. You are caring and loveable. I love you so much!

Kayla Ortiz   Grade: 02
My mom shines like the sun and smells like a flower. She is like a diamond who looks like an angel and loves me.

Richard Rojes   Grade: 02
My mom deserves a diamond because she is like a rainbow. I will do anything for you, my beautiful mom. She is a great mom!

Brycen Sailors   Grade: 02
My mom deserves a diamond because she's bright like a star. She cares for me and we eat together. She is the best mom ever.'

Karissa Sugita   Grade: 02
My mom loves me. She is an angel. She's as bright as stars and rainbows. She cares for me and is beautiful.

Gisler (Robert) Elementary
Fountain Valley

Teacher: Tim Adams

Angaelos Hanna   Grade: 04
My mom deserves a diamond because she works hard, she gets whatever I want and she tries her best to make me happy.

Francesca Kadi   Grade: 04
My mom deserves a diamond because she is loving and is always nice to everyone and she's a single parent, and always has a smile.

Bridey Wood   Grade: 04
My mom deserves a diamond because she helps with my homework. She takes care of me when I'm sick. My mom is a great mom!

Teacher: Marion Benson

Chandler Brunelli   Grade: 05
My mom deserves a diamond because she cooks and cares for me and for once I think I should do something for her.

Aliya Conway   Grade: 05
My mom shines just like diamonds, she has been doing so many things for me. My mom deserves a diamond. I love her a lot.

Anthony Cort   Grade: 05
My mom deserves a diamond. She's flawless in every way. She is bright as the sun's beautiful rays. She's better than anyone day after day.

Ryan Erickson   Grade: 05
My outstanding mom deserves a diamond because she is hardworking and does not get paid. She should get a diamond.

Carolina Freitas   Grade: 05
My mom is very special in many ways. She always wants to help. She never walks away. My mom is great to me. Lucky me.

Kassidy Gamble   Grade: 05
My mom is magnificent because she cares about me, loves me, and does so much for me. My mom shows it every day.

Ruben Gutierrez   Grade: 05
My mom is as beautiful as a diamond and is as sweet as a cupcake, her gorgeous eyes twinkle like the stars up high at night.

Riley Hanson   Grade: 05
My mom is nice and gives me a lot of things, she treats me like a king. My mom is a supermom and I love her.

Bryan Hartzell   Grade: 05
Like a summer's sun and a winter's moon, her smile is very bright. She works very hard to make my day, a delightful day.

Yoanna Ishak   Grade: 05
My mother is the light of my heart. Her light is like a diamond, so pure. Without her, the world is dark. I love her.

Nicole Kolb   Grade: 05
My mom's eyes are sparkly like the shiny sun. My mom's love for me is very strong. That's why she's the best for me.

Clarence Kung   Grade: 05
My grandma raised me from when I was five years old. She works to guide me. Without her, I would not be happy. She's wonderful!

Rachael Layfield   Grade: 05
My mom deserves a diamond because she has the biggest heart. She adopted me and my sister, she loves us with all her heart.

Jana Milan   Grade: 05
My mom deserves a diamond because she is the light in my life. She cares for me and loves me with all her heart.

Grant Rincon   Grade: 05
My mother should receive a diamond because she is the architect that is building my life. My mother is the fire of my burning heart.

Nicholas Taylor   Grade: 05
My mom deserves a diamond because every time I look at her face I see joy not disgrace and I am thankful to be her boy.

Myles Teano   Grade: 05
My mom is flawless. She is special in many ways. She can cook and clean all day and be here too. She deserves a diamond.

Collin Tery   Grade: 05
My mom deserves the biggest diamond in the world because she is very loving, caring and she is the most beautiful person ever.

Brianna VonBargen   Grade: 05
My mom deserves a diamond because she means everything to me. Her eyes glisten like the stars in the moonlit sky. She's loving and caring.

Teacher: Stephanie Carnes

Dane Brown   Grade: 02
My mom deserves a diamond because she is kind and caring. She is brilliant and strong. My mom is one of a kind.

Wyatt Burris   Grade: 02
She sparkles like a pretty, crystal heart that twinkle in a golden lasting heart. Big and round as a beautiful gem, mom sparkles like crystals.

Wade Gerard   Grade: 02
My mom deserves to have a diamond because she glows in the sun. Her eyes match to my heart and diamonds, the sparkle in the sun.

IN THE NEWS!

Moms Celebrate a Gem of a Mother's Day

In Memory of Dorothy Jean

Dorothy Jean, Writer. 04-20-99.

In 1993, I was at Michael's store, Gallery of Diamonds, interviewing him for an article. Just then, his very first "Diamond Winner", a tenth-grader from Huntington Beach came in with her mom to pick out her prize, an unmounted diamond. I don't know who was more excited, the teenager, her mother, Michael, or me. All I know is that still feel tingly recalling that moment.

My article was shelved and never saw print, but I've covered the WHY MOM DESERVES A DIAMOND® award ceremonies ever since and am always thrilled for the kids, their moms and for Michael. The annual event is a happy, heart-felt, almost super-human endeavor for a man who wants kids to be sure to tell their moms that they love them.

"I sponsor the contest to encourage children to think and write about how they appreciate their moms," says Michael, who for 20 years, searched for his birth mother.

"Although reared by a wonderful adoptive mother, I never knew my biological mother." Unfortunately, he never got to tell the woman he cared for her because she died before he discovered her whereabouts.

The jeweler personally judges every submittal. His wife, Carmen, and his staff help process and organize the thousands of pieces of paper that are stacked in boxes almost to the ceiling.

The Legendary Contest®

Trace Shelton. InStore Magazine. April, 2005.

It began in 1993 as an event to honor store owner Michael Watson's adoptive mother and the birth mother he had never known. In the twelve years since, more than 150,000 children have submitted essays to prove their mothers should receive one of three quarter-carat diamonds awarded annually by Gallery of Diamonds.

The first contest, which garnered 250 entries, awarded only one diamond to the most creative contestant. However, Watson also selected 50 second-place winners and awarded each a red African garnet. The strategy proved to be a brilliant one. The annual event soon put Gallery of Diamonds on the map - first locally, then nationally. With 22,629 entries in 2005, the company touts the contest as, "The greatest tribute to mom in the nation." The contest now takes eight months of preparation. Today, Gallery of Diamonds awards two diamonds locally in Orange County, and one nationally.

The Why Mom Deserves a Diamond® contest created by Gallery of Diamonds is by far the highest-profile, most successful, to date.

What others are saying about the WHY MOM DESERVES A DIAMOND® contest.

My daughter's essay has touched me forever. My diamond has not only become a symbol of love but also a reminder of how precious she is."
Michele Connella.
2001 Diamond Mom.

"Thank you for sponsoring such a special event. You touched my heart and gave me a diamond heart that will always be treasured!"
Geryln Glidden.
2007 Diamond Mom.

"My students were so excited to write about their moms and this turned out to be a very good lesson in finding the positive aspects of others."
C. Martin. S. B. Anthony.
Westminster, CA.

"We offer our warmest congratulations on your contest having created such an outstanding institution in Orange County."
John Adams. Orange County Librarian.

"It's so great to have (my students) writing extend beyond the walls of the classroom to be appreciated. The real miracle is simply to have them pause and give thought in expressing appreciating of their mothers, something they might not otherwise take time to do.

I thank you also for giving me a sparkling highlight in my year when my students are inspired, recognized, rewarded, and made aware of how fortunate they are to have their wonderful mothers."
Patricia Lane., teacher
Huntington Beach , CA.

"Thank you again for making your wonderful contest available to Orange County students. You have put a smile on the mothers' and children's faces - with feelings of success, love and inspiration for others. Thank you for your fine contribution for our children and families!"
Mrs. Pauline Rosenthal, teacher.
Irvine, CA.

"What a treat it was to go to your beautiful store with my daughter and receive such a tribute. When (she) read her poem, my eyes filled up with tears, and all the way home I felt full. What a wonderful and sweet adventure for Jenny and me."
Betsy Spradley.

"What a marvelous idea! Congratulations on your creativity and thoughtfulness in honoring motherhood."
Gloria Koss. River Rouge, MI.

".an awesome assignment, a great learning experience, and a challenge that could be met at any level. .all children come away with a feeling of pride and self-accomplishment. Thank you for creating a room full of smiles."
M. Craney. St. Malachy.
Brownsburg, IN.

"All day today, students have been sharing the details of when they picked up their garnets, and it sounds like a happy day for everyone."
A. Schwartz. Dale Jr. High.
Anaheim, CA.

"Thank you! . As teachers, we appreciate your effort making writing a fun and purposeful exercise. "
K. Moore, V. La Frossia, K. McDaniel and S. Hanauer. MacArthur Fund., Santa Ana, CA.

"Thank you for your graciousness. I really enjoy watching my students labor over their entries for your contest. We all do this from our hearts."
Robin Williams. Arroyo Seco.
Valencia, CA.

"Thank you so much for providing such a wonderful way to recognize moms!"
Susan Lee. Peters Canyon.
Tustin, CA

Madison Giles   Grade: 02
My mom is beautiful in the sky. My mom is pretty as I see her in my heart. My mom's eyes twinkle in the sun.

Caylin Lucio   Grade: 02
My mom shines like the beautiful sparkling sun. She always works hard. She is the most kindest person I have ever met in my life.

Maraya Mohr   Grade: 02
Mom's eyes are prettier than a crystal gem. She is as beautiful as a golden princess that has a big heart. She is lovely.

Emaan Sial   Grade: 02
My mom shines in the sun. She is like a princess cut in the sun. She does hard work. She is lovely to me now.

Teacher: Joanna Knobel

Kobi Ayres   Grade: 02
Her eyes dazzle in the sunset. The sunrises just to see her. Her radiance will last forever.

Andrew Ballas   Grade: 02
My mom deserves a diamond because she has eyes as precious as a gem. A diamond is a girl's best friend, but she is mine.

Emily Baumgartner   Grade: 02
My mom's eyes are rare, sparkly like a gem. She glimmers like a jewel. She glows with great beauty and will always be like that.

Jakob Bixler   Grade: 02
My mom is a princess that glows. Her eyes are so pretty when you look into them they sparkle.

Kristin Chandler   Grade: 02
Mom deserves a diamond because her eyes sparkle and glow like a beautiful gem. A diamond is a perfect thing and so is my mom.

Raquel Medina   Grade: 02
Her brilliance shines in her intelligence and beauty and that is a rare gift. She is a precious jewel that is flawless and shines strongly.

Nicholas Nguyen   Grade: 02
My mom is a rare jewel to me forever. She glimmers as a precious gem. She shines strong and radiant in the shining light.

Zoe Utterback   Grade: 02
There is one rare gem that is worth her weight in gold. She sparkles before them all. The precious glimmer in her eyes is forever!

Jake Whitcomb   Grade: 02
My mom is a diamond that will last forever and a rare glowing jewel. She is strong and shines like a beautiful gem of intelligence.

Teacher: Anne Rogers

Maddie Chaffin   Grade: 05
Why my mom deserves a diamond because she's caring, always by my side, encourages me to do best. That's why my mom deserves a diamond.

Canon Giambona   Grade: 05
My mommy deserves a diamond because she loves me. She has the greatest smile and face and love written all over it. Mommy loves hugs.

Stacie Higgins   Grade: 05
She cares for me and will stop whatever she is doing to help me with my homework, and I can talk to her about anything.

Tara Reece   Grade: 05
My mom's like a diamond. She sparkles and is rare. She's always there to care. She's more than a mom to me, but a friend.

Sarah Steinhaus   Grade: 05
I love my mom because she always sings around the house. It makes me feel cheerful and happy to hear her wonderful voice.

Gavin Wilson-Honeyborne   Grade: 05
Because she has done so much for me. She helps me on a lot of things and that she is always there for me.

Glenview Elementary
Anaheim

Teacher: Wendy Humphrey

Renee Beverly   Grade: 02
My mom deserves a diamond because she plays with me. And helps me get better when I get sick.

Jesse Cole   Grade: 02
My mom deserves a diamond because she is nice, she takes me places and plays with me. I love my mom so much.

Jocelyn De La Torre   Grade: 02
My mom deserves a diamond because she is very talented, wonderful and she never gives up. That's why I love her very much.

Ashlymn Donaldson   Grade: 02
My mom takes care of me when I'm sick. She is loving and caring. She helps me with my homework. She feeds me vegetables.

Taylor Halverson   Grade: 02
My mom deserves a diamond because she is beautiful and helps me do things. She is wonderful and helpful.

Spencer Lund   Grade: 02
My mom deserves a diamond because she is loving and caring to people. She is the nicest person to everyone in the world. She rocks.

Cory Mater   Grade: 02
My mom is very pretty. She is very cute and she loves me very much and I love her very much.

Melissa Morales   Grade: 02
My mom deserves a diamond because she likes to help me with my homework. She likes diamonds.

Jessica Suruor   Grade: 02
My mom deserves a diamond because she helps me clean my room and she is also good at doing her job because she gets money.

Hailey Whittaker   Grade: 02
My mom deserves a diamond because she helps me do stuff that is hard like do homework, and helps clean my room and she's awesome.

Kailey Wolf   Grade: 02
My mom deserves a diamond because she has been single. She has been taking care of me for a long time and I love her.

Teacher: Donna Simester

Mason Cruz   Grade: 03
My mom is nice to me. She shines like a diamond. Her eyes glow like a diamond. She makes me happy when I am sad.

Emily De Casas   Grade: 03
Her eyes shines like the sun. She twinkles like an angel. My God picked her out just like the sunshine shines like the sun.

Tommy Garcia   Grade: 03
My mom deserves a diamond because she glows like a diamond, looks pretty and has shiny eyes like a diamond and glows like one too.

Matthew Gomez   Grade: 03
My mom is nice to us and she shines like the sun and the moon. Her eyes are like a rainbow and a star.

Tomas Hernandez   **Grade: 03**
My mom deserves a diamond because she is the one who gave me birth. She taught me how to love and how to respect others.

Aline Monroy   Grade: 03
Her eyes are like a shiny star. Her heart is my heart and my heart is hers.

Ricardo Monroy   Grade: 03
My mom deserves a diamond because she is beautiful diamond. Her eyes shine like the beautiful moon and ocean.

Destiny Moreno   Grade: 03
My mom is the best thing that ever happened to me. She cares for me and loves me. I love her very much.

Melissa Rodriguez   Grade: 03
My mom deserves a diamond because she shines like a star. Her heart belongs to me and my heart belongs to her.

Pablo Serrano   **Grade: 03**
Mom is nice. She cares for me and brother. I love her with all my might. She is pretty and she loves us.

Mark Wyse   **Grade: 03**
I like my mom. She shines like a diamond. Her heart beat is like a ruby. Her eyes shine like sapphires on a lake.

Golden Elementary
Placentia

Teacher: Sara DeLand

Tatum Cazin   **Grade: 01**
My mom deserves a diamond because my mom is a queen! She is the best mom ever. She takes care of me.

Kristen Chang   Grade: 01
My mom works hard for me. She takes care of me when I get sick. She should win because she is really respectful and nice.

McKenzie Fossum   Grade: 01
My mom deserves a diamond because she loves me. She helps me with my homework. She looks like a princess. She worries about me.

Danielle Frobenius   Grade: 01
My mom is a great cook. She is pretty as a diamond. She takes care of me. She is the nicest in the world.

Sydney Mills   **Grade: 01**
I love my mom so much. She is the best mom ever. I have fun with her. My mom loves me so much.

Aditya Mody   Grade: 01
My mom carried me in her stomach for 9 months. She loves me so much and takes me to art classes.

Shelby Mumma   Grade: 01
I love my mom so much. My mom deserves a diamond because she is the best mom. I love my mom because she is pretty.

Dominic Nieves   **Grade: 01**
My mom deserves a diamond because my mom loves me. She is a good mom. She is a princess.

Jackson Solheid   Grade: 01
I always think of my mom. My mom is excellent so she should win a diamond. My mom is so special. I love my mom.

Ashelyn Villicana   Grade: 01
My mom deserves the diamond because she is pretty as a star.

Teacher: Lisa Fraser

Ebin Arroyo   Grade: 02
My mom deserves a diamond because she works around the house a lot and she cooks me dinner and she vacuums the house.

Makenna Calderon   **Grade: 02**
My mom deserves a diamond because she is the best mom ever and she takes care of my sisters and me. I love her.

Connor Carlson   Grade: 02
My mom deserves a diamond because she works hard to keep me happy and designs all my parties in my class.

Tom Chaney   Grade: 02
My mom deserves a diamond because she works really hard everyday. She cleans the house and takes care of me. My mom is really helpful.

Grace Cheng   Grade: 02
My mom deserves a diamond because she helps me and care for me. She makes me food. She cleans the house and takes me everywhere.

Kiri Oshiro   Grade: 02
My mom deserves a diamond because she is the best mother in the world. She loves me the most in the whole world.

Jake Schwab   **Grade: 02**
My mom deserves a diamond because she does everything she can for me and she loves me and I love her.

Isabelle Valdez   Grade: 02
My mom deserves a diamond because I love and care for her. She takes me to the park and feeds me. I love her.

Jake Wong   Grade: 02
My mom deserves a diamond because she works hard and keeps an eye on the puppy because he bites people.

Kelly Yu   **Grade: 02**
I think my mom should win a diamond because she takes good care of me and she keeps me safe.

Teacher: Jennifer Rasic

Ryan Bethencourt   **Grade: 01**
My mom deserves a diamond. Her smile is like glittery gold. She loves me so much. When she cuddles me up, I get so warm.

Terence Lee   **Grade: 01**
My mom is special as a diamond because she gives lots of love everyday. She has sparkly shining eyes, she is precious to me.

Jay Louie   **Grade: 01**
My mom is very precious like a shooting star. She shines like a star and she smells just swell like a flower in the sun.

Zachary Matl   Grade: 01
My mom is a flower from a beautiful garden and a night star beautiful bird.

Jared Mc Nair   Grade: 01
My mom deserves a diamond because she makes me feel good as a bee. She helps me good.

Aubry New   Grade: 01
My mommy is my favorite mom ever. My mom is the best mom because she makes me laugh.

Corinne Padar   Grade: 01
I love my mom. I make her special and happy. She looks like a diamond. She has a big smile.

Joelle Park   Grade: 01
My mom is beautiful as a diamond. She is graceful as a dove. She is very gentle as a feather.

Andrew Puch   Grade: 01
My mom makes me happy. My mom is very pretty. She is very nice to me and my brother.

* Amethyst winners in bold.

Mikaylee Watkins   Grade: 01
My mom makes me feel special. My mom is special to me. You make my day happy. You are really nice so you deserve a diamond.

Greentree Elementary
Irvine

Teacher: Yvonne Vedell

Eric Chung   Grade: 03
My mom is so nice, my mom is so beautiful, my mom deserves a diamond. I really think she is nice and loving.

Jennifer Lin   Grade: 03
The shine of my mom warms my heart. She sparkles to me to brighten the way to my dream.

Samantha Nguyen   Grade: 03
My mom shines in spotlight and is terrific to me. I love her so much that I would give her anything. My mom is the best.

Dan Nguyen   Grade: 03
I love my mom because her big smile makes me happy. She always blows kisses at me every time she goes to work. I love mom!

Crystal Webb   Grade: 03
Her eyes sparkle. Her eye lashes glitter. She cooks for the family and waves with a shimmer.

Greenville Fundamental
Santa Ana

Teacher: Sally Myers

Jonathan Abellera   Grade: 05
I think my mom deserves the diamond because she takes care of me when I am sick and she loves me and I love her.

Adrian Aguilar   Grade: 05
My mom is like an angel. Her eyes sparkle bright like a star. Her smile brightens my day. Her beauty wakens my soul.

Carl Bastillo   Grade: 05
I think my mom deserves a diamond because she works very hard to keep my family moving. My mom is very important to me.

Tina Bui   Grade: 05
Mom shines. Mom glows. In my heart, she is my queen. She is a wonderful mom to be. The queen that will be mine forever.

Riki Gallardo   Grade: 05
My mom is a very sparkly gem, or like a flower on it's stem. She is smart for she will always have my loving heart.

Julissa Gaytan   Grade: 05
My mom deserves a diamond because she does all the chores of her sister without complaining. She is wonderful mother and friend. She's the best.

Martin Madrigal   Grade: 05
In the morning, my mother's eyes shine like a new sparkling diamond. She has patience, she's understanding and she gives me lots of love.

Nicholas Martinez   Grade: 05
My mom should deserve a diamond because she is a hardworking mom and she always puts her kids before anything else and loves us.

Rosette Pham   Grade: 05
My mom deserves a diamond because she is not a liar, her love can't take me any higher, as I follow my hearts desire.

Carolyn Ta   Grade: 05
My mom is like light so smart and very bright. She shines like a diamond when it's dawn. She'll always be in my heart no matter what.

Ricardo Zarate   Grade: 05
My mom is the best in the world because her eyes glow brighter than the sun and her smile is as beautiful as the ocean.

Hankey (Carl H.) Elem.
Mission Viejo

Teacher: Rocklyn Meserve

Sanaz Ardehali   Grade: 05
My mom deserves a diamond because she works so hard just to make me happy. That's why she deserved a diamond.

Jeremy Bukacek   Grade: 05
My mom deserves a diamond because she raises me and works hard for everybody and never gets a treat.

Karen Catalan   Grade: 05
My mom deserves a diamond because she is always there when I need her. She is like my sun on a rainy day. She deserves it.

Guadalupe Cervantes   Grade: 05
My mom deserves a diamond because she is nice to anyone. She shines like a rainbow. She likes to play with us.

Julia Esquivel   Grade: 05
My mom deserves a diamond because she cares for me and my family. My mom also deserves one because she is a loving person.

Kassandra Estrada   Grade: 05
My mom is like jewels shimmering throughout the night sky. She takes care of me. She is like an angel smiling.

Alex Friehling   Grade: 05
She is an angel a descendant of God. She acts likes a shield for me. She is my mom.

Jessica Hernandez   Grade: 05
My mom deserves a diamond because she has always been there for me when I need her and is as pretty as a shining diamond.

Noah Husband   Grade: 05
The way my mom takes care of me is really, really neat. She makes sure that I'm happy from my head to my feet.

Alberto Lopez   Grade: 05
My mom deserves a diamond because she always does things for me. My mom is like a diamond glimmering in the night. I love my mom.

Caitlin McFann   Grade: 05
I think of love, I see mom. Your love for me, my love for you - immeasurable. Mom's voice - music. Mom.

Lindsey Moorhead   Grade: 05
My mom deserves a diamond. Let me tell you why, her voice is pure syrup which makes me feel high. I love my mom!

Bridget Ocampo   Grade: 05
My mom deserves a diamond because she is sweet like a fresh apple, and she protects us like a mama bear protects her cubs.

Erica Sanson   Grade: 05
My mom deserves a diamond because she has been taking care of me since I was born, and I want to give something back to her.

Makayla Stevens   Grade: 05
My mom deserves a diamond because she does everything for me and she loves me a lot so I wanted to do something nice for her.

Josiah Wittrock   Grade: 05
My mom deserves a diamond because she smiles like a rainbow. She is as sweet as a bunny and I love her more than anything.

Harbour View Elementary
Huntington Beach

Teacher: Gretchen Long

Alec Anderson   Grade: 04
My mom is great. She always makes dinner. She works at home all day. My mom deserves a diamond because she's the best mom.

Madison Brooks   Grade: 04
My mom deserves a diamond because she's very nice, proud, strong, and never gives up and she always helps others before herself. She is the best.

Matthew Carney   Grade: 04
My mom deserves a diamond because she is kind, gentle, loving and she is always willing to make me happy.

Daniela De La Rosa   Grade: 04
My mom deserves a diamond because she takes care of me and loves me and makes me feel good when I'm sick.

Riley Earles   Grade: 04
My mom deserves a diamond because she is like the most important person in the world and I wouldn't be alive without her.

Colin Fathauer   Grade: 04
I think my mom deserves a diamond because ever since kindergarten, she's volunteered in my class. When I have a game, she comes to it.

Michael Gonzales   Grade: 04
My mom deserves a diamond because she cares about me. She also helps me whenever I'm stuck on a problem in homework. She's the best.

Grant Haber   Grade: 04
My mom deserves a diamond because she takes care of me, she loves me, and she is always there for me.

Michael Lauermann   Grade: 04
My mom Susan deserves a diamond because she's a hard worker and she helps people in need. She is Super, Understanding, Spectacular, Awesome, and Nice.

Kelianne Leong   Grade: 04
Mom deserves a diamond because she treats me like I'm a very important gem, but to me she is the beautiful crystal of my heart.

Sarah Lin   Grade: 04
A is accepting. N is noble. D is dear. R is respect. E is entertaining. A is active. That spells my mom, Andrea.

Jenna Pajunen   Grade: 04
My mom deserves a diamond because she is kind and caring. She is also very helpful and gives me good advice.

Sierra Vukelich   Grade: 04
My mom deserves a diamond because she's been a really good mother to me and she always cares for me and loves me so much.

Sahar Walkman   Grade: 04
My mom deserves a diamond because she takes care of me. She always feeds me. She is always helping me. Mom will always love me.

Jasmine Zavala   Grade: 04
My mom deserves a diamond because she is kind to others, she makes people shine like a diamond, and she has a crystal smile.

Teacher: Jennifer Rilling

Jennifer Berge   Grade: 04
My mom deserves a diamond because she always works hard doing her job and cleaning the house and dishes and does a lot of hard work there.

Adam Blanchard   Grade: 04
My mom deserves a diamond because she works very hard and usually goes to sleep at one o'clock. She tucks me in at night.

Brooke Cyprus   Grade: 04
My mom is kind, helpful, caring, and nice to all. She does a lot for my family and I. My mom will do anything.

Ricardo Europa   Grade: 04
My mom deserves a diamond because she is nice, careful, helpful, outstanding, trustful, courteous and she always does things for me, even when she's tired.

Renee Levin   Grade: 04
My mom deserves a diamond because she is always looking out for the better of me and my family.

Michael Lombardo   Grade: 04
My mom deserves a diamond because she works so hard to take care of me.

Noah Murchison   Grade: 04
My mom deserves a diamond because she is funny and takes care of me.

Nathan Murphy   Grade: 04
My mom deserves a diamond because she always cooks for me and washes my clothes. Also, she always helps me. Also, she always loves me.

Jesus Ortiz   Grade: 04
My mom deserves the diamond because she is a loving and hardworking mom and she works hard everyday to keep the house clean.

Brook Rogers   Grade: 04
My mom deserves a diamond because she is caring, nice, beautiful, helpful, sweet and she is beautiful as a diamond.

Jordan Rovano   Grade: 04
My mom deserves a diamond because she always is doing too much work and going places. So I think she deserves something special for one day.

Keelyn Thompson   Grade: 04
My mom should win a diamond because she is a wonderful person and she does everything in the house and every mom should be rewarded.

Dylan Tran   Grade: 04
My mom should get a diamond because she is kind, loving, caring, helpful, funny, generous, creative, huggable, and she always makes sure I am safe.

Isaac Wright   Grade: 04
My mom deserves a diamond because she has loved me my whole life and cares for others and respects other people's will and she is kind.

Teacher: Grace Soldan

Elyse Manzo   Grade: 05
She is a shining star in the sky. It leads me to harmony inside. She is the brightest star at night. Her name is mom.

Sarah Stanfield   Grade: 05
My mom is a wonderful mother. So gentle, yet so strong. The many ways you show care always makes me feel I belong.

Katie Thorson   Grade: 05
My mom deserves a diamond because she's caring like a butterfly, beautiful as a blossomed daisy, thought for others, and loving to me and friends.

Paul Verdugo   Grade: 05
There's a special ingredient in my heart. The ingredient is my special mother and that ingredient will stay in my heart forever until I die.

* Amethyst winners in bold.

Hertiage Oak Private Edu.
Yorba Linda

Teacher: Amritha Acharya

Leena Carvalho　　　　　Grade: 03
My mom's eyes shine like the sun so bright, it makes me blind but what everybody sees is her glowing heart inside.

Daniela Firkle　　　　　Grade: 03
Her eyes are crystal, her hands are as warm as the sun. Her voice is the angels, and she is one of God's favorites.

Nadia HaLahan　　　　　Grade: 03
Her eyes twinkle. Her cheeks sparkly peaches. Her lips, soft rose petals. Her heart pure gold. She's always filled with love. She's my mom.

Katrina Hung　　　　　Grade: 03
My mom is a beauty. She shines brighter than the sun. If anyone competes with her, she will win for sure. She deserves that diamond.

Alison Mendrella　　　　Grade: 03
You have a smile that is beautiful like a lovely lily blooming. You have the natural beauty inside and out. You are my mommy.

Teacher: Cambare

Taylor Fischer　　　　　Grade: 04
My mom is the twinkle of the stars. The whistle of the wind. The happiness of very happy children. This floating breeze deserves a diamond.

Joey Gutierrez　　　　　Grade: 04
Her hair is as smooth as silk. She has blue eyes that shimmer in the sun. Without her I would not ever be complete.

Fiona Hines　　　　　Grade: 04
My mom cares for me when I fall off my bike, she carries me home and wipes away my tears. For her, I'd do anything.

Charlotte Kim　　　　　Grade: 04
My mom is like a beautiful, delicate snowflake riding in a gust of wind when she wears glittering jewelry. My mom deserves a spectacular diamond.

Shayan Rauf　　　　　Grade: 04
Each morning when I come down, my mom looks even more charming then the most beautiful crown. Each time I see her she is smiling!

Torin Siegel　　　　　Grade: 04
My caring mother deserves a diamond because she is loving and big hearted. She is also sweet like honey which she likes in her tea.

Teacher: Jane Frisz

Sun Choi　　　　　Grade: 06
She's worth a beautiful diamond. Smile worth a pearl and personality worth much more. But it's her heart that lights up the world.

Daniel Chu　　　　　Grade: 06
Oh my beautiful mother, eyes of diamond a heart of gold, your face shines like a str. I love you my dear mother.

Brady Edwards　　　　　Grade: 06
Her eyes shine like the stars above because she gives me all her love. Because she's the seed of the tree, I'm soon to be.

Lauren Jackson　　　　　Grade: 06
My mom is sweet like Skittles. I love her very much, eyes like two chocolate balls, lips like licorice whips. My mom's the sweetest treat!

Abby Kim　　　　　Grade: 06
My mom loves me and cares about me no matter what. Her smile makes me feel better and her cookies are awesome.

Ashley Moser　　　　　Grade: 06
Pretty and perfect, flawless and fine. Mom is the one, on my mind, dark or light, day or night. She loves with all her might.

Brandon Zirkle　　　　　Grade: 06
I see a shining light that is coming from the heaven's above. The light is so bright that people are blinded. I see that it's my mother.

Teacher: Purvi Holmes

Olivia Chung　　　　　Grade: 04
Her eyes as bold as the sunshine. Her heart as deep as the sea with her love for me. I love you mom.

Madison Drummond　　　　Grade: 04
My mom is as beautiful as pure white snow on a cold winter day. She is the best mom I could wish for.

Carlos Fregoso　　　　　Grade: 04
Sunlight and a pinch of glittering fairy dust shining in her eyes makes my mom. The queen of all. That's why she deserves a diamond.

Chris Koel　　　　　Grade: 04
Eyes more radiant than the sun. Sparkling more than all the diamonds in the world. A heart full of love and compassion. She's so awesome.

Evan Mei　　　　　Grade: 04
My mom as sparkling as a gem in the afternoon sun. More peaceful than a relaxing hot tub. More helpful than the internet.

Claire Park　　　　　Grade: 04
Her eyes shine like a lightening bug glowing in the night. Her voice sounds as clear as a crystal. It cheers me all the time.

Sean Savage　　　　　Grade: 04
My mom's eyes sparkle like bright diamonds. She is as beautiful as a rainbow and her smile is as bright as the sun.

Teacher: Lindsay Johnson

Kayla Alcaraz　　　　　Grade: 08
A dream so real with me beside her, but an angel comes saying "Heaven". I cried, she turned and said these words, "I love you".

Lauren Byrne　　　　　Grade: 08
My mother is the sun in my life, showing me the way. Day and night, she is by my side. I love her.

Matthew Cevallos　　　　Grade: 08
Like the moon in the night, she shines very bright. She glows in the radiance of her love. My mom, my own, my dove.

Vasilios Fasoulis　　　　Grade: 08
Mom, you are my guardian angel. You protect me from everything that's bad and you are more beautiful than flowers in spring. I love you.

Hussain Hemani　　　　　Grade: 08
Laila. So gentle, so sweet. Kind and lovable. The flower is a vast garden in the center of that flower lays a bright diamond. Hemani

Carly Johnson　　　　　Grade: 08
Like Venus with her shining face. Like sisters with their warm embrace. As endless as the sky could be. I'm so glad that my mom loves me.

Mackenzie Kaiser　　　　Grade: 08
Jacqui is her name, smiling is her fame. Always cheerful, always peaceful making you and the sunshine.

Victoria Lew　　　　　Grade: 08
Beautiful and glowing, inside and out. She brings me love and happiness and makes me want to shout.

Benjamin Pun   Grade: 08
Her caring heart and her bright attitude are always with me. Her effort to make my life the fullest is something I'll remember for life.

Alejandro Sanchez   Grade: 08
My mom deserves a diamond because of her passionate self. She puts others before herself no matter what.

Kayla Vizcarra   Grade: 08
Her smile fills your heart. Her hug can cure all parts. She runs wherever she's called. Her name is probably, Mom.

Teacher: Julie Mullings

Taylor Bruce   Grade: 03
Her eyes sparkle like the biggest, prettiest diamond. Her laugh has joy of laughter. Her heart is the place she loves me so very much.

Anna Dalton   Grade: 03
My mom smells like beautiful garden roses. Her eyes look like sparkling diamonds. She makes everybody feel very special.

Hailey Jeare   Grade: 03
A drop of love, a drop of laughter together it makes my mom. She is as precious as a diamond. I love you, Mom.

Kate Matthews   Grade: 03
My mom's heart is made of diamonds and her eyes sparkle with love and care for me. She protects me from the danger around us.

Celine Smith   Grade: 03
My mom's cooking wafts through my heart. Her heart is a diamond that glows in my eyes. If separated, I would simply just cry.

Teacher: Christy Overholtzer

Sahej Chawla   Grade: 03
My mom deserves a diamond because she is darling and so sweet. She twinkles like a star. My mom looks like an angel.

Suhna Choi   Grade: 03
When I go in my house, what do I see is a beautiful woman waiting for me. This is why my mom deserves a diamond.

Megan Lee   Grade: 03
My mom deserves a diamond because she helps me and she loves me. And she's perfectly fine. I love her just the way she is.

Teacher: Nancy Pace

Chloe Adler   Grade: 05
My mom is always there for me when I get hurt or sad. We'll love and cherish each other forever. I'll never stop loving her.

Klarisse Andre de St. Amant   Grade: 05
She shines and glitters like an evening star and when she says she loves me. My happiness travel far.

Manon Andre de St. Amant   Grade: 05
Liquid pools of silver shimmering crystals are my mother's eyes. It's love, undeniable love. There's no fiction in the beauty of unstoppable love.

Ryan Byrne   Grade: 05
My mom deserves a diamond because she guides like an arrow to the target. Her heart Is a flashlight showing me the way. She deserves a diamond.

Ashley Cheah   Grade: 05
My mother's sweet, she keeps things neat. When she smiles, it shows then like a diamond, it glows. My mother's the light of my heart.

Celeste Chen   Grade: 05
My mom is my hero, I am her sword. Together, we fight, through evil and good. Through life and love. She is a warrior.

Casey Cummins   Grade: 05
I love my mom. She brings me joy everyday. When I wake up, she is as bright as the sun and as sweet as candy.

Alec Jacques   Grade: 05
I was an imagination. That became reality. Now I give her love and eternal happiness.

Sue Jang   Grade: 05
I was in mom's womb. After I saw the world, I could smile, cry and laugh. Feelings are from heart, but heart was from mom.

Allan Jeong   Grade: 05
I was a mother's dream. That grew through her love and care. Now, she is my inspiration. Thank you for giving me life and love.

Evan McFerran   Grade: 05
Your eyes are crystal pools of love. Your heart beats like the sun's heat. Your smile warms up my heart so you deserves a diamond.

Mathieu Pham   Grade: 05
She dreamed for me. She waited for me. She struggled for me. She gave me birth. I am her life and she is my inspiration.

Alyssa Steinfeld   Grade: 05
I am the flower from my mom that blooms through her love. Now she is the water that nourishes me so I can blossom.

Alek Stevens   Grade: 05
My mom deserves a diamond because she is so beautiful. She is like a white swan or the snowy mountains.

Jennifer Winn   Grade: 05
Her eyes gleam in the darkness like the glimmering moon in the night sky. Her smile is like a contagious simper. Her love is mine.

Teacher: Tami Shirota

Mitchell Burke   Grade: 04
I think my mom should win a diamond because every night she gives me hugs and kisses me, then reads me part of a book.

Ammara Dadabhoy   Grade: 04
Her smile is like a crest. Her eyes twinkle like the sun. Her face is like a heart. Her voice is like a song.

Luke Gober   Grade: 04
I think my mom deserves a diamond because she is an honest, fair, and well known person with a good heart.

Willie Jackson   Grade: 04
It would match her because she's the sparkling diamond in my life. She is not like any other mom because she is special.

Isabela Kimmel   Grade: 04
Thank you God for making moms. They're so beautiful like a diamond. What would we do without moms? Really.

Angelo Scarsi   Grade: 04
My mother makes everyone smile. She's as nice as she could be. When I get scared, she comforts me. I love her so much.

Kevin Adler   Grade: 07
My mother helps me when I'm down and needing help. She never gives up on me. When I need her most, she's there for me.

Justin Anderson   Grade: 07
My mom deserves a diamond because she fills me with love. She tucks me in every night with a loving heart and a warming kiss.

Christine Budds   Grade: 07
My mom is like a beautiful rainbow. Her personality is colorful. Her heart is loving. She is always there with open arms. I love her.

* Amethyst winners in bold.

Evan Colburn   Grade: 07
My mother is like my guardian angel. She is my sunshine on a cloudy day, her eyes glisten like a diamond in the sunbeams.

Natasha Holden   Grade: 07
My mom not only deserves a diamond. Her beauty is beyond compare, she glistens when she smiles, and she is flawless.

Ama Koranteng   Grade: 07
She's the essence of my day; the hug that never goes away, the kiss that's always there, and the roots of my dark brown hair.

Timothy Park   Grade: 07
Her heart is a vast ocean of flowing love and warmth. Support dwells in every nook and cranny. I believe that my mother deserves diamonds.

Jamie Reyes   Grade: 07
She has dark brown, luminous eyes that shine like the sun. She is the light that makes my day bright. She is my loving mother.

Sabrina Weeks   **Grade: 07**
Her heart is like a vast ocean of generosity, kindness, and joy. When I'm able, she uses her wisdom to save me from my sorrow.

Hidden Hills Elementary
Laguna Niguel

Teacher: Laurie Asakowicz

Lolani Campos   Grade: 02
My mom is like the sun gazing at me every day. She has thoughtful thoughts. She is a rose to me.

Cyrus Hatami   Grade: 02
She is a flower in the ground and a beautiful angel in the sky. She is respectful to other people. I love my mom.

Joe Heneghan   Grade: 02
My mom deserves a diamond because her eyes shine like the ocean. She always reminds me about important stuff.

Allyson Jacobson   Grade: 02
My mom is so graceful. She is so nice. She sparkles like a diamond in clear sky light. I have faith in mom.

Elisa Lopez-Sanchez   Grade: 02
My mom is as beautiful as white clouds in the sky. She is a special mom. She is kind to everybody.

Giovanny Martinez   Grade: 02
MY mom is nice to my brother and me. She is cute and sweet. With a happy smile my mom is special.

Andrew Solte   Grade: 02
My mom has sparkling eyes, a crystal heart because she is a good smile.

Justin Stitt   Grade: 02
My mom is my soul. She is like a sparkling diamond up in the sky. She is like a diamond to me. I love her.

Teacher: Eve Benjoya

Nicolette Coleman- Poggi   Grade: 03
My mom is as sweet as a wish come true and I get to snuggle up with her at the end of the day.

Alana McKnight   Grade: 03
My mom deserves a diamond because she's sweet, responsible and respectful to all. She's also is going to take very good care of the diamond.

Parisa Meghdadi   Grade: 03
My mom is the universe's greatest mom ever. She is so nice and sweet. She is the one who should get something!

German Quiroga   Grade: 03
Mom, in Heaven. You're my real mother. You're not just a diamond, you're my mom.

Teacher: Tracy Botting

Camille Haroutunian   Grade: 02
My mom deserves a diamond because she pays a lot of bills. She also works hard everyday. She works for my school in my classroom.

Adrienne McNamar   Grade: 02
My mom deserves a diamond because she is a military mom. My dad is gone a lot so my mom and I are all alone.

Alberto Pizana   Grade: 02
My mom deserves a diamond because she works so hard. She has two kids, both are smart and a little bit of a trouble maker.

Brooke Podres   Grade: 02
My mom deserves a diamond because she works for a church. I love my mom everyday and every night. Our church loves her too.

Teacher: Laura Humphrey

Sebastion Clavijo   Grade: 03
My mom deserves a diamond because she prays for me that I'm healthy when I am sick and she makes me very happy.

Michael Cummings   Grade: 03
My mom deserves a diamond because she cleans our house every day. At the end of the day she is exhausted but still helps all three kids.

Averee Dovsek   Grade: 03
She gave birth to me and she raised me to be smart and friendly to everybody throughout my life. She's fabulous and hardworking 24/7.

Jillian Gellatly   Grade: 03
My mom loves me without a diamond but I would like to get her one! My mom suffers through for me and I love her.

Gabriellla Munez   Grade: 03
My mother deserves a diamond because she's always caring to me. One time fell off bike so mom ran so fast to get a band aid.

Sahar Said   **Grade: 03**
Every time I sleep or leave we say "love love". Our love means more than anything. Every time we see each other our hearts connect.

Meelad Taufiq   Grade: 03
My mom deserves a diamond because she takes care of five kids in her day care alone and she always listens to what I say.

Teacher: Julie Lamb

Madison Bellah   Grade: 02
I feel my mom deserves a diamond because she is fun, happy, loving, funny, pretty, helpful and the best lady in the world; a diamond.

Yasaman Ebrahimi   Grade: 02
My mom deserves a diamond because she brought me to the United States from Iran. So I wouldn't have to wear three jackets at school.

Amit Galatzer   Grade: 02
I feel my mom deserves a diamond because she is loving and sweet. It will make my mom so happy. When she's happy, I'm happy.

Atziry Ocotecatl   Grade: 02
Mom, you work hard everyday. I think you deserve a gift and a seven day vacation. I think you're sweet. I love you mom.

Teacher: Linda Waters

Dylan Campeau   Grade: 04
My mother is butterfly that flies in my heart. She keeps me healthy and smart. She is always there for me no matter what!

Maria Cayetano   **Grade: 04**
I thank God that I have a wonderful mom. I do not care if I win or lose, what matters is I have a mom.

Daniela Hernandez   Grade: 04
My mom deserves a diamond because she has earned it. She shines like the colors of the rainbow! She's my pot of gold!

Kiana Mannani   Grade: 04
Moms are like the sun and moon in the sky. Moms are like the seasons of the year. My mom is loving most of all.

Jessie Peterson   Grade: 04
My mom's eyes sparkle like the sea. She is so special to me. She loves me true.... Give her the diamond, I know Kung Fu!

Danny Zotelo   Grade: 04
Her eyes are like black pearls. Her lips are like rubies. She is the most beautiful woman on Earth, and I love her.

Hillsborough School
Anaheim Hills

Teacher: Kathryn Batarse

Nick Abassi   Grade: 05
My mom deserves a diamond because she is always there for me when there's a problem. If I'm in danger she protects - no matter what.

Lily Abrams   Grade: 05
Mom deserves a diamond because diamonds are very rare and special and she is my shining diamond. She is one of a kind, my mom.

Percilla Mirhadi   Grade: 05
My mom deserves a diamond because she has gone through many hardships. When I look at a rose, I think of her.

Ali Nas   Grade: 05
My mom deserves a diamond because she works hard all the time. I just got a new mom and I never gave her a present.

Teacher: Darcy Hammond

Nolan Clapp   Grade: 03
My mom deserves a diamond because she is loving, kind and all owed me to have a dog. That's why my mom deserves a diamond.

Cole De Luca   Grade: 03
My mom deserves a diamond because she is loving and caring. I couldn't ask for a better mom.

Tessa De Viso   Grade: 03
My mom deserves a diamond because she is beautiful, nice, caring, loving, sweet, amazing and the best mom in the world. She'll always be nice.

John Le   Grade: 03
My mom deserves that diamond because she's not a princess, not a queen, just the coolest mom you've ever seen.

Teacher: Tracey Parkhurst

Tommy Cho   Grade: 06
My mother is courageous, understanding, and kind. She helps me with everything, I appreciate her because she had helped me get better education in U.S.A.

Kiera De Viso   Grade: 06
Pure gentleness, pure love, pure loveliness is my mom. There are more than a million words to say about her. She is my wonderful diamond.

Aaron Ford   **Grade: 06**
When my mom looks at me, she stares into my soul and sees all the work that she has put into me has blossomed beautifully.

Mona Lee   Grade: 06
My mom is one person I know I will have forever. Her love is endless and my love for her reaches the infinity and beyond.

Aaron See   Grade: 06
God has given to me a mom, who's humble, kind, and strong, who picks me up when I'm down, and never ever makes me frown.

Sarah Yount   Grade: 06
I think my mom deserves a diamond; she is very special. She has two jobs and always works. She never has time to go shopping.

Stella Cho   Grade: 08
My mom studied and worked hard to achieve her goal as a doctor. I admire and love her as a doctor and mom.

Teacher: Lindsey Sanders

Bahar Ameen   Grade: 04
My mom helps me with my homework. All the money she has, she spends on me and she gets the left over's. She works hard.

Seth Cho   Grade: 04
She spends her life helping everyone. She spends everything on me. She doesn't get anything, only the diamond I want to give her.

Ashray Kapuria   Grade: 04
My mommy deserves a diamond because she is wise and takes care of all the family. She also is lively, active, spirited and has love.

Peter Le   **Grade: 04**
My mom is powerful, fresh, and fluid. She's impressive to start and is sure to flourish. That's why she deserves that diamond. Yes, yes, yes!

Tommy Lee   Grade: 04
My mommy deserves a diamond because she handles three children; one headed to college, another graduating from high school, and me in elementary. XOXO

Teacher: Cathy Villavicencio

Mary Aragaki   Grade: 02
My mom deserves a diamond because she takes me to the movies. I love her. The mostest to the hostess to the twinkly!

Trenton Blanchard   Grade: 02
my mom is a great mom. She cares about me and my family. She is nice to people in my neighborhood.

Elizabeth Finley   Grade: 02
My mom deserves a diamond because she helps me with my homework, she give me good food, she gives me a hug.

Mikey Pratt   Grade: 02
My mom is special because she respects God and respects me. She makes me happy.

Holy Family Cathedral Sch.
Orange

Teacher: Jennifer Kromling

Lili Alba-Hernandez   Grade: 05
My mom has a soul of a kind and gentle saint. Her eyes sparkle like a star when she smiles. She is a true gift.

Roisin Allaeddini   Grade: 05
My mom has such blue eyes that look like the serene sea reflecting it's true beauty. Her heart is as genuine as a sparkling gem.

Taylor Ashmore   Grade: 05
My mother deserves a diamond for her bright heart. When she's happy, I can see it glowing bright. A diamond is no match for her.

*** Amethyst winners in bold.**

Michael Avila   Grade: 05
Loving, caring, compassionate, and caring, even there word pale in compassion to my mother's glowing personality. Even the sun is dull, compared to her sunshine.

Adam Bauer   Grade: 05
My mom deserves a diamond because her heart is like a fountain of love and grace. She loves me unconditionally.

Mattie Cross   Grade: 05
My mom deserves a diamond. She has four kids and a crazy life. She does a lot for our school and dance studio. Thanks, Mom.

Lea Delgadillo   Grade: 05
My mom deserves a diamond because she is loving, caring, helpful, and patient. But mostly, she makes me laugh and supports me throughout my life.

Andrew Dvorak   Grade: 05
The glow of my mother's eyes in my soul. It burns in my soul because of her love.

Delaney Galindo   Grade: 05
My mother, the diamond of my life is better than all the riches of the world. Her heart, the gem of all gems shines within.

Lauren Galvan   Grade: 05
My mom is an angel sent from above. She teaches me values and makes life perfect and graceful. She is a true gift of love.

Francesca Hughes   Grade: 05
My caring mother who is extremely smart and has a very big heart. You are so very kind. I love you with all my heart.

Amanda Jaramillo   Grade: 05
My caring mother who is very sweet like candy, loves me very much. Just like a diamond, she is very difficult to replace if lost.

Emily Leyva   Grade: 05
My mom deserves a diamond because she is caring, helpful, and loving. Even though she is a busy bee. She will always love me.

Kaitlyn Minnis   Grade: 05
My mom deserves a diamond because she is so gentle to me. She gives me warm hugs when I'm sad. Her kisses are so sweet.

Micayla Nguyen   Grade: 05
My mom deserves a diamond because she is really smart and has a big heart. She is like an angel and guides me through life.

Maeve O' Connor   Grade: 05
My mom is so caring. She says, "Go do your homework, so you can play. She deserves a diamond because we create so much stress.

Kyanna Oyervides   Grade: 05
Mom, the shining lady I admire, no star can outshine her love and gentle heart. She has an angel touch and an admirable personality.

Bailey Prado   Grade: 05
Her hair, eyes and heart sparkles like one of God's diamonds sent down to help me with life. She deserves everything great and wonderful.

Nick Rodriguez   Grade: 05
Light as a feather, holy as an angel, loyal as a dog. My mom is these things and more.

Grace Sutton   Grade: 05
Her eyes so fine, her heart of gold, her sapphires soul. My mom a jewel above all jewels is mine forever more.

Jason Tirtorahardjo   Grade: 05
As the morning sun gently reflects off my mother's face, her mouth widens to a smile. Her eyes are as dark as the earth itself.

Brennan To   Grade: 05
My mom deserves a diamond because she's loving, helpful and cheerful. Also, she always cheers me on. This is why my mom deserves a diamond.

Nolan To   Grade: 05
Her diamond eyes burn into mine like diamonds from above. A dab of peace, a handful of love nothing outshines my mom.

Kyle Vu   Grade: 05
She has a diamond heart that reflects on all my problems. She is a part of me, my jewel, my mom.

Huntington Seacliff Elem.
Huntington Beach

Teacher: Alyssa Mauro

Riley Bartlett   Grade: 02
My mom is rare like the rarest of diamonds. My mom deserves that diamond because she's the star and sparkle of the diamonds.

Mason Corkett   Grade: 02
A diamond shines like my mom's heart. She will love you no matter what. She will never give up on you.

Annabel Hwang   **Grade: 02**
My mom is the diamond in our family. Strong and hard outside. Shining and brightening us whenever we are sad. A diamond for my diamond.

Taylor Jackson   Grade: 02
Diamonds sine and are rare like my wonderful mother. That's why my mom deserves the most rarest shiniest diamond in the entire world.

Seth Knorr   Grade: 02
A diamond may twinkle but my mom glows. My mom deserves a diamond because she is one herself.

Isabelle Krajewski   Grade: 02
Diamonds sparkle and shine just like my mom. My mom deserves a diamond because she's the rarest of the bunch.

Rachel Leou   Grade: 02
My mom is unique just like a diamond. I love the way she cheers me up when I'm sad. I want to brighten her day!

Tiffanie Lin   Grade: 02
A diamond shines brightly just like my mother. I feel that my mother deserves a diamond because she glows like that in her loving heart.

Ryan Rector   Grade: 02
Diamonds shimmer and shine just like my mom's heart. She deserves a diamond because she gives to everyone else and never to herself.

Donnie Schulte   Grade: 02
My mom has a gleaming heart of joy that's exactly like a diamond and that heart has lovable happiness and she deserves a legend able diamond.

Imperial Elementary
Anaheim

Teacher: Laurie Parke

Kelly Burns   Grade: 03
My mom is pretty, kind and thoughtful. She shines like the star in the moonlight. My mom is the best.

Tyler Coleman   Grade: 03
My mom is funny. My mom is nice. My mom's eyes shine brightly when the sun is out. I love my mom.

Chase Cromevoets   Grade: 03
My mom is so pretty and kind. She helps me with homework. She makes me food and helps me make good decisions.

Samantha English   Grade: 03
My mom deserves a reward because she's as sweet as candy. She shines like the stars. She looks like any angel. I love her always.

Jake Horton   Grade: 03
My mom is the best. I love her so much. She won't let me down. I can feel in my heart.

Quinlyn Howerth   Grade: 03
My mom is pretty and kind. She supports me. She helps me with my homework. She shines like the sun and the moon.

Juliana LaRosa   Grade: 03
My mom is as special as a rose. She helps me when I need help. My mom is a caring person. Her eyes glitter beautifully.

Philip Lee   Grade: 03
My mom is so pretty. She is really a nice mom. My mom is smart. My mom speaks so beautifully. People like her a lot.

Sara Leonard   Grade: 03
My mom takes me many places. She does many things for me. I like my mom a lot. My mom is the best.

Rylie Logan   Grade: 03
My mom is as sweet as chocolate. Her eyes sparkle and her heart is filled with love. That's why I love her.

Connor Mahaney   Grade: 03
My mom is so pretty. She is very sweet. She take care of me. I love her so much. Her eyes look like stars.

Lisa Namekawa   Grade: 03
My mom is pretty. She is always helpful and kind. She always tucks me into my bed and sleeps with me.

Phoebe Ngo   Grade: 03
My mom is so nice. She cooks me good food. She helps me with homework and projects. She is good with fashion.

Rebecca Steege   Grade: 03
My mom is very nice and kind. She will love me forever. She is like a special jewel. She is as gold as the stars.

Zach Zeman   Grade: 03
My mom shines like stars. I think she's very sweet. She is the best. She would pass any test. She loves me. I love her.

Independence Christian
Orange

Teacher: Corey Fisher

Alexander Aguirre   Grade: 06
When my mom walks into the room, it illuminates and everybody feels warm inside. She is loving and caring. I love my mom so much.

Alyssa Hanson   Grade: 06
When I am shy, my mom helps me shine. When I'm sad, my mom holds my hand. And when I cry, she holds me tight.

Tiffany Rose Lerfald   Grade: 06
I love my mom, she shimmers like a star. She loves music's song and she has a big heart.

Alexandra Olivarez   Grade: 06
My mommy cooks for me when I'm hungry. She takes good care of me when I'm sick. She is so thoughtful and caring.

Micaela Perez   Grade: 06
She is loving, kind, caring and always sharing. When I see her, I smile. She's always there for me, and I can tell her anything.

Kemy Purcell   Grade: 06
She is a star and shines with radiant beauty. Her voice is like a bird's, calm and soothing. Her eyes are lovely like sparkling emeralds.

Thomas Rafter   Grade: 06
My mom is glowing in joy and is a gem in the sea, like a delicate pearl, like a sapphire in the radiant Sahara Desert.

Alyssa Bloom   Grade: 07
My mom listens to my needs, and follows God's deeds. She is very kind and is completely mine.

David Fischer   Grade: 07
My mom is nice, amazing and has a twinkle in her eye, just like a diamond and the stars in the sky.

Paige Hines-Walker   Grade: 07
I love my mom. She is the bomb. She rocks, she rolls. She is totally in control. I love her and she loves me.

Kevin Hoskins   Grade: 07
My mom deserves a diamond because she has been nice to me even when I was not nice to her. She makes my bed.

Jack Huitt   Grade: 07
She is loving and kind. She has a bigger heart than anyone. She doesn't just love me; she loves others too.

Ashleigh Landry   Grade: 07
She is a great mom because she cares about me more than anyone and she's worth more than 10,000 diamonds to me.

Ismael Medina   Grade: 07
My mom is a blessing. She is so great, there are so many words for her; there are more than eight.

Mikena Parker   Grade: 07
She has a loving heart, full of joy, works hard, has a smile on when it's bad, and thinks of others instead of herself.

Priscilla Solares   Grade: 07
My mom has the illuminating shine in her eyes just like a diamond and she glows like one too.

Nicolas Urrea   Grade: 07
She organized two auctions for my school and asked for nothing in return. I can actually see God in her eyes when I'm with her.

Lizzy Grant   Grade: 08
She shines like a star that could be seen from near and far, a star that is so close to my heart.

Amanda Hicks   Grade: 08
She gave birth to cherish and love each moment in my life, to see me cry, to see me laugh, to see me love her.

Jacqueline Huff   Grade: 08
When I'm home by myself, I get scared. When the time for her to get home passes, I worry. When she's there, I'm calm.

Kayla Searcy   Grade: 08
From tiny ears with which she hears everything far and near. To her mouth, from which nothing bad spouts. She's the best through and throughout.

Kanani Soares   Grade: 08
From birth through growth, watching me learn. Teaching me rules for life with much concern and with many dreams for me, she does so yearn.

Teacher: Paula Gregg

April Albers   Grade: 04
Makes me happy when I'm sad. Comforts me when I'm mad. Always makes me glad.

* Amethyst winners in bold.

Dylan Capps   Grade: 04
My mom deserves a diamond because she is always nice to everyone including animals. She's also generous, joyful, and loyal. I'm happy she is my mom.

Cameron DeMarco   Grade: 04
My mom deserves a diamond because she's nice and takes me to amusement parks and forgives me when I do something wrong. I love her.

Ariana Gonzales   Grade: 04
My mom is the best mom in the world. She is always helpful. I love her so much. That's why she deserves a diamond.

John Hanson   Grade: 04
My mom takes care of me, cleans the house, helps with my homework, takes me places, and loves me. I'm glad she's my mom.

Ashley Isasi   **Grade: 04**
My mom is the sun in my day and my moon at night. She is my role model every day.

Justin Lightfoot   **Grade: 04**
She plays baseball, memorized all the DC comics, and she memorized all the Star Wars movies because she knew she was having a boy.

Jacob Monarres   **Grade: 04**
She has a heart made of gold. I am blessed by her words of mercy falling like diamonds from her mouth.

Laurel Morey   Grade: 04
When I'm sad, she makes me happy as can be. She always says, "I love you". She is the right mom for me.

Charles Obinma   Grade: 04
My mom deserves a diamond she is the most beautiful mom I ever had. I love you mom and thank you mom for loving me.

Brielle Schiermeyer   Grade: 04
My mom plays games with me; she makes it as easy as one, two, three!

Emily Storey   Grade: 04
My mom is a diamond. She treats me like a gem. She takes care of me very well. I will love her until the end.

Dylan Simon   Grade: 06
I treasure my mom. She is my prime. She is an angel; I am glad she is mine.

Teacher: Carol Lancaster

Abby Anastasi   Grade: 01
She got me a hamster and she loves me. She works hard. She works on getting us a house. We didn't find that many.

Grace Brisco   Grade: 01
She plays with me all the time. She lets me stay up late. She hugs me all the time.

Hailey Chaplin   **Grade: 01**
My mom is special because she is truthful and she is loving. She is the best mom I've ever seen because God made her.

Rylee Gordon   **Grade: 01**
She loves everybody. She loves to play. My mom is kind. She loves me no matter what she is the best mom in the world.

Finn Morey   **Grade: 01**
My mom deserves a diamond because she is really nice. She loves me a lot. She makes me hot chocolate when I ask her.

Nathan Perez   Grade: 01
My mom deserves a diamond because she is really nice to me. I love my mom so much.

Sophie Robertson   Grade: 01
When I don't feel well, she gives medicine and she tries to help me feel better. She gives me gifts.

Chelsea Robles   Grade: 01
My mom is special to me. In the summer, she takes me everywhere. That's why my mom is so special.

Jazzy Vosper   Grade: 01
My mommy is sweet and my mommy is kind and special to me.

Faith Woodrum   **Grade: 01**
She keeps me healthy. She reads Bible books to me. She is the nicest mom ever and I love her very much. She's the best.

Teacher: Jan McMasters

Jane Morin   Grade: 05
I think all moms are great, in that I will not debate. I also think my mom's the best, much better than all the rest.

Hannah Purcell   Grade: 05
My mom has many deeds like taking care of my needs. She holds me tight; she doesn't let me out of sight. Mom loves me.

Nicole Reigel   **Grade: 05**
My mom deserves a diamond because she cares for everyone. When she says no, I know it's because she wants what's best. I love her.

Aidan Scott   Grade: 05
Why my mom deserves diamonds? There are many reasons why. Mine's because she's loving to me, never gives up on me and is totally kind.

Teacher: Nick Morey B.

Gabe DuLong   **Grade: 02**
My mom deserves a diamond because she is nice as diamonds, she has eyes that sparkle brightly and it looks like heaven.

Wade Dutcher   Grade: 02
My mom deserves a diamond because she is sweet like a diamond, she is shiny like a diamond and she is wonderful like a diamond.

Jaclyn Evans   Grade: 02
My mom deserves a diamond because she loves Jesus and she also loves me very much.

Sierra Golden   Grade: 02
My mom deserves a diamond because she helps our country. She is a very good mom. I love her.

Noah Urrea   Grade: 02
My mom deserves a diamond because she loves me and she watches over me.

Anthony Bechelian   Grade: 03
My mom deserve a diamond because she tries her best to please me and she helps old people and she is so nice.

Jaylene Bronson   Grade: 03
I love when you spend time with me and I love you when you help me up when I'm down. I love you so much.

Meagan Fama   Grade: 03
Thank you for everything you do for me. You make me smile and very bright. I love you like a cat loves her kittens.

Sephina Frazer   Grade: 03
Mom, thank you so much for my pets and thank you for how much you love me. And I love you so very much.

Lillian Friedman   **Grade: 03**
My heart is full of love for my mom. She is my hero. I look up to her. I love you mom.

Joshua Galvan   Grade: 03
My mom likes to go hiking with me. She likes it when the whole family goes. I love her like a lion loves its cub.

Hana Giamrone Grade: 03
My mom is a great mom. She enjoys going shopping and helps me when I'm hurt or sick. She also helps around the house.

Lyndsie Howes Grade: 03
Thank you for all the wonderful things that you do for me everyday. I really appreciate that, Mommy. I love you very much.

Ian Rafter Grade: 03
I don't get my mom a lot of stuff. But she gets me stuff. That's why I want to get her a diamond.

Karl Vanderwatt Grade: 03
I'm glad I have my mom so I can make the right choices and be a Christian. I love my mom more than gold.

Irvine High
Irvine

Teacher: Julie Braun

Annie Chang Grade: 09
The first snows of winter slowly vanish beneath golden rays...Even beautiful spring blossoms do not last eternally. But one thing does: A mother's love.

Melissa Falz Grade: 09
She is a diamond - hard and sharp when needed, cool and smooth when she wants to be. But when you look inside, excruciating, euphoric beauty.

Nicole Kim Grade: 09
A diamond stays strong and endures like you. A diamond remains beautiful with age like you, but no diamond could ever compare to you.

Jerry Lee Grade: 09
Through my mom's unrelenting effort to nurture me, she's given me the best possible life I could wish for. She's irreplaceable and deserves a diamond.

Trisha Nguyen Grade: 09
My mom deserves a diamond because she has already given me thousands of diamonds. Her endless lectures will soon transform into priceless gemstones of knowledge.

Clinton O'Grady Grade: 09
You are there to understand. You are there to be my friend. You are there to love me and you are mine.

Stephanie Wang Grade: 09
When day ends and pretense falls. When mourners cry and traffic stalls. When children laugh and grow too tall. She will love me throughout all.

Erwin Wang Grade: 09
My loving mother, oh so sweet. She brought me love, up on my feet. And I love her, very dearly, which why I write these yearly.

Natalie Wei Grade: 09
My mother's constant love is strong and never steers me wrong. She ranks me highest in my mind. My mother's truly someone hard to find.

Teacher: Karen Harwood

Andrew Bain Grade: 11
She's my anchor, keeping me grounded and focused on what's important. She's my friend, talking me through my problems and worries. She's my mom.

Roni Bracha Grade: 11
You taught me something books never could - to live, laugh, grow, understand; understand that life is a road with swivels and turns, ups and downs.

Razleen Brar Grade: 11
Mama is a ruby radiating love, an emerald emitting compassion. Mama is my role model, selfless and successful. This sparkling woman deserves a sparkling diamond.

Sarah Chang Grade: 11
Mom is a lighthouse on the sea. She is an angel guarding me. Troubled, into her arms I flee and her love sets me free.

Vivi Chen Grade: 11
Every star in the night sky. Every hint of a smile on a soft face. Every radiant facet of a diamond. Belongs to my mother.

Alexandra DeLeon Grade: 11
Working late hours. Driving to school, to fencing, to friend's houses. Volunteering on weekends. Mending broken hearts. Teaching, loving, caring. My mother is my hero.

Helena Do Grade: 11
Showing me compassion and care, mom's words, melodies, flow through the air. Her faith in me is more than divine. Our love, forever will intertwine.

Rachel Kim Grade: 11
You stand your ground when the world turns away with outstretched arms you welcome me. Mom, you make life worth living everyday.

Vincent Lang Grade: 11
You gave my eyes first light, you helped me aim my sight. My soul will never get tired of loving you, my mother.

Kathy Le Grade: 11
Mom, you are a pillar of kindness and comfort for me to learn on. Your strength and knowledge guide me to the right path.

Brian Lee Grade: 11
Wakes up again, to go to work 7 p.m., makes us dinner, hears me complain. I pray nothing happens. I haven't yet said, I'm thankful.

Thu Luu Grade: 11
From Vietnam to America, leaving what you knew for an unknown world. For us, you strive. For you, we triumph

Sean Pan Grade: 11
Your goblet of love is full. I am fortunate to be swimming. Swimming in an endless pool of love you have given me.

Jenny Pham Grade: 11
On grave and solemn days, with your bright and cheerful ways. You give me hope. You show me bliss. You teach me love.

Adeline Tang Grade: 11
I was young and all alone. You held me and set me right. Though soon I'll be away from home. I'll remember your bright light.

Beverly Tieu Grade: 11
My mother is the moon. Her care glows with radiance. Her advice lights up a path that despairs darkness, she watches over her world, me.

Samantha Tran Grade: 11
She is the superhero in my dreams. The trampoline when I fall, the sun that lights my day. The compass to my success.

Chris Wang Grade: 11
Your soft hands blessed with affection. And the compassionate tenderness I've adored. Oh, my sweet grandmother. How I will love you. Forever and more.

Sarita Wanichpan Grade: 11
The umbrella for rainy days, the eraser for mistakes, the consequence for poor actions, the source of endless, unconditional love - my mother is my diamond.

Benjamin Weon Grade: 11
Love is not an emotion, but an ability, and I am amazed at how flawlessly she has mastered the ability to love me.

* Amethyst winners in bold.

The Four C's
by Michael C. Watson

Color

Although diamonds are found in nearly every color of the rainbow, a pure white diamond is one of the most prized and expensive. The absence of color is considered pure white. Most all diamonds have traces of yellow and brown and many famous diamonds are different colors (the Hope Diamond is blue.) The color scale designated by GIA starts at "D" for the whitest grade, then descends through the alphabet as the stone becomes more and more yellow.

When choosing a diamond, let your eyes tell you which color is the most appealing. If you feel an G color diamond is more or equally as beautiful as the E you are comparing it to at twice the price, don't be influenced to purchase the whiter gem just because the certificate sounds more impressive.

Clarity

Clarity refers to a diamonds lack of imperfections, or "inclusions." Although many diamonds have carbon crystals or feathers that may be viewed with the unaided eyes, very rare and expensive diamonds have few or no flaws. A diamond in which no flaws can be seen by an expert at 10X magnification is said to be "flawless." Most diamonds do not fall into this category, and it usually takes the expertise of a gemologist to help a consumer distinguish how one diamond has a higher clarity than another.

The scale used by reputable jewelers is the one designated by GIA. The highest clarity grade given to a diamond is "flawless," then descends down the scale depending on: how many inclusions the stone has, the nature of the inclusions, the color of the inclusions, and the position of the inclusions.

The scale adapted from the Gemological Institute of America is as follows:
FL- Flawless. Free from all inclusions or blemishes at 10x magnification.
IF - Internally Flawless. No inclusions visible at 10x; insignificant surface blemishes.
VVS (VVS1-2) - Very, Very Slightly included. Minute inclusions - Extremely difficult to very difficult to see at 10x.
VS (VS1-2) - Very Slightly included. Minor inclusions - Difficult to somewhat easy to see face-up at 10x.
SI (SI1-2) - Slightly Included. Noticeable inclusions - Easy to very easy to see at 10x. May be visible through the pavilion to unaided eye.
I (I1-I2-I3) - Imperfect . Obvious inclusions at 10x - Visible - easily visible - very visible to the unaided eye.

The presence of inclusions do not necessarily hinder the brilliance or beauty of a diamond. In fact, a flawless diamond that is held next to an SI1 clarity diamond of equal cut and color may be indiscernible to the naked eye, and can only be distinguished by a 10X loupe.

Inclusions are not necessarily bad, and are sometimes nature's way of telling us a diamond is genuine. Jewelers should point out notable or interesting inclusions to buyers, especially for identification purposes.

Although it is possible for a diamond to have the same carat weight or color as another diamond, it is the limitless combination of nature's inclusions that prevent any two diamonds from being exactly alike.

Carat Weight

The carat weight of a diamond is simply the weight, usually expressed in points. (100 points equal one carat). Weight is not in direct proportion to a diamond's size. For example, if you put three, one-carat diamonds side by side the diameters could be very different depending on the gem's cut. The term "carat" comes from the carob seed. In ancient times, gemstones were compared to the weight of this seed, which measured approximately what we express as *one-carat* today.

Even with today's technology, a rough diamond crystal loses about half its weight when fully cut. Because diamonds are exponentially rarer the larger they get, the value of a polished diamond twice the weight will be worth much more than twice as much.

Some people wonder if it is better to get a small, high quality diamond or a larger one that is not as perfect. There is no right or wrong answer, and it is largely a matter of personal preference. Since most all diamonds have some sort of inclusions, many women might prefer a larger diamond with a few small inclusions. Other women do not mind sacrificing the larger size for a more perfect gem.

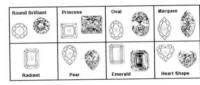

Cut

Of all the characteristics of diamond grading, cut is the most fascinating. Clarity and color are innate attributes of diamonds, given to them by the forces of nature. Cut, on the other hand, is the work and science of man. It is the expert proportioning of rough diamonds that brings them to sparkling life.

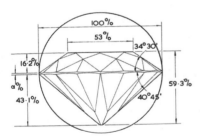

Cut refers to the shape, size and finish of the facets and their relative angles to one another. That is the main reason why no two diamonds are alike, for there are infinite possibilities of its final proportion.

A diamond may be referred to as ideal, fine cut, shallow, or deep. There are many diamonds that do not sparkle because they have been cut without beauty in mind. Even though nature may have given the stone an appealing clarity and color, the cutter may have sacrificed the ultimate beauty of the stone in order to salvage the largest carat weight possible.

Although not every jeweler volunteers this important information, one should always ask questions and also look at the stone to see if it handles light reflections well. In general, a diamond that has been cut too spread, or "shallow", might have good perimeter sparkle but look glassy on the interior. One that is too deep will look lifeless and display a dark spot in the center, sometimes known as a "nailhead."

My advice is let your eyes be the judge, for not all diamonds sparkle the same.

Jun-You Wu   Grade: 11
The wind storms, the rain pours. I feel I'm going to tear. At times a house and others an umbrella. My mom is always there.

Paulina Young   Grade: 11
My mom is a bounce house, graciously supportive, giving wide berth as I soar to new heights, and always there to catch me when I fall.

Jordan Elementary
Orange

Teacher: Sandy Lombardo

Ahtziri Callejas   Grade: 05
She sparkles and shines, just like the moon. Inside her heart there's sweetness and love. She's not perfect, but to me she is... My mother.

Jacqueline Carballo   Grade: 05
A whispered voice, a flawless face. My crystal heart for her gemstone eyes. Superhero mom with a golden heart. No words can describe my mom.

Esmeralda Castillo   Grade: 05
There are many words about my mom, but these are the most important. She is worth more than a diamond multiplied a zillion times.

Arizbeth Celestino   Grade: 05
She is my diamond. She is my love. She is my life, and she's my heart. No one can replace her, because she's my mom.

Hector Chavez   Grade: 05
She's the best mom. She buys me things I want. She's beautiful. I like when her eyes sparkle. She's the best mom I've ever had.

Noemi Chopin   Grade: 05
My mom is caring and loving, she sacrifices her time for us. My mom is not only my mom; she is my friend, my companion.

Sandra Cortes   Grade: 05
My mother deserves a diamond because she is beautiful, and she loves me, and always takes care of me. My mother is a beautiful angel.

Alejandro Cortez   Grade: 05
My mother smiles like an angel. Her face looks like it has been carved by beautiful angels. She is very nice, beautiful and a queen.

Amy Fernandez   Grade: 05
My mom deserves a diamond because whenever I need someone, she will lend me a hand. She loves me, and I will always love her.

Ana Fragoso   Grade: 05
My mother is like a meadow of beautiful flowers surrounding me. She shares my suffering and protects me.

Karla Garcia   Grade: 05
My mom shines for me like the sun everyday and the moon every night. I want to repay her with a diamond bright.

Gabriel Gomez   Grade: 05
She glows as a diamond. Her voice is like music beating on your heart. She is the one diamond. My mother.

Arturo Guevara   Grade: 05
She sparkles like diamonds when the sun shines on her. She's there whenever I need her, she smells like fresh roses. She's my beautiful mother.

Vanessa Gutierrez   Grade: 05
Mom is more than just my mom. She is an angel to me, and when I need help, she is always there for me.

Ahilin Hernandez   Grade: 05
My mom is a diamond shining so bright; she lightens my heart whenever she smiles, which makes me smile too.

Christopher Luong   Grade: 05
She always treats me with love and care and always has enough share. No one's as special as my mom. She means everything to me.

Luis Perez   Grade: 05
My mother is the shining light in my heart and also a sparkling diamond that shines like the sun.

Teacher: Scott Mitten

Jose Alvarez   Grade: 04
My mom would be happy if I brought her a diamond. Her smile would be as bright as a beautiful diamond.

Chris Avelar   Grade: 04
My mom is hardworking and is the best because she never gives up in her work. She is God's best creation in the world.

Mayra Barojas   Grade: 04
I feel that my mom needs to get a diamond because I want to see her cry with real diamond tears on her beautiful face.

Angel DeRosas   Grade: 04
Roses are red and diamonds are white. My mom is beautiful and that's alright. But a diamond for her is just out of sight.

Lizardro Hernandez   Grade: 04
My mother would cry with joy and her heart would beat. She will kiss and hug me every morning with her love.

Jasmine Martinez   Grade: 04
I hope my mom cries with joy because she is kind, takes care of me when I am sick, and she takes me everywhere.

Alexander Martinez   Grade: 04
My mom has done the best job taking care of me over these past years. I love my mom to death. Please pick my mom.

Johanna Ocampo   Grade: 04
My mom is the nicest. She pays attention to what ever I say. I love my mom so much.

Angelica Rodriguez   Grade: 04
Mother gave me birth and took care of me. If she was your mother you would love her. I love my mom. She's the best.

Matthew Sanchez   Grade: 04
I want her to cry with joy. I'd show her how much I love her with the diamond. She'll hug me with loving care.

Sabrina Subia   Grade: 04
My mom would be happy if she got a diamond. If she was your mom, you would get her a diamond too. Wouldn't you?

Mallandy Torres   Grade: 04
My mom needs a diamond because she never had one and I wonder how it will look in her hands that always cooked for me.

Kaiser (Heinz) Elementary
Costa Mesa

Teacher: Cynthia Blackwell

Jasmine Chau   Grade: 04
My mom deserves a diamond because she's always busy with everything. She's also lovely, caring, giving, and she's amazing.

Daniel DeBassio   Grade: 04
My mom deserves a diamond because she loves all people. She is kind, caring and very smart. She is a person to come to.

Haley Farnsworth   Grade: 04
My mom deserves a diamond because she loves me. My mom also thinks that I am wonderful. I want to do one thing for her.

Michael Jarboe   Grade: 04
My mom deserves a diamond because she is a great mom. Also, because she has been there for anyone in need and works very hard.

Jasmine Lomeli   Grade: 04
My mom deserves a diamond because she is a very sweet and loving mom. She also deserves a diamond because she is an amazing person.

Ingrid Marin   Grade: 04
Why my mother deserves a diamond is because she sacrifices a lot for me. So now it is time to give her what she deserves.

Ricardo Martinez   Grade: 04
My mom deserves a diamond because she is very kind. Another reason is because when she tells us something. It is because she cares.

Janie McDaniel   Grade: 04
My mom deserves a diamond because she gives me love, food, energy, and computer time. She also gives me clothes, shoes, pets and support.

Alexis Palacio   Grade: 04
My mom deserves a diamond because she loves me and gives me shelter. When I'm sad, she comforts me. That's why she deserves a diamond.

Julian Rodgers   Grade: 04
My mom deserves a diamond. She hardly has any jewels. She is nice and she doesn't yell.

Nicole Sanchez   Grade: 04
My mom deserves a diamond because she cares about people, helps people and because she loves kids and babies.

Alexandria Shen   Grade: 04
My mom deserves a diamond because she takes care of me. She gives me love and care. I love her. I couldn't live without her.

Summer Shorey   Grade: 04
My mom is a hardworking mother. She has a newborn baby that is now one year old and she is very tired. Please.

Teacher: Sherrilyn Dangl

Jennifer Balcazar   Grade: 03
My mom feeds me delicious food. My mom helps me with my homework. My mom cares for me a lot and she loves me too.

Max Chaffee   Grade: 03
My mom takes care of me and has nurtured me my whole life. She gives me stuff I need to survive. Thanks for reading.

Joshua Estes   Grade: 03
She protects and watches over me. My mom comforts me when I'm scared. She gave me my birth, feeds me, and cooks food for me.

Delaney Gendron   Grade: 03
She loves us and is nice. She cooks homemade food and helps me by driving me to school. She is wonderful and works hard.

Mike Hoffman   Grade: 03
She cooks my food. She takes me places and get me surprises for my birthday and in the summer time.

Daniel Knapp   Grade: 03
My mom helps me with my homework. She works very hard and cooks good food for me. The last thing she is very, very fun.

Ernesto Martinez   Grade: 03
She gives me food to grow big and strong. She also protects me from strangers. She buys me clothes to be warm and not cold.

Meagan Pistacchi   Grade: 03
My mom cooks yummy food and gives me confidence in doing my best with my homework. She lets me have sleep over with my friends.

Teacher: Shirley Kwan

Griffin Brockhoff   Grade: 03
My mom deserves a diamond because she helps out in class, she's in the PTA. She does our hair in the morning; that's why.

Oderico Buran   Grade: 03
My mom deserves a diamond because she cares about me and knows the true meaning of love. She is a very loving mom.

Mina Kirchhoff   Grade: 03
I think my mom deserves a diamond because she makes necklaces and bracelets and always takes good care of them.

Claire Leiby   Grade: 03
I think my mom deserves a diamond. She always helps me. She is having a baby and I want to do something nice for her.

Kobe Richardson   Grade: 03
My mom deserves a diamond because she lets her three kids do a lot in life. She is a hard worker. I hope you can help.

Trae Russell   Grade: 03
The reason why my mom should win this diamond is because she's a nice mom and she has always been a nice mom forever.

Amber Varela   Grade: 03
My mom deserves a diamond because she is the best thing in my life. She helps me with everything. I love my mom. I am excited.

Teacher: Jiffy MacMaster

Kaitlyn Alford   Grade: 04
My mom deserves a diamond because whenever she's around, my heart feels loved and if I won, that would warm her heart.

Siena Amoroso   Grade: 04
My mom deserves a diamond. She gives me love and support. When the sun beats down, she shimmers in the light. I lover her dearly.

Orion Carter   Grade: 04
I think my mother deserves a diamond because my mother is kind as a kitten, as sweet as sugar and as loving as a puppy.

Isabel Jeremias   Grade: 04
My mom is the best in every way. When I'm feeling blue, she makes my day. I love her and she loves me.

Abigail Judge   Grade: 04
My mom deserves a diamond because she is kind, loving and caring to everyone. I can always count on her. She rocks.

McKenzie Lambert   Grade: 04
My mom deserves a diamond because she is a good mom and never gives up on her family.

Brock Marz   Grade: 04
The reason my mom deserves a diamond is she works non-stop and always listens no matter what.

Cassandra Mounsey   Grade: 04
I think my mom deserves a diamond because she makes me feel special inside of me and she has a very beautiful face.

Kathryn Peters   Grade: 04
My mom deserves a diamond because she works very hard educating young preschoolers and always puts us before herself. She hardly ever gets a treat.

Briana Rabaga   Grade: 04
I think my mom deserves a diamond because she is always there for me when I need her. She also makes me be strong.

* Amethyst winners in bold.

Wulfi Seraphin — Grade: 04
My mom deserves a diamond because she helps me with my homework and kisses me and hugs me and comforts me when I feel bad.

Alex Stamy — **Grade: 04**
My mom's eyes sparkle like a diamond and wherever she goes foot prints of gold follow. She warms my heart whenever she's around.

Paul Steiner — Grade: 04
My mom deserves a diamond because she warms my heart when it's cold and does the best for me and others.

Teacher: Liz Slezak

Jordan Blosser — Grade: 05
A mom is mindful, sympathetic and attentive. She's encouraging, helpful, positive, thought of as a treasure gem and valuable. Thankfully, that's my mom.

Helena Davis — Grade: 05
Mother, cooks every meal. When she leaves, I know she's thinking about me. She sparkles like a star in the sky. She is my star.

Adam Freeman — Grade: 05
My mother shines like a diamond in our house. Like a diamond, she is loveable, valuable, and a treasure. She is an elegant special gift.

Danek Guerin — **Grade: 05**
Born poor girl, picking rise on a province. Becoming a mother, knowing possibilities ever since. She's still staying strong, with father not along.

Jesse Marquez — Grade: 05
My mom has loved me with her whole heart. She's the best mother you can have. She's loving, caring, comforting, unselfcentered, kind and funny.

Mariah McEntyre — Grade: 05
Mother's eyes care like the sparkling sea. Her hair is as soft as a bunny rabbit's fur. Her voice is like the rain forest.

Isel Romero — **Grade: 05**
My mom beautiful, magnificent, loving, caring, the one that brought me to earth. My mom is wonderful and what have I done in reward?

Adrian Santistevan — **Grade: 05**
With lovely starlight eyes, a warm ruby heart. The heavenly moonlight sparkles on her. She is an angel and the greatest mother of all time.

Josiah Sotomayor — Grade: 05
My mom is caring, loving, kind, highly educated, awesome and cool, athletic, thoughtful, has a sense of humor. And best of all, she loves me.

Kailynn Thomas — **Grade: 05**
My mother is tough like diamonds and pretty like twinkles in her eyes. Diamonds and her are like twins in the blue sky.

Natalia Tortorello — Grade: 05
Sparkling, glimmering, elegant, expensive like a diamond. She's one of a kind. Friendly, loving, helpful and beautiful. A mom like this is hard to find.

Katelin Turner — Grade: 05
My mother is flawless and she is practically like a diamond. She works so hard to keep me happy and healthy. She is so awesome.

Cole Whitacre — Grade: 05
She is a kind, passionate, selfless angel. I want her to possess something beautiful like a diamond as I do her.

Kennedy (John F.) High
La Palma

Teacher: Lisa Holley B.

Mark Gaa — Grade: 09
Mom is the sweetest of all; she's the type of mom that will never fall. She has unconditional love, one as graceful as a dove.

Ramses Ochoa — Grade: 09
My mom always protected and tried to get our necessities, even though we didn't have the money for it. My siblings and I love her.

Sangeeta Songu — **Grade: 09**
She takes night jobs no one wants, so she can be there for us. She never complains, just makes sacrifices for us with a smile.

Killybrooke Elementary
Costa Mesa

Teacher: Michelle Arbuzow

Sofia Rice — **Grade: 02**
My mom deserves a diamond because she is loveable, nice and sweet. She takes care of my family; in fact, she is amazing.

Teacher: Debbra Demarco

Destiny O' Neal — Grade: 02
My mom deserves a diamond because she works very hard. After she gets off of work she goes to school so she can give us nice clothes..

Felicia Crenshaw — Grade: 03
I love you mom, you are the best. Even though you like tea and I like sports, you will always be in my heart.

Clara Gallegos — **Grade: 03**
Nice, helpful, all-knowing. Whether we are good or bad, we are still beautiful to her. I love you mommy!

Alexia Gonzalez — Grade: 03
I love my mom. She's nice and sometimes very funny. She always helps me when I'm stuck. Her eyes are like the moon at night.

Jacob Jones — **Grade: 03**
Pretty angel she is. Her eyes glow like the moon. Looking in her eyes is like the best dream ever.

Christina Laty — Grade: 03
Mothers' eyes show the look of love. Her smile the warmth of caring. As I cuddle in her arms I wish her a big diamond.

Ashley Morales — **Grade: 03**
Angelic, glowing like the sun. She is the only one. Caring, giving, loving.

Nick Worth — Grade: 03
Her eyes are as light as the moon. She is nice to me and other people every day. She is like an angel to me.

Teacher: Polly Demkiw

Litzy Alverez — Grade: 03
My mom is always there for me. She is kind , helpful, nice, fun and loving. She is thankful.

Kyle Bado — Grade: 03
I love my mom because she is sweet. She is kind to others. She is thankful for her job and her home.

Sophie Beazley — **Grade: 03**
My mom is so special. She is always gentle. When she looks at pictures of me she becomes sentimental. I love her!

Sierra Dixon — Grade: 03
My mom deserves a diamond because she is respected, selfless, and caring. She is also happy, loving, helpful and sweet. My mom is joyous.

Jessica Gonzalez — Grade: 03
My mom is a caring and funny person. I love her because she is nice and loving. When I come home she has a smile.

Michelle Pham — Grade: 03
My mom is beautiful an bright. She tucks me in at night. She is so kind. I don't mind. She is so caring. She loves sharing.

Ian Robbs — Grade: 03
My mom is always there for me. She is kind and is the sweetest person ever. I love my mom and she loves me back.

Citlally Rodriguez — Grade: 03
My mom is the prettiest, sweetest, most caring and special person in the whole wide world. She is so kind and happy every day.

Walter Rodriguez — Grade: 03
My mom is amazing when helping me with my reading comprehension. I pray for her to keep herself safe. She is amazing at cooking dinner.

Teacher: Dianne Elizondo

Sean Bond — Grade: 04
My mom deserves a diamond ring because she glows like the sun. she is kind-hearted, sweet, intelligent and as beautiful as a diamond.

Luis Contreras — Grade: 04
Mom, you have more value than a diamond. You don't compare to all the money in the world. I cant imagine life without you.

Mario Henriquez — Grade: 04
My mom deserves a diamond because she protects me. Her eyes are like diamonds. She guides me out of trouble. I love my mom.

Kintak Keju — Grade: 04
My mom deserves a diamond because she teaches me right from wrong. She is my charm and the best charm in the world.

Lauren Kiefer — Grade: 04
My mom helps me when I'm sad. When I make her laugh she has a bright smile like a diamond. I love my mom!

Karlee Kisher — Grade: 04
She takes care of me. She's been there every second. I love her. She loves me. She's beautiful inside and out. We are together forever.

Brandon Luna — Grade: 04
My mom deserves a diamond because she has a heart of gold. I will never trade her for anything. She takes care of me.

Bronwyn Mazzarella — Grade: 04
My mom deserves a diamond because her smile warms my heart, and all through the day she'll embrace me and care for me.

Rodney Munoz — Grade: 04
My mom deserves a diamond because her eyes sparkle like the stars. She makes my family happy and she is special to me.

Valery Quiroz — Grade: 04
Mom, you're the sparkle in my eye. You make me shine every day. There will always be a special place for you in my heart.

Holly Reiland — Grade: 04
My mom deserves a diamond because she is as sweet as sugar and her eyes sparkle in the sun. Her hugs are warm as summer.

Braulio Rodriguez — Grade: 04
My mom deserves a diamond because when I look in her eyes they sparkle like diamonds. When I hug her I feel oh so safe.

Vanessa Valdivia — Grade: 04
My mom deserves a diamond because she has a heart of gold. I wouldn't trade you for anything. Mom, you are all I ever wanted.

Jessica Vasquez — Grade: 04
Your eyes shine like stars in the sky. Your warm heart warms mine. You have a heart like a jewel. I love you mom!

Teacher: Angela Ivey

Sarah Bordelon — Grade: 04
My mom is brighter than the sun and more protective than a mama bear. She's a giant diamond and needs a baby diamond. She's awesome.

David Ceballos — Grade: 04
Because she's nice, kind, and has beautiful eyes like the sea. She smells like a rose and is as pretty as a diamond.

Ileana Hernandez — Grade: 04
My mom's heart is as big as the ocean and her kindness is as enormous as the sky. My mom's love will never end.

Paola Hernandez — Grade: 04
I love my mom because she is sweeter than sugar and her eyes sparkle as bright as the sun. Her love is deeper than anything.

Cindy Jimenez — Grade: 04
My mom is valuable to me. She's sweet like an apple and like a flower that never dies. She's the stars in the high sky.

Elias Laty — Grade: 04
My mom deserves a diamond because she is always there to help me. She is as sweet as sugar and she loves me very much.

Analisa Maddox — Grade: 04
My mom glitters in the moonlight, her love is as deep as the sea. My mom is the best mom in the whole wide world.

James Miramadi — Grade: 04
My mom is like a diamond, she makes everybody happy. She loves me more than anything, she comforts me when I'm mad and sad.

Alexis Parks — Grade: 04
Some of my days are cloudy, some are rather droopy but I'm brightened up by the pearl white smile of my mother.

Kenny Remmel — Grade: 04
My mom is too sweet. My mom deserves something good. I would give her a diamond if I could.

Mahena Seal — Grade: 04
My mom is so special in everything she does. When she smiles she makes me smile and feel happy. When she laughs I laugh too.

Alexandra Villapando — Grade: 04
She tucks me in at night and tells me everything is going to be all right. She is priceless and is extraordinary. That's mom!

Willie Worth — Grade: 04
My mom deserves a diamond because she is so sweet. Lawful like God but gentle like angels. I love my mom ,yes I do.

Esperanza Zambrano — Grade: 04
My mom deserves a diamond because she is nice and helpful at home. Her eyes shine and sparkle. She is also lovely and sweet every day.

Teacher: Kristen Karlin

Princess Castellano — Grade: 03
She's the one who's there for me. Funny, smart and very loving. There will never be another. That one person is my mother.

Andrea Cordero — Grade: 03
My mom deserves a diamond. She is the best mom because she told us to try to touch the stars and she's helpful to me.

* Amethyst winners in bold.

Lance Faeldan   Grade: 03
My mom deserves a diamond because she is the light of our family but most of all she is the greatest in the whole world.

Tatiana Jimenez   Grade: 03
My mom deserves a diamond because she puts me and my siblings before anything. She works hard to give me the best that she can.

Catherine McTague   Grade: 03
My mom is sweet, my mom is fine. I want to give her the diamond for all her time.

Valerie Sanchez   Grade: 03
My mom is very special to me. My mom is more than a mom, she is a diamond. I love her the way she is.

Teacher: Giao-Ahn Le

Dylan Clovenger   Grade: 05
Today I wake up, and see her smiling face, as shiny as stars all throughout space.

Diana DeLaCruz-Garcia   Grade: 05
Mom is as valuable as diamonds. Mom is here, hope and happiness is there too. I admire my mom because her heart is a treasure.

Gabriel Godinez   Grade: 05
Like an angel from above, she descended from heaven to give me love. She's as bright as the suns light. She's the fun loving mom.

Katherine Lawrence   Grade: 05
She is like an emerald, her smile is like a gem. A path to heaven and love, she is the key to the impossible.

Summer Lawson   Grade: 05
Mom, the dark hole that is my life has only one ray of hope. The chance to see you smile once more.

Jesse Lopez   Grade: 05
In the darkness I see monsters up ahead. Then a beautiful woman appears in the mist. I realize it is my lovely mother protecting me.

Anani Loredo   Grade: 05
As I run, I feel like someone is following me. Danger. Suddenly a beautiful angel, my mom, holds me tight. I'm safe.

Sophia Maddox   Grade: 05
Gloom fills the air, clouds fill the sky. But with your love I can fly. Turn the world upside-down, everything's joyous when you're around.

Roshni Maharaj   Grade: 05
Mom, your eyes shine like your beautiful heart. I seek upon a lovely star, but that star is you. That is why I love you.

Mark Mathenge   Grade: 05
Her eyes are a ray of light during the dark times. Her smile is the path to greatness. My diamond deserves a diamond.

Estefania Mendoza   Grade: 05
Mom, your eyes are as shiny as a precious diamond in the sky. Your love is precious to me, that is why I love you.

David Moya   Grade: 05
As my mother runs her finger through my hair, it flows like a river with love and care. I love my mother.

Catherine Pimentel   Grade: 05
The light to my future, my role model, my leader to everything. She encourages me to try my best. No one can replace her, Mom!

Stephanie Rojas   Grade: 05
When all is lost, my mom is there to bring me love and care. In the dark my mom shines bright, she is my light!

Daniel Salazar   Grade: 05
Mom, your eyes are beautiful as the night sky. You're more valuable than a diamond. This is why you are everything I need.

Ivan Shikhelman   Grade: 05
Her eyes glisten in the light, as I watch her sing a sweet melody like a beautiful bird.

Mason Tufuga   Grade: 05
My shell when I was peanut, the mother bear for a cub. I love her with all my heart, to see the reaction of love.

Teacher: Janet Sugiyama

Cheyenne Davis   Grade: 05
To give me time to relax, she cares for my little brother, feeding him, cleaning him, changing his diapers and never having time for herself.

Jasmine Pineda   Grade: 05
My mother is as graceful as a flower in the meadow. She smells like a gorgeous sweet rose. She's as beautiful as a lovely butterfly.

Fernando Salgado   Grade: 05
My mom gives me happiness more than any other mom. She is like a flower that will grow forever like a beautiful red rose.

Bernice Tadique   Grade: 05
She's a good role model, I see, I know she loves me. When I'm a mother some day I want to be her in every way.

Jake Winters   Grade: 05
My mother is awesome, She is my alarm clock in the morning. She brings me breakfast in bed when I'm sick. She'll love me every day.

Estefany Amado   Grade: 06
Day and night, a mothers love is never tiring. Her love never rests, her soul never stops caring, her energy inspires everyone around her.

Gabriel Arroyo   Grade: 06
You've lectured and talked and given advice. You've worried and watched and tried to be nice. You've listened and cared and you've understood. You rock!

Regina Cordero   Grade: 06
My mom is caring and sweet. She always supports us even if we're sad. She always encourages us to reach for the stars.

Mayra Gonzalez   Grade: 06
She's very special like no other. She always encourages me. She helps me with my problems. I know I can always turn to her.

Michelle Magallanes   Grade: 06
My moms eyes are sparkling gold like a star. I love m mom dearly. She gives me love and support. That is a real mom.

Max Nguyen   Grade: 06
My mom is a beautiful and gentle woman. She is kind and nice to everybody. She works hard for my family. She deserves the best.

Genisis Pineda   Grade: 06
The love for my mom is endless. Her eyes shine like stars. Her heart is like gold and my passion for her will never end.

Marcela Ramirez   Grade: 06
Oh mother how I love you, you are so sweet and kind. You are my special woman. You're my whole entire life.

Dyanara Ramirez   Grade: 06
graceful as the white feathered swan, glistens like a midnight star. Calm as the ocean blue, beats the beauty of a rose with dew.

Jennifer Rodriguez   Grade: 06
A precious angel and hero. A brilliant shiny, colorful, perfect dazzling star. Sparkles with love and happiness. She is my mom I love her.

Daniel Salgado   Grade: 06
My mom is beautiful. Her eyes sparkle like the moon when it shines down on the water. Her heart is filled with love and joy.

Elijah Sanchez   Grade: 06
My mom is awesome! She supports two thankful kids on her own she shows determination in my school projects and sports. She rocks!

cristian Soriano   Grade: 06
My mom deserves this more than any other mom. She enlightens the house with joy when she comes from work. She is a beautiful goddess

Teacher: Phyllis Vliss

Cyrene Cledera   Grade: 06
Mom, beauty is your game, but to me you are always beautiful. Love is your strength and compassion is your power. I love you mom!

Abagail Escalante   Grade: 06
My mom deserves a diamond because her inner beauty sparkles like s star under the moonlight.

Valery Gama   Grade: 06
After years of taking my mother for granted, I wanted to let you know how beautiful you are and how grateful I am to have you.

Jens Guevara   Grade: 06
My mom's sweeter than cake, willing to help others, and full of heart and joy. She's beautiful as a rose and shines like a sparkling diamond.

Rachel Keane   Grade: 06
Her eyes shine like the moon, her heart glitters like the stars. She is bright like the sun. My mom glows like the night sky.

Mark Makram   Grade: 06
My mom is so pretty, loving and caring. She knows how I feel and we are really connected, just like one person.

Yanci Martinez   Grade: 06
My mothers voice sounds like a sweet soothing violin when she speaks to me. Her eyes look like sparkling blue diamonds in the morning horizon.

Shannan McCormick   Grade: 06
Her eyes glitter in the sunlight like diamonds just polished. My heart pounds when I see her. She is the heart that makes me complete.

Matthew Mildamati   Grade: 06
My mom is incredible, can you not see? She will do completely anything for me. She's beautiful and smart but it's not hard to see.

Neil Zagada   Grade: 06
Diamonds, rubies, pearls and jewels all seem the same. Unlike my mother who is unique, like her ways.

Ladera Vista Junior High
Fullerton

Teacher: Carlos Donnelly

Adrian Aguero   Grade: 07
The light that shines through the darkest of days, brighter than any diamond or jewel, and an endless love, my mom.

Gavyn Alexander   Grade: 07
Bright brown eyes so shiny and sweet. A loving heart that glows like the afternoon sun. The compassion of an angel loving me so much.

Taylor Barnes   Grade: 07
A gentle spark in her eye, always without a guy, raising me for all my years, never any sad tears. A person I call mom.

Anthony Barone   Grade: 07
Every minute of everyday, I feel my mom's love go through my soul, like an everlasting river. Her eyes sparkle like so many stars.

Adena Bentley   Grade: 07
My mom is always shining. A heart as bright as gold. A smile warm as the Earth. Guarding my life for me.

Elizabeth Chen   Grade: 07
She works so hard to provide for me. She sacrifices everything and goes through so much trouble. She is my role model. My hero.

Sarahi Contreras   Grade: 07
Good natured as can be. Very friendly, hardworking and thoughtful is she. My mom is my companion. She is truly a beautiful angel sent to me.

Rachael Diaz   Grade: 07
She's unique in many ways. She gives off a radiant glow. She shines brighter than the sun and stars. I'm grateful to have my mom.

Eric Flores   Grade: 07
If you take a heart of an angel, the body of a beautiful girl and the bag of kindness, you will get my mom.

Jesse Flores   Grade: 07
Like a shining diamond on a ring. She's the priceless diamond in my life. So loving, so sweet, I wouldn't trade her for anything.

Tiffany Fowler   Grade: 07
Like a Band-Aid, mommy heals my boo-boos with her heart. Whenever I need one, she gives me a hug.

Caroline Gallagher   Grade: 07
Thank you so much for just living life, for battling sadness and all of the strife for that I am grateful for that you shine.

Jacob Golumbic   Grade: 07
Her teeth sparkle like a diamond; her soft, warm voice comforts me when I'm down. My mom, a precious jewel herself is worth millions.

David Gonzalez   Grade: 07
She takes my heart until the end. Her eyes twinkle when the sun hits her glamorous face. She's the most lovely lady in my life.

Hannah Green   Grade: 07
She sparkles like a diamond in the drop of moonlight, the flawless light shines within her soul, my love can never be exclaimed to her.

Emma Guzman   Grade: 07
Without my mom, there would be no me. She gave me a gift, the gift of life.

Brendan Hanson   Grade: 07
My mom has eyes that shine like a star. She calms my storm and helps me through the day. She is my life.

Jessica Harrica   Grade: 07
Though you are in a wheel chair, you still have lots of care. I know you'd giant the world for me. I'll love you for eternity.

Isaiah Hernandez   Grade: 07
One reason mother is a sparkling rock. She is the sparkle in my eyes. Mother is my life. Mother is my shining, beautiful, precious diamond.

James Hubbard   Grade: 07
So sweet and gentle, just like a flower. Her love is anything but sour. From east to west, she is by far the very best.

Kristin Kepley   Grade: 07
There are so many ways to describe my mother, she's sweet and more caring than any other.

Theodore King   Grade: 07
She is a burning flame that guides me home from a cold winter night. Her heart glows like a full moon in a dark night.

* Amethyst winners in bold.

Alexandra Kraus   Grade: 07
In the night, she cools my anger. At dawn, she warms my sorrow. She caresses my falling tears away, and hugs me until the morrow.

Josh Krieger   Grade: 07
Like a slice of the sun guiding me through the dark or a bite of heaven healing my wounds with only my love in return.

Allison Kubo   Grade: 07
She's the mother tree of my forest, standing tall and proud; casting her branches out, overlooking faults, and loving me with a diamond heart.

Elizabeth Lowe   Grade: 07
Gazing at me lovingly, her eyes shining like stars, always leading me through a dark path, my heart, my shelter, my mom.

Megan Maple   Grade: 07
A little bit of laughter, a lot of love, she is the one to drown my heart with happiness and fill the sky with sunshine.

Alejandra Medina   Grade: 07
We've been through a lot, she's seen it all. My mom is my best friend, sister, and someone I can talk to. I love you mom.

Kenneth Moralez   Grade: 07
Your heart is sweet and mellow like a clear deep blue sea which glimmers in the sun and shines bright in the night.

Mikalynn Morita   Grade: 07
You brighten my way from despair, the light and warmth shows that you care. You are my life; you are my sky.

Matty Nakahiro   Grade: 07
When eyes are flooded or face is red, her kind gentle touch and soft sweet words imprison the outraging emotion and mop up the tears.

Jonathan Nunez   Grade: 07
Mom's have no price. She is irreplaceable. Nothing can compare; she is more valuable than the world's biggest diamond.

Julian Pastor   Grade: 07
Embraces my feelings with thoughts that are unimaginable. She's pieces in my heart that balance me. A diamond shining like glitter glimpsing at an angel.

Emily Paulsen   Grade: 07
Your heart blooms with love. Your soul dances with the kindness you share. Mom, you open my eyes and take my hand in your hand.

Tyler Place   Grade: 07
In the night like the moonlight she shines upon me she is my protector and guidance and she is my life and love.

Destiney Ramirez   Grade: 07
She never has a frown, I know she'll never let me down. She wipes away my tears, she helps me get through my fears.

Shelby Rogers   Grade: 07
Mommy, the center of my heart, the ground beneath my feet, my world even when it's upside down. I love you like no other.

Miranda Scales   Grade: 07
Her voice like sweet music, cascades throughout the night. Her eyes are never ending crystals that keep me safe from fright.

Evan Sonny   Grade: 07
A touch of happiness, a pinch of honor, a lot of loving compassion. Mix that all together and see what comes out, my mom together forever.

Matthew Sorensen   Grade: 07
Her heart is full of gold. Her eyes are like the nighttime sky. Her smile is bright like the sun. Glad that I'm her son.

Madison Stover   Grade: 07
A winter day; a summer day comes the seasons change as we change together. We are never far apart. Our hearts are like one.

John Styffe   Grade: 07
All the love you need; a dash of logic, two pinches of smarts, all the hugs and kisses you desire and you have my mom.

David Tsuda   Grade: 07
When a wave of sorrow comes over me. When I'm down in shame. I see a ray of sunshine between the clouds. It's my mom.

Athena Wingate   Grade: 07
Shining in the night, my mom is like a star as perfect as can be, always watching me, teaching me what there is to know.

Nathan Zamora   Grade: 07
Her candy smile like a twinkle upon a star, she bore me with pride, she reared me with love. She will embrace me for eternity.

Teacher: Lynda Hodges

Kasuni Bodinayake   Grade: 07
My mother is a selfless, hardworking person. She is always tired from working to support us. She deserves more than a diamond, she deserves the world.

Matthieu Bouchard   Grade: 07
My mom is the most wonderful person on earth. She is creative, loving and caring. She is worth more than any diamond in the world.

Kimber Carter   Grade: 07
My mom deserves a diamond because she is magnificent in so many ways. One reason is she cares and loves me each and every day.

Michaela Chapman   Grade: 07
My mom shines like the ocean blue. Every day she glistens like new; her eyes sparkle like the stars so bright. She gleams like morning light.

Adina Corke   Grade: 07
A diamond for mom. My mom is like a diamond. Shiny, unique…priceless.

Jordan Davis   Grade: 07
My mom is like a diamond, she dazzles, twinkles, and cares like no other and most importantly, she is always there for me.

Tyler Davis   Grade: 07
My mom deserves a diamond because she's never selfish. My mom cares about other people more than herself. I think she deserves something of recognition.

Susan Day   Grade: 07
My mom is amazing. Even though she is a mother of five. A grandmother of four. She still has room in her heart for more.

Shannon Grossman   Grade: 07
Sagacious, compassionate, disciplinary, and strong. Mom, because of these characteristics of yours, I am confident you will do me no wrong.

Natalie Hoover   Grade: 07
She is sweet, smart, gorgeous and funny. When I have a sore throat, she gives me tea with honey. My mother loves her daughter.

Ashlyn Hulin   Grade: 07
I still don't know the half of how my mom does things. I pray every starry night for her to receive something great. I'm faithful.

Alex Kemp   Grade: 07
The sparkling, heart-warming diamond is identical to my beautiful, caring mother. A picture is worth a thousand words, but my mother is worth a billion.

John Pierre Khoury   Grade: 07
My mom is nice, fun and helpful. She always helps me when I'm sick and takes us to our soccer games on Saturdays.

Leah Kim   Grade: 07
My mom is amazing. She helps me through my ups and downs. She is the most important woman in my life.

Susanna Kwon   Grade: 07
My mom cheers me up when I'm down, does everything she can to show her love and no words can describe the care she provides.

Ayla Laurencio   Grade: 07
My mom is my best friend. She is a single mom, hardworking, honest, and most important loving. Being on her own, she's an amazing mother.

Andrew Liou   Grade: 07
My mom is charming as a rose and has a heart of gold. She's optimistic through times of less. My mom is a true hero.

Angela Liou   Grade: 07
Supermom. Taking on challenges with optimism. Golden words treasured forever from you to me. My mom loves me endlessly, the idol shining in my heart.

Kenzo Mann   Grade: 07
My mom deserves more than a diamond. She is loving, caring, kind, helpful, smart, funny. In fact, my mom is the diamond of our family.

Julia Monson   Grade: 07
My mom has many characteristics of a diamond, just like a diamond she shines like no other. She is unique and is the most beautiful.

Grant Murthi   Grade: 07
Mom always makes me happy. She gives me hugs when sad or scared. She makes me feel secure and safe. My mom loves me.

Veronica Navarro   Grade: 07
My mother is beautiful, her smile lights up my day. She's all a daughter could ever ask for. I am lucky to have her.

Erin Olsen   Grade: 07
I will say that mom is perfect to me. She isn't rich and doesn't spoil me. I guess that's what I love - she cares.

Jason Ortiz   Grade: 07
My mom loves me forever. My mom is as tough as nails. My mom glistens through the dark. My mom is a diamond.

Brenna Schaffell   Grade: 07
When I'm down, she'll make meg glad, looking out for me. Shining minds, brightening souls, my mom is always there.

Robert Shin   Grade: 07
My mother is a hardworking, charismatic, and loving person. She wipes my tears when I cry. Encourages me when I struggle. She's the greatest mom.

Layla Silva   Grade: 07
A beautiful, loyal, heartwarming person is my mom. She brings happiness to the family and everyone loves her.

Scott Stedman   Grade: 07
My mom is the most optimistic person you will ever meet. She goes above and beyond what she should do and never says a peep.

Malcolm Sun   Grade: 07
My mom, amazing. Awesome, charming, cheerful, elegant, enthusiastic, fantastic, heroic, graceful, jolly, and stylish. Boy, am I lucky to have my magnificent mom.

Erica Trujillo   Grade: 07
My mom deserves so much, that God gave her me my mom, stood by me in pain and happiness and we are still standing strong.

Emily Williams   Grade: 07
Sue, my mom is a delightful person. She's a homemaker and loves what she does. Her mind knows that she's wonderful and everyone else does too.

Andy Yu   Grade: 07
Her love is an angel, giving, feeling so secure. Her voice sings sweetly, promising to assure, as mom's heart is a diamond, eternal and pure.

Teacher: John Mac Murray

Dennys Aguilar   Grade: 07
I know someone that's hardworking. I'm her loving son. She's loving and caring. She's my best friend, and I'll love her to the end.

Dalia Alvarado   Grade: 07
My mom is a beautiful lady, she could make a diamond shine with her soft hands as if she were an angel.

Dakota Amman   Grade: 07
She helps people all the time. She helps my neighbor when he couldn't drive. She helped me when I stepped on glass. She's a diamond.

Alaina Aparicio   Grade: 07
My mom is a beautiful and intelligent woman. She cares for me and loves me. Even though she doesn't get a lot. She has me.

Marisa Aragon   Grade: 07
I love my mom, and she gives me that love in return. Whenever I'm around her, I feel safe. She is very precious to me.

Esther Armenta   Grade: 07
When I feel sad or bad, she makes me feel much better and she is the best mother ever. And I love her.

Ashleigh Barnes-Szabo   Grade: 07
The reason why my mom deserves a diamond is that she always does things for my sisters and me, but never anything for herself.

Joey Batrez   Grade: 07
My mom deserves a diamond because she is beautiful and trustworthy. She loves when I give her something. So please make her diamond special.

Belinda Bravo   Grade: 07
Her eyes are shiny. Her smile is bright. Her personality is sweet, but most of all her fragile heart is the real "diamond".

Gladys Carrillo   Grade: 07
My mom's always there when I need her no matter what happens. She sacrifices herself and goes beyond the limit to take care of us.

Gabriela Castorena   Grade: 07
My mom is like a diamond; beautiful, strong and powerful, but there is something else inside her, a tiny spark glowing both day and night.

Nicholas Coca   Grade: 07
It would be a perfect reminder each and everyday of how much I appreciate her great love and hard work.

Sky Conner   Grade: 07
My mom is the most intelligent, justifying, noble, and ravishing woman that I know of. She is the most kind-hearted, respectful, and awesome mentor.

Rebecca Creighton   Grade: 07
You shine like a jewel without a doubt. The love you give is beyond measure, sparkling inside and out. Mom, you're my greatest treasure.

Jaqueline Cruz   Grade: 07
The one and only best mom in the universe deserves a diamond for her kindness and loyalty. My mom is the best in the world.

Lauren Foster   Grade: 07
Mom,. I thank you for your care for warm hugs and being there. I hope when you think of me, a beautiful woman you'll see.

Izelle Guerrero   Grade: 07
My wonderful mother puts everyone before herself and helps when she can. If she gets this diamond, she will feel special, great and independent.

Egriselda Guillen   Grade: 07
It's our day, and what's seen? A beautiful smile that cares for me. Without you, I have no soul; I'm nothing but a hollow hole.

Kaity Hernandez   Grade: 07
Although my mom has five kids, she still can work the rest. But I want to give her something that is the very best.

Nicole Hostert   Grade: 07
My mom deserves a diamond because when my dad was on dialysis waiting for a kidney, she gave him one. My mom saved his life.

Nishat Islam   Grade: 07
There are numerous reasons why I think my mom should deserve a diamond. She cooks, cleans, and is very helpful. Plus I love her.

Dakota Kramer   Grade: 07
Why my mom deserves a diamond. My mom deserves a perfect diamond because she is the perfect mom. She is the most caring, trusting, mom ever.

Aldo Marichi   Grade: 07
My mom deserves a diamond because she's very sweet. She loves me so much, and she's friendly with everyone she meets.

James Michael   Grade: 07
Giving my mom a diamond is the least I can do after all of the wonderfully good things we have been through.

Brenda Miranda   Grade: 07
I can give you a million reasons why my mom deserves a diamond. Love, because of love, my mom loves me more than anything, seriously.

Sarah Muma   Grade: 07
My mom deserves a diamond. Why do you ask? Her cooking is out of this world. She has the best patience and the greatest love.

Angus Penderaross   Grade: 07
You don't know, so it's up to me to show, she cleans, she works, she love, she shows. That's why my mom deserves a diamond.

Kristina Rietveld   Grade: 07
I'm fortunate that I was born to someone like you; I love you not just as my mom, but for what you are and do.

Lynda Rodriguez   Grade: 07
When times are difficult, she follows through. Tries her hardest no matter what. Gives hope when there is none there. That's why we love her.

Brittany Routledge   Grade: 07
Mom's generous, loving, kind. Birds sing when she steps outside. She loves her family, her children, too. You deserve a diamond, mom, here's to you.

Kimberly Runyan   Grade: 07
Mom, you're my inspirational guide, no diamond can sparkle like you. You've always been there for me, this jewel was meant for you.

Sergio Sanchez   Grade: 07
My mom is the most loving and caring person in my life. She knows right from wrong, and this is why she deserves a diamond.

Dakota Smith   Grade: 07
My mom was a single mother for eleven years and has always given to people and I think she should get a diamond back.

Nicholas Vaillette   Grade: 07
My mom deserves a diamond because she is a kind, loving, and hardworking mother. She is also always there when I am hurting.

Angelica Valadez   Grade: 07
My mom has taken her five children in her arms. She makes our hearts warm with love. Independent, caring, dependable, special to me…my mom.

Hana Vaughan   Grade: 07
She loves me like no other. My role model who takes care of three kids without a father, the one I like to call my mother.

Joyden Weatners   Grade: 07
My mom is sweet, innocent, helpful and lots of things. I am extremely lucky to have a mom that likes me. My mom is cool.

Paola Yepez   Grade: 07
She loves and cares for our family. She is a hard worker and never gives up on anything. That's why I think she deserves a diamond.

Yuri Yu   Grade: 07
My mom is a reflection of a diamond. A diamond shines in the caring soul of my flawless mom. Just like a diamond.

Brenda Zarate   Grade: 07
She is the best you'll meet. She will fill hearts with joy. She's my rose model and many things that will fill millions of pages.

Teacher: Jennifer Rovira

Alina Alayev   Grade: 07
Through difficult and simple times, my mother is always there. She would gladly give her own happiness to make someone else feel blissful and radiant.

Dillon Barney   Grade: 07
My mom makes me smile; she'll drive me miles and miles. She'll take me anywhere. She fills my heart with love and care.

Mark Bocz   Grade: 07
What my mom does…she serves, oh, what a diamond she deserves. She cooks, she cleans, she runs about, but all throughout she never pouts.

Sabah Chaudhry   Grade: 07
Because she has a full-time job. She cleans the house, cooks everyday, cooks everyday, helps with homework and loves unconditionally.

Joanna Marquez   Grade: 07
My mom deserves a diamond because she's magnificent, loving and caring. I would never want to lose her. Love my mom. She's always there for me.

Minna Mattis   Grade: 07
Like a diamond she sparkles, precious like one too. A diamond can barely compare to how much she will love you.

Ariana Miller   Grade: 07
My mom loves me and that's all that matters. She's worth WAY more than a diamond, or any other stone.

Grace Poteet   Grade: 07
My mom deserves a diamond because she has always been there for me. So I would like to thank her in a sparkly way.

Jordana Rohm   Grade: 07
My mom is lovely and generous. She thinks of me first, I think she works hard for me. She cooks, cleans, and runs with me.

Shivam Thapar   Grade: 07
She's the heaven residing on Earth. The refuge that engulfs all pain. The warmth that makes me melt. The miracle that happens again and again.

Laguna Hills High
Laguna Hills

Teacher: Lynn Jax

Olivia Chen   Grade: 09
A star, the diamond of the sky, always guiding, always caring, fighting for me, loving me forever. My precious mom.

Daniel Hwang   Grade: 09
Guardian angel in darkest of night took away fear and brought back the light.

Lauren Lamparter   Grade: 09
My mom is a wonderful, kind-hearted, loving, selfless, godly woman. Even through her struggle with breast cancer, she never gave up on her family.

Luke Mitchell   Grade: 09
Sunshine and love, given by my mother. She's as sweet as a dove. She has no equal or other.

Paige Ramos   Grade: 09
The angel of radiance and strength birthed the daughter of imperfection and fear. The angel gave always; the daughter gives back now.

Brady Runyon   Grade: 09
Every time you make me laugh, every time you make me smile, I wonder what life would be like without you. I love you, mom.

Andrew Walraven   Grade: 09
Mom. She loves, she lives, she is the reason I love to live. She loves, she cares. She cares about my love. I love her.

Laguna Niguel Elementary
Laguna Niguel

Teacher: Linda Cardwell

Hayden Burnight   Grade: 03
My mom cleans as is she were a vacuum. She is very smart, nice and funny. She is very hardworking. I love her.

Joshua Cassarino   Grade: 03
Mom, friendly, smart, cleaning, caring, exercising, loves hugs and cares all about me - Buddy.

Jonah Dewing   Grade: 03
Mom, smart, hilarious, loving, caring, hugging, a hardworking medical doctor.

Samantha E - Grant   Grade: 03
Mommy, funny, smart, cooking, running, comforting. I couldn't live without her love.

Ethan Greely   Grade: 03
Mom, smart, funny, counseling, smiling, hugging, always kind and calm. Love.

Matthew Gutierrez   Grade: 03
Mom, friendly, hilarious, loving, teaching, helping. A teaching bundle of love - Mother.

Nathan Kim   Grade: 03
Mother, smart, hilarious, caring, comforting, loving. A warm joyful piece of love.

Yvette Ochoa   Grade: 03
Mommy, loving, pretty, adoring, caring, kissing. A woman full of love and caring.

Ethan Reed   Grade: 03
My mom is as bright as an angel. She has a warm caring heart. She is like Jesus to me because Jesus could do everything.

Angeles Rosales   Grade: 03
Mom, smart, kind, caring, helping, loving, a playful beautiful, hardworking woman.

Dominique St. Laurent   Grade: 03
Mom, smart, funny, caring, helping, adoring, super joyful and always happy.

Teacher: Michelle Fialho

Richelle Ennis   Grade: 03
A dab of laughter, a pinch of kindness, a hand full of love, and most importantly, beauty.

Keegan Flynn   Grade: 03
She is the star on top of my tree. As she is my hero and as soft as the sea.

Kimberly Fraser   Grade: 03
Mom! I would be nothing without her, I would not be here without her. She is a shining beautiful diamond.

Jimmy Garvey   Grade: 03
Mom shines so bright that I have to wear shades. Her kindness is worth more. She is so smart. I think she is so flawless.

Jillian Naffziger   Grade: 03
My mom is just like a shining pearl. She is my treasure, and I love her better than a diamond.

Nasim Razavi   Grade: 03
She shines like a diamond and who is she? She is my mom. I would rather have her instead of a diamond.

Celeste Rock   Grade: 03
She is a spectacular mom and she is always there when I need her. Her heart and kindness are bigger than these words.

Gigi Ruddins   Grade: 03
My mom is sweet like honey and smells like flowers. Her green eyes twinkle in the gleaming moonlight. She loves everyone, everyday.

Ashley Simonson   Grade: 03
Mom's heart warms up the room. As her eyes twinkle so bright. My mother is fantastic to me. Everyday and every night.

Neal Spencer   Grade: 03
She is a caring and welcoming person and sparkles like a gem. Her kind heart is worth more than a diamond.

Teacher: Vanessa Napolitano

Megan Ferrell   Grade: 03
Flowers are pretty and my mom is pretty. My mom is as pretty as a flower on a stem. I love my mom a lot.

Golnaz Khazeni   Grade: 03
My mommy is sweet and loving. She sits with me. She eats with me. She plays with me and more. I will always love her.

Connor Meehan   Grade: 03
My mom is as sweet as pie. She is like a sunset on a cool summer day. Her personality is a flower. She loves me.

Brendan Nugent   Grade: 03
My mom is so pretty, she is as pretty as the sun at night reflecting off of the lake. My mom is kind and friendly.

Chase Reichenback   Grade: 03
My mom is one in a million. She helps me with a lot of things like my homework. My mom is so nice to everyone.

Humza Ruhmani   Grade: 03
She always has a good attitude. I love her more than anything. She is the best mom I can ask for.

Kai Schaeffer   Grade: 03
My mom is very sweet. She is as beautiful as a gem. Also, she is the best mother ever in the world.

* Amethyst winners in bold.

Allison Tran   Grade: 03
My mom is very special to me. She takes care of me and most of all, she loves me. She is brighter than a diamond.

Teacher: Lu Neely

Michael Carranza   Grade: 03
My mom's long black hair is like a river. She smiles like the sun in summer. She's my own special kind of diamond.

Taylor Dyssegard   Grade: 03
My mom is sweet like a cupcake. She is like an angel to me. She deserves to wear a diamond on her angel wings.

Olivia Gasparian   Grade: 03
My mom deserves a diamond because she is as beautiful as a daisy blooming and she works as hard as a busy beaver.

Victoria Gong   Grade: 03
My mom is as sweet as a piece of candy and she deserves a diamond because she shines like the brightest star in the sky.

Faith Johnson   Grade: 03
My mom is as smart as a dictionary. She is as pretty as a new born star. That's why she deserves a diamond.

Kate McHenry   Grade: 03
My mom is as pretty as a rose. She shines like the beautiful sun in the sky. Her love is as big as the world.

Jack Polucha   Grade: 03
My mom is as sweet as ice cream. She is as beautiful as a movie star and she is as bright as the sun in the sky.

Mackenzie Sprong   Grade: 03
My mom is caring like a mommy cat to her baby kittens at daybreak and sweet as pie and organized as a hopping kangaroo.

Nicky Valdivia   Grade: 03
My mom deserves a diamond because she does so much in one day; ten other people couldn't do so much in one month.

Allyson Villasenor   Grade: 03
My mom is as sweet as sugar. Her eyes are as blue as the ocean. She puts the fun in my world.

Laguna Road Elementary
Fullerton

Teacher: Janet Diamant

Elina Bougas   Grade: 02
My mom's eyes are like sapphires, her lips like a rose, her voice like birds chirping, her heart full of love.

Cynthia Choi   Grade: 02
My mom deserves a diamond because she is special, smiles all the time, has eyes like shining crystals, and smiles as beautiful as a pearl.

Stephanie Hu   Grade: 02
I believe my mom deserves a diamond because she loves me and takes care of me, and I think she deserves a little surprise.

Joshua Kang   Grade: 02
I believe my mom deserves a diamond because she is very special, she always smiles, and I know she loves me more than a mile.

Elise Lau   Grade: 02
My mommy's love is sure to win. Her love is number 1. Her eyes shine like the shining sun, and always by my side.

Zuzia McMurry   Grade: 02
Twinkling like a star, bright as a diamond. Her heart as a crystal, so loved by me.

Claire Minohan   Grade: 02
She sparkles like a crystal. She shines like a star. She is as colorful as a rainbow. She always has a smile on her face.

Lake Forest Elementary
Lake Forest

Teacher: Patty Fox

Kassandra Alonzo   Grade: 01
My mom's hair is chocolate brown. Her snuggles calm me and so do her pretty warm eyes. Her love flows like a river.

Carter Aram   Grade: 01
My mom's heart is as warm as the golden sun and her eyes are as beautiful as crystals, her cheeks are as warm as hot chocolate.

Silas Arreola   Grade: 01
My mom loves me more than the world. She helps and saves me. She is my diamond.

Savonte Bayless   Grade: 01
Mom is cooler than the Raiders. She's the best mom in whole world. She is the golden grace. Her eyes are calming blue water.

Trent Bliss   Grade: 01
My mom is better than my Nintendo DS. Her pretty eyes make me melt like the sun. She is a trophy

Timothy Brander   Grade: 01
My mom's eyes are as black as hot chocolate. Her hair glistens like diamonds reflecting in the sun. She is my gold.

Zole Burns   Grade: 01
My mom's hugs are warmer than hot chocolate. Her love is like air as it surrounds me. She is my best friend.

Belleare De La Cruz   Grade: 01
My mom is better than hot chocolate. Her warm love snuggles me like a blanket. Her eyes shine like diamonds when we're together.

Rocco Dipippo   Grade: 01
My mom is more gorgeous than flowers. My mom's beautiful black hair is constantly on my mind, and so is her love.

Madeline Essman   Grade: 01
My mom's hair is as dark as a jaguar's fur and her eyes sparkle like glitter because my mom is a star.

Abby Gilkey   Grade: 01
My mom is as pretty as a diamond. She is as wonderful as a rose. Her hugs are tighter than a bear's.

Steven Gutierrez   Grade: 01
My mom is the diamond of everybody. Her love flows like an eagle soaring over the world. Her beauty amazes the earth.

Emma Johanson   Grade: 01
My mom's eyes are like the sunshine. She is as pretty as a deep red rose.

Jenna Jung   Grade: 01
My mom is as pretty as a penguin walking. My mom's eyes shine like diamonds. She can wake and love a tired girl.

Jonathan Katrowski   Grade: 01
My mom's pretty eyes are as beautiful as her loving heart. Her pretty lips melt me like hot chocolate. She's better than the whole world.

Nika Keshavavs   Grade: 01
My mom has beautiful brown Hair. Her warm smile is brighter than sunshine. Her love beats inside me. She is true love.

Jacob Klein Grade: 01
Beautiful roses I see remind me of her eyes. Her hair is like dark chocolate. She is my gem of life.

Dimitri Kupanaf Grade: 01
Her eyes are like sparkly jewelry when she's with me. Her flowing black hair is as soft as a lamb and so is her heart.

Brandon Leyvas Grade: 01
My mom has orange red hair like the sun. Her brown eyes sparkle like diamonds. She is my rock of life.

Shayne Simpson Grade: 01
My mom's shiny blue eyes are like the ocean. Her cooking is better than Betty Crocker. Her love is stronger than the Yankee's Don Maddinly.

Teacher: Nanci Gordon

Christine Cartagena Grade: 03
My mom deserves a diamond because she's like a star that sparkles in the night. She takes great care of us and loves us a lot.

Scott Collin Grade: 03
My mom deserves a diamond because she cares about me and my family. She's really nice to everyone she knows.

Sarah Dahlstrom Grade: 03
My mom deserves a diamond because she sparkles like a jewel. She is like an elf at Santa's workshop always busy taking care of me.

Christina Galindo Grade: 03
My mom deserves a diamond because she always takes care of me and she sparkles like a gem filled with beauty.

Austin Harvard Grade: 03
My mom deserves a diamond because she works really hard to keep me and my sister happy and smart.

Danielle Johnson Grade: 03
My mom deserves a diamond because she cares for me no matter what. She helps me with homework and she is always nice to me.

Ariana Jones Harvey Grade: 03
My mom deserves a diamond because she's always there when I get hurt or someone is mean to me, she really cares about me.

Cameron Mann Grade: 03
My mom deserves a diamond because she's as pretty as the moonlight. She takes great care of my three brothers and me.

Morgan Miller Grade: 03
My mom deserves a diamond because she's a great winner and I know she can do anything. A diamond is special and so are you.

Noelle Ness Grade: 03
My mom deserves a diamond because she is the best mom. She takes care of me. She is a mom that sparkles at night.

Rebecca Pascual Grade: 03
My mom deserves a diamond because she has loved, cared, fed me for so long. When you look at my mom, her eyes shine.

Isabella Polito Grade: 03
My mom deserves a diamond because she's nice, caring, loving. She helps me and is friendly, giving, awesome, and thoughtful. She's always there for me.

Isabelle Tobin Grade: 03
My mom deserves a diamond because she is like a shooting star that sparkles as bright as the moon in the dark night sky.

Erik Tolman Grade: 03
My mom is so nice. She takes me on trips to baseball and football games. She's the only mom in the world I would like.

Alyssa Willis Grade: 03
My mom deserves a diamond because when my dad goes out of town, she makes good food and loves me double.

Teacher: Michelle Pellow

Rachel Andrews Grade: 04
My mom is like a shooting star, and even though flowers are very neat. Only my mom is just as sweet. My mom = happiness.

Eileen Bermudez Grade: 04
My mom is as pretty as a rose and as bright as a star. She cares for me and she loves me.

Zahra Elhanbaly Grade: 04
My mom is very special. A diamond she deserves from everything she gets us. To every meal she serves.

Yanna Garcia Grade: 04
Mom deserves a diamond because she shines like one, and she is as pretty as one. Plus she is a shiny diamond in my heart.

Nagina Hamid Grade: 04
My mom deserves a diamond because my mom is beautiful. When she walks, she sparkles like a shooting star. My mom is my heart.

Jordyn Krohn Grade: 04
She deserves a diamond to tell her she's the brightest star in my sky. No one's as special as her. She deserves the brightest diamond.

Jade Ross Grade: 04
My mother is my love bug inside of me. She makes me feel loved and special. Also, she's the best loving thing that ever happened to me.

Delaney Ryan Grade: 04
My mom deserves a diamond because she loves me and takes care of me. She deserves something very special. I love my mom.

Dean Soderman Grade: 04
Mom deserves a diamond because she is the best mom in the world; she is always there for me and she is loving.

Jacquelyn Vallesillo Grade: 04
To see you happy makes me realize it's good to have you by my side. When I was little, you were my guide.

Siena Yusi Grade: 04
Sweeter than a lollipop, cooler than the breeze. My mom's love to me will never stop. My mom and me, a diamond for my mom.

Lakeview Elementary
Yorba Linda

Teacher: Brenda Dimopoulos

Christopher Fu Grade: 01
She is the best mom ever. She wants me to eat good food.

Michael Geraghty Grade: 01
She takes very good care of me. She makes sure I don't get poisoned.

Andy Hon Grade: 01
My mom is the best because she is nice. She is the best and she is playful.

Allison Sweeney Grade: 01
My beautiful mom deserves a diamond because if I say my food is cold, when will get right up and put in the microwave.

Lampson Grove Day Sch.
Garden Grove

Teacher: Alexandra Hilario

Jesus Alvaras Grade: 05
My mom is the best. She's always around, she never upsets me. She is all I care about. My mom is great. I love her.

* Amethyst winners in bold.

Evelyn Cisneros   Grade: 05
My mom is my angel and I am her bunny. I love her giggle and smile and I love to be her child.

Georgie Garcia   **Grade: 05**
She's a star that shines in the night sky. Whose love shines forever. Her sweetness won my heart and will help her win a diamond.

Finnigan Horan   Grade: 05
My mom is very nice. She's a great mom. She's the best. She tells me right from wrong. She loves me forever long.

Nikki Kinney   Grade: 05
My mom does a lot for me. She loves me very much. She is made of love. Her heart is pure and caring.

Danielle Kintop   **Grade: 05**
We watch TV. together. We play with our dogs. She cooks good dinners. She loves me so much and I love her back.

Justin Lovato   **Grade: 05**
My mom gives colors to my world, and joy to my life. She is loving and careful and the best friend of my life.

Richard Nelson   Grade: 05
My mom deserves a diamond because she cares for me and loves me when I'm sick or sad. She is the love of my life.

Austin Urena   Grade: 05
She loves me and I love her. When I first saw her I thought she was the most beautiful thing I ever saw.

Karina Valenzuela   Grade: 05
My mom is so sweet, that's why the birds so tweet, tweet. My mom cooks so good. That's why everyone likes her in the neighborhood.

Teacher: Rebecca Lambert

Diandra Catrinescu   **Grade: 01**
My mom deserves a diamond because she gave me a beautiful cake for my birthday. She takes me to the park and plays with me.

Millie Garcia   Grade: 01
My mom deserves a diamond because she makes my favorite food macaroni and cheese. She helps me with my homework. She is nice.

Kennedy Hilario   Grade: 01
My mom cooks good food so I can get healthy and strong. Her heart is as sweet as a rose and made from heaven.

Sabrina Lomri   **Grade: 01**
My mom is always nice to me. She helps me up when I am down. My mom puts me to bed and kisses me.

Kirsten Normand   Grade: 01
My mom is special because she takes me places. She gives me chocolate milk. She is funny and makes me laugh.

Joshua Haynes   Grade: 02
My mom deserves a diamond because she surprises me with stuff. My mom has nice eyes and pretty eye lashes.

Nathan Mendoza   Grade: 02
My mom deserves a diamond because she teaches me new thing. She is the best mom I could ever have.

Gabriel Nguyen   Grade: 02
My mom deserves a diamond because she takes care of me. She makes me laugh. My mom is so beautiful. She let's me play.

Sean Von ting   **Grade: 02**
My mom deserves a diamond because she keeps me safe. She's beautiful and she's good to me. She's the best mom in the world.

Matthew Weddle   **Grade: 02**
My mom deserves a diamond because she is the most beautiful thing in the universe. She's rose picked out of Jesus' garden.

Las Flores Middle
Los Flores

Teacher: Susie Barca

Chandler Bauer   Grade: 06
Mom deserves a diamond because her heart is strong, her soul is pure. She cares for all, we should too. My mom deserves a diamond.

Cassidy Houschild   Grade: 06
My mom deserves a diamond. She works hard for everyone. She truly cares and helps people learn more. I want to get something special.

Tyler Kratzat   Grade: 06
My mom deserves a diamond because she is helpful, nice and caring. I want to win, so that I make my mom feel appreciated.

Garrett Landau   Grade: 06
My mom deserves a diamond because she is grateful, wonderful, kind, and special. She does so much hard work, she deserves a diamond.

Heather Malick   Grade: 06
My mom deserves a diamond because she is kind and caring, also helpful. She does not let me down and she always helps me.

Nicole Mehring   Grade: 06
Through time, my mother has watched me grow. She was the hand that helped me in every way possible. She deserves more than anything.

Rachel Neiman   Grade: 06
My mom deserves a diamond because she's a hardworking single mom that never gives up. She never thanks about her self - only others.

Juliana Regis   **Grade: 06**
My mom deserves a diamond because her heart is a diamond pure and strong. She is beautiful and kind and I truly love her.

Eemil Selanne   **Grade: 06**
My mom deserves a diamond because she helps us in everything we need in our life. She works so hard for us. She loves us.

Hali Stokes   Grade: 06
She helps me with everything wrong. She feeds my family. She is calm in bad situations. She always know what to do. She is amazing.

Casey Swoboda   **Grade: 06**
Mom deserves a diamond because she cares, she shares and she is super thoughtful. I love her more than anything in the world.

Shawn Trejo   **Grade: 06**
Through my life, I see my mom supporting our family with sweat and tears. But with the diamond I can say, you've earned it.

Brooke Triplett   Grade: 06
My mom deserves a diamond because she's a hardworking mother and cares about one another. She cares about me and is easy to please.

Dmitry Tunic   Grade: 06
As perfect as a diamond, she's brighter than a star. My mom deserves a diamond because she's number one. So mom, thank you for everything.

Teacher: Laurie Cummings

Mady Adair   Grade: 08
My mom should win a diamond, this is very clear to me. She loves me like no other, and is as gentle as the sea.

Tara Aitken   Grade: 08
My mom is like a diamond, for she has her flaws but can be a girl's best friend, which is why she deserves one.

Karly Alleman   **Grade: 08**
She has no flicker or doubt with the decisions she makes, her gestures destroy any sign of dismay. She deserves a diamond in every way.

Tiffany Allen   **Grade: 08**
My mom, the key to my heart, my breath of life, more needed then oxygen, I can't imagine one day of my life without her.

Tyler Allen   Grade: 08
Her affection to me is like no other. She is a diamond among dirt like a rose among weeds. My mom deserves a diamond always.

Makensie Bates   Grade: 08
My mom is like friendship, caring and sweet. No matter where I am I know I have her, she will last forever in my heart.

Katherine Beliles   Grade: 08
She held me when I cried, my tears she dried. My mother is my caretaker. Now it's my turn to take care of her.

Bria Burchianti   **Grade: 08**
Moonlight, stars, flowers and diamonds all are wonderful things. This is nice, but nothing can compare, my mom is more than just a diamond.

Angela Celo   **Grade: 08**
Like a caterpillar that transforms into a butterfly, everything beautiful begins as a lump of coal. Thank you mom, for seeing the diamond in everyone.

Brandon Chen   Grade: 08
Hardworking and caring, that's my mom. Feeding you her love, in the way only mothers can. Always there for you, always ready to help.

Jacob Clarke   **Grade: 08**
What spirit shines beyond the mourning voices of murmuring crowd, glimmering as a prized jewel among the crowded sands below the heavens? My mother.

Sarah Clausing   Grade: 08
My mom is all I could ask for and more. Her love for me is endless. Whether I'm sad, scared, or happy, she is there.

Jordan Colombs   Grade: 08
Like the stars in the night sky, the tender sand in the desert, and the water in the ocean. My mom and I are inseparable.

Travis Corbin   Grade: 08
With so much grace and heart and beauty, work and devotion, peace and love, my mother is the treasure of my day, night and life.

Columbia Crandell   **Grade: 08**
Mother is a word for the fiercely loyal and those who have the capacity for infinite love. My mother humbly reflects that perfect beauty.

Allie Crupi   Grade: 08
Music swells upon the night air; waves break upon the shore. These sounds so loved by everyone. My mother loves me more.

Darby Curtis   Grade: 08
The moon shining at night, the light in my day. My mom is my hero and I would not have her any other way.

Hunter Dimler   **Grade: 08**
Funny and radiant, her warming spirit brings joy to all. Her beauty glistens like autumn's glow, and makes me want to love her more.

Kevin Domagala   Grade: 08
My mom's a full time worker, she's also a mother of four. Twenty-five words can't describe her. I need a whole lot more.

Kendall Donaldson   Grade: 08
Shining bright from sea to sea. My mom means everything to me. Words can't describe her love, flying around me like a dove.

Brandon Ellert   **Grade: 08**
Teenage life, an ocean. The ebbing tides flow. The waves roar. A nurturing mother can settle the seas and calm the chasms of adolescent existence.

Kristen Fejas   Grade: 08
My teacher, my support, and my defender. My mother is a star shedding her light and guiding me through the dark times.

Will Foster   **Grade: 08**
I started as a seed; she planted me. As I grew, she watered me. And now, because of her, I am a blooming flower.

Brody Franzen   **Grade: 08**
A diamond, flawless and pure. Just like a mom,. Making the unknown clear. Knowledgeable and caring, guidance through fears. Purely a diamond, clear and crystalline.

Taylor Gordon   **Grade: 08**
My mom is something that you just can't explain. She's caring, comforting. And loving all the same. She deserves this diamond, that is obviously plain.

Natalie Grabowski   **Grade: 08**
My mother's heart is admirable and pure. Her compassionate eyes sparkle like the diamonds in the sky, and her smile lights up my world.

Nicole Hagen   Grade: 08
She brought me to earth and gave me my name. She made me what I am now, and for that she deserves one thing.

Brett Hall   **Grade: 08**
Pregnant with beauty and priceless like the Mona Lisa, my mom is a garden filled with exotic flowers. She has created love that overwhelms cupid.

Christian Halvorsen   **Grade: 08**
Like a warm breeze on a mid-summer day, my mom's everlasting love and comfort means more than I can say. My mom is my diamond.

Katherine Harbison   **Grade: 08**
My mother is my best friend, she listens to me and she is always there for me. I will love my mother forever and ever.

Hunter Hite   **Grade: 08**
My mother deserving so much, getting much less. Elegant as a diamond, her love is priceless. Fun, fortune us and all together, flawless.

Adam Jones   **Grade: 08**
Loving and caring, beautiful and young. My mother has been my support and ally during times of hardship. Her memory and soul will last forever.

Melanie Kim   Grade: 08
Guiding me down the road of life, turning me towards the highway to heaven. She'd sacrifice herself for me instantly. Mom, my loving guardian angel.

Karli Ladwig   **Grade: 08**
My mom who cares more about others than herself, who provides everyone with warmth and comfort, and who has a large and loving heart.

Quinn Lancaster   Grade: 08
Mom, caring, loving, helpful. She is a treasure. I am very affectionate to her and I think she deserves a diamond. I love you, Mom.

* Amethyst winners in bold.

Mckenzi Latchford   Grade: 08
My mother is special, my mom is clear. She's a precious treasure from above and will always love and be loved no matter what.

Lindsay Liegler   Grade: 08
Fierce and beautiful, yet delicate as a rose. Her love as deep as the sea. The greatest creation this world has ever known. My mother.

Jessica Lim   Grade: 08
A ray of light which guides my soul through times of sadness that strike my heart into the abyss. My mother, my pillar of life.

Zachary Lowe   Grade: 08
My mom deserves a diamond because she is like the sun with all her blazing beauty and bright personality.

Denae Luce   Grade: 08
My mom is as sweet as a lollipop, as brave as a lion. She is as loving as an angel, as beautiful as a diamond.

Emily Martin   Grade: 08
My mom is a diamond among stones. Her facets reflect warmth to the cold world. A diamond would represent her in all of her wonders.

Kaitlyn Mataya   Grade: 08
Cheerful, thoughtful, helping, sharing, my mother is the best at caring. She taught me life, she taught me love, while keeping peace, like a dove.

Brooke Maushund   **Grade: 08**
My mom is the wax to my surfboard. Without her, I would slip off the edge and plunder into the darkness of life, without hope.

Nicolette McNair   Grade: 08
She drives me near and far, whenever I need her, she's there in her car, her love is so dear that I never feel fear.

Ryan Mirza   Grade: 08
Just like a diamond, a mother's love is forever. My mom's love for my brothers and I will never stop, ever.

Megan Mittleman   Grade: 08
Her smile is used often but perfect. Her heart is old, yet it's love is eternal. My mom is a diamond to me from God.

Tori Morrison   Grade: 08
When I feel like crying, she sings me old songs that make me smile again.

Madeline Oi   Grade: 08
My mother wouldn't care if I was fat or ugly. Caring only if I'm happy, I'm so fortunate to have her. I couldn't be happier.

Monika Patel   Grade: 08
Diamonds, radiant, glistening. Attracting all the attention, amazing and lovable, cherished and beautiful. My mother is the same, she deserves a jewel to match.

Dane Petersen   **Grade: 08**
Eyes sparkling, like an iridescent pond. Love shining out, like a lustrous full moon. Dedication penetrating deeper than space. I love you mom.

Scott Phillips   Grade: 08
My mom is a diamond; steady and unchanging through the toughest of times; more beautiful than the sunset after a majestic summer day; my hero.

Caroline Pohl   Grade: 08
Like a shining star on a moonless night, like a lifeline reeling me in. My mom, loving and thoughtful, deserves more than a single diamond.

Kyle Robb   **Grade: 08**
My mother is a shining star with rays of optimism and hope. She is the treasure of golden utopias, and makes my day a diamond.

Travis Sovronec   Grade: 08
My mom is loving, she is protective; she is the warm sun rays piercing the depressing clouds; she comforts the frightened and solves all calamities.

Miranda Stomp   Grade: 08
My mom's luscious red hair glistens like a shiny medal, who loves me day and night, through thick and thin.

Hubert Ta   Grade: 08
My mom is endless as space with beauty extending on past the shining sea. Glowing like neon, she is bright and extends on through life.

Natalie Tate   Grade: 08
Angelic, sparkling eyes. A sweet, melodic voice. A caring, patient spirit. An aura of joy and happiness. My mom.

Jack Taylor   Grade: 08
My mom, worthy, loving, caring, unselfish and a truly great mom. She is the one that you will want to receive this diamond of honor.

Erin Theodorakis   Grade: 08
Bitter and misleading is the dark. But she cloaks me in her affectionate arms. Warm and tender, her grin bids me safety and guidance.

Jack Vanderford   Grade: 08
Her heart as warm as a summer day. Majestic as the sun, each and every ray. I thank god I have her, every single day.

Kaitlin Vick   Grade: 08
My mom is a gardener, caring and nourishing, gentle and replenishing. Her smile is a barrier, strong and protective, passionate and reflective.

Yana Williams   Grade: 08
One of the few people who has known me my entire life, my beautiful mother deserves a diamond symbolic of my undying love.

Ryan Yoo   Grade: 08
My mother's love enraptures me. It guides me along the path of life. When I need perfect love, she will always be there. Mom's love.

Chandler Zinke   **Grade: 08**
Treasure, life, diamonds, gold; my sweet mother's soul forms the mold, of which my life, formed of steel, forms my happiness, the love I feel.

Lexington Junior High
Cypress

Teacher: Laura Miller

Nina Amoranio   Grade: 08
My mom makes me happy everyday because I know she's the person that gave me life, which is the greatest gift I have ever received.

Priscilla An   **Grade: 08**
A bubbling laugh comes out from her lips, her cool hand brushes my cheek, she mouths the words, "I love you" and my heart soars.

Kristina Bae   Grade: 08
A smile like sunshine, a heart of gold. The lovely face is the person I behold. My mother.

Elizabeth Black   **Grade: 08**
My mom has her own 4 "Cs". Cheerful to everyone she meets. Character that is strong. Caring heart. Classy lady. My mom is a cool gem.

Yessenia Borja   **Grade: 08**
Stars above us, oh so high. My mom among them shines the brightest. Bursting with love and never a pout, illuminating from the inside out.

Moriah Brookins   Grade: 08
Essence of people tumbling from heaven. An origin from Africa. Strong, yet a kiss of a dove. A true gem. She is...Mom.

Brittney Burroughs   Grade: 08
Her eyes shine like stars in the moonlight. Her skin is as calm and gentle as a babies. There is no one like her.

Anthony Cabrera   Grade: 08
My mother our life, she loves us more than we'll know, from birth she watched us grow, her eyes dazzle, like amazing stars.

Julianna Carbonaro   Grade: 08
Her eyes sparkle like a diamond upon the sky, her voice makes my body quiver, not stubborn but sweet. The number one in my heart.

Minji Chai   Grade: 08
Mom deserves a diamond. Her heart is wide as a pond. She is my destiny and bond. We're a fond mother and daughter.

Angela Chang   **Grade: 08**
Eyes like pearls in the sea, she smells like sweet pea, smiles warm me throughout the day, when I called, she comes with no delay.

Brenda Chang   Grade: 08
Sparkling, intelligent, wonderful, caring, loving, there is no word in this whole entire world to describe how great you are. You are my light.

Alexander Chen   **Grade: 08**
More brilliant than the sun's light, more elegant than the moon at night. More precious than any other. Is my one and only mother.

Alexis Chen   Grade: 08
Her eyes shine like a polished gem, gleaming brilliantly like rays of the sun. Her warmth makes my heart open, I love her, my mom.

Sharon Chong   Grade: 08
Her love shines brighter than the biggest diamond. Her heart is as pure as a crystal. I love her, she loves me.

Eunice Chung   **Grade: 08**
Depression...sadness...mistakes, all erase the road of my life. I see somebody...carefully paving the erased road of mine. Yes! I see mom.

Christine Culhane   Grade: 08
Just like twinkling stars, her smile brightens my day always with a warm heart.

Joseph Desimone   Grade: 08
Flirting, kind, it cuts and swerves this carbon crystal show, it's curves created by fire, but made of ice, it catches rainbows in its vice.

Cindy Doan-Tran   Grade: 08
My mother, my special person. She loves, shares, cares and shelters. She watched me before I was one. My mother, the sun of my day.

Garrick Estes   Grade: 08
My mom deserves a diamond because she is nice, her love is unconditional, it doesn't have a price.

Sterling Garrett   Grade: 08
The light on my path. The give of all, my mop of life, the one that I love above all.

Emily Hut   Grade: 08
Mom is more than just a word. Mom is my hero, my heart, my everything. She is life itself.

Jessica Huynh   Grade: 08
When there is nothing but darkness pulling me in, the only person keeping me from falling in was my mom. The light of my life.

Sang Yoon Hwang   Grade: 08
No matter the pain, the worry, she is there each day with a smile, embracing everyone lovingly.

Susie Hwang   Grade: 08
My one and only mother, the one who love we most, who always worked hard. When I look at her, my heart feels at ease.

Dennis Hyon   Grade: 08
My mom's eyes may sparkle like a diamond. Her smiles may shine the sun. But it's her heart of gold that really counts.

Edgar Jaramillo   **Grade: 08**
She is my rising and my setting, my day, my night. She is my constant, my forever. She give me purpose, she gave me life.

DaEun Jeon   Grade: 08
Her love touches my heart; it endures forever to take me home. Her smiles make my heart beat. Her tears for me freeze to diamond.

Samuel Joo   **Grade: 08**
She's so fly, it isn't no lie. She makes me want to cry. Her love never runs dry. She's the reason I'm under the sky.

Ijya Karki   Grade: 08
Her sparkling eyes shimmer like the nights' star. Her words so wise led my life this far. Her smile so cheerful, she's my precious crystal.

Margaret Kim   **Grade: 08**
Mom to me is like the sun to earth. I cannot function without her. I look up to her as the earth to the sun.

Ye-Eun Kim   **Grade: 08**
The image of my mother, helping another to her utmost ability, appears in my train of thoughts, when I think of the word MOTHER.

Lauren Kim   **Grade: 08**
One who shows kindness. One who shows me their love, warms my heart. Why not show my heart to that loved one?

Deborah Kim   Grade: 08
Each and every wrinkle symbolizes the joy and pain that had drifted by. As she ages day by day, the sparkle in her eyes remain.

Grace Kim   Grade: 08
Warming smile that everyone greets. Dedication and with her soul and all lives her remarkable life. A loyal wife, mother and friend who stands tall.

Sharon Kim   Grade: 08
My mother loves from the deep inside of her heart and as she prays , I can feel her love.

Daniel Kim   Grade: 08
Unconditional love flows with her, which shows through thoughtfulness and caring ways. So warm do I feel from her compassion, she is like the sun.

Stacey Kim   Grade: 08
My mother, who never hurt a soul. Her heart is warm as hot cocoa during Christmas Day. Mom is whom I'll protect during my years.

Jinyeong Kwon   Grade: 08
Most common people, moms. Most rare people, moms. Rarest of the rarest, own moms. The rarest - My Mom.

Kungsun Lee   Grade: 08
Sparkling in the light, the diamond represents my mom as a treasured jewel.

Jennah Lee   Grade: 08
Sitting on the rooftop, watching the setting sun, it reminds me of my mother who hoped for the best. This makes me cry out.

* Amethyst winners in bold.

Shileah Lewis — Grade: 08
My mom doesn't deserve a diamond. She deserves a lot more. She provides everything for me. So giving her something she deserves wouldn't hurt.

Tatiana Lu — Grade: 08
My mom, irreplaceable, loving, wonderful, unperceivable, passionate, courageous, unpredictable, caring, indescribable, hero, role model. Mom.

Oksana Lubyanaya — Grade: 08
She twinkles like a diamond. Has eyes that shine bright. Her smile has light that affects the sunlight.

Jonathon May — Grade: 08
My mom has a smile so beautiful and bright. It shines like the moon on a dark winter night. It is an extraordinary sight.

Brandon Mendenhall — **Grade: 08**
Her heart is gold. Her soul is a diamond mold. When cat is near, it purrs. This is why the diamond is rightfully hers.

Andrea Miloslavic — Grade: 08
I love my mom, oh so dearly. I hope you can read this clearly. She's the center of my heart, nothing can take us apart.

Taylor Morrison — Grade: 08
My mom deserves a diamond because she is a great mom. She is beautiful and loving. She teaches me how to be a better person.

Jenny Mun — Grade: 08
She's the single, hardworking mom who saves the best for her child, and take the scraps for herself. Mom, I love you. I truly do.

Emily Nakamoto — **Grade: 08**
Her warm honey thick aura has the essence of a rushing waterfall entwined with pure, genuine waves immersing and swirling straight into the hearts of others.

Nancy Navarro — Grade: 08
She gave me life, so I want to than her for everything she did for me by giving her a diamond as beautiful as her.

Lauren Navarro — Grade: 08
Heart of crystal, beautiful, yet strong. Helps me pave a shining road to my future. Lightening when in angst. A gem that belongs.

Michael Nunez — Grade: 08
When I look her in the eyes, I get that special feeling that appears on every kids first Christmas and makes me smile with love.

Alex Ouklore — Grade: 08
Mommy is special to me with beautiful eyes, she can see. There is never a day that I cannot say, "I love you for eternity".

Kaitlyn Paek — **Grade: 08**
The most colorful rainbow, the most beautiful flower, the sweetest scent, the softest pillow. Eyes sparkling, lips shining. My best friend, Mom.

Maya Reyes — Grade: 08
My mother is a star, she shines so bright, she loves me, she cares for me, she's my everlasting diamond.

Emily Rhee — Grade: 08
I fall, fail, and fall on my road to success. Every time it hurts, it stings, but I come up every time for one reason…My mom.

Sharon Ro — Grade: 08
My mom has always been the most hardworking reason I know. She's one of the two pillars that has kept me standing. She deserves this.

Michelle Rojas — Grade: 08
As she rises with the sun, she shines like an angel when night has arrived, she sparkles under the moonlight…No diamond can compare.

Safya Sajjad — Grade: 08
"Mom", you deserve a diamond because "I love you". No other words in any language are more powerful than "I love you".

Hali Sanchez — Grade: 08
My mom, the diamond of my heart. The sparkle of my eyes, the twinkle of my smile. The shiny star of my life.

Patrick Shim — Grade: 08
Her eyes sparkle with love and care. Every time I am with her is a splendid day. Her heart is a garnet the size of a star.

Frankie Simpson — Grade: 08
She is always pushing me to do my best so I will have a good future. My mom cares about me and my future.

Briahni Walker — Grade: 08
My superwoman does more than one million things. She works, cooks, and takes care of me, a teenager. A worthy prize for my superwoman, mommy.

Teacher: Marianne Stewart

Jensen Aguino — Grade: 07
My mom deserves the diamond because she is really generous to other people and always insists to help or do good things for someone.

Meghan Arce — Grade: 07
My mom deserves a diamond because she always gives up things for me. She loves my family so much. To me, she's priceless.

Aja Bair — Grade: 07
My mom 's strong, a guitarist, model, actress, singer, volleyball girl. She drives me everywhere, she loves me so much. She makes me a strong, young lady.

Emily Bierei — **Grade: 07**
My mom is special but isn't everybody's? My mom accepts me for who I am when no one else does. My mom deserves a diamond.

Destiny Castro — Grade: 07
My mom is unique, she's spontaneous, supporting, strong, when I need a boast. She's rare with a friendly, generous smile. Her contagious laugh with joy.

Kelsey Conkle — Grade: 07
My mom deserves this diamond for many reasons. This might be cheesy to the readers, but this is true. She is exotic, fantastic and lovable.

Alex Cool — **Grade: 07**
Moms are like diamonds, pure and irreplaceable. Diamonds and moms are priceless, but I would rather have a mom every day of my life.

Andrew Crow — Grade: 07
My mom deserves a diamond because she does so much for me and needs to be told or showed how much she's worthy and loved.

Kai Crowe — Grade: 07
My mom deserves the diamond because she is as strong as a diamond. Even though the hardest times, she is just like a diamond, strong.

Kaitlyn Curry — Grade: 07
My mom deserves a diamond because she always cares for me with all her heart. Her eye sparkles when she smiles.

Daniel Davila — Grade: 07
My mom deserves a diamond because she's special. She's more valuable than anything I have, like as if she's a diamond. You only have one mom.

Shawn Dettmer Grade: 07
My mom deserves a diamond because she works every day and never stops. She listens, cares, and loves me for the way I am.

Elizabeth Duran Grade: 07
She's a prized jewel herself. Smile's appear on people's faces when she walks by. I want to show her how much I love her.

Holly Fosmire Grade: 07
Diamonds and my mom are rare, strong, bright. They never loose their luster. They always shine in strong beauty to make me smile.

Sean Frank Grade: 07
My mom is like a jewel. You would have to be a fool to not have her win. I will present it in a tin.

Connor Freeman Grade: 07
Her eyes are so bright. She fills me up with delight. Loves me all the time.

Kyle fujitani Grade: 07
Mom, that's a word everyone knows, a word that means love, helpfulness, kind, puts up with you and will not get angry. Mom.

Amy Galvez Grade: 07
My mom deserves a diamond because she is strong and shines like a diamond. She is rare and delicate and hard to break.

Makenna Gibson Grade: 07
My mom is special, she's beautiful inside and out. And she deserves a diamond as beautiful as her.

Alexis Guerra Grade: 07
She works very hard for my family at home and work. She's always been there for me. With arms open for me, makes me better always.

Tyler Hernandez Grade: 07
To be honest, my mom deserves a diamond because it matches her personality. Diamonds are pure, they shine, and are tough just like my mother.

Alex Huang Grade: 07
My mom deserves a diamond because she works very hard to keep us healthy. Mostly my mom helps me learn the good and the bad.

Alexandria Ibarra Grade: 07
My mom deserves a diamond because she has put all her strength into helping me and I want to show her she's doing divine.

Lea Jacobsen Grade: 07
A diamond is a very beautiful an unique gem that can never be replaced, just like my mom.

Justin Kane Grade: 07
Like a diamond, my mom is flawless forever. My mom is more than a diamond, even more than all the stars in the universe.

Jenny Keung Grade: 07
My mom is the shining star of mu life. She gave me the gift of life. It's my destiny to bring hope in her heart.

Jann Kim Grade: 07
My mom deserves a diamond because even though she's small, she is worth a lot for me, just like little diamonds that costs lots of money.

Seth Kington Grade: 07
My mom is a diamond. She puts a smile on whoever she encounters. Her eyes twinkle in the sunlight. It lights up the entire room.

Edward Lagrone Grade: 07
My mom deserves a diamond because like a diamond she is shining, brilliant and rock hard, that shines out with all her love.

Timothy Lee Grade: 07
Why do you not think my mom deserves a diamond? I know why she deserves it. She will withstand anything for me like a diamond.

Hayleigh Magdaleno Grade: 07
My mom deserves a diamond because she works like a waterfall, long and hard. When she gets home, she sparkles and that completes my mom.

Richard Martinez Grade: 07
My mom deserves a diamond because she is patient like how a diamond takes a long time to make and also my mom is unique.

Kendra Medina Grade: 07
My mom deserves a diamond because diamonds last forever. She doesn't break easily, and everyday she shines as bright as one.

Joseph Mercado Grade: 07
My mom deserves a diamond because they have a lot in common. She does because she is bright, she is pretty and she is rare.

Lucas Mok Grade: 07
My mom deserves a diamond because she's kind, because of her I got a great mind, like a diamond, she would shine. She's my guideline.

Nicole Murry Grade: 07
If my mom were a diamond, I could spot her among a million. She's unique and as such a special person and no one else can compare.

Trent Porter Grade: 07
My mom deserves a diamond because she's the best mom ever. She is priceless like a diamond. She loves me.

Natalie Punkay Grade: 07
My mom is a diamond. She is worth so much to me, sparkling with beauty and kindness.

Dylan Quintero Grade: 07
Mom's are like fires, blazing hot and fierce. They burn with a raw passion and are never put out. Their blistering intensity warms my heart.

Kristen Reitz Grade: 07
My mom is like a diamond because she lights up the room when she walks in and she is always shining bright in the light.

Tori Richmond Grade: 07
My mother is always with me, not time, not space, not even death will ever separate me from her.

Jonathan Sevilla Grade: 07
My mom deserves a diamond because she is flawless. Her eyes sparkle like a pond in the moonlight, and her hair flows like a waterfall.

Allison Smalley Grade: 07
We all know our moms love us, my mom is way more. She is just like a diamond. She is so strong. I love her.

Jamie Speake Grade: 07
My mom shines like a diamond. My mom gleams when she smiles. She makes the whole mom light up, when she comes home from work.

Haley Swanson Grade: 07
My mom deserves a diamond because she is a diamond. She shines brighter than any diamond. She's my diamond. I wouldn't trade her for the world.

Lisa Thompson Grade: 07
My mom is strong, smart, working person. She is a rare person devoting herself to volunteering. That is why my mom deserves the diamond.

* Amethyst winners in bold.

Andrew Tuttle   Grade: 07
My mom deserves a diamond because she has eyes like diamonds that sparkle in the sun's light. She makes me smile and laugh so much.

Raquel Umbarila   Grade: 07
My mom deserves a diamond because she is loving to everyone, caring, and very beautiful on the inside and the outside.

Brooke Warken   Grade: 07
I am positive my mom deserves a diamond because to me her love is priceless just like the prize I hope to win for her.

Allison Wixom   Grade: 07
My mom deserves a diamond because she understands me and I can go to her for anything. She's my best friend, she deserves a diamond.

Daniel Zembower   Grade: 07
My mom deserves a diamond because her smile shines brightly just like a diamond in the mid-day sun.

Carlos Zumaya   Grade: 07
My mom should get a diamond because she is strong, she is the rarest mom and she is special to me. So please, oh please.

Elise Burlace   Grade: 08
My mom is a teacher, ray of sunshine on a bleak day, shelter from the harshest glow and most of all, my very best friend.

Liberty Christian School
Huntington Beach

Teacher: Carol Boswith

Christopher Antimie   Grade: 04
My mom guides and corrects. Her heart is as soft as a fluffy pillow. She's strong, spiritually and makes sacrifices for me.

Mia Boccanfuso   Grade: 04
Her eyes like stars in a moonlit summer sky. Her touch like delicate snowflakes. Her heart overflowing. She is a cozy place for me to rest.

Hannah Burkholder   Grade: 04
My mom's heart is magic. She's like the stars that shine at night. Her eyes are indescribable. Her love is everlasting.

Spencer Cendejas   Grade: 04
A loving mom, heart pure as clouds. Eyes watching over me like sun across the endless ocean. Her sacrifices, love, protection, like a lioness.

Justus Dae   Grade: 04
Mom's heart bigger than the universe, warmer than summer beaches. Her face, more gorgeous than roses, more pleasant than angels. Her love, eternal.

Noah Gane   Grade: 04
My mom is a diamond. She keeps me safe and sound. Also, strong and proud and her food is almost as good as her love.

Jacob Gane   Grade: 04
Mom's soft eyes gaze lovingly at me - like being wrapped in the coziest blanket, sitting next to a fire. She's elegant, exquisite, stunning, breathtaking.

Madison Haney   Grade: 04
Her love, red as rose. Her eyes glisten in the sun. Her comfort, calm as a meadow. Her smile, warm and cozy. Her kiss, magical.

Levon Lester   Grade: 04
My mom is awesome! Her eyes like sparkling crystals. Her heart, like big red roses. Her time given to comfort me. That's a deserving mom.

Jay Milne   Grade: 04
My mom's eyes are like sapphires, gleaming in the sun. She makes me feel elated when she holds me.

Rosa Nguyen   Grade: 04
Her eyes like two stars in a moonlit sky. Her smile as warm as a fireplace. Her hug, as heartfelt and magical as snowflakes.

Kitty Nguyen   Grade: 04
Her eyes as gorgeous as luminous gems in the sky. Her kiss as tender as a butterfly's wings, her passion indescribable. Mom - my precious diamond.

Lillie Richardson   Grade: 04
I think my mom deserves a diamond. When she hugs, I feel like I'm in paradise. When she gives her sacrificial time, it warms my heart.

Austin Suzukin   Grade: 04
My mom's eyes are like diamonds. Her kiss is like roses. When she hugs, I feel cozy and tender. She is tough like a gem.

Teacher: Sean Coffee B.

Crystal Eckman   Grade: 06
Her hair dark as midnight, lips as pink as a rose. Her eyes, stars in the night. She tells me I'm her world and stars.

Heather Parsons   Grade: 06
Mom. She cooks, she cleans, she loves, she gave me life for Pete's sake. I would buy her a million diamonds if I could.

Natalie Starr   Grade: 06
Her eyes are like the sun beams beaming down on me. Her voice is that of an angel picking me up when I'm sad.

Teacher: Jessica Davis

Evan Garner   Grade: 03
My mom deserves a diamond because she is the sweetest peach in the tree. She watches over me like a bird soaring in the sky.

Ezra Kelly   Grade: 03
My mom is so sweet to me. She deserves something great. She thinks anything will do the honor. But I think it should be precious.

Katherine Maloney   Grade: 03
My mom is like a snowflake. She is sweet as syrup. Her eyes are as beautiful as a diamond.

Julianne Matthews   Grade: 03
Mom is a faithful, truthful breeze, an angel in the air, she is perfect in every way, my love for her is here to stay.

Joel Navarro   Grade: 03
My mom deserves a diamond because she has a sweet heart and she is as beautiful as a butterfly and I love her kisses too.

Ethan Olguin   Grade: 03
My mom deserves the diamond, she is as beautiful as a daisy. Then when we get it, we will give it to charity.

Abigail Spitzer   Grade: 03
My mom is cute, she's lovable and smart but best of all, she's a work of art.

Shaun Turner   Grade: 03
I love my mom so much and she's as sweet as a bee's honey. She watches over me like a bear with her cubs.

Teacher: Robin Smith

Carissa Graham   Grade: 01
My mom deserves a diamond because she babysits other kids and takes care of me too.

Skylar Thompson   Grade: 01
My mom deserves a diamond because she is trying her best to be a teacher and she takes good care of me. I love her.

Dakota Whitmire Grade: 01
My mom deserves a diamond because she is a good teacher and she helps me read.

Teacher: Jan Wessels

JoAnna Arellano **Grade: 05**
My mom deserves a diamond because she's beautiful like white roses and is sweet like honey. She loves like God. I like her twinkling eyes the most.

Paul Fowler Grade: 05
My mom is a diamond - she enlightens my day for every day I see her, my troubles go away. You always get me through, mom.

Alexandra Maloney Grade: 05
My mom's as bright as a light, sweeter than candy, and as pretty as a flower. She's special doing so much for me.

Elizabeth Noson Grade: 05
My mom deserves a diamond because she is as pretty as Niagara Falls and intelligent as Einstein, but the best thing she is kind as birds.

Molly Perry Grade: 05
I'll not always be with my mother, someday she'll be gone forever. I'll enjoy my life with her now.

Delanie Ragan **Grade: 05**
More precious than a diamond, my mother is to me. With faith and love, she guides me in who I am supposed to be.

Sierra Whitmire Grade: 05
My mom's as pretty as a red rose, as caring as a school nurse, and she's as delightful as a beautiful summer day.

Teacher: Vangie Yeager

Jeffrey Braun **Grade: 02**
My mom is kind because she is helpful. My mom has eyes that shine whenever she looks at me. I think of stars bright.

Taylor Lee Grade: 02
My mom is the best mom because she reads the Bible with me and she does homework with me and she loves me very much.

Jake Lindborg Grade: 02
My mom is shining with joy in the morning, the afternoon, and night. My mom has a great smile on her face every single day.

Matthew Maloney **Grade: 02**
My mom is beautiful. She deserves the diamond because she works very hard. She sparkles like the shining stars. She is so kind. She does everything.

Athena Schlusemeyer Grade: 02
My mom is helpful. When I get hurt, she kisses my boo boo. She has brown shining eyes and dark brown hair. My mom's playful and nice.

Lily Stokes Grade: 02
My mom sparkles like a star. She is like a shining diamond at night. I am blessed. She is my mom.

Dylan Stokes Grade: 02
My mom is blessed from God. My mom's eyes sparkle and shine. She is really huggable. My mom sometimes cooks dinner. My mom is caring.

Chelsea Stokes Grade: 02
My mom shines. She is sweet and kind. She is helpful and prays with me. She sparkles like a diamond. I like her beautiful eyes.

Lincoln (Abraham) Elemen.
Santa Ana

Teacher: Baltazar

Ana Linares Grade: 04
My mom deserves a diamond because she has been a great mom always. Also, my mom deserves the diamond, why? Because she inspires me always.

Jennifer Lopez **Grade: 04**
My mother is beautiful, my mother is lovely. She shines like one little diamond above the sky.

Teacher: Paulette Dunn

Eric Aguilar Grade: 04
My mom shines brightly like the sun. Every time I see her, she is like a sparkle in my eye.

Rufina Bustamonte Grade: 04
My mom should win a diamond because she is the light of my heart. Her angel wings touch the heavens.

Jovany Carlos **Grade: 04**
My mom deserves a diamond because she sparkles. She has won my heart, and I love her because she is my most precious gem.

George Carreno Grade: 04
My mom deserves a diamond because she is special in so many ways. She is my lucky charm because she makes me feel special too.

Stephany Chavez Grade: 04
My mom deserves a diamond because when I feel blue, my mom says I am a piece of her heart and her shimmering light.

Misael Cruz Grade: 04
My mom deserves this diamond because she gave me my life. She loves me and takes care of me every moment I am with her.

Natalie Gonzalez Grade: 04
My mom is my life. She always has faith in me. My mom's eyes sparkle like diamonds and she looks like a brilliant, jeweled angel.

Yvette Hernandez Grade: 04
My mom is a hard worker who never gives up. She cares about me and my studies. She also looks as bright as a jewel.

Dania Jenkins **Grade: 04**
My mom is my everything; best friend, heroine, the glue that holds me together. I couldn't live without her. She is unique to my life.

Liliana Ledezma **Grade: 04**
Her sparkling eyes look after me. The warmth of her arms protect me, and the love from her heart says, "I love you".

Sandra Lopez **Grade: 04**
My mom deserves a diamond because she is my number one. "I wouldn't change her for all the diamonds in the world."

Ana Lopez Grade: 04
My mom gave birth to me and taught me to be helpful, respectful and honorable just like her. She is my guiding light.

Jose Manriquez **Grade: 04**
My mom is a gift from above. She makes my heart soar. I love her because she is my special gem.

Diana Ninez Grade: 04
My mom is an angel from heaven. She takes care of me and is always by my side to guide and help me through life.

Ashley Robles Grade: 04
My mother deserves a shiny, sparkling diamond. First, she is always there for me. She is also very trustworthy, good-hearted, and tender towards me.

Ricardo Ruiz Grade: 04
I think my mom should get a diamond because she's always there for me. When I have problems, she always talks me through them.

* Amethyst winners in bold.

Emmanuel Salcedo   Grade: 04
My mom is so gracious and filled with elegance like an angel from heaven to earth. She is my special gift.

Sofia Sanchez   Grade: 04
My mom is the golden light of the sun. When she's sad, the sun does not rise. She's everything in my bright and sparkly world.

Lizet Vargas   Grade: 04
I have a warm and loving mom. She is like a soft cloud. She comforts means she holds me close to her.

Ricky Vazquez   Grade: 04
My mom's love to me is loyal and true, no matter if I'm happy or blue. My mom is my soul, deep in my heart.

Zulema Vazquez   Grade: 04
This diamond, my mom is someone wonderful who I think of with fondness. She brightens my day, even when I'm feeling sad.

Adeline Velazquez   Grade: 04
My mom is a real angel. Her smile is like sunshine. I love her more than all the diamonds in the world.

Linda Vista Elementary
Mission Viejo

Teacher: Miriam Keilar

Marco Almaguer   Grade: 06
My mom deserves a diamond because she is like an angel from up above with hugs and kisses that makes my day.

Karla Avila   Grade: 06
Mom, you are a soul beneath my heart. I love you so, you're always there no matter what. You shine like a star in heaven.

Whitney Bagley   Grade: 06
My mom deserves a diamond because a sun is bright and so is she. Except the sun can't replace my mom, no one can.

Brianna Cabello   Grade: 06
My mom is like a diamond. She's someone you wouldn't want to lose. You would love and appreciate her. You wouldn't want anyone but her.

Isabel Castaneda   Grade: 06
My mom deserves a diamond because she is my guardian. She is like an angel that watches over me, that shines in the light. Mom.

Leanna Cockerham   Grade: 06
My mom deserves a diamond because she is loving to people the way she loves me. She blooms like a flower, pretty as can be.

Tracy Flores   Grade: 06
Two reasons why my mother deserves a diamond: She is the rose in my garden, the light in my life. I love you, mom.

Maria Hernandez   Grade: 06
Shiny like a diamond. Huggable as a teddy bear. Sweet as a lollipop. Loveable as if she were Valentine's Day.

Christina Komoto   Grade: 06
My mom deserves a diamond. My mother's personality is like ice cream. It will make you happy like a dream. I love you, Mom.

Benjamin Rumbaugh   Grade: 06
Even though my mom is more shiny, magnificent and much better than all the diamonds in the world, she would be proud to get one.

Costas Soler   Grade: 06
Your eyes like diamonds glistening in the morning sunlight, your hair like a beautiful river flowing out to sea. Your sweet love of all things.

Ava Stone   Grade: 06
My mom deserves a diamond because she is like a sun that always shines. A heart that never breaks. I love you, mom.

Jocelyne Vera   Grade: 06
I'll tell you twice, there is no price for this precious jewel I hold so dear. It's so bright, it's like a light.

Keith Waite   Grade: 06
My mom deserves a diamond because she helps me when I'm down and she spreads cheer whenever she's around.

Linda Vista Elemen.
Orange

Teacher: Orlene Burd

Quinton Buss   Grade: 04
My mom loves me very much while she give me great ideas. She helps me with my homework while I feel the kindness.

Jenna Conine   Grade: 04
Birds singing, flowers growing, sun's shining, her beauty's here, the twinkle in her eye sparkles everywhere, listen to your heart and say, "I love you."

Izick Larios   Grade: 04
Your beautiful as a flower and you smell like a rose but most of all you're my loveable mom.

Evan Mariesin   Grade: 04
My mother's heart is like a rose, always open, always loving, my mother is always kind and appreciates whatever I do, I love her.

Matthew McGinns   Grade: 04
My mom caring like the moon to the stars. As loving as clouds to the sky. As graceful and gentle as a deer.

Lily Nguyen   Grade: 04
Mom, you are so special in everything you do. You're so sweet and gentle. Your looks and your love is so heavenly sweet.

Skylar Schrank   Grade: 04
My mom is faithful and grateful. She loves me so much. She has a touch of love everywhere. She's my me and only mom.

Faith Truitt   Grade: 04
Her eyes sparkle like the sun. She's as sweet as cotton candy and the best part is she's all mine. I love you, mommy.

Libby Zenke   Grade: 04
For me, she's as sweet as tea. She fills me with joy, just like a toy. She's the right mother for me.

Teacher: Janet Peal

Savannah Davis   Grade: 05
Her eyes are like the ocean when it hits the sun and when she smiles at me, she makes me feel like I'm number one.

Alyssa Kelsey   Grade: 05
I love my mom. I love her lots. She is so sweet. She's never not. She is mighty fine and I'm glad she's all mine.

Moddy Medina   Grade: 05
I'll never say my mom is perfect, because nobody is. I can say she is beautiful, and loving to me. Hopefully, that's what you'll see.

Kelsey Mercado   Grade: 05
Her eyes glow like a moonlit sky. Her heart is sweet like candy. Her smile brightens up the day. She brings peace to my life.

Alexandria Patrick   Grade: 05
I love the way you look at me. Like I am special to you. Your beautiful eyes and heart so pure. I'll always love you.

Jerry Sandoval   Grade: 05
Mom, you are truly one of God's greatest gifts to me. I thank God for my mother more than any other gift. I love her.

Teacher: Kelly Ward

Kathleen Cunningham   Grade: 04
Her voice, a singing angel. Her soul, a mysterious wonder, her triumphant mind, a beautiful light, my mom, a loveable charm.

Madison Jenkins   Grade: 04
A little bit of moonlight and a little bit of sparkle. My mom is sparkling like the sun. She's the one.

Kaitlyn Meeder   Grade: 04
She cures me when I'm sick. Her heart and my heart stick. She's the one who gave me life, without her I'd not be alive.

Ethan Plettinck   Grade: 04
My mom is like light even at night. She is what makes the sun rise, she's the reason why I'm not afraid to live.

Kate Taylor   Grade: 04
My mom has heart. Her heart is as big as the earth and filled with love too. She loves me for who I am.

Los Alamitos Elementary
Los Alamitos

Teacher: Marilyn Schefski

Megan Bowers   Grade: 04
Mom, you have a heart of gold. You are always so bold. You are the prettiest, kindest, flower. You're a beautiful queen in a tower.

Algernon Carillo   Grade: 04
My mom has a caring heart. She is also loving, funny and very smart. She deserves the grand prize because she has such beautiful eyes.

Chloe Kwak   Grade: 04
My mom, I really need. She always puts me in the lead. She'll love me forever more, because she's the one with the winning score.

Ryan Lee   Grade: 04
My mom's the best. If she was a bird, she'd give me her nest. She's always there for me. She makes me smile in glee.

Justin Min   Grade: 04
People want to see how moms are always there to please. My mom's always taking care of me. So they'll pick her, wait and see.

Michael Oh   Grade: 04
My mom is always fair. That is why she likes to share. My beautiful mom is really great. Because of that, she has no hate.

Kaitlyn Tamares   Grade: 04
My mom's my saddle on my horse. She keeps me on my course. She cares when I am reckless. She deserves a diamond even a necklace.

Los Coyotes Elementary
La Palma

Teacher: Nicole Lamping

Colby Deterding   Grade: 02
My mom is the sweetest mom on Earth. She is as pretty as a rose. She is as sweet as pumpkin pie.

Joseph Kim   Grade: 02
My mom deserves a pretty diamond. My mom is so sweet to me. She protects me from all the danger. She loves me always.

Teacher: Leigh Logan

Krystin Cota   Grade: 05
Eyes like diamonds in the night sky, beautiful, funny, loving, all words to describe her. When she smiles I am blinded by her beautiful beam.

Conner Goen   Grade: 05
My mom shines like the morning sun, her hugs provide the warmth of a fire. And, she was my best Christmas present ever.

Scott Im   Grade: 05
My mom is the music to me. She helps me, feeds me, and talks to me. She's an angel from heaven and made from God.

Alicia Kim   Grade: 05
Cups of kindness and buckets of love. Love keeps filling like stars above. She arrives bringing arms around me. Mom means the world to me.

Sarah Park   Grade: 05
My mom is as sweet as the sweetest fruit in the whole wide world. She loves me with a big heart and I love her back too.

Caleb Rallo   Grade: 05
My mom deserves a diamond because her heart is as big as an ocean liner. Also if you look into her eyes they look like gold.

Samantha Santana   Grade: 05
My mom has a lovely face like an angel, her kisses are like everlasting love for me. Lastly her eyes are like a sunshine.

Justin Smart   Grade: 05
My mom deserves a diamond . Her eyes shine like stars. Her voice is like angels singing a song and her heart is like gold.

Lauren Wada   Grade: 05
My mom fills me with love and kindness. Mom makes me laugh. She comforts me in hard times. She encourages me to do my best.

Teacher: Pat Luft

Tony Chiang   Grade: 05
She fills me with her precious love, she voice is sweet like pure honey, her life is like a light which guides me to the future.

Rylee Clark   Grade: 05
In the purple twilight, there is a light. The first star out tonight, watching over me. That wondrous, kind, beautiful and smart star, is mom.

Kaitlyn Cota   Grade: 05
A hug that makes me feel safe. A smile that lights up my heart. "I love you" she tells me. I'll always love my mom.

Audrey Hoang   Grade: 05
As lovely as the dawn, as beautiful as the sunset, cheerful as always, who loves me very much. Always watching over me like an angel.

Emily Hsiao   Grade: 05
Overwhelming me in her kindness, flooding me with joy, a sea of diamond is nothing compared to mom's love.

Ariana Lee   Grade: 05
With eyes that shine and filled , who loves me wherever she is? Who can that be? It is my "All-Star" mother.

Nathan Marasigan   Grade: 05
My mother, loving and kind, guides me like the North Star, cares for me so much, the best one by far.

Khushbu Nadasia   Grade: 05
Her smile is like the sunshine. Her eyes are bright as the moon. Her lips are like a ruby and she shimmers at noon.

* Amethyst winners in bold.

Amanda One   Grade: 05
A river with a gentle wave, a meadow with the lightest breeze, my mother is more beautiful than all of these. My special mother.

Sara Shin   Grade: 05
Apple of my eye, affection sweet as heaven, guiding me through darkness, toward light, joy and laughter, like shooting stars. Mom, my everlasting love.

Zerena Varghese   Grade: 05
When I look into her eyes, I am looking into a valuable diamond. After she hugs me I feel loved and cared for greatly.

Anthony Won   Grade: 05
My mom brings joy and happiness even in the coldest nights. She helps me with the chores and my homework, so she deserves that diamond.

Phil Biala   Grade: 06
Her smile is what lights up my day. Her love is what makes my heart shimmer and she is the star in my sky.

Stephanie Cha   Grade: 06
My mom is my everything, she is like an angel from above, not only is she my mom, but she is also my forever diamond.

Kristine Galiger   Grade: 06
My mom is my diamond, my biggest prize possession, My mom is my life, the reason I'm alive.

Taylor Harper   Grade: 06
Saving me, day by day. Smiling to light the way. Hugging me to suffocate all the pain, and saying I love you day after day.

Kellyann Huey   Grade: 06
She's my guidance through the dark. Her smile glows and her eyes spark. She gave my life and my breath, I'll never, ever, ever forget.

Taylor Kennon   Grade: 06
She is a gem herself. She takes care of the family, she loves us, and feeds us as though we were gems too. I love her.

Joshua Kim   Grade: 06
My beautiful kind, mom deserves a diamond. She shines brightly like the sun and wherever someone needs help, she is there to help me.

Eliza Ngo   Grade: 06
Your heart is as pure as gold, kindness you will always hold. Your arms spread out with love, like the wings of a dove.

Evan Pascual   Grade: 06
I love my mother very much, her lovely eyes and gentle touch, her glistening smile like a star, she's cooler than a fancy car.

Shivani Patel   Grade: 06
A smile that makes my day, a hug that shows me the way, "I love you and I always will" she says, I believe her.

Emily Yao   Grade: 06
My mom is sweet and kind, she loves me far and near, when troubles come rushing down, my mom is always my savior.

Teacher: Mrs. Mollenkramer

Arman Abdolsalehi   Grade: 04
My mom is like an angel in the sky. She raised me and took care of me. I love her and she loves me.

Kaila Chen   Grade: 04
My mom's heart is caring and kind. She always believes that I could do it and never loses faith in me.

Aaron Chiong   Grade: 04
My mom deserves a diamond because she works hard for me. She gives me everything I want. The most important is, she gives me love.

Devin Claure   Grade: 04
Her love is like a river flowing to my heart. She smells like the beautiful poppies in California. She is the most beautiful angel floating.

Lauren Hester   Grade: 04
My mom deserves a diamond because she works hard, helps me, does fun things with me and she does her best at everything.

Jay Hong   Grade: 04
I think my mom deserves a diamond because she's generous, she's helpful and she cherishes me so much. I think my mom deserves a diamond.

Menka Jagad   Grade: 04
Dear mom, you give me so much love, and you are as beautiful as a dove. You give me so much pleasure, that I can't even measure.

Annie Kim   Grade: 04
Mother, you're so fearless. You're all hugs and kisses. You taught me many things I know. Your tenderness is like sunshine on my face.

Jimmy Kim   Grade: 04
My mom is like angel because she washes away my sorrows. She plays with me when I feel lonely, that's why I love my mom.

Brian Lee   Grade: 04
My mom is an angel making me happy when I am gloomy. She is important to me like a diamond and I love her.

Natalie Ozawa   Grade: 04
My mother cuddles with me at night, and hugs me really tight. She's there with me day and night, no matter what I'll be alright.

Tom Tran   Grade: 04
She is a hard working person and we tell our secrets, and helps me whenever I need it. I love her and she does too.

Vivian Wu   Grade: 04
My mom deserves a diamond because she cherishes me every day. Her heart is full of love and care. She is always elegant and joyful.

Jonathan Yang   Grade: 04
My mom deserves a diamond because she has always cherished me. So I want to show her and I really care about her.

Teacher: Anna Smith

Devin Antony   Grade: 06
My mom deserves a diamond because she shines brighter than the sun and she gave me life. She's invaluable and is finer than jewelry.

Tiffany Chang   Grade: 06
When the sun shines down on my mom and she smiles that perfect smile, she looks like an angel from heaven itself.

Christopher Concepcion   Grade: 06
My mom deserves a diamond not only she cleans up around the house, she cares about me. She meets my hearts desire with the hugs she gives.

Annie Fu   Grade: 06
My mom deserves a diamond because she is sweet and caring, when I'm sad she brightens up my day and blows my rain cloud away.

Clara Ju   Grade: 06
My mom deserves a diamond because she is sweeter than chocolate, more graceful and flawless than a goddess and brighter than the sun.

Eunice Kim   Grade: 06
She meets my hearts desire with every hug she gives. "My everything" is engraved on her forehead foe she is made of pure gold.

Allison Mattern   Grade: 06
Her hair is as golden as the sun on a hot summer day. Her lips are as red as an apple. I love my mom.

Emily Moscoso   Grade: 06
Her eyes are filled with care and joy, brimming with the feelings of a mother. Through mischief and scolding, her eyes show nothing but love.

Anjali Patel   Grade: 06
My mom is like a diamond, she sparkles in the sun and she glows at night like the full moon.

Travis Peralta   Grade: 06
My mom deserves a diamond because she is as graceful as a swan and as pretty as one too.

Grace Seo   Grade: 06
My mom deserves a diamond because she has a heart of hold and lots of determination. I'd love to have a hold of her imagination.

Salman Tailor   Grade: 06
Shows   Most   conspicuous   love imaginable, she Obliviates all my sorrows, cheering up mu glum expression, her Magnificent appearance makes me love even more!

Nicholes Torres   Grade: 06
She's not only mom, she's a friend. She cares for me no matter what. She works harder than anybody else. I love her no matter what.

Andrew Won   Grade: 06
My mom deserves a diamond because she is heartwarming, she will protect me at all costs and her smile is something I can't buy.

Teacher: Robin St. Hilaire

Michael Alfrante   Grade: 05
My mother should have one of these diamonds because her eyes sparkle like the diamond she is, and her smile shines like the sun above.

Aileen Arellano   Grade: 05
My mom has glamorous eyes, they sparkle like diamonds. She's as charming as an angel. I could never live without her. I love her.

Brittany Bardin   Grade: 05
My mom is an angel from above. Her smile is bright and beautiful. Her eyes twinkle in the sunlight. She is a pretty diamond.

Arianna Carmona   Grade: 05
My mother deserves a diamond because her heart is a warm safe place I can call home. My mother and I will always be together.

Blake Clark   Grade: 05
My mom is the best. Her eyes are like a sparkling diamond in the sun shining at me. She is the best mom ever.

Carson Deterding   Grade: 05
My mom is the best ever! She loves me and supports me. Her hair is red as a rose. I love my mom so much!!

Jimmy Huang   Grade: 05
My mom is like gold to me. Her mind is always thoughtful when she's doing things. She is the best mom in the world.

Sean Hutson   Grade: 05
My mom deserves a diamond because her eyes are as beautiful as the ocean. Her hair sways as fine as palm trees in the wind..

Noel John   Grade: 05
My mom is as precious as a diamond. She is a kind and loving mom. I wouldn't be here if it weren't for my mom.

Christine Kim   Grade: 05
My life is beautiful because my mom looks like a big diamond. I'm thankful that I have a mom and I love her.

Alex Noh   Grade: 05
Our main part of my family is mom. I love her and she loves me. That's why we're family, a very, very happy family.

Hanna Norton   Grade: 05
She smells like a rose, with crystals in her eyes, and as soft as the first snowflake of winter hitting the ground. She deserves one.

Deja Rice   Grade: 05
She understands me and how I feel. She has a heart of gold and she uses it. I learned from her to follow my heart.

Nicole Turudic   Grade: 05
My moms eyes are beautiful as the sky, her hair is brown like a brownie, she is beautiful. I could not live without her.

Teacher: Muntzi Verga

Kasandra Alverez   Grade: 04
My mom is like an angel taking away my sorrowful moments. She is like a river filled with love. She is my beautiful gemstone.

Alex Antos   Grade: 04
My mom is loving and supportive. She helps everybody. My mom is always giving. I compare her with an angel. She always looking her best.

Darshanie Botejue   Grade: 04
Holding me close mom is like Mother Nature. Her face is the sun. Her hair is the air. Her voice is the birds chirping beautifully.

Aaron Corrillo   Grade: 04
My mom is the sweetest mom in the world. When I hear her voice it is as soft as my favorite blanket.

Luis Escolano   Grade: 04
Carrying me in her arms, that's when I knew she deserved a diamond. She deserves a diamond because she's mother anyone could have.

Kimberley Friday   Grade: 04
As pure as gold, my mom is the best. She is sweeter than candy. She is gentle and kind. She loves our family. She's lovely.

Karina Gomez   Grade: 04
Holding hands with my mother makes me feel so safe. I never feel afraid when I'm with her. My mom is always there for me.

Noah Hernandez   Grade: 04
My mom is loving and caring. Her beautiful green eyes gleam when she looks at me. Her hugs make me feel so wonderful.

Jessica Jackson   Grade: 04
Every day my precious as a glistening sea that sparkles like a diamond. She gives up her time to spend worth me.

Jonathon Kim   Grade: 04
My mom is like the Queen of Hearts because she was so much love in her heart for my family.

Sarah Lee   Grade: 04
When it's dark she is like a bright light. When I'm sad she cheers me up. When I'm afraid she is like a safe place.

* Amethyst winners in bold.

Lemuel Lee Grade: 04
Cradling me into a silky quilt, my mom did on a sunny day. Holding me with all her love, "precious son" she whispered to me.

Karissa Mumford Grade: 04
Hard working, caring, loving, wonderful, fantastic, kind mother. She cares and loves me for who I am. She is always here for me.

Ashlee Noh Grade: 04
Always keeping so cuddly and warm...in her soft milky hands, like an angel...since I was born.

Cameron Paninsoro Grade: 04
Loving and caring for me. Mom is always watching out for me. She tells me bedtime stories before I fall asleep. She is a diamond

Lindsey Pike Grade: 04
I love my mom, she is the best. She keeps me warm and loves me so. She is like lightening in my life.

Mariah Preciado Grade: 04
My mom is a very nice person, she always makes my eyes sparkle with love. She's always there for me when I need her.

Robert Ross Grade: 04
When I first saw her I knew she was my true diamond. She sparkles, shines and glows in the midnight light. She's my gemstone mother.

Andrew Solares Grade: 04
Out of your body I came. The moment I heard your voice it was smooth as silk. Beautiful you were the moment I saw you.

Emily Spencer Grade: 04
Soaring, gliding through the sky, my mom is like a mother bird who cares and loves her little ones.

Brian Ta Grade: 04
My mom is caring and loving. She helps me understand and get ready for tests. Her hugs warm me like the sun.

Wesley Wan Grade: 04
When I need help my mom is here for me. Her love flows like a waterfall. She is like a garden of roses to me.

Kirstin White Grade: 04
The feelings she gives me when I greet her is the best. She helps me stay on task. My mom is number one.

Teacher: Shannon Vey

Nick Hisamoto Grade: 06
She is like a star gleaming in the sky. Her eyes are as beautiful as a flower. She smells like a rose in a garden.

Allie Howe Grade: 06
My mother is loving from the heart. With her dazzling smile and caring arms, I'm positive that she will guide me down the right path.

Kaitlyn Jenkins Grade: 06
Her heart-melting eyes. Her golden heart, her love is stronger than anything in the world . She is known as Super Mom to me.

Austin Kasaka Grade: 06
My mom deserves a diamond because like a tree she carefully watches me grow and she never looks away because she knows I might go.

Matthew Kim Grade: 06
My mom is the conductor of the life around her. Without her, life will fall into a shadow of despair, but that isn't out destiny.

Justin Lee Grade: 06
Why does my mom deserve a diamond? For she is as constant as the sun and as righteous as the moon. I love my mom.

Lauren Lukacsa Grade: 06
My mother is so tender and she's as sweet as a rose, as well as being fun and exciting, she's also so unique.

Shannon Mc Guinness Grade: 06
My mother shines like the stars. She never turns anyone down. The fire in her heart glows everywhere she goes. I love her so.

Sophia Moon Grade: 06
We shared laughter, teardrops, and love. You turned my life black to white. You helped through hard times. I love you mom!

Michelle Moreno Grade: 06
Her voice is as sweet as flowers, her face is soft as silk. You'll wonder who this person is, she's my sweet-hearted mother.

Alyssa Pascual Grade: 06
My mom is diligent, caring and very loving. She's as sweet as chocolate and as unique as a dove and she'll always love me.

Melissa Pena Grade: 06
My mom is sweet like a rose, pure as the sun and the way her eyes shine it's like a glistening moon in the sky.

Jacob Pereira Grade: 06
My mom deserves a diamond because she is beautiful like the night sky and the stars sparkle in her beautiful eyes.

Zonia Roland Grade: 06
My mom is as perfect as a diamond, she's the only one I've got, when ever I don't get my homework, she's there to help.

Angelique Santos Grade: 06
The mother of mine that's loving and sweet always shines on my day because I know she's one of the stars that always glances at me.

Hannah Son Grade: 06
Mom deserves a diamond, she's a diligent worker I adore. She tries to give me what I want. I think it's time to exchange sides.

Susmitha Varghese Grade: 06
Eyes sparkle like night time stars, lips red as a radiant ruby, heart as gold, two words to describe all this: My mom.

Cody Westbrook Grade: 06
She's as benevolent as they come, a perfect soul. She never hurts anyone and loves everything. Perfect, fun, and loving, these words describe my mom.

Troy Yamaguchi Grade: 06
She is not perfect, as no one is but the next best thing my mother is wise, kind and fair. Always treating others with care.

Mac Arthur (Douglas) Fundamental Inter
Santa Ana

Teacher: Cristina Barber

Melissa Aguirre Grade: 06
Never let me go mom, never. You are a rose protecting me with your thorns. Together we are complete. Without you I am nothing.

Angel Banfill Grade: 06
My mom is the ember of my life, the one thing that keeps me living, if that ember ever went out I would be no more

Melanie De La Cruz Grade: 06
My mom is like a gold coin that sparkles in the sunlight. My mom is like a diamond that she flashes like a camera.

Natalie De La Rosa Grade: 06
Whenever I see my mom she shines like the beautiful horizon, she is as gentle as the water and smooth as air

Mariela Diaz — Grade: 06
I love my mom, she's the light of an angel who shine from the sky. She's the treasure to my heart that I'll keep inside

Eduardo Duarte — Grade: 06
My mom is fabulous just like a blooming red rose. She's just like gold when she shines in my heart.

Jessica Fotiades — Grade: 06
my mom is a blooming gardenia. Her love is essential. She is a dove soaring through the sky, she is the wind beneath my wings.

Briana Gomez — Grade: 06
My mom deserves everything. She's like a bunny that I could hug any time. My mom is like a diamond because she shines every day.

Sharon Hernandez — Grade: 06
You love me like I love you. Since my birth you took care of me. When you get old I will take care of you

Christian Mejia — Grade: 06
Her love is stronger than a lions roar. Her love is as valued as a diamond. Her honesty is as strong as a blazing fire.

Kassandra Munoz — Grade: 06
When I hug my mom I feel the heat of her love that is warm like the sun and hot like fire

Michael Nava — Grade: 06
My mom, she is an angel sent from heaven above to guide me through life, care, protect, and the number one thing is love

Angel Perez — Grade: 06
My mom is special like a diamond, she is sweet as a puppy, strong like a redwood tree, she is as gentle as a breeze.

Karen Quintana — Grade: 06
Mom is a diamond shiny and bright. A rainbow in the blue sky. I know she'll be on my side. This love will never die.

Jasmine Rea — Grade: 06
She's like a unicorn, magical and remarkable. Mom is my number one. She is always going to be my diamond, enjoyable, lovable and charming.

Justine Reyes — Grade: 06
My mom cuddles me like a puppy. She is gold that always sparkles. Like a sunflower, my mom's love grows. You're the number one mom.

Delilah Rojo — Grade: 06
You made my heart. My heart keeps beating because of you. I look in your eyes, they sparkle like diamond with special love for me.

Brandon Smith — Grade: 06
My mom is the greatest thing in the world. My mom is a diamond, unbreakable and forever. I love my mom.

Anthony Teran — Grade: 06
Mom is the person that made my heart beat, the one that has the heart of an angel.

Teacher: Julee Blair

Juan Abarca — Grade: 06
her beauty shines forever like a star in the sky. Her eyes represent heaven and all that's pure. She's the best mom ever to live.

Alondra Aguirre — Grade: 06
She's blissful air I breathe. A blanket that keeps me warm and medicine I take to make me feel better. My mom is my hero.

Marilyn Avina — Grade: 06
She is like a blazing sun shining down on me, uncovering the darkness and leading me to the right path on every step I take.

Metztli Beas — Grade: 06
Her love shines brighter than the sun… heals me when I'm hurt…never stops loving me when we fight…is always there to protect me.

Brianna Casillas — Grade: 06
She is calm and quiet, full of peace like the simple breeze, In my eyes nobody else will be so perfect to me but her.

Michael Cecere — Grade: 06
Like the sun. a day is never bright without her. Ring as the day awakes to shine upon other's fates. Her light never burns out.

Erick Chavez — Grade: 06
Her smell is like the morning breeze in my face. Her smile is the shiniest star in the sky. She's more precious than a diamond.

Brian Chuong — Grade: 06
The sun shines bright and the moon as well. As strong as the bond of my years, my mother and her enlightening, proud, encouraging smile.

Daniel Cruz — Grade: 06
She's the sunlight of my day, brightening and making my day joyful. She is also like Mother Nature giving her plants sunlight, water and soil.

Kenari Drayton — Grade: 06
Gentle like the midnight breeze filling me with courage, always by my side for my protection. She is the one I love, my mother.

Anne Duong — Grade: 06
Delicate as a flower filled with glistening dew, my mother encourages me through complex obstacles like thorns on roses to my destiny, toward relieving petals.

Jamar Edwards — Grade: 06
Angel sent from God. Being precious and open-hearted to her adoring children and family who feels she is rapidly shining like the June sun.

Vanessa Estrada — Grade: 06
Mom is as graceful as a grown swan. She is a rare flower who blossoms once in a lifetime. My mommy is loving, caring and hardworking.

Kayla Fausto — Grade: 06
Mom is my friend, mom is my life in a battle together we fight…mom is my heart that sparkles above, in the cloudy sky.

Gabriel Flores — Grade: 06
With love as strong as Mr. T, I really think she is sweeter than candy. Being with my mom is as pleasant as a tropical breeze.

Kevin Gonzalez — Grade: 06
My mom is like the sparkling sea of hope, every drop is an ounce of love. She's willing to sacrifice her personal space for me.

Juan Gonzalez — Grade: 06
She caresses me with love. Her sparkling face brings joy to me. She is a rainbow amidst the rain. She is like a peaceful river.

Eduardo Guapilla — Grade: 06
Mom is always there when I fall. She helps me to the top. If it wasn't for her I wouldn't be where I am now.

Brenna Hanly — Grade: 06
Shines my way through hard times. Encourages me to fill my destiny. Shines like a bright star, as a guiding point, in the night sky.

Christian Lopez — Grade: 06
A gift from the heavens, so graceful and sweet. Shining a light for me in the darkest of days. Helping me find the right way.

* Amethyst winners in bold.

Dayilynn Macias   Grade: 06
Like a star in the deep blue sky, shining toward my destination.   Picking me up every time I fall down. Loving me endlessly until time.

Crystal Mejia   Grade: 06
She shines like the sun up in the glorious sky. When the wind blows it blows with pride and love in the air like mom.

Peter Nguyen   Grade: 06
Like a swaying tree in the rustling wind. She is strong and courageous with a determined heart but also calm like the radiant flowers in the pasture.

Nolan Nguyen   Grade: 06
The rose of my life, she blooms comfort and kindness.   Worth more than any diamond, the sun on her side, both smile down upon me.

Isai Ocampo   Grade: 06
Always with a benevolent attitude. Like starlight's blaze lighting my route. Always wanting the destiny of wisdom in my life. Her love for me…Infinite.

Victoria Ortega   Grade: 06
Mom sparkles like stars in the midnight sky, stands out more than any diamond. A wonderful role model and a wonderful person, my mom.

Ivette Parra   Grade: 06
My mom carries me through life to get to my destiny. She does what is best for me, even it feels unfair. Mom knows best.

Crystal Peng   Grade: 06
Her happiness shines like the golden rays of the daylight sun. Her cheery, warm skin keeps me safely secured under the stars. Most cherished, mother.

Ethan Pham   Grade: 06
A glistening star shining brightly in the pitch black night.   Raining glorious amounts of light to reveal my future path of success, glory and brilliance.

Alicia Quintero   Grade: 06
My mother is like Christmas morning, joyful and full of excitement. Hearing her laugh is like hearing angels singing hallelujah in the highest. She's my everything.

Giovanna Rebollar   Grade: 06
She pushes me towards my future, encourages me all the way. Never lets me feel as if I can't win an A. This is mom.

Nael Reyes   Grade: 06
Her love is more valuable than any diamond. The one who raised me, gave birth to me, and gives unconditional love. When enters darkness fades.

Anthony Saaverda   Grade: 06
Funny as a comic who cooks and cleans. Pretty as a flower who smells as fragrant as a field of honeysuckle that loves and cares.

Adrian Salgado   Grade: 06
Like a lovely blossoming rose blooming radiantly everyday. Each fragrant flower petal is the different kind of love that she always shows me each day.

Javeria Syed   Grade: 06
My role model to accomplishment, a person who's my hero. Graceful wings protecting me like guards. A delicate jewel I will never lot go of.

Mellanie Tran   Grade: 06
A brilliant rose in bloom. So hardworking, yet always serene. She brings out the best in everyone. A radiant sunbeam. More precious than priceless gemstones.

Alexis Tran   Grade: 06
Eyes that stare at me as I go. A voice whom I listen to for help. The one I believe, trust, honor and respect.

Moises Villegas   Grade: 06
A seed becoming a flower. My mom's love grows bigger everyday in good times or bad. I know I can count on my mom.

Ashley Vu   Grade: 06
Graceful and elegant like an orchid gently, delicately floating on ice blue water. Every day looking more heavenly than ever. Is and will be irrevocably treasured

Raiven Williams-Tidwell   Grade: 06
My mother, like a ray of light , fills my life with joy and happiness. Her heart as big as the sun. She's a shining star.

Teacher: Sandi Clifford

Isaac Ambriz   Grade: 07
Her sweet and sensitive heart is as strong as her personality.   She never puts you down in a bad situation.

Kailyn Araiza   Grade: 07
Always need them by your side. I couldn't have asked for a better one. It's my mom, loving, caring and like an angel to me.

Adrianna Banuelos   Grade: 07
She is a magical lady who sparkles like stars during night. She is fabulous because she can do any thing unlike anyone else. She's my mom.

Daniel Chau   Grade: 07
Her smile like a sparkling stone. Her love created from blazing sun. An eternal flame encrusted in her gift to me everlasting. My mom.

Sarah Correa   Grade: 07
She is strong like bamboo. I am her little cub.   She shelters me and cares for me. She is my fierce and caring mother.

Rosalia Delgado   Grade: 07
She is a friend for me. She is the one I reach for help. She is a loving and caring person. She is my mom.

Michaela Gideon   Grade: 07
She's perfect in every way. She shines just like the diamond she deserves. She's my hero and nothing can change her love for me.

Daniel Gonzalez   Grade: 07
You're a treasure all your own. You don't need fancy stones. Your love is worth more than million dollars.   You love me, that's what matters!

Melissa Hernandez   Grade: 07
The times we've spent together are unforgettable, it makes me realize how much you mean to me. I will always cherish moments we've spent together.

Michael Martinez   Grade: 07
Many ways you show you care, mom. Your love to me is deeper than the ocean. It seems you can do anything to help me.

Magali Martinez   Grade: 07
She is as strong and beautiful as waves. Her eyes sparkle like the radiant stars. I will never let her go. She is my mom.

Steve Pineda   Grade: 07
God gave me an angel so beautiful and so loving. He told me to trust my angel, give her respect. I should call her mom.

Karina Ramirez   Grade: 07
She's as sweet as an apple in the springtime, following me through life, blessing my heart, like an angel, she's the best mom ever.

Justin Reeves   Grade: 07
My mom's voice is velvet when she talks and she could brighten up any day when she smiles. Her eyes can warm anybody's heart.

Michelle Sanchez Grade: 07
Some mothers sparkle others glow. Mine shines like a star in the dark of the sky. Loved by family, friends and even dogs too.

Daisy Taamilo Grade: 07
My mom is everything, she is gentle like the palms of my hands and as sweet as a banana cream pie. My mom is everything!

Joselyne Velez **Grade: 07**
For her beauty and kindness, she deserves a diamond. She sparkles and radiates light unto others. She is one of a kind, a true treasure.

Adrian Villegas Grade: 07
She shines like a star in the sky. Looks like the moon, even brighter. I lover her more than anyone else.

Teacher: Deborah Davis

Saul Flores Grade: 08
Mother's love is as pure as an angel from the heavens. Her love is medicine to my soul when I'm upset.

Jennifer Molina **Grade: 08**
My mommy is as delicate as a glass and as beautiful as a sunset on the beach. My mom twinkles like a star at night.

Marilyn Oum Grade: 08
Mothers are a blessing sent from heaven above spreading warmth and tenderness with kindness and love.

Alejandra Perez Grade: 08
My mom is like an angel. A goddess in a dream. One with a heart of gold to share with the entire universe.

Daniel Rodriguez Grade: 08
Mom is like my sun. She also is my fun. She teaches me manners and shows me right from wrong because she is my mom.

Angel Santiago Grade: 08
Put some soul. Put a little compassion. Add a heart made of gold. Put lots of love and you made my mom.

Jasmin Silva **Grade: 08**
My mom is my inspiration. She's my shoulder to lean on, she's the sunshine to my days and I owe her the world and more.

Samuel Sosa Grade: 08
My mom is like the sun. She always brings light into my world. In the night, she is the moon the one who guides me.

Teacher: John De Gree

Melissa Barrera Grade: 07
Mom, I love you from the bottom of my heart. As long as I have blood rushing through my veins. I will always love you.

Sarena Bloeser Grade: 07
Shining stars in the dark blue sky shines like my mothers eyes. Her heart is as pure as the golden shining sun.

Alexander q Bustos Grade: 07
My mom deserves a diamond because without her I am nothing. She is worth to me more than any diamond in the world.

Jake Cathey Grade: 07
Mom, she had a diamond for a heart, she's as sweet as a tart, she'll never let you fall because she is kind to all.

Cristian Chanon Grade: 07
My moms eyes sparkle like diamonds in sun, her skin, soft as a rose petal, her heart, big and soft as a dozen roses.

Tiana Gamino Grade: 07
Your eyes dazzle like the stars. You smell like a bloom of flowers. Your looks are so fly in sky because you are my mom.

Bryan Gonzalez Grade: 07
First I called her mommy, then mom, now she's my hero. I'm small and helpless. How about you? Here is my mother to the rescue.

Richard Hernandez Grade: 07
When the sun hits her eyes they twinkle, when the moon hits them they glow, she deserves it because she shines like a diamond.

Miguel Hernandez Grade: 07
The one in my very soul. My heart glitters like millions of crystals. She is like a beautiful Earth Angel

Matthew Magana Grade: 07
My mom deserves a diamond because she always puts herself last and she's a giver and not a taker. I would love to bless her.

Nicholas Nunez Grade: 07
My mom is the one who brings me joy and laughter. She's never let me down and never will. She is always by my side.

Jessica Orellana Grade: 07
She shines in the luminous sun. Her eyes glow like the moonlight. She will always have a place in my heart.

Mike Ortega Grade: 07
Mother with affection that gives so much devotion. She blooms my life when I'm gloom in life. She guides me and stays beside me!

Austin Phillips **Grade: 07**
I look into her eyes, they twinkle like a diamond. Her heart engraved with love, her voice is like those of beautiful golden doves.

Maury Quintana **Grade: 07**
Her eyes shine as if I'm looking at the bright sunlight. One look at her face tells me that this day shall have no night.

Michael Serrano Grade: 07
My mom means the world to me. I love her like I love my sports. She is all I need to go on.

Irvin Urquiza Grade: 07
My mom is a royal queen. Beautiful like an angel in the sky. She is worth more than diamonds and gold. She is my mom.

Adriana Valencia Grade: 07
My mothers brown eyes bring no frown, her song flows through the air when she sings. Until this day I still say I love you!

Teacher: Maria La Frossia

Kaitlyn Ascencio **Grade: 07**
Her heart, the size of the world. Her hugs, like mountains. She is always there for me. The little things she does make a difference.

Rita Caballero Grade: 07
My mom is like a shining, bright star. Her hugs are warm like her heart. She's like a diamond and a star to me.

Monica Cardenas **Grade: 07**
She rises over the horizon. She's better than Wonder Woman. One word can describe her, Super! She's a friend, a doctor, and she's mom.

Kristy Duarte Grade: 07
MY mom is kind and sweet. Loving and gentle. Brings joy wherever she goes. She can bring peace to the troubled mind.

Alex Garcia Grade: 07
Mom is another word for love. She is as peaceful and graceful as a dove, very nice and calm. I'll always love my mom!

Luis Garcia **Grade: 07**
Your skilled fingers, your gentle voice, your sparkly attitude. You are the springtime in the winter of my life.

* Amethyst winners in bold.

Danny Gomez Grade: 07
My angel, my heart, my mom is the fire in my soul. She gets me by everyday. I know the heavens gave her to me.

Karla Gomez Grade: 07
She shines like sunlight day and night. Her hair curly as curly fires. The way she kisses us goodnight. That's why she deserves a diamond.

Allen Huang Grade: 07
Her voice like the chiming nightingale. Soothes the dingiest nightmares. With that motherly affection to protect her family even winter feels tender by her side.

Louie Jota Grade: 07
Her soft touch from her gentle hands. The brightness of her beauty is seen throughout foreign lands. Her sweet voice and protection. My special mother.

Melissa Kusinsky Grade: 07
My mom, she has a heart of gold, a smile that shines bright and eyes that sparkle like diamonds. I love my mom very much.

Jordyn Louis Grade: 07
As I wake up early morning. I see mother's face. She then gives me her words of warmth. "Good morning, honey". Now I feel safe.

Carlos Muro Grade: 07
Like sunset's glow, she glistens in moonlight. Her expression, like bursts of laughter. Her arms, wings from an angel, so gentle. I love you, Mom.

Priscilla Ramirez Grade: 07
A light in my dark sky. A jewel in a pile of nothing. You my mother, the one who gave me life. Mom, I love you!

Jessica Riestra Grade: 07
Without her, rain will be around every corner. She's my soul, the wind surrounding me. She's a true hero and patriotic, that I love.

Rodolfo Rodriguez Grade: 07
Mom is a shining star. She loves me for who I am. I wouldn't be able to live without her. I love her so dear.

Amber Rodriguez Grade: 07
Mom, such a beautiful word. My mom is the sunshine of my day and the beautiful shining stars of the night. I appreciate everything she does.

Chantal Ruvalcaba Grade: 07
She is my one and only hero. She has super powers that make me love her more and more each day. She is my mom!

Casey Tran Grade: 07
Her skin, smooth as a diamond. Her touch, soft and delicate as a feather. Her beauty, like no other. Her love, I will cherish forever.

Aaron Villanueva Grade: 07
My mom is a magnificent person with a great personality. She is sweeter than the sweetest sugar. She is more beautiful than a summer's sunset.

Teacher: Kathleen Peterson

Viviana Borroel Grade: 07
When I'm passing through the darkness, my mom is my guiding light. Even in the thickest mist...my shining star on a storm night.

Juan Contreras Grade: 07
Her heart is made of pure gold. Her eyes are like bright shining stars. Nobody can take her place, God gave this mother to me.

Angie Joaquin Grade: 07
When it rains, the waves from the ocean are strong, but not as strong as the love that my mom has for her family.

Abigail Nolasco Grade: 07
My mothers love is like a poem with just the right rhyme,. Her love touches my heart and is always on my mind.

America Quintana Grade: 07
When I wake, light consumes me. She is the star in my sky, the fire in my heart, for she is my mom, forever mine.

Jason Rojas Grade: 07
The word "mom" doesn't fit what I consider mine to be, which is my best friend, a friend I know I'll have for life.

Joseph Sandoval-Rios Grade: 07
My mom loves us so much. She never makes us feel like we disappoint her. Her love is deeper than the sea.

Miguel Tapia Grade: 07
My mother, my strongest motivation. There was never a single day that my mom wasn't there. Because of her I know I could accomplish anything.

Teacher: Christine Yellin

Crystal Altamirano Grade: 06
My mom so bright, as an endless light. Her eyes like stars, as they twinkle through night. She is the golden key to my heart.

Erick Alvarez Grade: 06
My mom's eyes shine like starry night. Her heart is as golden as the sunset. She is the goddess of me, her little gem.

Albert Alvarez Grade: 06
She brings me hope and joy. She's positive and caring. I love her like you do. Of course, she's my mother.

Lisa Anzurez Grade: 06
Your eyes are lights that guide us through. Your voice helps us pick the right paths, your hands gives us hugs that never fade away.

Eliane Castiglione Grade: 06
The crystal in her eyes that shine out waiting for a call. The relaxing words coming out her mouth and all the warmth from one gentle hug.

Teresa Chavez Grade: 06
Her golden heart is beating. She cleanses my soul. She is my everything. She is my gift from God. I'm proud to call her mom.

Adrian Delgado Grade: 06
Mom, you're the beat of my heart. You are the only one who can touch my soul. You are the thing that makes me encouraged.

Jasmin Diaz Grade: 06
My mom is always there for me. She never gives up. She is the best mom I could ask for.

Tiana Esera Grade: 06
The grass deep in her eyes. Her smile that she embraces. My mother, so unique, so beautiful. I love her as I say it.

Miguel Guillen Grade: 06
Mom. The brightest of stars. Stands out among the rest. Her voice, a nice soothing sound. Always a delight looking at her sweet smiles. Mom.

Kevin Hanly Grade: 06
Her eyes- shining crystals. Her love is my light, the deeds she has done are like an Angel's. She is the work of God's compassion.

Adrian Hernandez Grade: 06
My mom wouldn't hurt a fly. Her voice is like stitches to my broken heart. To me, she is a star in the middle of the sky.

Jesus Huerta Grade: 06
Her shiny eyes fill the sky with light. Her niceness warms anybody from head to toe. Her smile can make a pile of stars shimmer.

Myriah Ibarra   Grade: 06
My mom is the glue that keeps me together, she is beautiful in every single way. She is the one I will love forever and always.

James Lopez   Grade: 06
Her compassion warms my heart, her eyes shine like a pearl in a clam. Her loving care fills me up with joy.

Andrew May   Grade: 06
Her brown eyes are golden shining stars. Her crystal clear voice soothes and comforts me. Her flawless hands pick me up when I fall.

Justine Mills   Grade: 06
Her voice as soothing as a lullaby. Her love more powerful than a nuclear bomb. She is the star that shines in my soul.

Vanessa Morales   Grade: 06
My ocean of love, sky of compassion. A forest of sunshine. Stars of cherishment. My individual sun of unique, a part of my soul. My mom.

Albert Nghiem   Grade: 06
I am lost in darkness wandering into unknown places. My mother's crystal light finds me, protects me with her shield of love.

Maria Oum   Grade: 06
God created a special mother. Her eyes are brown like the Earth. Heart like pure sunshine. And God gave that special mother to me.

Noemi Quezada   Grade: 06
She's like an endless light flowing through my heart. Her love, like a warm blanket. Her eyes, like a star in the moonlight, protecting me.

Jeremiah Rengal   Grade: 06
Mom's crystallized heart shines in the dimmest light. She speaks words as valued as gold. Her love can't be replaced. Mom, the source of life.

Vanessa Rosario   Grade: 06
Her smile is as majestic as her laugh. Her eyes twinkle in the moonlight. She is sweeter than apple pie. She is wonderful.

Rosa Salazar   Grade: 06
Her eyes shine like stars. A heart filled with gold. When she talks to me, I hear words of joy. She is my one hero.

Abraham Sanchez   Grade: 06
Your eyes are like gems sparkling in the sunshine. Your heart and emotions shine like a gold mine. Those emotions are worth more than gold.

RaeAnn Sandoval   Grade: 06
Her eyes twinkle bright as stars. You can see them both from Mars. She is special like a gem. She won't be sad ever again.

Brystal Torres   Grade: 06
Each day my mom's eyes dissolve into my heart. She is like canvas, I can express myself when she's around. I love my mom.

Pablo Urtiz   Grade: 06
Her eyes shine like the morning sun. Her words of life make the birds sing. She glows like a full, bright moon. My mother.

Macolm (John) Elementary
Laguna Niguel

Teacher: Colleen Dilloughery

Nicole Dec   **Grade: 03**
She's a dove giving peace to the world. She has a smile to brighten up the room. She's a heart flowing to give warm love.

Armmon Kianipey   Grade: 03
My mom deserves a diamond because she's nice and caring. She's nice as a dog licking you. That's why she deserves a diamond.

Sophia LaVoie   Grade: 03
She is a great worker and she is clever. When I'm sad she makes me laugh. She is kind and beautiful. She's very sweet.

Michaela Mahoney   **Grade: 03**
She is beautiful and strong, brave and caring. Her mom named her Harmony and I know why, because that's what she brings to everybody, Harmony.

Nicholas Revolinski   Grade: 03
My mom is always helpful. She is always eager to help me with my homework. She is always nice to others. She is the best mom.

Teacher: Lia Haubert

Ashley Gant   **Grade: 03**
My mom deserves a diamond because she has a Grammy award winning smile. She is always there for me because she loves me.

Caroline Halloran   Grade: 03
My mom is always there for me. I love her so much. My mom only doesn't deserve a diamond, she is a diamond.

Roman Jones   **Grade: 03**
My mom deserves a diamond because she never left my side. She is the diamond of my life. I love my mom so much.

Conner Onesto   Grade: 03
My mo is loving and helpful. She deserves a diamond. My mom always cheers me up when I am crying. My mom is the best!

Sophia Rzankowski   **Grade: 03**
She shines like a magnificent diamond. Her eyes are like big beautiful diamonds. She is one. She needs one.

Teacher: Megan Hunner

A J Baker   Grade: 03
My mom deserves a diamond because she's warm hearted. She helps me when I feel bad and when I'm down. She's lovely!

Ryan Borovinsky   Grade: 03
my mom deserves a diamond because she is a shining star in the sky. She's caring, lovely and nice and she is quiet when I concentrate.

Cameron Cecil   Grade: 03
My mom deserves a diamond because she shimmers and shines just like one. She also deserves one because she's thoughtful and caring. I love her!

Andrew Davis   Grade: 03
My mom deserves a diamond because she cares about me and helps me with my homework. She greets me each day with her radiant smile.

Robbie Jaimerena   **Grade: 03**
Out of all the things my mom loved, she loved me the most. She cared unselfishly for others. My beautiful mom is phenomenal.

Max Maier   Grade: 03
My mom deserves a diamond because she is beautiful and shines brighter that the sun. She loves my family a lot. She's a great mom.

Caroline Meredith   **Grade: 03**
My mom is like no other mom. She's warm-hearted and gracious. She's bright just like a diamond. She's also enjoyable to be around.

Jacquelyn Porter   Grade: 03
My mom deserves a diamond, she is as clever as a leprechaun and as jolly as a snowflake. She shines brighter than a star.

Erin Tilley   Grade: 03
My mom deserves a diamond because she's a shining star. She makes everything reflect on a rainy day. She brightens up the day!

* Amethyst winners in bold.

Aline Tusan   Grade: 03
My mom deserves a diamond because she's special. She helps me with my homework and she teaches me to cook. We pretend and play together.

Bella Vejar   Grade: 03
My mom shines like the stars in the beautiful sky at night. She's happy like dancing snowmen and cute as a butterfly. She's lovely.

David Wong   Grade: 03
My mom is very clever, lovely and playful. She is remarkable. She is always filled with care. She's the most splendid mom ever!!

Teacher: Michelle Kennedy

Taylor Cross   Grade: 03
My mom is a shining star in the sky and her smile is like the clouds above our heads. Her eyes are like diamonds.

Jenna Harris   Grade: 03
My mom deserves a diamond because she is beautiful, talented and loves me a lot. She understands me when I am sad. Thank you mom.

Haily Hunner   Grade: 03
My mom is very generous to give her time to teach third   Grade. That is why my mom deserves a diamond.

Laha Ljoka   Grade: 03
To make my mom, I have to mix my grandma and my grandpa. To love her all I need is love and hope.

Dana Mackensen   Grade: 03
The sunlight and moonlight shone on my mom and that means she is kind, nice and a very beautiful person

Todd Mortenson   Grade: 03
Mom, your eyes sparkle like glitter, your heart beats like a drum. You are my mom.

Kimya Pezeshki   Grade: 03
My mom deserves a diamond because she I the light in my eyes. She's a mom that I love. She's the stars in the sky.

John Pratt   Grade: 03
My mom is light. She's brighter than moonlight. She Is caring, loving and she is my mother. Terrific, fantastic, brilliant is my mother.

Jack Sterner   Grade: 03
My mom deserves a diamond because she never stops loving me. She always is a helper in class and at home. I love my mom.

Summer Woods   Grade: 03
My mom deserves a diamond because she is as beautiful as the sun, because she is as loving as a heart could be. Thank you!

Teacher: Tiffany Torres

Garrettt Jackson   Grade: 03
MY mothers eyes gleam in the sky like the beautiful stars. She shines like the horizon in the distance. I love my mom the most.

Claire Lisle   Grade: 03
My mom is like a shimmering stream. The brightest sunshine. As loving as an angel. She is like a beautiful rose. My mom.

Riley Lloyd   Grade: 03
My mom is the grand wave crashing in the ocean. She is my god and angel sent from above. She is my own heaven.

Reid Morrison   Grade: 03
She is the moon in the night. As you sleep she'll shine so bright like a night light coming through your window. She's the best.

Jennifer Santos   Grade: 03
Mother is beautiful like a blooming flower in spring. Calm like the waves that pass my side. She rises up like an angel above.

Chase Snyder   Grade: 03
My mom is the wind soft and breezy. She flows like an angel through the sky. She whispers in my ear as she floats.

Jackson Spencer-Shook   Grade: 03
My mom is like a golden flower that grows in the winter that cannot be picked. I love mother.

Nicholas Ushiyama   Grade: 03
My mom is as graceful as the waves in the sea and no one can compare to her diamond-like eyes. This is her surprise.

Joseph Wilske   Grade: 03
Joyful, she is happy. She knows how to improve. She dislikes hate and does not wait t make a better world. I love my mother.

Kaitlin Wright   Grade: 03
My mom, the rushing light that puts me to bed every night. Her skin is as soft as snow. She is my mother I know.

Marblehead Elementary
San Clemente

Teacher: Babara Maroshek

Brenna Bardzilowski   Grade: 05
Her lustrous blue eyes are like the deep blue of a Hawaiian sea that lighten up me at every chance that I can see.

Natalia Daly   Grade: 05
Her extraordinary voice calls my name. Makes me feel like I have no shame. We both love each other very much that matters to me.

Patrick Furlong   Grade: 05
She gave me life to live, a breath to breathe, a heart to love.   Smart as Einstein, a beautiful charm, my mom.

Kaitlyn Hagan   Grade: 05
Her eyes glitter in the light like stars. Her smile is like the horizon.   With the sun shining over her, I love her even more.

Jaren Harrell   Grade: 05
More valuable than the universe, more precious than gold. I love her much, I love her so. My mother, better than gold.

Nikki Houston   Grade: 05
Her smile is made up of one million stars. Turquoise and grey make her eyes sparkle. Loving arms wrap around me with care.

Evie Mcgarry   Grade: 05
My mom is a glistening diamond that shines brighter than the brightest star in the jewel of my heart that shines brighter than the sun.

Molly Morris   Grade: 05
Her smile sparkles like the sun. So caring, kind and gentle is her heart. The person who loves me most, my mom.

Alyssa Nusbaum   Grade: 05
A body of pearls, golden curls. A heart made of ruby and gold, emerald eyes. She is but the rarest gemstone of all. My mother.

Tristan Patterson   Grade: 05
Your eyes shine like two pots of gold, your heart shines like a rainbow in the sky, and your hair shines like a crystal.

Jade Sommer   Grade: 05
My mother's eyes are greener than grass, brighter than stars, her voice sounds like an angel's from the heavens, she's prettier than the gods.

Madison Tangeman   Grade: 05
Sparkling hazel eyes, they look so gorgeous. Her compassionate heart sounds like gold. My mother's soul will be mine forever.

Michael Wood   Grade: 05
Eyes as blue as the ocean, as smile as bright as the stars. Who is this woman? My mother and all her love.

Cole Ybarra   Grade: 05
My mom is as bright as stars. Her eyes glisten in the moonlight. Her love is as strong as a tiger. Mom deserves a diamond.

Cooper Zediker   Grade: 05
Her eyes look like the twinkling night sky, and whenever I look at her she fills my heart with joy.

Teacher: Betsy Milner

Joshua Barragan   Grade: 02
My mom deserves a diamond because she brings love to my heart because she reads me books. She gives me hugs, kisses, and she is special.

Maresa Fazio   Grade: 02
My mom deserves a diamond because she's always cheerful and dazzling. She cares for me and love me. I play with her all the time.

Ayden Madsen   Grade: 02
My mom's eyes are like the diamond that I know, she's going to win. If it wasn't for her I wouldn't be here today.

Macayla Norman   Grade: 02
She spends time with me. She cares about me. Her eyes shine like a glittery diamond in the sky. She brings love in my house.

Carlos Ramirez   Grade: 02
You put love in the house, you're the gold in my heart and beautiful like the moon. She's my valentine, I love her.

Karina Repaire   Grade: 02
My mom deserves a diamond because she is kind and loving. She takes me fun places and has snuggle time with me.

Avery Scott   Grade: 02
My mom's eyes are so bright, beautiful, and loving. With her, play time is so fun. Her lap, so soft and comfortable. Loving, fantastic.

Riley Shiroke   Grade: 02
My mom deserves the diamond because she has shiny eyes, she plays with me, she tickles me and I love her.

Mariners Christian School
Costa Mesa

Teacher: Jan Bryant

Catherine Allen   Grade: 06
Her love is like a circle, never-ending and always pure. When I am feeling lonely, her smile is the only cure.

Aaron Boaity   Grade: 06
My mom's hugs are indescribable; her love is like the ocean deep and pure. She loves me for who I am. She is perfect.

Anna Chin   Grade: 06
Mom has true beauty inside and out. She sparkles like diamonds without a doubt. With a heart pure of love, she's an angel from above.

Trey Crossley   Grade: 06
Her sparkling eyes are pure blue water of the sea, she accepts me for who I want to be, a poem to thee, my mother.

David Daran   Grade: 06
Her love is deeper than any ocean, her eyes sparkle like the shiniest diamond there is, she is more amazing than any person I know.

Brennan Hall   Grade: 06
My mother's love, does not come in a package. My mother's love, shows not one flaw. My mother's love is a treasure I will treasure.

Kaitlyn Hicks   Grade: 06
My mother's hair runs like a river of silk, a perfect rose with the perfect amount of water and nutrients. My mother - I love her.

Zachary Hoenecke   Grade: 06
Mother's love has no end. She comforts me around each bend, she gives me hope for a whole new day, she loves me all day.

Rachel Howard   Grade: 06
My mother, a beautiful wonder. Her smile is like a touch of heaven. Her love for me is never-ending, my mom is...

Caitie Incledon   Grade: 06
Her courage is good, her intentions are great. She has awesome values, and the mental and physical strength to do anything. She is my inspiration.

Holly Mc Ruer   Grade: 06
She loves, hugs, and inspires me unconditionally. Her heart is kind and made of gold. My mom is like an angel sent by God.

Brooke Meer   Grade: 06
My mom is rare, she is a breath of fresh air. She is very pretty, and oh so witty. My mom; a diamond in the moonlight.

Mylan Metzger   Grade: 06
Inner beauty and outer beauty. My mom has them both. Her outer beauty shines like a ruby, but her inner beauty is radiant like diamonds.

Abbey Pickett   Grade: 06
This diamond belongs to my mom, she deserves this beautiful gem. She's there for me when I'm sad and celebrates with me when I'm glad.

Alyssa Randall   Grade: 06
My mother is the fire in my heart, the music in my soul, she is a comfort when I'm hurting. My mother is my all.

Michael Reese   Grade: 06
Mom. Her hair's like flowing fields of wheat, reflecting in golden sunset. Her eyes are beautiful as emerald water of a koi pond. My mom.

Jackson Rhodes   Grade: 06
My mother's soft voice is as gentle as can be, her loving personality glitters within her, sparkling like a beautiful jewel in the heaven's above.

Mandie Sinclair   Grade: 06
My mom's voice is as sweet as the morning dew; she's soothing like honey and she's the most loving mom I could ever have.

Lauren Solaas   Grade: 06
Why my mom deserves a diamond because she loves me so. Her care, her kindness, her love, and her heart does overflow.

Jessica Stone   Grade: 06
My mom is the hero of my dreams, her care so tender, hugs so warm, she is the diamond of my heart.

Walker Thurston   Grade: 06
Her eyes sparkle like diamonds. Her heart as big as the sea. Who is this special person? The mother of me.

Natalie Ward   Grade: 06
My mom's heart is pure as a diamond. Her eyes sparkle like precious gemstones. To me, she is a priceless gift that will last eternally.

Nicholas Whitelaw   Grade: 06
My mom is the most beautiful diamond in heaven; she sparkles like the stars above us. She is my perfect diamond.

* Amethyst winners in bold.

Kate Allen   Grade: 07
My mom is like a starry night. Her smile shines, her eyes twinkle and her hair flows like a river.

Clay Carr   Grade: 07
Mom, always there, perfect peace, super smiley, soft touch, always optimistic, strong in faith, dedicated worker, special person. Mom.

Rachel Chandler   Grade: 07
My mom, a tree, strong and steady provides love and food always ready. When times come, when I feel down, she is always my clown.

Cassidy Davis   Grade: 07
Her love, her smile, her hug, her kiss. Nothing in her heart is amiss. No mother can compare to the one I love so much.

Christina Nelson   Grade: 07
Eyes sparkling like a deep sea pearl. All day long seeming to whirl. Her soothing voice sings like birds chirping. Her heart bubbles with joy.

Tracy Williams   Grade: 07
My mom is like a sweet song. As gentle as a dove, she gives me so much love. She is like an angel from above.

Teacher: Krista Esswein

Katalina Aviles   Grade: 04
My mom's the diamond shining inside me. Her eyes are always a twinkly sensation. She gave me life, that's why I love her.

Julianna Dahlke   Grade: 04
She shines like a star in the sky. She's as kind as a diamond quite so find. She's my heart, a shining crystal.

Christian Del Rey   Grade: 04
Sparkles like a diamond, pretty as a ruby. More glamorous than a golden treasure chest. My one of a kind mom.

Nathan Foster   Grade: 04
My mom is so beautiful, her eyes shine like a diamond and they glisten like the sea. She is as perfect as a sapphire.

Brock Malliet   Grade: 04
My mom's eyes are crystals. My mom is a diamond, but the best this is, she is better than any jewelry, she is my mom.

Ali Pfleger   Grade: 04
Her heart is like a ruby. Her eyes sparkle like crystals. She is kind and loving. She is sweet like honey.

Trenton Rhodes   Grade: 04
She glitters like a garnet and dances everywhere, she's as perfect as a pearl, honest and fair. Her eyes are made of diamonds shining forever more.

Mark Schaefer   Grade: 04
She's the apple of my eye. Like a brand new ruby. Everyday I feel like I've been showered with her love. She's my diamond.

Ashley Sheward   Grade: 04
Mother's words are like diamonds made with love and care. She is kind in every way. She is the most stunning person. I love her.

Parker Thurston   Grade: 04
My mom deserves a diamond as big as the moon. But money can't buy such a thing. Love is the only key to that prize.

Tami Thurston

Jeremy Fukushima   Grade: 07
She is as beautiful as a flower and she is not sour. She is my closest friend and every broken heart she will mend.

Emilee Haskell   Grade: 07
She's been there since the beginning. She's raising me and loves me. Anything I ever needed, she provided and she's made everyday my best day.

Ethan Hold   Grade: 07
Mom serves with a loving heart, gives to all, does her part. She spreads joy, like the sun and to every occasion brings much fun.

Jeshurun Kim   Grade: 07
My mom loves all, is kind to all, helps all, tries all, benefits all, and above all, my mom perseveres through all.

Joseph Lee   Grade: 07
Oh, how I love my mother so. If only she had a diamond though. Her love for me is amazing. She is my everything.

Luke Napolitano   Grade: 07
My mom is always there for me. No matter what I do, her love is unconditional. You would give her the diamond if you knew.

Megan Roach   Grade: 07
Why my mom deserves a diamond, it's simple you see. Whenever she smiles, her face sparkles at me.

Megan Sweeney   Grade: 08
Her voice as soft as waves on a beach, her love is never hard to reach. A smile reaching thousands of miles, nothing can compare.

Mariposa Elementary
Brea

Teacher: Kathleen Hales

Emily Hwang   Grade: 05
Eyes shining with soft moonlight, filled with loving care. At twilight, it shall be yours, the little shining star that exactly matches mom's brown eyes.

Grace Lee   Grade: 05
Like a dazzling petunia blooming gracefully in spring filled with abundant loving care, her smile is warm, seemingly glistening from the stars.

Nicole Martinez   Grade: 05
Twinkling eyes shine like the sun, she perks up your day. There is nobody else that can do it my mom's way.

Daniel Parahnevich   Grade: 05
Mother's splendid love. Smiling brown eyes bring a lustrous shine, like that of a brilliant gem, and the warmth like that of a gleaming sun.

Rishi Patel   Grade: 05
Graceful like a smooth stream of beautiful flowing water, the glistening of the sun's sparkling rays, beautiful as my mom's eyes look at me.

Alyssa Placencia   Grade: 05
In my mom's precious eyes, there's a loving, hardworking person, bad or good day she brings out the sun, and always cares for everyone.

Morgan Potts   Grade: 05
My graceful, mother's character stands out in the twilight of dusk as her eyes shine as beautiful diamonds and her heart is pure gold.

Payton Quaranta   Grade: 05
Graceful as a flowing river, much more glorious than a shooting star, nothing can truly ever compare to mother's warm and phenomenal glowing heart.

Luke Sandoval   Grade: 05
My mom glows in the twilight between night and dawn, because her love for me is so bright the whole world can see it.

John David Stendahl   Grade: 05
She is as pretty as a bird, and as caring as an angel. Do not forget she is as graceful as the ocean.

Sara Trejo Grade: 05
As she stands out in the afterglow of a blazing sunset. Her eyes dazzle like diamonds, her smile like the soft velvet of night.

Masuda (Kazúo) Middle
Fountain Valley

Teacher: Wendy Baker

Samuel Beidokhti Grade: 06
My mother is a golden angel from heaven. She's perfect in more ways than one. She's smart, beautiful and a lot more. She is the best.

Lauren Eisele **Grade: 06**
My mom is an angel sent from above. A diamond in the rough, the diamond of my soul. My mom, my heart, my love, forever.

Jeffery Lim Grade: 06
My mom gives me love and affection so a beautiful diamond is what she should get. I am her star and she is my sky.

Julie Ransom Grade: 06
My mom deserves a diamond for the twinkle in her eyes, for being very kind. She might be small but is very big inside.

Aaron stark Grade: 06
Inside my house, there is a mom and in that mom there is a heart. In that heart, there is love and purity for all.

Teacher: Leslie Bennett

Cristeen Ahn Grade: 07
Mom deserves a ;diamond because it shines like her mind. It's beautiful like her heart. Mom deserves a diamond.

Jeremy Arucela Grade: 07
My mom deserves a diamond because she is the best mom in the world. She would do anything for me. I love her.

Charles Bennett, Jr. **Grade: 07**
My mom, the diamond in my eyes. She sparkles ever so bright, as a star in the night sky, always to shine so bright.

Jessica Gonzalez **Grade: 07**
My mom deserves a diamond because they would get along perfectly. When they're in the sun, they both shimmer and shine. They're both really beautiful.

Destiny Maciel Grade: 07
My mom shows me so much love, gives me the biggest hugs even though we have our ups and downs and never shows me any frowns.

Teacher: Charlene Bosl

Ann Dinh Grade: 08
Twinkle, twinkle, you're a big star that shines in me. You soar to great heights in all you do. Because of that, I love you.

Muaz Ilyas Grade: 08
My mom comforts me, she's very beautiful. Her eyes sparkle like a diamond. Her smile is as incredible as a ruby. I love my mother.

Summer Johns **Grade: 08**
Her beauty like a red rose. Her eyes like fresh dew drops on crisp, new grass. Her smile like a colorful rainbow. My Mother Nature.

Vartan Kazezian Grade: 08
Mom - an angel from above. Mom - has everlasting love. Mom - your heart is ever so large. Mom - she's the center of my heart.

Brianna Martinez **Grade: 08**
When I picture her in my mind, I don't see beauty, I see an endearing strong woman; someone who doesn't need expensive stuff, just me.

Jonathan Nguyen Grade: 08
She is sparkles of love that stare at your eyes and make you smile with joy. My mom is all I have to love.

Jordyn Sanchez Grade: 08
My mom, the most amazing person I have ever met. She is my world, best friend, mother, and my hero. God bless her!

Hunter Tejada **Grade: 08**
A personality as sweet as chocolate. Eyes glittering like stars, a heart pure as gold, a smile gleaming like diamonds. That's my wonderful, flawless mother.

Jennifer Temores Grade: 08
My mom, unlike other moms, is special. Patient, loving, caring mother whose first priority are her children. My mom deserves a diamond!

Linsey Tran Grade: 08
My mom is the best, she deserves it all. Whenever I'm lonely, she's right down the hall. She loves me immensely, my best friend.

David Tucker Grade: 08
My mom is the sweetest person on earth. She would give anything just for me. Her eyes sparkle like the stars in the sky.

Toby Vanderveer Grade: 08
My mom is the most expensive thing in the world, for you only have one. This is why she deserves a diamond. She is one.

Meagen Walter Grade: 08
My grandma is my best friend. She encourages loves and helps me when I'm down. There are no words to describe how much I love her.

Teacher: Alisha Garnett

Denise Avent **Grade: 08**
Her hair, a flowing waterfall. Her eyes shine with knowledge and love. She is an irreplaceable work of love. She is my mother.

Kaylianne Hartman Grade: 08
My mom deserves a diamond because she's big in many ways. Her brain is huge, her feelings are strong, her heart is like a maze.

Yesenia Juarez Grade: 08
My mom deserves a diamond because she is a wonderful mom. She sacrifices her life for us everyday. She's the most beautiful in my eyes.

Victor Le Grade: 08
An everlasting heart for I have crushed upon her soul so I must nurture the fading flame of her heart.

Tasneen Madie **Grade: 08**
She takes care of me well. Stays all night up when I'm in and loves me today, tomorrow, and always mom deserves a diamond everyday.

Shawnna Ramady Grade: 08
My mother is amazing, brilliant and brave, always there for her children, always there to care. She's loving and kind for others to share.

* Amethyst winners in bold.

Melody Strickler   Grade: 08
When people ask me why my mom deserves a diamond, I say, "Because my mom's spirit shines like a diamond, guiding me when I'm lost."

Teacher: Beth Gillis

Robert Arellano   Grade: 06
I have a diamond, it makes me happy, it makes my heart turn to gold and it's with me forever and it is my mom.

Bin Hill   Grade: 06
Her eyes gaze into my eyes. Her heart is as beautiful as gold. A little sun and her eyes sparkle up like diamonds.

Rachel Henze

Dolly Dang   Grade: 07
My mom is like the most precious gem in the world. She changes my frown upside down. My mom deserves a diamond again and again.

Jennifer Quan   Grade: 07
You're part of me, like I'm part of you. You gave me life and I gave you laughter. No matter where, we'll always be together.

Kora Tseng   Grade: 07
My mom is the most important person in my life. She created me. I would be nothing without her. I love my mom!

Teacher: Jennifer Johnson

Calvin Bui   Grade: 06
My mom is amazing. She is nice and caring. My mom entertains me and always keeps me happy. She puts a smile on my face.

Lauren Clary   Grade: 06
My mom is my diamond. She's fragile and rare. She sparkles with love and shines her heart for all who cares. She's my flawless diamond.

Campbell Grihalva   Grade: 06
My mother is nice like a cold drink on a hot day like the wind on your face. She cares for me. She is kind.

Becca Kirkland   Grade: 06
Her voice is velvet, her hair is silk. Her personality outshines her beauty. In the sun she sparkles. I'm irrevocably in love with her.

Anna Nakamura   Grade: 06
Her warm smile gazing upon me. Her beautiful eyes watching as I sleep. That's why mother needs a shiny stone such as a diamond.

Steve O'Neil   Grade: 06
My mom is the care of my soul. The loving diamond in my heart. She is there for me through thick and thin.

Marcelo Santana   Grade: 06
Her heart so warm, her arms so welcoming. Her eyes filled with joy. My mom so selfless, I wish all were made like her.

Samantha Stanish   Grade: 06
My mom is amazing, she is like a firework on the Fourth of July, always entertaining and always puts a smile on my face.

Sarah Sulewski   Grade: 06
My mother sparkles like the sun, she flies like a dove through the wind until dawn. She's got it all. What can I say, "Mom".

Sarah Telford   Grade: 06
My mommy's eyes are the green grass. Her smile is the bright sun. She loves me and I love her. Mommy's heart is in diamonds.

Jonathan Tran   Grade: 06
My mom has a heart of diamonds. She is a flawless diamond sparkling when a ray of light hits it.

Francisco Valladares   Grade: 06
She is beautiful. She is kind. She is caring and her soul is pure like a diamond.

Jake Wells   Grade: 06
I wouldn't be here now if it wasn't for mom. She gave me everything I wanted. She gave me life. She is my life's diamond.

Teacher: Thomas Warf

Raven Aloe   Grade: 07
My mom is a shoulder to cry on. She is the sun to my shine and the laughter in my life. I love my mom.

Alec Brown   Grade: 07
My mom deserves a diamond because she is an angel on Earth. She is as pure and reliable as the very air we breathe.

Kayla Cung   Grade: 07
My mom is the biggest heart in a sweetheart box. She's sweet like a yummy treat. When I'm down, she turns my frown upside down.

Victoria Ellard   Grade: 07
I love my mom with all my heart, always together, never apart. She's my best friend until the end. She deserves a diamond again and again.

David Hill   Grade: 07
My mom's worth more than a diamond, more than a house or a personal island. All the money in the world's nothing compared to her.

Melissa Ly   Grade: 07
Every morning when I go to school, it's like a rush hour for mom. Even though she's tired, there's always a smile on her face.

Kristina Nolff   Grade: 07
My mom is very sweet. For that she can't be beat. She gives me great pride when I am close to her side.

Michael Querry   Grade: 07
My mom deserves a diamond because she is as beautiful as a diamond. She is more precious than a diamond. She is my best friend.

Zury Ramirez   Grade: 07
My mom's a beautiful rose, that makes me smile. She's the sun that shines. She's my one teacher that teaches me. She's my mom.

Andrea Suarez   Grade: 07
My mom deserves a diamond because she's mom and dad for me since I was born. She's always by my side and works hard for me.

Thomas Tran   Grade: 07
My mom deserves a diamond because she has done, but she wants out of everything is my very happy love.

Summer Williams   Grade: 07
My mother's heart is as sweet the cookies she bakes. She brings joy in the family and her eyes sparkle like a diamond.

Teacher: Norma Young

Russell Barie   Grade: 06
My mom is sweet as candy. She's like a morning sun. She's like a shining star at night. The only one I love.

Kenneth Barrios   Grade: 06
Her eyes are as bright as the stars above. She is the one I will always love. My mom is always a goddess to me.

Elysa Basquez   Grade: 06
My mom sparkles like the stars at night. Her round eyes so blue and bright. She's so passionate and caring. So brave and very daring.

Kristin Bayle   Grade: 06
Her warm smile is like a pocket of sunshine. Her voice is like music. Her eyes, they shine like the diamond she deserves.

Kitty Bennett   Grade: 06
Her smile lights up the room. Her laugh fills the room with joy. Her heart is warm and gentle like the simple summer breeze.

Avery Gonzales   Grade: 06
My mom, she lights up my day. She's the reason I don't fray. She gave me life, she helped me live. Oh, how I love her so.

Jeffrey Huang   Grade: 06
Your smile makes me feel loved. Your eyes sparkle under the moonlight. You're as sweet as sugar. You're my inspiration, Mom.

Jessie Le   Grade: 06
Eyes like warm melted pools of chocolate. Voice like a talented harpist's notes. Hair like soft rose petals. My mom.

Lily Mooney   Grade: 06
Mother is love, mother is joy. Mother, oh what a wonderful word. How she makes you want to sing, the taste of sweetness lasts forever.

Thomas Mundi   Grade: 06
Her soul is pure gold. Her heart is a gleaming ruby. None can compare to her voice of diamond, singing the song of love.

Theresa Nguyen   Grade: 06
The sun's shine. The dews' twinkle. And the brightest star in the darkest night. Makes the perfect diamond my mom deserves.

VanAnh Nguyen   Grade: 06
The meaning of my mom, she's sweeter than sugar. A heart filled with love. She's bound to be a saint. Forever a charm, my mom.

Sy Pham   Grade: 06
Delicate as a feather on a rare bird. My mother is a flower and I her hummingbird.

Danielle Popovich   Grade: 06
Her eyes shine like diamonds. Her heart is made of gold. She comforts me and loves me. Her kindness is untold.

Kasey Reeve   Grade: 06
My mom's eyes are like twinkle stars. Her face shines like polished glass. She will always be remembered in my soul as a wonderful mother.

Shea Sueda   Grade: 06
She is as loving as the waves she surfs at the beach. She is always behind my shoulder, ready to teach, my mother , the greatest.

Joyce Yoo   Grade: 06
My mom twinkles like a star. You can see her from afar. I really like the way she shines. I am glad that she's mine.

Mc Auliffe (Sharon Christa) Middle
Los Alamitos

Teacher: Barbara O' Connor

Sabrina Adjiri   Grade: 07
My mom deserves a diamond because she is the most fun, most loving mom in the world. She is always thinking of others.

Aly Bailey   Grade: 07
Most loving, everyday she is there for me. Off the hook, mom, out of everyone in the world, you deserve this diamond.

Kimberly Banda   Grade: 07
Motherly, aspiring to learn. Respectful to others. Intelligent. Aiming to be better at her English.

Nick Bistocchi   Grade: 07
I think my mom deserves a diamond because she is a hardworking mother and needs something else to hold onto besides me.

Bobby Burton   Grade: 07
Magnificent person. Occupying my greatest days. Making the road ahead, brighter for me to shine.

Jenna Marie Course   Grade: 07
My mom deserves a diamond because her heart sparkles. She's loving, loyal and always thinks of others before herself. She glows from the inside out.

Victoria Deremiah   Grade: 07
My mom deserves a diamond because she is as beautiful as one, and that is what our house looks like after she cleans it.

Lyndsey Evans   Grade: 07
Do you want to know spectacular? Well, meet my mom. She's great, always there, always on the ball, but, best of all. She's lovable.

Aaron Fawcett   Grade: 07
Loving, caring, peaceful, sweet and happy. My mom is always optimistic no matter what the situation may be.

Mark Frankenberg   Grade: 07
My mom deserves a diamond because diamonds are forever. I want to show that my love for my mom will last forever.

Jana Hammoud   Grade: 07
Oh, mother, how much you love me for who I am. I love you, too, but not enough. Whatever you do is always enough.

Nicole Hipsher   Grade: 07
My mom has always been there when I need her. She always knows what to do. I love you dearly, mom.

Ross Hutter   Grade: 07
Oh my mom, you're so sweet. Oh my mom, you're so neat. Oh my mom, you're brighter than sun's. Oh, my mom, you're so fun.

Samantha Lai   Grade: 07
I think my mom deserves a diamond. She's always helpful, an inspirational role model, and a hard worker who's always caring about others.

Noel LImfueco   Grade: 07
She has a smile of sunshine and a heart of gold. Her eyes are stars that shine, and I am happy she is my mom.

Eizin Lin   Grade: 07
My mom should deserve a diamond. She is kind-hearted, nice and loveable. She's the one who makes me who I am today. The best!

Jessica Lui   Grade: 07
Bird scratches the earth; bird scratches to feed brood; scratches and finds stones; young bird falls, landing; bird leaves stones to retrieve brood; motherly love.

Kari Maelara   Grade: 07
Thoughts of my mom reach so incredibly deep in my heart that nobody in the entire universe could reach that special place that is irreplaceable.

Bryan Neal   Grade: 07
My mom is the best. She shows love for me everyday no matter what. She shows me, she always care.

Savannah Nieman   Grade: 07
You can experience mental and emotional rebirth with the bittersweet love with your mother's heart at your side.

* Amethyst winners in bold.

Makenna Oberst Grade: 07
Mom, there are so many words I can say about you. You're my best friend, and I can't live without you. I love you, mom.

Clark Olson Grade: 07
My mom is the best mom ever, and she deserves whatever she wants because she has always been there and is so supportive.

Kelly Peterson Grade: 07
She is smart, she is tall. She likes to go to the mall. She makes my diner everyday, but sometimes she will pay.

Caelan Plank Grade: 07
My mom deserves a diamond because she supports whatever I do and does everything she can do to give me a good life.

Anthony Ricaldi Grade: 07
My mom deserves a diamond. She is kind, sweet, and helpful to all. She has been a great mother that I want to repay her.

Sierra Thompson Grade: 07
My mom deserves a diamond because she has an amazing personality. She's very gentle and is slow to anger. She is overly kind to everyone.

Sydnie Woods Grade: 07
Your hair is blond, so is mine. We're two peas in a pod. You're important to me as I am to you. Love you, Mom.

Teacher: Joanne Tajima

Audrey Choi Grade: 07
It is difficult to express my mother into words; she is too spectacular to describe. A heart of gold and knowledgeable mind makes her beautiful.

Shelby Edmondson Grade: 07
Perfectly flawless, a role model to me. She wants me to be the best I can be. My mom, both a teacher and a friend.

Tara Egigian Grade: 07
Amazing person, very caring, helps me, protects me. Love me, hardworking, always entertaining, movie buddy. Role model, best friend, always there, perfect mother.

Kellie Guggiana Grade: 07
She is understanding, caring and deserving. Her love for me is never poor. My mom is a better mom than I could have asked for.

Joshua Holmes Grade: 07
My mom deserves a diamond for her pure and loving heart. My mom deserves a diamond because she's nice and very smart.

Sophie Joslyn Grade: 07
My mom is always there for me with anything, for help or advice. She is always willing, and gives me the best.

Sara Kass Grade: 07
Mu mom is the hardest worker I know. She always tries her best to show. How much she loves my family so.

Michelle Lewis Grade: 07
No jewel can sparkle like the diamond, she is my mom, is the brightest diamond of them all.

Adam Manoogian Grade: 07
Mom's full of love and care. Always will to share. Yet always polite and fair. One of a kind, unique and rare.

Shannon O' Farrell Grade: 07
There's a light at the end of a tunnel. When I get farther, a stronger light shines. I find that brilliant light is mom.

Rachel O' Sullivan Grade: 07
Mom is like a rose, delicate and beautiful. She is wonderful. She is also smart, loving, and caring to me. I love my mother.

Bree Otto Grade: 07
"Diamonds are Forever", as many people like to say. Yet, mom's love for her family, and kindness for everyone will withstand for eternity.

Chris Powelson Grade: 07
Soaring, flying with wings as noble as an eagle's with eyes as striking as a lightning bolt. Mom is the queen of the clouds.

Lyn Stoler Grade: 07
In every aspect, she outshines any other. She adds wonder, awe, and magnificence to all the world. Mom is a wonder for all to behold.

Holly Tinturin Grade: 07
A brave single mother and hero of two, as beautiful as the sun, deserves her chance to shine with pride because she is number one.

Willow Urquidi Grade: 07
Mom, a true child at heart. Pure and happy, a beautiful art. Help me flourish with knowledge I live me you nourish, happiness you give.

Ryan Woyshner Grade: 07
My mom is very sweet. She helps everyone she can meet. I like the way she smiles. Her love can last for miles.

Benjamin Yeh Grade: 07
My mom is more than a diamond. She is a jewel in the sky. Her eyes winkle; her smile twinkle. My mom deserves a diamond.

Mc Dowell Private Elemen.
Laguna Niguel

Teacher: Ingrid Mc Kibben

Brooke Bradley Grade: 03
Her eyes glow right into my soul. Like a whole crystal heart. She understood from the start, I never want to be apart.

Richard Chin Grade: 03
My mom is cotton candy dipped in maple syrup, mixed with sweet, fresh chocolate in chewy fruit candy. My mother...the sweetest one.

Taylor Davey Grade: 03
My mom 's eyes glow into my heart. She is the crystal of my soul. My mom deserves a diamond.

Tarika Gujral Grade: 03
I can always count on mom this is why she keeps me like a diamond in her heart with a twinkle in her eye.

Sophie Lindborg Grade: 03
Mom's strong, healthy, caring. Mom's tough, don't be daring. Mom is like a mermaid in the sea. Mom is the best she could be.

Carson Matthews Grade: 03
My mom's eyes sparkle throughout the day and night and her teeth are so white that they can lead through the darkest cave at night.

Catherine Orihuela Grade: 03
Emerald eyes glistening like jewels in the moonlight. Her heart is my constant world. Her never-ending smile and love are fun and cheerful.

Melanie Shams Grade: 03
My mom's everyone's angel. Her care and compassion endless. Her heart pure and unselfish. The sparkle in her eyes. Reflects the gem that she is.

Brandon Wu Grade: 03
I can see she looks out for me. Her eyes glow bigger than stars. We will always be together as strong as bars.

Teacher: Linda Peotter

Rostin Amirani   Grade: 05
My mom; gives me shelter, cooks, dinner, drives me everywhere, and is my pursuit of happiness. You have to agree. My mom deserves a diamond.

Jessica Chin   **Grade: 05**
My generous, loving, amazing, mom. With a sweet, caring, wonderful heart. Her eyes shine like amber glistening in the morning sun.

Kristina Coffin   Grade: 05
I am lucky to have a person like my mom because she is my model, helper and most of all the best storyteller ever.

William Miyamoto   **Grade: 05**
When I gaze into my mother's eyes. It warms me up around inside. That gentle look that's soft and fun warms the inside of everyone.

Teacher: Lisa Schoenhoefer

Jake Hanes   Grade: 04
I love my mom, she's the one, when I frown you make me smile when I need help you're the one. I love you.

Sara Khoshniyat   Grade: 04
For all her hard work, kindness, understanding, and sacrifices. My mom deserves more than anything I can give her. A diamond is the least she deserves.

Gwen Martin   Grade: 04
My mother deserves a diamond because like the diamond she is unique, beautiful and a rare jewel.

Mc Gaugh (J.H.) Elemen.
Seal Beach

Teacher: Raymond Crutcher

Brian Beggs   Grade: 05
Diamonds are rare, so is my mom. You can see her smile for miles and miles long. She cooks, she cleans, she's a mom machine.

Anna Bullock   Grade: 05
My mom has a lot of love. She shares it with our family. Her eyes are shiny with laughter. She cares for people, like me.

Justin Calub   Grade: 05
My mom's golden hearts as pure as a newborn. Her love's as rare as an ancient diamond. My mom's unique and special. I love her.

Rhaiel Cepeda   **Grade: 05**
Her beautiful eyes reminds me of ocean pearls. Her voice sounds like a wonderful melody, I love her more than a diamond more than anything.

Kennedy Faulkner   Grade: 05
Mom's eyes sparkle like a diamond. Her heart's love surrounds me and my sister, her hand reaches out and comforts us, my mom.

Sarah Gollub   Grade: 05
My mom has a smile that can be seem from a mile. Her hands warm my heart, now I know we'll never be apart.

Megan Haynes   **Grade: 05**
My mother's heart is like a beautiful meadow. Her care and love is like a blanket that bundles around me. I love her so much.

Italia Jones   **Grade: 05**
My mother's heart is bursting with love like an explosion of fireworks. Her face is like a beautiful queen that needs a crown.

Elizabeth Kerzie   Grade: 05
The sparkle in her eye reminds me of a diamond. The pupil in her eye reminds me of a beautiful pearl. I love her.

Tamara Lee   Grade: 05
The pearls in her eyes remind me of soothing waves. Her care and love makes me give all the love I have. My mom.

Sydney Loomis   Grade: 05
Crystals and gems have a dash of sunlight. In this light my mom shines very bright. Her soul is as big as the night.

Carmen Parker   Grade: 05
Her eyes sparkle in the light of love. Her voice sounds like a melody to my ear. I always will love her.

Skyler Pyle   **Grade: 05**
I cherish the lipstick marks on my cheek. The ocean of your eyes. The "I love you's", when I go to school I cherish mom.

Kurtis Rios   Grade: 05
My mother is as sweet as berries and as cool as snow. I know I don't say this enough, but mom, I love you.

Adam Simonetti   **Grade: 05**
Walking on a narrow path, looking at the street lights guarding the night sparkling like diamonds. My mom is special to me, she's my diamond.

Emily Soule   Grade: 05
Her eye are like shining star. Her heart is as big as the moon. As I look up, I see my beautiful mother.

Sarah Thomas   Grade: 05
Love is with my mother, I can see her near and far. My mother shines like a diamond no matter where you are.

Macey Vera   Grade: 05
Her eyes sparkle in the sunlight. Her smile runs for a mile. Her voice sounds like waves in an ocean. She's the gem I love.

Teacher: Lisa Halvorsen

Pauline Foster   Grade: 05
My compassion for my mother is as strong as a diamond shining in the sun, and her smile is my treasure. I shall always keep.

Spencer Lopez   **Grade: 05**
My mom is always there for me. Whenever I feel sad, lonely, or discouraged. She always says the right words to make me feel better.

Calista Rodrigue   **Grade: 05**
Her eyes sparkle like the stars above. Her smile brightens my day. My mom is the treasure of my life.

Isabella Shean   **Grade: 05**
My mom, twinkling eyes, bright soul, warming heart, protecting me, helping me, always there for me, teaching me the rights and wrongs of life.

Shelby Snyder   Grade: 05
Her eyes sparkle like glistening sand on the beach. Her heart is so big like the moon.

Jessica Winslow   Grade: 05
My mom is so special. She's the center of my heart and no matter what they say, we're never apart.

Teacher: Carol Kile

Nico Collins   Grade: 03
She takes care of me. When I'm hurt or very sick and when my grandpa died she sat next to me at the funeral.

Olyvia Evans   Grade: 03
I'll always remember the great time we've had. I love you all the way to the moon and back. You are the star of my life.

August Haeffner   Grade: 03
She has done things with me. Example making cookies right besides me. She is my guardian angel. And her love lives forever in my heart.

* Amethyst winners in bold.

Brittney Jansta   Grade: 03
When I have gymnastics, I always hear you yell, never give up. Now I cheer, go mom, because you cheered for me. I love you.

Gillian Kienitz   Grade: 03
My mom deserves a diamond because she is my Girl Scout leader. She does book orders for my class and she bakes cookies with me.

Max Madrzyk   Grade: 03
I love my mom. Whenever I go to a soccer game, she's always cheering me on "Go, Max!" She's flawless like a diamond. Go Mom.

Ashlyn Nicholson   Grade: 03
I think my mom is the best. I was so sick, she ran out the door and she came back in 20 seconds with medicine.

Teacher: Vicki Newman

Kieren Duncan   Grade: 03
My mom deserves a diamond because she always volunteers. She is helpful. My mom is full of joy and happiness.

Nicole Elder   **Grade: 03**
Sweet, loveable, kind and she cares about me. She has a very kind heart. When I'm hurt, she helps me. She loves my family.

Bronsyn Ledgard   Grade: 03
My mom deserves a diamond because she always takes care of me when I'm sick, takes us places without complaining and is very lovable.

Anneliese Marsh   Grade: 03
My mom deserves a diamond because she's generous. Sometimes I get frustrated and she calmly helps me out. There isn't a mom like mine.

McKenna Reutershan   Grade: 03
My mom deserves a diamond because she is sweet and generous and always helping people. And of course, she is very pretty. I love her.

Teacher: Michelle Brien

Kate Gammel   Grade: 05
Everyday of my life, I'll always be a mom, my girl. She loves me in everyway, a kid could be loved. She's my devoted mom.

Christine Van De Velde   Grade: 05
Kind, special, beautiful, nice, loving, caring. My mom, the best mom in the world. She works hard everyday to make sure things are finished. The best.

Teacher: Lisa Wright

Chloe Carpenter   **Grade: 05**
Mom deserves a diamond because her eyes sparkle like a diamond and her heart shines like rubies, her smile glints like a sapphire so pretty.

Isaac Collins   Grade: 05
My mom deserves a diamond because she works hard to help me with my homework, and she is very nice.

Lauren Dvonch   Grade: 05
My grandma deserves a diamond because even after her husband recently died, she always stayed strong for me and my family.

Olivia Elvidge   Grade: 05
My mom deserves a diamond because she is a loving, caring, mom and really deserves a diamond for her hard work.

Kaylie Harrington   Grade: 05
My mom is pregnant. She works hard even though she's pregnant. She deserves a little papering for all the work she does. I love her.

Sarah Hermann   Grade: 05
My mom deserves a diamond because she always cares and looks out for me and doesn't always get a reward for everything nice for me.

Hannah Horn   Grade: 05
She deserves a diamond because she is one. Kind and beautiful, she is never seen without a smile on her face. I love her.

Eben Humes   Grade: 05
My mom deserves a diamond more than anyone I know, because she is nice, caring, but best of all, she is really fun.

Dani Iwami   **Grade: 05**
My mother is the light in the darkness. In her arms, I feel safe like a pearl in a oyster. Without her, heaven never existed.

Mina Mizutani   **Grade: 05**
Her eyes gleam in the sunlight and her smile brightens the day. Giving her hugs warms my heart. My mom deserves a diamond.

Sophia Schade   Grade: 05
My mom deserves a diamond because she works very hard. Happy or sad, mad, or joyful. She still loves me and I love her.

Wyatt Snyder   Grade: 05
My mom deserves a diamond because she helps me with homework, always forgives and she is nice as a warm summer day.

Molly Wray   Grade: 05
I would try to measure how much I love my mom, but all the rulers, scale, and thermometers in the world couldn't do that.

McPherson Magnet
Orange

Teacher: Wes Bishop

Natalie Barnett   Grade: 04
My mom is the light in my life and there is never going to be a day when she is not bright. She's my diamond.

Madeline Chung   Grade: 04
Mom, you are a rainbow in my heart. Nothing can tear us apart. You love to care. You are my gemstone everywhere.

Jake Lopez   **Grade: 04**
A diamond is all the colors of the rainbow as my mom is all the colors of my life. Her heart is full of colors.

Nathan Ly   Grade: 04
My mother is perfection. She watches over me. Her eyes are diamonds. She smiles sunshine. But best of all, without her I wouldn't be here.

Nick Tanner   **Grade: 04**
My mom is like a diamond, she is bright and shiny. She has many facets. She is funny, kind, and loving. She's a rare gem.

Emma Vander Wall   Grade: 04
My mom is as graceful as a swan. Her eyes sparkle like the brightest star. My mom is my diamond. I love you mom.

Jacob Zimmerman   **Grade: 04**
Always by my side, she is helping me out, without a doubt. She's the best mom ever a boy could ever wish for.

Teacher: Judy Denenny

Madeleine Anginli   **Grade: 06**
My heart fills with love when I see her, she has eyes that twinkle back at me. Her glistening heart like gold. I love her.

Mariann Bui   **Grade: 06**
She's as beautiful as a dove and as fuzzy as a bee, but it's her love that gives me the courage to be me.

Karen DeLeon   Grade: 06
She shines like a twinkling star. She brightens my soul in every way. When she smiles it's like I'm in a whole different world.

Colin Eacobellis   Grade: 06
My mom's eyes sparkle in the moonlight like a star. When she speaks, it sounds like a magical violin. She is the diamond in me.

Danielle George   Grade: 06
A diamond is nothing compared to my mom's love. She is prettier than any gem. Sweeter than an angel, my mom loves.

Devin Ghidella   Grade: 06
Splish, splash, splish, splash, her hair is like a wave of laughter crashing into the rocks of wonder. That is all about her.

Brooke Glover   Grade: 06
My mom is the fire in my heart. She is the angel in my soul. Eyes shining like a ruby. Mom, my special gem.

Paul Gomez   Grade: 06
Like a hare in the field, my mother's always there. Without her my life would be despair, mother with her hair swirling in the air.

Alejandra Gutierrez   Grade: 06
My mom, the center of my heart. The one that believes in me. She's like a beautiful diamond. I see her face in the constellations.

Andrew Hamilton   Grade: 06
Eyes sparkling in the morning sun, soul as clear as crystal. A smile filled with warmth and comfort, my mom is the diamond of me.

Natasha Heim   Grade: 06
She runs to me, her hands reflecting in the starlight and a soft glow in her hazel eyes. Mom is my passion and love within.

Anthony Holland   Grade: 06
My mom's eyes glisten in the sparkling waters of the deep sea. I see her passion in the moonlit sky as she looks upon me.

Aishwqrya Jayabharathi   Grade: 06
A flower's fragrance reminds me of my mother who is like no other. And bathed or not in moonlight. She always glows to me.

Chris Kelly   Grade: 06
One million different stars. One million different planets. One million different beings all of them have mothers, but only mine has that special gleam.

Dakota Kolosky   Grade: 06
My mom's heart and voice are golden seas of love and compassion. She puts joy into people's hearts. Her eyes are galaxies compressed into packages.

Isaac Lopez   Grade: 06
My mom is like a rose in the wind. Her voice is soothing like the ocean. She's sweeter than a strawberry.

Javier Madrid   Grade: 06
Everyday when I see her. Her eyes gleam in the sunlight. Her heart pieces through mine and becomes one.

Jake Marcel   Grade: 06
My mom is the diamond in my soul. She keeps me going dusk until dawn. At night she protects me, at day she is mom.

Zoey Montano   Grade: 06
My mom's eyes remind me of the moon. She's my role model and always answers my challenging questions. My mom is a star that always shines.

Joseph Naples   Grade: 06
So secure and sweet, her heart warming hugs cannot be beat. She cares for me each day, as if I'm baby Jesus laying in hay.

Zair Ocampo   Grade: 06
My mother's eyes gleam as the sparkling ruby passes her, flowing away with the wind, over the hills and out into the glimmering ocean.

Alexis Palomo   Grade: 06
She spreads her wings like an angel. She comes down from heaven like a crystal. She's a gift from God that came to love me.

Jennie Palomo   Grade: 06
My mom is an angel with a halo over her head that was sent from the sky just for me.

Jessica Patterson   Grade: 06
Her flawless features sure impress. She brightens my day with a single kiss on my cheek. One, two, three. I love her, she loves me.

Chase Pike   Grade: 06
My mom's heart beats with the pulse of love and compassion. Her smile makes my soul a bright star shining in the night sky.

Collin Reyes   Grade: 06
On the beach a treasure to standing. She takes care of me everyday as if I were her shining diamond. She is like no other.

Austin Rivada   Grade: 06
My mom's heart is like gold. Her eyes are like blue stars in the night sky. There is a great angel in her.

Daniel Savage   Grade: 06
My mom is bright as the moon and peaceful as the stars. From the sea to me, her love runs deeply in and around me.

Ryan Slivkeff   Grade: 06
My mom's eyes are bright and shiny like a ruby. The beat in her heart is as strong as a diamond. She is the gem in my life.

Riley Stein   Grade: 06
She brings light to gloomy days. She smiles in special ways. She always hears me when I call. My mom's the best gem of all!

Brian Stocks   Grade: 06
My lovely mom gave me life for that she is a diamond in my eye forever. She will sparkle in my life.

Emma Sturdivant   Grade: 06
My mother's smile shines down on me. She lights my world like the fiery sun, my mother's like a daisy growing stronger everyday!

Cassandra Vagliently   Grade: 06
Her hair has the beauty of the sun. Her eyes shine in the moonlight. Her heart is as big as a whale. She's flawless.

Claire Vargas   Grade: 06
The glory in her eyes, the laughter in her smile, the power in her thoughts. She whispers in my ear, her thoughts touch my heart.

Teacher: Kimberly Hays

Brian Camey   Grade: 05
My mom is a rose in a garden. Her heart warms my soul. She's the light which guides my life and my choices.

Caitlin Cruz   Grade: 05
She is loving, carrying a beautiful rose. She's the one I love the most. She's the perfect mother.

Joey Harrington   Grade: 05
My mom is like an angel making everyone happy. The light from her eyes fade all my fears. She's a perfect mom.

* Amethyst winners in bold.

How do you say, "I love my mother?"

Words are living things. Positive words give us hope and comfort when they are read. When we say or read them from our lips, they have the amazing power to heal, encourage and inspire us. Throughout our lives, we remember beautiful words that are spoken to us. That is why it is a requirement for essay winners to recite their words to their mothers when they come to receive their prizes.

Orange County is the home of families from many different cultures and the WHY MOM DESERVES A DIAMOND® contest has shown that the common denominator of everyone's heart is our mother. The following thirty expressions say, "I love my mother." Each was written by mothers, fathers and essay winners whose origins trace to the far corners of the world. Used by permission, each expression is handwritten in their own language for others to enjoy.

Kocham moją mamę
Polish

Аз обичам моята майка!
Bulgarian

Armenian

Sign language

我愛我的母親
Chinese

JA VOLIM MOJU MAJKU
Croatian

Ethiopian

Farsi

J'aime ma mère
French

Hebrew

Tôi yêu mẹ tôi.
Vietnamese

मैं मैशा मता को प्यार करता हूँ
Hindi (Main Indian language)

నా అమ్మను నేను ప్రేమిస్తున్నాను.
Telugu (another Indian language)

ﺐﺣ ﺃ ﻲﻣ ﺃ
Arabic

ខ្ញុំ ស្រឡាញ់ម្តាយ
Cambodian

Mahal ko ang inay ko.
Tagalog

Braille

私は お母さん が 大好き
Japanese

Annemi gok seviyorum
Turkish

Aku sayang Ibu
Indonesian

ﺎﻧﺍ ﺐﺣﺍ ﻲﻣﺃ
Egyptian

ಬಹಳ ಇಷ್ಟ ಬಹುಶಃ ಶ್ರೇಷ್ಠ
Kannada (another Indian language)

Jag älskar min mama.
Swedish

저의 어머를 사랑합니다.
Korean

ຂ້ອຍ ຮັກ ແມ່ ຂ້ອຍ
Lao (Laos language)

T'hibirkem yemma
Bereber (Language used in North Africa)

Я люблю мою маму;
Russian

Georgian

Yo quiero a mi mama
Spanish

நான் என் அம்மாவை மிகவும் நேசிக்கிறேன்
Tamil

* Amethyst winners in bold.

Edgar Hernandez   Grade: 05
My mom is a glorious rose in a mystical garden. When anyone sees her they think of a magnificent world.

Serge Johnson   **Grade: 05**
She's a wild lily with lots of love in her eyes. Happiness and warmth in her heart. Without her my whole life would be darkness.

Bailey Layton   Grade: 05
smart as a teacher. Sparkles like the stars. Her eyes twinkle like golden treasures. Her smile warms my heart.

Hannah Marquez   **Grade: 05**
Boom! The ball went flying. My mom heard me crying in the middle of the street and she saved my life in a heart beat.

James Ordonez   **Grade: 05**
She fills my heart with love and care. She sparkles like the stars beyond. She cares about me and fills my heart with golden cheers.

Chayse Pena   **Grade: 05**
When I'm down, I want my mom around because she will hold me tight and tell me it's alright throughout the silent night.

Scott Stewart   Grade: 05
My mom twinkles like a star above. She spins my world like the earth. She shines brighter than the sun. She's smarter than an astronaut.

Teacher: Jane Layton

Michael Elmore   Grade: 05
My mom, oh, mom pretty and fine, thoughtful and sweet. My mom, mom prettiest sight on a beach of sunset. My mommy, mom.

Ally Flanagan   **Grade: 05**
As peaceful as a white dove, as bright as the North Star, loving and tender, a shining diamond leading the way through life, my mom.

Jeffrey Hosmer   Grade: 05
When she smiles, I smile. When she is in pain, I am in pain. We are connected in a way even we do not understand.

Nicolas Jackson   **Grade: 05**
My mother, as beautiful as the starry night. Her eyes glisten like the sun. Her presence brightens the day. My mother, the best of all.

Madison Victer   Grade: 05
She is an elegant as a butterfly. Her beauty sparkles. She would never strike at you. I will always have her deep in my heart.

Teacher: Denise McGraw

Lexa Aguilar   **Grade: 01**
My mommy loves me so much. She reads me a book before bed. I love my mommy and because of this, I love you forever.

Race Carter   Grade: 01
My mom is kind to others. She cooks food for me and takes me places. She takes care of me.

Andrew Looney   Grade: 01
My mommy tucks me in bed. She makes me breakfast and takes me to Downtown Disney. She helped me when I was sick. Mommy cares.

Sarah McWhirter   Grade: 01
My mom cares about me and my sisters and she loves us because she helps us clean the house.

Joseph Palacios   Grade: 01
My mom loves me because she makes me breakfast and takes me to school and takes me into bed.

Justis Pearce   **Grade: 01**
My mommy cares for me. My mommy sleeps in my bed sometimes and my mommy lets me sleep in her bed too.

Nicole Rose   Grade: 01
My mommy helps me with my homework. She helps me with breakfast. She takes me to school.

Hailey Thyden   **Grade: 01**
My mommy gives me hugs and kisses. My mommy takes me to get my nails done. My mom makes me cookies.

Teacher: Bonnie Morse

Sinclair Adams   Grade: 04
My mom is the best. She's important to me. I couldn't live without her. She loves me. She is deserving and I love her!

Allen Badolian   **Grade: 04**
My mom is the best mom in the world. Her smile shines bright and she is worth more than gold. I love my mom.

Nareg Donabedian   Grade: 04
My mom is loving. She is special in my life. She is helpful. She is radiant too. She loves me and I love her.

Riley Fink   Grade: 04
My mom is totally cool. She's pretty as a princess. She's queen of our house, and everything in it.

Conrad Frisch   Grade: 04
My mom is my loving princess of niceness. She is my arm full of love.

Lauren Gullion   **Grade: 04**
My mom causes the sun to rise because of her sweet eyes. They glitter in the sun and shine in the night. She is colorful.

Rosalinda Gutierrez   Grade: 04
My mom makes me feel better by saying that I am the princess. I think she is the princess. She's loving, caring, and helpful.

Isabelle Huffman   **Grade: 04**
My mom is as beautiful as the sunshine. She's the queen of love. Her eyes are blue like a swimming pool of sweetness.

Kelly Lazarus   Grade: 04
My mom is a radiant gem. She is better than gold. She is the queen of love and sweet as ice cream.

Teacher: Cheryl Robertson

Seth Ambrose   **Grade: 04**
She's the water in my lake. The nutrients in my food. The goodness in heaven, but most importantly, she's my mom and I love her.

Alexandra Anthony   Grade: 04
My mom is sweet and nice. She's always there for me, would shield me in a blazing fire. She deserves to be the queen mom.

Jourdan Clark   Grade: 04
My mom is special for taking care of me. She shines so bright like the sun. The most beautiful mom. Her eyes are like pearls.

Lukas Franco   Grade: 04
My mom is a river that always flows with energy and love. She cares for me a lot and is always there for me.

Nicholas Godoy   Grade: 04
My mom is caring, loving, fun, nice and important to the family. She helps me with a lot of things. She is the best.

Keely Ann Hare   Grade: 04
She is a flower that never dries out. A candy that's always sweet. A waterfall that always flows. Smells as sweet as a rose, Mom.

Parker Jones Grade: 04
My mom is wonderful. She is smart and intelligent. She is like an angel only better. She is very helpful. She is the best Mom!

Amanda Neely Grade: 04
I love my mom. She is a heart that never wears out. She is a flower that never dies. That is my mom.

Lan Thi Nguyem Grade: 04
She's as soft and gentle as a puppy. She loves me with all heart. She cuddles me like a little lamb. My wonderful mother.

Anthony Soza Grade: 04
A heart that never breaks. Love mom. A flower that never dies. A candle that never blows out. A diamond that never goes away.

Anabita Swingle Grade: 04
She is wonderful. The morning's freshness, coldness and sunlight reminds me of her. She sparkles more than a star. She is a great gift.

Mia Vasquez Grade: 04
You are the brightest star of the history of stars. You are a delicate flower with a lot of power. You are my only mother.

Elizabeth Zimmerman Grade: 04
She loves me like a golden treasure. Her words flow like the ocean when she says "I love you, Liz". She is my Mother.

Teacher: Maureen Robinson

Gillian Fennessy Grade: 05
When my mom hugs me, I wish that she'd never let go. Her eyes are brown as chocolate. When she kisses me, I feel warmth.

Brooke Hayes Grade: 05
Starry night, sky so bright. Purple, yellow, green, and white. All the colors of the light. That's my mother in the night. Colors so bright.

Victoria Higareda Grade: 05
She's the closest thing I know. She's my peace of Heaven. I'd never know the true reason of life if it wasn't for her presence.

Blake Leatherman Grade: 05
My mom's a glorious person, just to protect me, that is everything to me, as her eyes sparkle like diamonds. She loves me as I do.

Samantha Luley Grade: 05
She fills my heart with love, her eyes sparkle like diamonds, her hair is like garnets and I love her like the moon loves stars.

Maddy Masters Grade: 05
A golden angel from Heaven. A sparkle from the light. With the beauty of a dove, sparkling crystal blue sea. I love her so much.

Alexis Montgomery Grade: 05
Hair shimmering in sun like a beautiful diamond. Beauty that is so rare to life, is pretty as an angel that has flown from Heaven.

Kianna Snow Grade: 05
Walks along the shore with the wind in her face while keeping up the pace. She finds an almond and trades it for a diamond.

Miller (George B.) Elemen.
La Palma

Teacher: Cyndi Burgess

Matthew Devera Grade: 03
My mom deserves a diamond because she is a wonderful mom, she helps us learn so we can be smart when we grow up.

DaSol Lee Grade: 03
When I was a little kid, I drowned in the swimming pool, then my mom jumped in and saved me.

Rianne Monroy Cruz Grade: 03
My mom's always there for me. She's always there when I get awards. But my mom deserves a special diamond because she's a special mom.

Emilie Ramos Grade: 03
My mother comforts me each and every day. At the bay or in the sleigh, she says, I love you and protects me as I play.

Angela Larzo

Brittany Barreraz Grade: 04
I'd never give up my favorite joy. The person who lightens up my day. Joyful, kind, sweet as candy. Mom, I love you now and forever.

Joshua Chang Grade: 04
Eyes that shine like the moon, beautiful as an angel, goddess of love and peace. These words are my mom.

Roselynn DeCastro Grade: 04
My mom gets love from me everyday. Her eyes shine like the stars above. Her lips are red roses. My mom is like moonlight.

Michael Edwards Grade: 04
Sweet as candy. Eyes that shine. I love you so much. I'm glad you are my mom.

Andrew Gad Grade: 04
My mother's eyes shine like the stars in the night and the moon that shines right and right when she kisses me, I am heaven.

Jaiden Guitteriez Grade: 04
I love my mom and she loves me. We're a happy family. We go to places to have fun. We both like to run.

Alex Iwan Grade: 04
My mom's eyes are like stars in the sky, glowing bright, just like her personality. She deserves a shiny diamond just like her smile.

Monica Jensen Grade: 04
Eyes like stars, sweet as honey, hair as bright as the sun, and hardworking too. Mom, I will always love you.

Faith Kington Grade: 04
My mom's the moon, she has eyes like stars. Her hair is as dark as a moonless and starless night. She's the fairy of love.

Grace Lee Grade: 04
I have a mom that has a kind heart. She has a big smile everyday and night, and she always cares for me.

Hailey Martinez Grade: 04
My mom is the apple of my eye, she is caring and kind, my mom loves me when I'm sad, mad, she twinkles like diamonds.

Danny Nungaray Grade: 04
As perfect as the moon, as bright as the sun, she twinkles like magic. You know why that happened because she is my mom.

Christian Otto Grade: 04
My mom's eyes twinkle like the midnight stars. Her smile is really white. Her voice is like an angel. I will love her always.

Harrison Park Grade: 04
I see a brilliant, dazzling, and gleaming goddess over me. I feel pure and truthful. This person is a person I truly love, my mom.

* Amethyst winners in bold.

Julpa Rajyaguru   Grade: 04
My mom deserves to be as shiny as the noon day sun with her sparkling eyes and because she's the best.

Mari Wada   Grade: 04
My mom is caring and kind and she sparkles the sunlight. When I'm sad she cheers me up. I love mom a lot.

Jeongmin Yoo   Grade: 04
My mom's big heart is bigger than the world. She means everything in the world to me. Her eyes sparkles like a star.

Mission Hills Christian Sch
Rancho Santa Margarita

Teacher: Cameron Montefu

McKenna Almand   Grade: 03
Her eyes dazzle in my soul like a star up in heaven. She is so sweet and gentle, I love my mom so.

Sarah Boots   Grade: 03
My mom dazzles like light in the deepest, darkest cave. She is a gem of life to me, from darkness to light in a cave.

Quentin Buchman   Grade: 03
Her eyes like polished gems. Her hands like a sweet angel. Her heart like a flawless dove. Her hair a pure, dazzling star.

Kellie Chou   Grade: 03
Her loving hands touch my soul. Her shining heart is full of gold. Though she travels near and far. She is always in my heart.

Stephanie Connell   Grade: 03
My mom is some light of the moon. She is a flower from heaven. She is my diamond; my flower.

Mitch Dossey   Grade: 03
Her eyes shine like the sunset. She is my light in the darkness. She gives me grace everyday. Words can't explain how I love her.

Felice Gioia   Grade: 03
I don't deserve to have my mom. She helps me when I need her. She shines like diamonds. She is the gem of my heart.

Trestle Grohs   Grade: 03
My grandma shines like heaven. She is bright like a diamond. She is special the way God made her. She is a faithful person.

Abigail Hanson   Grade: 03
My mom is as bright as a diamond, as shiny as the moon. She's as sweet as a daisy. Her heart is golden.

Kaylie Holt   Grade: 03
My mom sparkles in the moonlight. She is my diamond. She dazzles in my eyes. She is wonderful beyond wonderful. She loves me.

Sam Ireland   Grade: 03
She is beautiful like a diamond. Her eyes sparkle in the moonlight. Her wonderful heart shines like a gem. I love my mother.

Marcus Johnson   Grade: 03
She shines like the sun and is very fun. My mom is honest and patient, but the best part is she loves me.

Pua Jung   Grade: 03
When I see my mom's sight, I feel so bright. Her hands glow in the sun, she is my only one. There is none other.

Jamison Kent   Grade: 03
My mom is magic in my heart. She's dazzling in my soul. She's heavenly in my mind. She's the only real diamond I know.

Kalani Lucas   Grade: 03
She shines in the night and she sparkles like the sun. She is my treasure. I know she is the one. My wonderful, flawless mom.

Emily Miller   Grade: 03
Her eyes dazzle like the sunlight. Her joyful heart is in my heart. The bright star that she is will always be there.

William Osier   Grade: 03
My mom is gentle and light. She outshines the stars and the moon. She is brighter than the sun and she is sweet and special.

Joshua Richter   Grade: 03
My mom guides my way. God shines like a gem in her heart. She is my diamond and I love her.

Skylar Rickabus   Grade: 03
My mom's the light of the sun. Her hair shines like a wonderful, dazzling diamond. She has diamond eyes and a flawless heart; my mom.

Danielle Sladek   Grade: 03
Her eyes sparkle. When I'm in danger, I can trust her. She makes me laugh. She holds me with her gentle hands. She is gorgeous.

Cole Sumner   Grade: 03
My mom is pure. She is honest and joyful. She shines like a gem. Her heart is flawless. She is magical. I love my mom.

Madison Theis   Grade: 03
My mom's beautiful eyes, stare right back at me. They are dazzling diamonds that will always be the key to my heart.

James Williams   Grade: 03
Her eyes are bright with hope. Her soul is flawless. Her hair is like gold strands of light. I already have my diamond, my mom.

Teacher: Christine Ramirez

Noah Barrette   Grade: 03
Mom helps me when I'm in trouble. She loves me more than anything. She helps me in scary places that pop up in my life.

Katelyn Bewley   Grade: 03
I love my mom, she's great to me. She is an angel, taught me God's word. Mom does so much for me, she is great.

Faith Fong   Grade: 03
Mom's an angel from heaven with round diamond eyes, like no other, she's calm as the moon. My mom cherishes me too.

Nicholas Greco   Grade: 03
My mom is a wonderful mom. She is an angel to me. I love my mom so much. She has a heart for me.

Sam Jakana   Grade: 03
I love my mom, she is so nice. Always there for me, she's the world in my life, like moonlight, she shines for me.

Kyle Kong   Grade: 03
My mom is loving and content. She is beautiful and nice. She is so generous, my mom cares just right.

Katelyn Mc Kinley   Grade: 03
My mom is a diamond, she is a gift from God. She is the light of my world. She is a diamond from God.

Zoe McFarlane   Grade: 03
I look into her heart. What do I see? I see a loving, truthful mom, who will always take care of me.

Kiersten Papst   Grade: 03
My mom is a gem because she shines like heaven. My mom is a diamond, she is always smiling. I love you mom.

Karisma Santalahti   Grade: 03
A little spice, a little Christ and you have everything just right. My mother can change your day, with her smile everyday.

Emily Sato   Grade: 03
My mom is so kind. She is God's gift from above. Her brown eyes twinkle, like the light of Heaven. She is a wonderful, Christian mom.

Peace Spearman   Grade: 03
I saw the moon. I thought of my beautiful mom. I saw her eyes, she's super mom. She encourages me when I am down.

Hannah Starrh   **Grade: 03**
She loves me more than gold. Her thoughts are kind and true. She loves the Lord with all her heart. She's the best mom too!

Alyssa Vieira   Grade: 03
My mom is very sweet. She is like a treat. She cares for me and loves me. I love her because she's there for me.

Teacher: Lisa Shore

Tanner Anderson   Grade: 04
My mom's eyes sparkle like the midnight blue. Her hair shines like the sun. She is my diamond.

Nicole Ballance   Grade: 04
My mom is sweet, caring, and loving. She has the sweetest voice. My mom loves me even if I make mistakes. She's the best.

Brianna Beller   Grade: 04
My mom has the sweetest heart, her beauty sparkles always. When her eyes shine, I know she loves me like it was meant to be.

Rheise Berro   **Grade: 04**
My mom is like a dove up in the sky, never-ending love is what is mine. I love her so and she is my mom.

Mary Desmond   Grade: 04
Mom's golden hair is a light in the darkness. She's not only beautiful on the outside, but her inner beauty sparkles everyday of her life.

Sarah Healy   **Grade: 04**
She shines like the golden sun shining down on the loveliest ocean. An angel is always with her making her inside and outside, beauty glisten.

Hannah Jackson   **Grade: 04**
Her eyes sparkle like the stars. Her beauty is much too hard to explain. I love her, and she loves me. She's my mom.

Bailey Kent   **Grade: 04**
My mom is overflowing with love. Her voice leads me in the darkness. Her voice is sweet as candy. I love her.

Carter Knauer   Grade: 04
My mom is the best, she would never love me less, she is just as sweet as the birds and the bees.

Nicholas Lofgren   Grade: 04
Her eyes shine on her face like diamonds, she's like an angel from heaven, she is super kind, and she's also very gentle.

Alexis MacMillin   Grade: 04
My mom is unlike other moms. She is like an angel gifted by God made with crystals in her eyes. Beauty always shines on her.

Chad Matthews   Grade: 04
My mom has beautiful eyes, they are always sparkling and flashing. Her teeth shine like gold. She is sweet like pie.

Nicholas McAteer   Grade: 04
I look at my mom in awe. She is loving and she is caring. Her heart is as red as a ruby. I love her.

Marcus Minardi   Grade: 04
My mom is great and sweet and her love can't be beat. I have loved her all my life. She is like sugar and spice.

Daniel Montefu   **Grade: 04**
My mom's eyes glisten in the moonlight. She is an angel who fell from heaven. She is full of joy and sweetness. She is love.

Graham Parton   **Grade: 04**
My mom sparkles in the sun. She is a wonderful bundle of fun. She shows courage and love. She is as beautiful as a dove.

Brandon Tappan   Grade: 04
Her eyes shine like the stars. Her smile is brighter than the sun. She is my mom and I am her son.

Heather Trivanovich   Grade: 04
I love my mom with all my heart. She has a twinkle in her eye, she has loved me from the start.

Connor Urbano   Grade: 04
My mom is sweet like an apple. She gives good advice and she cares for me. My mom keeps me healthy and strong.

Carter Vieira   **Grade: 04**
Her voice is the sound of the wind whispering in my ear. She's loving and kind and cares if I'm sick. I love my mom!

Teacher: Gigi Swanberg

Leah Boyd   Grade: 03
My mom is very neat, she is so very sweet. She's like a little lollipop that I would like to eat.

Tate Hamilton   Grade: 03
My mother is prettier than a diamond. Her eyes sparkle more than the brightest star. Hearing her voice is like hearing a bluebird's song.

Mikaela Hershock   **Grade: 03**
My mom's eyes are like diamonds. Her hair golden, just like her golden heart. She is priceless, but I have her in my heart.

Hana Strickfaden   Grade: 03
My mom is prettier than a flower. She smells as beautiful as a rose. She shows it to me because she has a beautiful heart.

Gehrig Urbano   Grade: 03
My mom is amazing, she's always happy and her eyes always twinkle in the sun. Also, she makes the best pancakes ever. Better watch out.

Mission Viejo High
Mission Viejo

Teacher: James Harris

Katlyn Adinolfi   Grade: 09
Long blonde hair and beautiful brown eyes. Everything she does is such a surprise. Since I was young, she cared for me.

Chelsea Aguero   Grade: 09
Loving, caring, giving. She does more than I could ever ask and expects nothing. She deserves everything I cold give her including a diamond.

Josh Auerbach   Grade: 09
She wakes up early, drives me and my sister to school, walks the dogs, cleans the house, buys groceries, cooks dinner…she deserves a diamond.

Mackenzie Ayers   Grade: 09
All the time adds up, night and day. For me, she labors. Why not give a diamond for the fruit of labor that never comes.

Christopher Baroni   Grade: 09
My mom deserves a diamond because she works very hard every day. She is always trying to help others feel better when they are down.

Daniel Bellomy   Grade: 09
My mom deserves a diamond because she is always there to help anyone and everyone with their problems, and is always there for me.

Cassidy Blythe   Grade: 09
My mom is very unique. She is very different unlike any other. There is no other woman like her. She is one of a kind.

Paul Bowker   Grade: 09
In my mom's high school years, she had trouble with bullies. Since then she has always been the one to protect the weak and defenseless.

Austin Caruana   Grade: 09
You are the gentle breezes of Earth, the warmth of the sun and the love of all people. Whatever happens, I still love you.

Celese Castillo   Grade: 09
Always there when you are down, tears of joy without a frown. Shines like a star when times are rough, comes through when it's tough.

Ashley Cerrudo   Grade: 09
My mom is a good mom, she helps me out a lot and I appreciate everything she's done. She's always nice to me.

Elisa Concepcion   Grade: 09
My mom deserves a diamond because she is beautiful and one of a kind. She deserves something that is beautiful and one of a kind.

Naya Deykes   Grade: 09
Precious as a stone, mommy smells like tea. Supportive and caring, lovely s can be. She deserves a diamond because she is everything to me.

Kris Freeman   Grade: 09
I believe all moms deserve a diamond because they are all special in their own way and went through all the trouble of having kids.

Sophia Fusco   Grade: 09
My mom deserves a diamond because she takes care of me and she teaches me life lessons. I love my mommy.

Chad Gauthier   Grade: 09
Mother and provider of seven. My mom has angel written all over. She works hard managing nurses, provides us with food, love. She's the best.

Jaime Gomez   Grade: 09
Mothers are beautiful like a diamond's shine. They make every day bright, because I've got mine.

Miranda Gonzales   Grade: 09
My mom is precious and delicate too. I think she deserves a diamond or two. I love my mom and you would too.

Shane Griffin   Grade: 09
A diamond is an elegant stone that shines in every mom's heart. My mom deserves a diamond because she is always there for my family.

Alison Griffin   Grade: 09
My mom deserves the world. My mom deserves everything. My mom deserves a diamond for everything she has done.

Christen Hagstrom   Grade: 09
It is simple, she respects me, so I respect her, it is simple.

Serena Harris   Grade: 09
Ever since the day I was born, she loves me more and more. Though we have our fights, she always seems to make it right.

Noelle Hunter   Grade: 09
My mom deserves a diamond because she is always taking care of people and housing people who are in need. I love her so much.

Abbie Ijanis   Grade: 09
My mom is extra special and practically perfect. Everyone loves her. She has an amazing personality and character.

Tanner Jackson   Grade: 09
My mom deserves more than a diamond. For all she does to help me succeed, there is nothing good enough, to show my gratitude.

Daniel Jorczak   Grade: 09
Who makes a wonderful dinner at night? Who taught you to stand up straight? Or to be disciplined? My mom's the reason I'm still alive.

Sara Kamieniecki   Grade: 09
My mom is a Girl Scout leader for two troops. She helps us work hard to achieve our goals. She's a really amazing person.

Garrett Kauss   Grade: 09
My mom deserves a diamond because she is a great role model and always ready to serve someone in need.

Jeff MacMonigle   Grade: 09
Mom deserves a diamond for working hard and helping to support our family. She doesn't get rewards, but a diamond is a reward for life.

Nairi Marderossian   Grade: 09
What's really a mom? Other than that person who truly cares. She's a part of everything in your life. A mom is a unique gift.

Joe Martin   Grade: 09
My mom gave up her life for her children. There is nothing I could do to repay her. But a diamond is a good start.

Connor McKee   Grade: 09
My mother deserves a diamond as thanks for her undying devotion to her family and friends; her love towards others is endless.

Brooke Millard   Grade: 09
My mom deserves a diamond because she means the world to me. She fills me with cheer and encourages me to do my best.

Scott Oberman   Grade: 09
My mother, my life giver and my shepherd. She has the undying grace of an angel and the patience of a saint.

Shelby Piersant   Grade: 09
She is smart, she is strong. She is kind and she is calm. She is incredibly special and she is my mom.

Alex Piwczynski   Grade: 09
The one who drives me to Los Angeles for hockey practice everyday during rush hour. The one who means the world to me; my mom.

Alexzandra Reed   Grade: 09
My mom is like a diamond in my eyes. She never stops shining and always tries in the end, she never gives up.

Sina Riahi   Grade: 09
My mom is the angel who brightens my day. She puts me before herself and sacrifices for my success. My mom is my true diamond.

Emily Ruth   Grade: 09
My mom deserves a diamond because she is caring and she loves me very much. She's funny and she always cares for me.

Taylor Savage   Grade: 09
I love her so much and she loves me back. She deserves the world so I can try and give her that.

Krystal Scavo — Grade: 09
I want to repay her anyway I can. She has always been there for me. She is the best a mom could be.

Ryan Scott — Grade: 09
My mom is a beautiful person who's always been there. I love her with all of my heart. Please show her that with a diamond.

Cole Stein — Grade: 09
My mom deserves a diamond because she loves her children, loves her husband, helps people in need, and helps the environment.

Kahn Van Toor — Grade: 09
My mom deserves a diamond because of her care, love, and support. She is simply the best mom ever.

Cheryl Waits — Grade: 09
My mom deserves a diamond as a reminder of what a wonderful mother she is. Like a diamond, my mom is beautiful, rare, and bright.

Kate Woodward — Grade: 09
The moon and stars, they're marvelous. You think nothing can compete, but you are wrong, she's stupendous. My mother makes me complete.

Carley Yegsigian — Grade: 09
The parting between my mother and I was less amicable than my parents' divorce. Whatever I say, she never stops trying to make it right.

Teacher: Jan Tattam

Lauren Beechler — Grade: 12
My mom deserves a diamond because she is a survivor, my best friend, a hero to many and an astounding mother.

Scott Clelland — Grade: 12
My mom deserves a diamond because she is cancer survivor, strong woman, supportive and a nice mom. Also, because she loves everything about life.

Brian Glynn — Grade: 12
My mom is nice, funny and sweet. She really deserves a treat, a diamond would sweet her off her feet.

Mitchell Elementary
Garden Grove

Teacher: Suzy Fauria

Ashley Bravo — Grade: 06
The reason why my mommy deserves a diamond is because she's my supermom, and she's my role model. She rocks my world.

Franco Fernandez — Grade: 06
I think my mom should win a diamond because she's hardworking and responsible. She also takes care of three boys. She's a model mom.

Helen Nguyen — Grade: 06
I want to get my mom a diamond because she's one special mom. She works hard for me. I wish I win my mom happiness.

Khanh Nguyen — Grade: 06
My mom deserves a diamond because she's the best mom I can ever have. She works hard to take care of our family.

Moiola (Fred) Elementary
Fountain Valley

Teacher: Emily Harvest

Maximilian Denembo — Grade: 04
My mom is funny and sweet, nice to me, pretty as a flower, busy as a bee. I would hate to see her leave.

Taylor Golden — Grade: 04
My mom is as pretty as a rose. As she watches my family grow, she always loves me at the end. She's my best friend.

Kennedy Jackson — Grade: 04
My mom is like a golden retriever because she's fast. She's light as snowflakes, kind as a bee, and I love her like a poodle.

Joseph Liu — Grade: 04
My mom is my dictionary. She is my problem solver. She is my chief chef. She is my chaperone. She is the best mom.

Heather Peterson — Grade: 04
She will never let me down. She feeds me and loves me. She plays with me. She tucks me into bed. Yes, she is my mom.

Kristen Prado — Grade: 04
My mom is a sweet, loving, caring mother who loves me with all her heart, no matter what, and I love her so much!

Cambria Stirrat — Grade: 04
My mom is a beautiful flower in the garden of good and great, she's fantastic on any given date, my mom's pure happiness, no hate.

Teacher: Melissa Housel

Chelsea Martinez — Grade: 07
My best friend in the world is as cool as she can be. She deserves a diamond because she will always be there for me.

Sidney McClelland — Grade: 07
My mom's eyes sparkle with forgiveness. Lips move with thanks. Body glows with beauty. Heart full of love for her five children, including me.

Kristine Nguyen — Grade: 07
I couldn't ask for more. I couldn't ask for better. She's already the best out there. No words could describe her.

Brittany Yates- Kelly — Grade: 07
My mom is the BEST! Her heart is like a giant ruby, always shining. So thoughtful to others, rarely thinking of herself. I love her!

Teacher: Laurel Kellogg

Aysia Buendia — Grade: 04
My mom is her own jewel. She sparkles in the moonlight. She is precious and valuable and I'm the twinkle in her eye.

Stefanie Eilders — Grade: 04
My mom has beautiful hair with golden stripes and gorgeous brown eyes like a diamond twinkling in the moonlight.

Caitlynn Evans — Grade: 04
She gave me life. Cares beyond belief. Master of teaching me. She is a "gem" herself!

Ryann Husain — Grade: 04
When she calls me, it sounds like the world's filled with gold. When I gaze into her eyes it looks like a path of diamonds.

Mackenzie Kohanek — Grade: 04
From the sun's shadow and the moonlight above, her heart is made of pure diamond and love.

Grace Mosher — Grade: 04
Moon and sun, yin and yang. The world's differences change anyone. She teaches me the differences by staying unchanging, a gem in my soul.

Vivienne Nguyen — Grade: 04
Her gleaming eyes are beautiful. Her face makes her shine. Whenever the sun shines at her, her heart is pure gold.

Jayme Pappas — Grade: 04
My mommy's eyes shine like from Heaven above. I'm lucky she always shares her love. I love her so much. She's the best mommy yet.

Courtney Suruki — Grade: 04
My mom's heart pure as gold and sparkles like her eyes. Her help to me is as helpful as my teacher is to me.

* Amethyst winners in bold.

Teacher: Kathleen Naughton

Amanda Lee   Grade: 05
Her eyes always shining. Her soul always caring. To you from me a golden heart. My mom, a loving angel.

Samantha Oliver   Grade: 05
Heart dazzling, eyes gleaming, my mom, a generous woman, is beautiful and deserving of a gorgeous, twinkling diamond.

R.J. Rahimi   Grade: 05
Her eyes glisten like the diamond that waits above. Her heart as gold as heaven. Her voice so soothing to me. I love her!

Katelynn Tran   Grade: 05
My mother's heart shines brighter than gold. For she's everything, but cold. She's greater than the sun. She's loads of fun. My mother, the angel.

Brandon Valdes   **Grade: 05**
Gem gleaming, diamond shining, a precious stone for my mom. Loving, hugging, protecting me like a precious diamond. The stone my mom deserves.

Teacher: Jody Phillips

Saika Batliwala   **Grade: 06**
She has taken care of me for years. Changed me into a beautiful person. I strive to be her. A treasure with a golden heart.

Mackenzie Brashier   **Grade: 06**
When I look into my mom's eyes I see reflected back at me the silent reassurance of unconditional love.

Aaron Campbell   Grade: 06
My mother is the apple of my eye. She is sweeter than homemade apple pie. My mom is glory and this is my story!

Alexandria Deovlet   **Grade: 06**
My mom is the diamond of my life, unique and irreplaceable. She is the diamond necklace dangling close to my heart. She is a rarity.

Mai-Han Do   Grade: 06
As I see my mother's eyes, they remind me of the day we met. As I see my mother's heart. It reminds me of love.

Amanda Graf   Grade: 06
My mom gives me love. She's like a pretty dove. Whenever I look in the sky above, I love her and she loves me.

Jonathon Jennings   Grade: 06
My mom's a goddess in her own way. She's loving and caring to me. So that's why I wanted to say, I love you mommy.

Anessa Longoria   **Grade: 06**
My mother loves me. When she hugs me I feel like a warm cup of tea. She is the key to tranquility for me.

Sarah Meskal   Grade: 06
My mom's a frappucino with whip cream on top, with caramel and chocolate which makes me hop, she's a flowing stream her eyes sparkle gleam.

Lucia Nguyen   Grade: 06
A heart of gold, her eyes of a tainted snowflake. As she, the goddess descends from the sky, her gifts everlasting, my love, my mother.

Thomas Price   Grade: 06
My mom's voice sounds like beautiful music; her eyes like brown beautiful gemstones; she has a body of an angel. She is my mom.

Mialinda Sepulveda   Grade: 06
When I look into my mother's hazelnut eyes, I see a wonderful, smart, beautiful woman underneath. I love her as much as she loves me.

Tien To   Grade: 06
My mother is the key to me. Her love is so untold. She loves me all with her heart of pure gold.

Teacher: Leslie Williams

Kaitlyn Danlinhton   **Grade: 04**
A touch of love, a life to live, breath to breathe, a golden heart, two twinkling eyes is what my mom is to me.

Ricky Gruenstein   **Grade: 04**
My mom's a sparkling heart, that loved me from the start. She's the only one, that's as bright as the sun. She is my heart.

Delaney Millican   **Grade: 04**
My mom makes my world bright and lights the burning candle in my heart. She is truly the nicest part of my life.

Connor Nelson   **Grade: 04**
A drop of sweetness, a ray of sun, a little bit of moonlight. She is my diamond, there to light my way. Mother, love.

Daniel Nguyen   Grade: 04
My mom makes me happy. I'll love her for a century. I am glad that I am her son. That's why she deserves a diamond.

Camile Nguyen   Grade: 04
My mom has a heart of fold that glitters like a rainbow. When I'm down, she helps me float because she's an angel.

Tracy Nguyen   Grade: 04
My mom's heart glitters like a rainbow. When I'm down, she helps me float. When I'm alone, she's always there. I know she loves me.

Dillon Roberts   Grade: 04
My mom is sweet, kind, and thoughtful. She's the love that makes me live. She works all day for us. She loves us all much.

Montevideo Elementary
Mission Viejo

Teacher: Cindy Busic

Harrison Bloom   Grade: 04
My mom is the best. She is like a diamond. She is as pure as gold. I don't know what I would do without her.

Nina Christodulou   Grade: 04
My mom works really hard. She is really loving. She's like a diamond to me. She always works for us. She always cares for me.

Samantha Dayles   Grade: 04
My mother's eyes are as pretty as diamonds. The sun shines because of her smile. She sounds like an angel. She is a gem.

Bayleigh Duarte   Grade: 04
You are more than silver. You are more than gold. You are more than anything in the world. I love you so dearly much.

Justin Evans   Grade: 04
My mother's eyes look like two diamonds shining in the sky. My mother is as perfect as she can be. My mom is perfect.

Victoria Ferry   **Grade: 04**
My mom is a loving and caring mother. Her heart is filled with all the good things in life. Her love makes me happy inside.

Jennifer Lezay   Grade: 04
You are the shine in my eye. You shine more than a diamond ring. You are not just a diamond, you are shinier than gold.

Melissa Mendez   **Grade: 04**
The wind through your hair. Your eyes like my soul. My mother means the world. Nothing is better than a diamond for my mother.

Joe Ramirez　　　　　　　Grade: 04
Her eyes glow in the moonlight like diamonds in the sun. Her love completes me. Her heart is made of gold.

Kayla Scord　　　　　　　Grade: 04
How did I get here? I turned around. There you were. I didn't think twice irrationalized. Mom, you are the greatest person. I love you.

Jenae Vancura　　　　　　Grade: 04
A mom that is special should be just like mine, made of roses grown by vines. She won a special place in my heart.

Amanda Wagner　　　　　　Grade: 04
My mom's eyes sparkle like the moonlight. Her heart is made of gold. She's sweeter than a peach. I love my mom more than anything.

Teacher: Cindi Hausheer

Marissa Aldridge　　　　　Grade: 04
Diamonds are beautiful and they are the most wonderful gift for someone special like my mom. She shows me everyday how much she loves me.

Kathy Barkhordar　　　　　Grade: 04
My mom is strong like a diamond in the rough days. She loves unconditionally no matter what. She feeds me and helps me grow too.

Bailey Clement　　　　　　Grade: 04
I believe my mom's value is more than a diamond's. I love my mom for always being there. My mom's the best. I love her.

Ethan Ignoffo　　　　　　Grade: 04
My mother is an excellent mother, she is always at my soccer games cheering me on. She also educates hundreds of kids during the day.

Joseph Nava　　　　　　　Grade: 04
I think my mom is really great. She makes sure that we are healthy. She is the one who feeds the family. I like my mom.

Deja Osborne　　　　　　Grade: 04
A diamond reminds me of my mom because she is unique and special. She is hardworking and helps me with a lot of things.

Sam Rose　　　　　　　　Grade: 04
Mom deserves a diamond because like a diamond my mom shines, shows her love and compassion, but unlike a diamond she is worth way more.

Kelly Savage　　　　　　Grade: 04
Like a diamond, she has a fire within. It shows by the four c's - like a diamond her c's are caring, cute, creative and crazy.

Natalie Zimmerman　　　　Grade: 04
Making history in the global banking business is how I think of my mom. She is a wonderful, intelligent, pleasant and reasonable woman.

Teacher: Carol Johnson

Catherine Brown　　　　　Grade: 06
Mom loves and cares day and night. She's a star, shines so bright. She's like a treasure from beyond and we have a great bond.

Nathan Cassens　　　　　Grade: 06
The eyes of a ruby, the heart of a diamond. That's my mom, the mom I love.

Chad Davis　　　　　　　Grade: 06
My mom is like outer space. Her heart, as bright as the sun, and her eyes like twinkling stars in the night sky.

Tim Denlinger　　　　　　Grade: 06
I think my mom's the best. She would like anything. I give her. But gems would amaze her. Win or lose, still happy.

Brittany Earnest　　　　　Grade: 06
My mom deserves a diamond more than anyone I know. She has always been there for me for encouragement and support. She's my best friend.

Sammy Goodman　　　　　Grade: 06
A mother's love is forever. A diamond to treasure. On a scale, she's a ten. Her love has no end.

Jesus Hernandez　　　　　Grade: 06
My mom is what I need, her eyes shine like two diamonds in the sun that the reflection shines back in my eyes.

Ben Hood　　　　　　　　Grade: 06
A beautiful diamond so perfect and flawless. Whose heart is so bright, it must be spotless.

Alyssa Jones　　　　　　Grade: 06
A beautiful mom deserves a gift as beautiful as her. I'd love to see her face when she sees the gift, joy and love.

Dana Kamieniecki　　　　Grade: 06
My mom is worth more than any treasure in the world. I would love to give her a diamond.

Ariana Kendrick　　　　　Grade: 06
Her eyes twinkle at night like a diamond in the sky, in the morning, she's a butterfly. She's flawless tonight, she shines like a ruby.

Tabitha Morris　　　　　　Grade: 06
With a heart of passion and personality of gold. My mom is the one person sparkling so bold and beautiful inside and out.

Matt Nelson　　　　　　　Grade: 06
Mom, you are the greatest mom in the world. All the other kids are raised by little girls. Mom, I love you from the heart.

Delaney Orr　　　　　　　Grade: 06
My mom has a heart full of gold and her beauty so bold, she's exactly for me and helps me when I scraped my knee.

Cole Paton　　　　　　　Grade: 06
My mom is like a diamond, she can't be scratched or touched. She is flawless. If I don't win, I will still have a diamond.

Darian Primer　　　　　　Grade: 06
My mother's eyes shine like the moon which from this day is shaped like a heart.

Kamila Sabat　　　　　　Grade: 06
She gave me life, she was there for me. She works her heart to keep us up. She is my mom.

Kara Shue　　　　　　　　Grade: 06
My mom is like the North Star that shines bright. My mom brightens my day when I'm feeling blue and that's why I love her.

Sidney Smiggs　　　　　　Grade: 06
My mother is the light of my soul. She is my precious gem, so fragile but so great. Her eyes sparkle, her heart glows.

Alli Zundel　　　　　　　Grade: 06
Such a precious sparkling diamond of a mom your tingling blue eyes, such a warm feeling inside.

Teacher: Patty Winger

Uriel Gallegos　　　　　　Grade: 06
My mother deserves a diamond because she is a very nice person. She is very loveable. She always takes care of me and her family.

Katy Iverson　　　　　　Grade: 06
My mom is wonderful and even though we don't have very much money, she still let's me play sports. My mom definitely deserves a diamond.

Julie Koch　　　　　　　Grade: 06
My mom deserves a diamond because she works all day, goes to school at night and everyone she still manages to give us attention.

* Amethyst winners in bold.

Samantha MacKay   Grade: 06
My mom does many things for me when it comes to soccer, especially supports me. She's loving and caring, I'm very thankful to have her.

McKenna Mire   Grade: 06
My mom will do anything for her children. She does a lot of things for us. My mom really deserves this diamond.

Jaime Valdivieso   Grade: 06
My mom is a helpful, fun-loving person that supplies people with food and that's why she deserves a diamond.

Morningside Elementary
Garden Grove

Teacher: Anita Griswold

Kathy Huynh   Grade: 06
Mom deserves a diamond because she takes care of us, loves us, cooks for us. She also gave birth to us.

Tina Nguyen   Grade: 06
My dad went to the army before 1975. My dad was captured by VC so my mom sold her wedding ring to care for us.

Morris (Juliet) Elementary
Cypress

Teacher: Mary Fenoglio

Kayla Ashton   Grade: 01
My mom is like
100 dollars. Her hair is like diamonds twinkling on a star at night. My mom loves me so much.

Raymond Barrera   Grade: 01
My mom is shiny like diamonds. She is beautiful and pretty. I love my mom a lot.

Daniel Cho   Grade: 01
Mom, beautiful hair, beautiful eyes. Cooking, sleeping, loving. Reads books to me.

Alex Do   Grade: 01
Your eyes sparkle in the light, your hair is almost a star in space at night. You're as beautiful as a diamond in the sky.

Jessica Paul   Grade: 01
My mom is so helpful to me because she does everything to make my happy. She's so beautiful and I think that is fine.

Bradley Weaver   Grade: 01
My mom shines like a star in the sky. She is beautiful like a diamond.

Marc Anthony Zaldana   Grade: 01
My mom has beautiful sparkling eyes of a star mixed with beautiful jewels. My mom is pretty. I love my pretty mom.

Teacher: Colleen Ferreira

Taylor Jackson   Grade: 01
If mom were the moon, I'd be stars. If she were castles, I'd be the moats. If she were the bear, I'd be the cave.

Daniel McCrary   Grade: 01
If mom were trees, I'd be leaves. If she were a flower, I'd be a bee. If she were a river, I'd be the water.

Tori Merten   Grade: 01
If mom were love, I'd be the heart. If mom were the sea, I'm a dolphin. If mom were the star, I'd be the sea.

Jeremiah Moon   Grade: 01
If mom were a moon, I'd be stars. If she were grass, I'd be soil. If she were the summer, I'd be a pool.

Ethan Wasserman   Grade: 01
If mom were a kiss, I'd be a hug. If she were trees, I'd be her leaves. If she were a wink, I'd be a nod.

Teacher: Michelle Moore

Abdallah Ahmed   Grade: 05
The reason my mom deserves a diamond because she cares about all my needs and even I make her angry, she still loves me.

Brandi Carrillo   Grade: 05
I think my mom deserves a diamond because she supports my family with my dad. She works twelve hours and she shows that she loves me.

Jacqueline Gonzalez   Grade: 05
My mom deserves a diamond because she is hardworking. She always has some time for me, but the most important thing is she loves me.

Leah Han   Grade: 05
My mom deserves a diamond because she gets stress from work, so she doesn't have to be sad. I want her to be 100% happy.

Madison Heckert   Grade: 05
My mom deserves a diamond because she can take are of three kids without bursting her bubble.

Alaina Irvine   Grade: 05
My mom deserves a diamond because she works full time and still loves us. She keeps our house and clothes sparkly clean, like a diamond.

Erica Lee   Grade: 05
My mom deserves a diamond because she raised me alone. Plus she pays my prep school so I can become an educated person. She's great.

Briana Milstead   Grade: 05
She deserves a diamond because she is flawless. Sometimes she doesn't have time for herself and helps me out. She always puts me first.

Justina yoo   Grade: 05
I think my mom should get it so later when we get older, she can look at the diamond remind her of the good times.

Teacher: Mindy Pfafflin

Abi Annis   Grade: 01
Her hugs are the best. She gives me the gifts I want. She keeps me warm when I'm cold. I'll never stop, loving her.

Zoe Chen   Grade: 01
Mom reads me stories. Mom is an angel in the sky. Mom is a dazzling princess. Mom is jolly like Santa. Mom is very clever.

Nick Groman   Grade: 01
I love my mom more than all the money. My mom is fabulous and an angel at baking.

Nolan Huisinga   Grade: 01
My mom is dazzling. She is like an angel to me. She makes the best brownies and cupcakes.

Karina Martin   Grade: 01
My mom is treasure and an angel and gold and silver. She is the best to me. She is my only love and truth to me.

Jeremy Matney   Grade: 01
She's like a red heart to me. She is dazzling diamonds.

Chelsea Stannard   Grade: 01
She is smart. My mom is like a lovely rose. My mom is an angel. I love mom.

Kayli Woodside   Grade: 01
My mom is the spirit in the sky, the angel of my heart, the brightness of the stars.
Teacher: Ann Steinbrink

Ahmad Dabbagh   Grade: 05
My beautiful mother's eyes are like shining as the moon and the sun mixed together.

Paige Edward   Grade: 05
My mom's like the sun in the sky. She's always up high, high, never gloomy like grey clouds. She's always there to make me proud.

Viviana Gonzalez Prido   Grade: 05
Sugar, spice and everything nice is what makes her up. That little sparkle in her eye. Makes the brightest star looks like a small dull glow.

Taylor Hermes   Grade: 05
My mom's a generous soul and fills the air with joy. Every time I see her, her eyes shimmer in the light like a polished diamond.

Jenna Hirao   Grade: 05
A cup of compassion, a ladle of love. The ingredients of where my mom came from above.

Andrew Kim   Grade: 05
She is nice and kind, when I dhow her a diamond, it might shine in her eyes with a burst of happiness.

Jordan Lewis   Grade: 05
A little bit of love and a little bit of happiness, you mix the two together and get my caring mother.

Jordan Macias   Grade: 05
My mom's eyes are like purple diamonds shining in the moonlight. Her voice sounds like it came from heaven.

Kevin Martin   Grade: 05
With heart of gold, two children to hold. A family kept together. Her love lasts forever. She is amazingly wonderful.

Madison Nelson   Grade: 05
Her eyes sparkle like a great, big diamond. Her heart is always filled of joy. But most of all, she is special to me.

Rachael Rodriguez   Grade: 05
The person I love, the most is in the heart of my soul. She's the one who's great and perfect and that always is mom.

Anisha Shinmar   Grade: 05
My mom is so lovely and shines like a star. She's my gem of good luck and warm in my heart. She's a perfect mom.

Hannah Sutkowski   Grade: 05
The moon shines bright, it reflects the light of a diamond. It's very big, but not nearly as big as my mom's heart.

Ben Winter   Grade: 05
The twinkle in her eyes is the real prize. You know, these are not true lies. Her beautiful face is no disguise.

Moulton Elementary
Laguna Niguel

Teacher: Kimberly Cashin

Ryan Harding   Grade: 02
My mom deserves a diamond because she works hard as a school teacher and she is a good cook and helps me with my homework.

Bridgit Hoolihan   Grade: 02
My mom means more than a diamond to me. She means the world to me. I love her to the moon and back.

Chloe Lukas   Grade: 02
My mom has to go to Asia for her job and misses me very much. The diamond will remind her of me when she's gone.

Teacher: Amy Zeppa

Lucas Blow   Grade: 03
My mother is as beautiful as the diamond. Also her eyes gleam like the diamond and she is as rare like the diamond.

Dylan Bruckheim   Grade: 03
Hot dogs, five dollars. Bus tickets, three dollars. Arcade, ten dollars. A 1/4 carat diamond, $600 dollars. My mom's love - PRICELESS.

Katherine Copeland   Grade: 03
She is like a precious gemstone to me, she is strong and resilient like a diamond.

Daniel Jelladian   Grade: 03
Mom deserves a diamond because her eyes are as shiny as crystals. Her heart's as strong as gold. She's the best mom in the universe.

Adam Kader   Grade: 03
My mom is my crystal. Heart, the jewel of my life. Her love is unbreakable for me. She is rarer than anything.

Staci Lin   Grade: 03
Her eyes are shimmering just like the stars. She is a priceless person and a caring one too. She is a special gift from God.

Parker McDaniel   Grade: 03
Her eyes are like gold. Her heart is a gem and her love is priceless. She is all mine.

Rebecca Morrow   Grade: 03
Mom's eyes twinkle like gems. She's unique like a diamond. Her love is rare and precious. She is priceless to buy.

Samantha Rush   Grade: 03
My mother is as expensive as diamonds. Her twinkling eyes are like jewels. She has a heart of gold. I love her very much.

Muir (John) Fundamental
Santa Ana

Teacher: Lisa Condon

Kimber Cruz   Grade: 03
My mom deserves a diamond because of what she thinks about me. My mom is so sweet that I will thank her with this.

Andrea Franco   Grade: 03
Roses are red, violets are blue. Her heart sparkles like stars too. She works hard day and night. She deserves a diamond. Am I right?

David Martinez   Grade: 03
My mom should have a diamond. She should have one because she has the best heart in the world. She'll love me a lot forever.

Aubrianna Nieto   Grade: 03
Of all the sweets I love to eat, my mom's heart is my favorite treat. That's why my mom deserves a diamond.

Joanna Ortiz   Grade: 03
My mom deserves a diamond because she shines as a star and I think she deserves more than I can give her.

Teacher: Suzanne Krill

Justin Dysome   Grade: 02
Roses are red, violets are blue. Your eyes shine like the moon. Your heart is sweet like you. You're as beautiful as a flower.

Kayla Laguna   Grade: 02
My mom is like an angel rising up in the sun. She always protects me and always is there for me when I need her.

Jonathan Lavenant   Grade: 02
Her eyes twinkle like a gem. Her heart so bright and shiny. She lights the world with great love and never lets me go.

Benjamin Lemus   Grade: 02
My mom is the gem of my soul. Her eyes glisten in the sun. Her kisses and hugs, fill me with love. I love her.

Elena Leyva   Grade: 02
My mom deserves a diamond because she is so very kind. She is like a blanket that won't let go. My mom is my gem.

* Amethyst winners in bold.

Drake McFaul   Grade: 02
My mom as peaceful as a dove, more beautiful than a swan, and touches my heart more often than needed but I like it.

Nia Parks   Grade: 02
She twinkles in the moonlight and shines in the sun. She smells like a rose. The most wonderful thing is. She is my mom.

Teacher: Sylvia Mc Pherson

Diego Enriquez   Grade: 02
My mom deserves a diamond for all the work she has done for my baby sisters, brother, big sister and me. She's the best.

Peter Gonzalez   Grade: 02
My mom deserves a diamond because it is incredible. She is helpful and smart. My mom can do a magic trick. I like my mom.

Alejandra Navarro   Grade: 02
My mom deserves a diamond for being a great mom and also for taking me to the cemetery to give flowers to my grandma, Yolanda.

Teacher: Jan Nelson-Orville

Julissa Acosta   Grade: 02
My mother deserves a diamond because she's very nice and sweet. Her eyes are like the stars in the sky that sparkle like a diamond.

Grace Elson   Grade: 02
My mom is beautiful like a butterfly. She smells like peaches. Her eyes are as green as lime drops. She is nice to me always.

Megan Logan   Grade: 02
My mom deserves a diamond because she shimmers like glitter. She reminds me of a diamond because she wears sparkly jewelry everyday. I love her.

Briana Mancillo   Grade: 02
My mom deserves a diamond because she is beautiful like an angel. She is like a rose. Her favorite color is red just like roses.

Andrew Medina   Grade: 02
My mom deserves a diamond because she is sweet and she's helpful. My mom deserves the best diamond because she's the best mom.

Anissa Orozco   Grade: 02
My mommy deserves a diamond because her eyes shine bright; very, very bright. Just like a beautiful shimmering diamond in the night. I love her.

Emily Ortiz   Grade: 02
Roses are red, violets are blue. My mom deserves a diamond, or two. She never says a lie. She is as pretty as a butterfly.

Monica Renteria   Grade: 02
I love my mom. She's beautiful like a diamond that sparkles in her brown eyes. She deserves a diamond because she is the best mom.

Veronica Rodriguez   Grade: 02
My mom deserves a diamond. She is very nice. She smiles very pretty. She hugs me a lot. Her eyes sparkle like a beautiful, diamond.

Adam Salguero   Grade: 02
My mom deserves a diamond because she's a part of my heart and I'm not me without her. I really need her.

Teacher: Wendy Quintana

Ashley Alvarez   Grade: 03
Of all the sweets in the world, my mom is the sweetest. She works really hard around the house. So she deserves the best.

Anapatricia Curiel   Grade: 03
My mom works until she drops and no one seems to notice. She deserves a diamond for all she gives without expecting anything in return.

Michael Logan   Grade: 03
My mom deserves a diamond because she's pretty as a rose and sweet like honey. She deserves a diamond because she has a glowing heart.

Paulina Robles   Grade: 03
My mom is sweet and funny. She deserves a diamond because she takes good care of us. She is hardworking. My mom deserves the best.

Teacher: Karen Stepanski

Isaiah Hernandez   Grade: 04
My mother deserves a gemstone because she works continuously to supervise, secure and nourish me along with five other children. She really deserves a diamond.

Michelle Lockington   Grade: 04
My mom deserves a beautiful diamond for her love and support to the family. Her smile brightens the darkest rooms in the house.

Stephanie Maturino   Grade: 04
My mom deserves a diamond because she's a mother who cherishes her four children. She tries to keep us safe like mother bears do.

Jacqueline Najera   Grade: 04
My mom procures a diamond because she is a superior woman and mother. She is a role model to my brother, family, friends, and me.

Jesus Ochoa   Grade: 04
My mom deserves a diamond because she's sweet as sugar. She encourages us to follow our dreams. She is very witty, cool and cooks good.

Ritu Sharma   Grade: 04
My mom deserves a diamond because she always fulfills my desires and my needs. She always protects my brother and me as a mother tiger.

Phillip Solis   Grade: 04
I think my mother deserves a diamond because she is the rose of love in the gardens of my heart which burst love for her.

Teacher: Christopher Yusi

Veronica Carrillo   Grade: 05
I think my mom deserves a diamond because she is pretty. I think she will be even prettier with a diamond on her hand.

Iliana Ibarra   Grade: 05
My mom deserves a diamond because she has always helped me. She always takes care of me. She tells me to do my best.

Valerie Reyes   Grade: 05
My mom deserves a diamond because she's the best. When I'm mad or sad, she's like a magical fairy that can fix anything. She's the best.

Delilah Roman   Grade: 05
My mom deserves a diamond because of all her hard work, her help, and her responsibility to keep me safe. My mom is the best.

Jasmine Ruiz   Grade: 05
My mom is very hardworking. She works head to toe. Her only goal this year is to spend as much times with the family.

Pablo Sanchez   Grade: 05
I think my mom deserves a diamond because she loves me, she does everything for me. She is the best mom in the whole world.

Hailey Vasquez   Grade: 05
My mom is exquisitely nice, made out of spice. She works very hard to give us a home. That is why my mom deserves one.

Kimberly Wong   Grade: 05
My mom deserves a diamond because she is always working. Sometimes she deserves the world but we can't give it to her. I love her.

Nelson (W.R.) Elementary
Tustin

Teacher: Laura Epstein

Adam Barajas   Grade: 03
My mom is a helpful, lovely and beautiful mom. She helps me a lot. She has loved me and takes care of me.

Darien Cai   Grade: 03
My mom is as sparkly as a diamond and as beautiful as a diamond. That's why I love her in all places.

Katie Dang   Grade: 03
My mom deserves a diamond because she is pretty and she gets what I really need. My mom deserves a diamond because she is nice.

Ciera Friel   Grade: 03
My mom deserves a diamond because you can always count on her. She is always working hard. She is very loving.

Gustavo Garcia   Grade: 03
My mom deserves a diamond because I appreciate all the things she's done for me. She always cares for me. She's a beautiful mom.

Kayla Gonzalez   Grade: 03
She loves me. She is beautiful. My mom cares about me. She protects me from danger. My mom is very nice and helps me.

Stephanie Guevara   Grade: 03
My mom deserves one because she is nice. She always has time to play with me time to help me with my homework. Love, Stephanie.

Elissa Ortiz   Grade: 03
My mom is fair and loving. She is as dazzling as a diamond. She has given me stuff that I like.

David Quinonez   Grade: 03
My mom deserves a diamond because she's beautiful and I appreciate her love for me. She is dazzling, beautiful and shiny like a diamond.

Newland (William T.) Elem.
Huntington Beach

Teacher: Erica Melcer

Connor Aoki   Grade: 03
My mom deserves a diamond because she helps me with everything I do and she gives whatever I need to have a nice life.

Savannah Bonifay   Grade: 03
Mother deserves a diamond because she is extraordinary in so many ways. Especially when she helps me cook soup and teaches me how to read hard books.

Megan Crutsinger   Grade: 03
My mom is a great mom for taking care of me. She is also thoughtful and caring. She always makes me laugh.

Marissa DeGeorge   Grade: 03
My mom deserves it because she is loving, caring, very kind and very nice. And because she loves me very much.

Shay Douphner   Grade: 03
My mom deserves a diamond because she is a nice mom and a kind one too. She is the best mom I could ever want.

Samantha Pearl Haines   Grade: 03
My mom deserves a diamond because she is nice, pretty and she is in a nursing home. So she is really lonely.

Eden Hawes   Grade: 03
My mom deserves a diamond because she is really fun, nice and beautiful. I think she would look great with a diamond necklace.

Joe Kang   Grade: 03
My mom deserves a diamond because she is nice, caring, honest and careful. I want a diamond for my mom. I want to say thanks.

Griffin Kosick   Grade: 03
My mom deserves a diamond because she is the one that tucks me in at night. She also squeezes me so tight. Please pick her.

Samantha Marlow   Grade: 03
My mom should win the diamond because she deserves it for being the most beautiful, helpful mom in the world. I hope she wins.

Jack Morrell   Grade: 03
I think my mom should get the diamond because she takes care of me and she is a very nice mom.

Bryan Phan   Grade: 03
Mom should get a diamond because she is very helpful and nice. When I don't understand something, she helps me. I hope she wins.

Connor Sandford   Grade: 03
My mom deserves a diamond because she is nice to me. A diamond is as beautiful as her. My mom is nice too.

Megan Schutt   Grade: 03
My mom deserves a diamond because she is always there for me. She takes care of me better than any other mom.

Katrina Ueno   Grade: 03
The beach is where my mom and I go. She's the best mom ever, don't you know? She always makes my heart glow.

Teacher: Michelle Siefker

Jamie Beck   Grade: 03
My mom is sweet and loving and beautiful like a diamond. Her eyes sparkle so bright just like a diamond.

Kelsey Crutsinger   Grade: 03
My mom is unbreakable in my heart. Her eyes sparkle in the night. She is like a rare diamond to me.
Teacher:

Jad El-Jurdi   Grade: 03
My mom loves and cares for me so very much and I love her with all my heart. She is ever so nice.

Jacob Elton   Grade: 03
My mother is more beautiful than any other diamond. Her eyes, shine brighter than the brightest star.

Jacob Ferris   Grade: 03
My mom is nice and caring. I would not trade her in for twenty million diamonds. I love her more than anything.

Nolan Funke   Grade: 03
A diamond is beautiful just like my mom. My mom is the nicest. She helps me when I need it.

Seth Haden   Grade: 03
When I look at the stars, it always reminds me that my mom's heart sparkles like a diamond of love.

Danielle Johnson   Grade: 03
My mom's heart is unbreakable as long as I'm with her. The diamond she will always wear will be as sparkly as her eyes.

Amy Lee   Grade: 03
My mom's eyes twinkle in the bright moonlight. Like the diamond on my window sill, they're gleaming with light.

Sabreena Nguyen   Grade: 03
My mom is pretty like a diamond. A diamond is rare like my mom. She is pretty and nice like a diamond.

*Amethyst winners in bold.

IN THE NEWS!

Words Worth A Diamond

Mission Viejo teenager writes a poem that wins his mother a heart-shaped gem
Amanda Glowish, Orange County Register. March 19, 2007.

The poetry contest was worth five extra points in class….and a diamond.

Wanting his five extra points, Michael Glidden, a junior at Capistrano Valley High School, entered the contest. He wrote a 25 word poem on WHY MOM DESERVES A DIAMOND®, a contest run by Gallery of Diamonds in Newport Beach.

Glidden, 16, almost didn't turn the poem in and his teacher, Laura Little, received it late but still accepted it. Little, a judge for the contest every year, encourages her students to parpicipate by offering them extra points.

MARILYNN YOUNG, STAFF PHOTOGRAPHER

A few weeks later, he found his words had won over the judges. He beat more than 15,000 other entries and won a ¼ carat heart-shaped diamond for his mother, Gerlyn. "Michael's poem won within the first 12 words," said Michael Watson, president of Gallery of Diamonds. "It's amazing."

Perhaps the best part of Glidden's victory was surprising his mother. He had kept the contest a secret from her and told his mom after finding out he was the winner.

"On Valentines Day he read it to me, which was very sweet," said Gerlyn Glidden. Knowing most people would use clichés about diamonds, Glidden said he thought about why it is that he loves his mother. He wrote two other poems and chose the one he liked the best. Always having a flair for writing, even he was surprised by his accomplishment.

"I didn't believe myself and I never won anything like that," said Glidden of Mission Viejo.

The contest, in its 15th year, requires the winner to read the poem to his or her mother in the jewelry store before being awarded with the diamond, worth $500. The diamond was unset and Gerlyn is having her ring set in two bands of diamonds with the heart in the middle. When it's complete, she plans on making it a regular accessory.

"I am hoping to wear it all the time. It could be something to pass down, maybe to his wife or his children," Gerlyn said. "It's a neat heirloom."
"

Free Diamonds!

Contest Fulfills the Diamond Dream.

By Susan Thea Posnock, National Jeweler Magazine. May 1, 2007. Pg. 24.

For 15 years, Gallery of Diamonds in Newport Beach, Calif., has been giving away diamonds as part of its trademarked WHY MOM DESERVES A DIAMOND® contest.

"It started very humbly. It was just kids from local schools that sent in essays, and now it's nationwide with 15,000 to 20,000 kids sending in essays about their mom," says Gallery of Diamonds president Michael Watson, who first started the contest to honor his adoptive mother.

"The contest is more than just prizes," says Watson. "It's business with meaning."

Reagan Parker   Grade: 03
A diamond shines so bright, but my mom's love is so much brighter. My mom loves me more than you.

Alyssa Sandford   Grade: 03
My mom is so great. She fills up my heart. Her love to me is unbreakable, like a diamond of some sort.

Jacob Tomin   Grade: 03
Mom, you're the best. Your heart is beating in your chest. A diamond is worth a million. Your worth a billion.

Jan Van Eyk   Grade: 03
My mom is as beautiful as a sparkly, shiny and rare diamond. The diamond is as unbreakable as my mom's eyes.

Matthew Van Heel   Grade: 03
My mom twinkles bright in the sky like her love. Diamonds are beautiful, but not as much as my mom.

Newport Coast Elementary
Newport Beach

Teacher: Nathan Gibbs

Michael Cage   Grade: 06
My mom is a swan gracefully gliding across the water. She's also like a pancake filling me up with joy. My mom deserves a diamond.

Kelsie Delaney   Grade: 06
My mom's eyes sparkle like a midnight star. They glisten and shine. Her love is as big as the deep sea. She deserves a diamond.

Emaan Jadali   Grade: 06
My mom is like the sun. She gives me power and warmth. My mom deserves a diamond because she is my wonderful and beautiful hero.

Morgan Merchat-Chambers   Grade: 06
My mom deserves a diamond because she is special to me. She is my hero, my own shining star. My mom is my sparkling diamond.

Cheyenne Thies   Grade: 06
She's the reason I wake up. She makes a dark alley clear as daylight. Words can't describe my love for her. She's my mom.

Teacher: Mariela Hayner

Tatyana Buchwald   Grade: 03
Her smile brings sunlight to the day. Her eyes makes rainbows in the sky. She is so nice. I love her.

Emma Goolsby   Grade: 03
My mom is a sparkling star. She has a heart as big as the sun. She's a beautiful angel. She's so loving. She's my mom.

Michael Gozali   Grade: 03
A wonderful, colorful gem. The stone of my life, she is the rainbow of beauty. Who is that shining light? She is my mom.

Alec Griffith   Grade: 03
Her eyes shine when she looks at me. She is the best mom. When I look at her, she fills my heart with joy.

Gabriel Hansen   Grade: 03
Her eyes sparkle, she is so beautiful. She always picks me up when I fall down, she is so amazing and she is my mom.

Joshua Hubbs   Grade: 03
My mom's eyes are like clear pools of water. Her eyes glisten in the sun when she looks at me, her love warm my heart.

Nolan Kaya   Grade: 03
When my mom smiles it is like a sunset. Her eyes are like a star. Most of all, she cares about me.

Leah Khalili   Grade: 03
My mom's eyes twinkle like stars. Her brown hair is as smooth as chocolate. She will stay in my heart forever.

Jake Nguyen   Grade: 03
Her eyes look at me like a shining star. Her smile shines like a bundle of gold. She is my mother, the one I love.

Delarai Sadeghitari   Grade: 03
Her heart is made of love and care. When she looks at me her eyes sparkle. I love her more than the world. My mother.

Jake Tsubota   Grade: 03
My mom gleams like a crystal. She shines like the stars. When I see her, I see her with a smile, she's the most beautiful.

Teacher: Anne Mink

Gillianne Archiquette   Grade: 02
Her eyes gleam like the sun and her face is always bright. She loves me and cares for me. I love her too.

Tyler Bates   Grade: 02
My mom is always happy and her eyes sparkle. Her smile cheers me up. She is always forgiving and she loves me.

Reece Berger   Grade: 02
Her eyes sparkle like two stars. She has a perfect face. Her heart is a shiny diamond.

Mallorie Cohen   Grade: 02
Every morning my mom wakes me up with a big hug and a kiss. I feel loved with my mom.

Brianna Fortmuller   Grade: 02
My mom is pretty and her eyes are like a diamond and she is the nicest mom you can have.

Alex Kermani   Grade: 02
My mom is the nicest person because she makes me happy when I see her. Her eyes make me proud and she loves me also.

Arman Roshannai   Grade: 02
My mom is loving and caring. Her hair shines and gleams. Her eyes are two clear pools of sparking water and she loves me so.

Nick Thompson   Grade: 02
My mom is love and caring because she makes me glad when I'm sad. Her eyes shine like the sun.

Sara Utner   Grade: 02
My mommy is the best. Her eyes sparkle with love. My mom loves diamonds. She deserves it.

Teacher: Ingrid Ohanian

Emmy Berger   Grade: 05
With that twinkle in her eyes, never will my mom ask why. She says that in life I will succeed. That's a fact she believes.

Vincent Ong   Grade: 05
My mom is so special because she gave birth to me. She is so brave for nourishing me. Giving a brother to me was good.

Rayna Schonwit   Grade: 05
If I traded moms for one day, I would lose my mind. Whenever I have problems, I go to her for the best solution.

Leila Shaygan   Grade: 05
A princess sitting one her throne. A goddess and everyone must know. My mother, beauty inside out. The diamond of my life, there's no doubt.

Teacher: Lisa Scott

Krista Anderson   Grade: 05
My mom deserves a diamond because she's my world. She's beyond pretty and beautiful put together. She's caring and loving in everyway, I love her.

Jordan Chun   Grade: 05
Her love is stronger than gravity. Her heart burns with love like a wildfire at night. That is why my mom deserves a diamond.

* Amethyst winners in bold.

Ty Comrie   Grade: 05
My mom deserves a diamond because in a million different ways. She is a kind hearted role model and a loving and caring person who loves me.

Katie Correnty   Grade: 05
My mom deserves a diamond because she works so hard and helps me with homework every night so she does not get time for herself.

Christopher Ford   Grade: 05
My mom deserves a diamond because she is beautiful on the inside as well as the outside. She is kind, caring, and an amazing mother.

Allison Freyman   Grade: 05
My mom deserves a diamond because she is the most generous caring mom I know. Even though we fight we will always love each other forever.

Sydney Ivey   Grade: 05
My mom deserves a diamond because she shines like stars in the night. Her eyes are like clouds in heaven. She deserves a beautiful diamond.

Kate Kim   Grade: 05
My mom is always there for me. Full of love and joy, she's like a precious crystal. For that, a diamond for thanks.

Taylor McMorrow   Grade: 05
She deserves a diamond because she is the most thoughtful and caring mother you could get. She would make dead flowers turn back to life.

Shelby Pollack   Grade: 05
My mom deserves a diamond because she is kind and friendly and won't let you down. I love my mom.

Kayla Rose   Grade: 05
My mom deserves a diamond because she's the sweetest mom anyone could ever have. Whenever I'm with her, I feel like I'm with an angel.

Nicolas Junior High
Fullerton

Teacher: Helen Flores

Unique Bennett   Grade: 08
Without my mom, I'd be a turtle in the forest. Her eyes sparkle when I look her way. She's as deep as the ocean.

Jane Cockar   Grade: 08
Hard worker, open hearted and loving, that is my mother: Always a giving person and wants nothing in return. Wouldn't trade her for anything.

Luis Covarrubias   Grade: 08
My mom is special because she doesn't give up on me and pushes me to my full extent.

Nicole Day   Grade: 08
My mom's like water in the sea. She's beautiful and she's always there for me. My mother is my diamond, She's my shinning star.

Alyssa Dominguez   Grade: 08
My mom always has good ideas, inspires us to be vegetarian and has a master's degree in English. Surprisingly, she still finds time for cook!

Marvin Gomez   Grade: 08
My mom really deserves a diamond because she cares for anyone. She's like a gem that really deserves another , especially a diamond.

Candice Lebs   Grade: 08
My mother shines like the northern sky. She love me with all her heart. She guides me with her smarts and she is me.

Jenny Matti   Grade: 08
My mom , Wow! She's the most benign, altruistic person in the universe. My mom is amazing because she would give up her life for me.

Eric Mendoza   Grade: 08
My mom does everything she can to make me happy and it would be nice if I can do the same for her

Elizabeth Morales
People are only complete when they have a mother to share all their passions and sorrows with and to start by them throughout their lives.

Nohali Padilla   Grade: 08
The loving mother always shows she cares. She cries to see you succeed. She's strong even when things go wrong. That's a true mom.

Brook Patterson   Grade: 08
Her eyes are always shining. Her smile is oh so blinding. My mom, she's loving, and is always cuddling.

Diego Peredo   Grade: 08
She deserves the diamond because she's the essence of life, without her my life would have no meaning. She shines in everything she does.

Oswaldo Ramirez   Grade: 08
My mom is very special. She shines like a sparkly diamond. She is the key to my treasure chest and the fire to my lamp.

Anthony Rodriguez   Grade: 08
My mom loves me. Just wait and see. She is as flawless as a diamond and she's even nice to my dog Simon.

Stephanie Salas   Grade: 08
Her personality shines like a diamond. Everything about her stands out without any flaws. Sweet and petit, like a diamond.

Jaqueline Villafane   Grade: 08
My mom is my love. When I wake up, I see her smile on her face and I know she will be there for me.

Teacher: Nancy Mizuno

Denise Arnaga   Grade: 08
My mom is so special to me. She's someone who I can trust. She wants the best for me and I love her so much!

Apolinas Barban   Grade: 08
My mom is like a map because she helps me whenever I need help and she shows me the right path to take.

Karen Crisanto   Grade: 08
She is my world, the person I love, the one I'll never forget. She will never be replaced, Mo Mom!

Lisa Dinh   Grade: 08
My mom is a legend. Her good deeds outnumber the stars in the sky. Such a graceful person as she has done wonders for me.

Selene Gonzalez   Grade: 08
My mom is like an angel. She watches me with care, Her smile like a star. Love like hers is rare.

Oscar Hurtado   Grade: 08
My mom is a Spring day. During the day, she warms me like the sun. During the night, she lights my life like the moon.

Rubicella Martinez   Grade: 08
Don't need medicine or a pill for when I'm feeling ill to prevent from falling apart, all I need is my mom in my heart.

Sergio Mejia   Grade: 08
My mom is my own guardian angel. She cares, loves, and watches me,. The love she shares is infinite. It fills me every day with glee.

Helen Munoz Grade: 08
My mom is like a star, she is full of light. She twinkles like a diamond in the deep blue sky.

Victor Munoz Grade: 08
My mom is like a teacher. She inspires me to do my best in class and to be a success in the world. I love you, Mom.

Karen Sanchez Grade: 08
When I cry, she gives me a hug. If I laugh,, she giggles. When I tell her I love her, she says, me too.

Miko Santos Grade: 08
Tender-hearted: the only one of her kind. Her love for me goes beyond all other loves. She loves me so dearly from head to toe.

Jessika Silva Grade: 08
What would be the night without the moon? What would be the day without the sun? What would I be without my Mom?

Georgia Sinclair Grade: 08
My mom is not flawless like a diamond nor flowing like a river. She is more like Velcro, that's why we bond so well.

Alan Tillmann Grade: 08
My mom is loving, my mom is caring. She never lets me break a smile. If I ask for a foot, she goes a mile

Rydell Urban Grade: 08
Mothers are like diamonds in all different shapes, colors, sizes, but I think my mother is the best, the greatest and the brightest.

Teacher: Marisa Ortega

Fiana Cruz Grade: 07
My mom deserves a diamond because she is the best. She cares about me, loves, helps, and understands me. I love my mommy.

Mariana Flores Grade: 07
My mom had been there when I most needed her and for that I think she deserves this diamond that I give her with all my heart.

Hai Nguyen Grade: 07
My mom deserves a diamond because she worked so hard to take care of me everyday and when I got sick. Mom's great.

Evangelina Perez Grade: 07
My mom deserves a diamond because all the work, pain and struggle she goes through each day. Just to make it as a single parent.

Elizabeth Rodriguez Grade: 07
My mom is a wonderful mother, she deserves a diamond because she is very helpful, loveable, and is always caring for me.

Teacher: Susan Wells

Josselin Acosta Grade: 07
My mom gave me life and a I am thankful. She brightens my path with her beautiful light. She is the angel that guides me.

David Anzueto Grade: 07
I love my mom. She does a lot for me in my life. Just like a single, unique star in the sky. She glows beautifully.

Daniel Cochran Grade: 07
She's the light to my darkness, the maker of my day who loves me without a doubt. My guardian angel from heaven. My mom.

Christen Hunter Grade: 07
Mom is like the sun, making every day bright. She sparkles like the stars up in the sky. Without her, my world would go dark.

Aloso Ikaninifo Grade: 07
My mom is like a rare, so delicate, so beautiful. My mom is like a baby, so loved and so precious to cherish and love.

Aneisha Johnson Grade: 07
There's nothing more fulfilling than a mother's touch, for her bundle of joy. She loves so much. I love my mom, my hero, my love.

Nancy Lara Grade: 07
My mom is like a dove. My mom is the one I love. Like an angel in the sky, she gave me life.

Stephanie Love Grade: 07
A little speck in the sky glimmers like my mother's eye. You, my mom are my gem.

Emm Luu Grade: 07
My oxygen, dying without her presence. Warm hands embrace me, and heaven's elegance surrounds. A diamond that outshines all stars. Like no other, my mother.

Jose Navarrete Grade: 07
Mom's shinier than shooting stars. She's a treasure inside my heart. I love at her in the eyes. I see the confidence in my life.

Chad Oltmanns Grade: 07
My mom is like a mother bird in nature. Nourishes me when I'm young. Then pushes me over the edge. I spread my wings and fly.

Jennifer Ortega Grade: 07
Her knowledge is as big as the sky, her heart is as big as the ocean and her love for me is unconditional, my mom.

Jennifer Reynoso Grade: 07
My mom is like my light in the right. She always knows what's right. She's the greatest value in my life.

Katie Simpson Grade: 07
Sitting in a room all alone, thinking life won't worsen, when light shines, and an angel appears when I realize it's only mommy, my diamond.

Alejandro Vargas Grade: 07
My mom is as bright as a diamond and as soft as a teddy bear. She is the inspiration in my life.

Ana Vazquez Grade: 07
My mom shines like a beautiful summer morning. When my mom sings, the birds join her.

Jason Walsh Grade: 07
Diamonds have every color of the world. My mom deserves a diamond because she is the color in my life. I'm nothing without her.

Jeremy Willis Grade: 07
My mom is the sand in my sandbox. The light to my dark cave. My mom is the best mom I could ever have.

Teacher: Linda Wingfield

Gilbert Ascencio Grade: 08
She is a caring, smart, mom and she is always trying to make me feel better every time. I'm sad. My mom is my angel.

Joseph Bocanegra Grade: 08
My mom sparkles like a diamond when I'm down. She shines when it's dark. My mom deserves a diamond because she's a superstar.

Paula Garcia Grade: 08
She is fun, she is cool. She is the coolest sister in the whole world. She makes me laugh. She makes me smile.

Griscelda Gomez Grade: 08
My mom is like medicine. When I'm feeling sad, she always makes me feel better. She's like a blanket so nice and soft.

Daniel Gonzalez Grade: 08
My mom is as strong as a diamond, she is beautiful as a rose. My mom is like a chocolate candy bar, nice and sweet.

* Amethyst winners in bold.

Casey Hernandez   Grade: 08
My mom is a bright shining star. She's as brave as a knight. She is like a dove in the sky.

Jaimie Loy   Grade: 08
By for all moms I've gotten to know, my mom is boss. She's the cheese to my macaroni. The one I can rely on.

Sonia Martinez   **Grade: 08**
My mom is my sun. She shines down on me during the day and at night, she is my moon, lighting up my dream world.

Andrea Munoz   Grade: 08
My mom's a mind reader. She knows when I'm mad, sad or hungry. She's an angel always on my side, without her, I'll be miserable.

Briana Toledo   Grade: 08
My mom is like the light of my life. She's always shining so bright. My mom is like a best friend I never had.

Martin Vera   **Grade: 08**
Her touch gives me comfort. Her smile brings me happiness. Her laugh spreads joy like a star shining over me. My mom is my everything.

Nohl Canyon Elementary
Anaheim

Teacher: Whitney Amsbary

Eddie Alexopoulos   Grade: 05
Mom deserves a diamond because she does everything for me. She loves ,e and she takes me places and now I need to give something back.

Sarah Jung   Grade: 05
My mom has eyes that shine like diamonds. She is very kind and gentle. She barely gets mad. She loves me all the time.

Olivia Kridle   Grade: 05
My mom is an angel that comforts me when I'm scared. She loves me and cares for my family and me.

Jared Medina   Grade: 05
My mom deserves a diamond because she works too hard and the love she gives me is better than anything.

Nicole Nguyen   Grade: 05
Mom deserves a diamond because she is the prettiest, most intelligent, and the best cook ever.

Daniel Otair   **Grade: 05**
My mom deserves a diamond because she is a diamond in my heart. She is strong, beautiful and precious. That's why she deserves a diamond.

Matthew Rose   Grade: 05
My mom deserves a diamond because she works so hard everyday and cares so much about my family and me.

Eric Vazquez   **Grade: 05**
My mom deserves a diamond because she has been my guide, my determination, my heart and soul and my protector and provider. Love you mom.

Teacher: Lesley Atwood

Leanne Ho   **Grade: 05**
My mom is a diamond to me, precious and sparkling. But she's worth more than any diamond; she is priceless.

Devin Hurt   Grade: 05
Why does my mom deserve a diamond? Well the answer is obvious. She's perfect the way she is.

Rylie Ith   Grade: 05
My mom is a light in my life that guides me. She's as sweet as a peach, and that's why my mom deserves a diamond.

Kevin Le   Grade: 05
My mom deserves a diamond because she loves me above all things and would sacrifice herself for me.

Pierson Marks   Grade: 05
The beauty of a rose, the shine of a star, the twinkle in her eyes, she is like a diamond in the skies.

Ashley Nguyen   **Grade: 05**
My mom is worth more than a diamond. Her love is all the wealth I need. Jewels can't compare to her. I love my mommy.

Max Olsthoorn   **Grade: 05**
My mother is a beaming star. She shows her heart to her loved ones. I wish on that star every night, how I love her.

Julia Reitkopp   Grade: 05
Mother, how beautiful and beloved you are to my heart. I desire that we will never part,. For you have loved me from the start.

Teline Tran   Grade: 05
Mom is full of valuables. Eyes like diamonds, lips as pink as rose quartz, and the best - a heart of gold.

Lauren Trent   Grade: 05
My mom's the diamond in my life. She shines just like a star. She's the gift that keeps on going, no matter where you are.

Kathryn Versteeg   **Grade: 05**
Her smile is as bright as the sun. Her joy is happiness for everyone. Her eyes glimmer like a crystal lake. She'll love me always.

Jordyn Walker   Grade: 05
My mom is like a shining star. She's the best there could be, no matter where or how far. Nobody can replace my amazing mom.

Kaylee Yoon   **Grade: 05**
My mom's heart is like diamond shimmering in the sunlight. Her twinkling smile lights my heart like a bright moon on a starry night.

Teacher: Kathy Beam

William Klos   Grade: 03
My mom deserves a diamond because she works hard around the house, and she substitutes for classes and works hard.

Stephanie Kwak   Grade: 03
My mom deserves a diamond because she helps me with my homework, and my mom comes to my piano recitals.

Joseph Molina   **Grade: 03**
My mom deserves a diamond because she is my guardian angel and cares for me and loves me. That's why she deserves a diamond.

Elianna Peng   Grade: 03
My mom deserves a diamond because she always lets me cuddle with her in her my bed, and I like it a lot.

Dylan Porter   **Grade: 03**
My mom deserves a diamond because she is brighter than the North Star. I love her more than life itself, and I love her.

Claire Powers   Grade: 03
As pretty as a flower, as sweet as a bird, as nice as an angel. This is why my mom deserves a diamond.

Collin Press   Grade: 03
Her eyes shine like emeralds. She should go through the rainbow of happiness. She cares for me. She feeds me and she helps me.

Chloe Sweeney   Grade: 03
My mom deserves a diamond because she helps out with the poor. She helps by volunteering in Mexico and at a local food shelter.

Teacher: Stephanie Mips

Brenna Davies   **Grade: 06**
When I'm down, she's always there, patient as can be. She's kind and loving, so exuberant, it amazes me. She's my mom, my number one.

McKenna Elsner   **Grade: 06**
Shines like the stars, watches like the moon. She is the center of my universe. My mother.

Ilan Ezra   Grade: 06
My mom is perfect. Her eyes sparkle like a diamond. My mom is flawless and kind to everyone. That's why she deserves a diamond.

Nolan Halal   Grade: 06
My mom deserves a diamond because she is the nicest mom in the world. She is an idol to other great moms. She's great.

Ryan Hitt   Grade: 06
As sweet as chocolate, as warm as the sun, her eyes are diamonds in the sky. Her voice like a symphony - my mom.

Melissa Maffei   Grade: 06
My mom is like a treasure chest. A strong, hardy cover, filled with the most precious items and her precious items are her family.

Sarah Palazzola   **Grade: 06**
Her eyes deep with compassion. Her soul cries out with joy. She loves me and that is the most precious thing there is to be.

Marcela Portales   Grade: 06
Her eyes shine like diamonds. Her heart is made of pure rubies. Her skills, gifts from the heavens. She is my beautiful, loving mother.

Sukhmani Punia   Grade: 06
She's like the sun; she shines so bright. She's like the moon; she watches over me during the night. My love is like her world.

Eddie Robles   Grade: 06

Eyes sparkle like the starry night. Hair smoother than silk made just right. Heart and passion warmer than the sun. She is always very fun.

Patricia Toon   Grade: 06
All the things she ever said. Loving me until each day's end. Good times, times of despair. She's always there. She can't be compared. Mom.

Ryan Velasco   Grade: 06
Her eyes sparkle like the sun on the sea. Loving and caring for me so greatly. My mom, beautiful in and out.

Sydney Walker   Grade: 06
Her eyes sparkle like stars in the Milky Way and her heart is full of love and compassion. She is great; she is my mom.

Derek Wong   Grade: 06
Her heart is filled with an infinite amount of love. It pours onto me. Forever, and I simply could not live without it. My mother.

Michael Yamasaki   Grade: 06
More helpful than any caretaker, a voice sweeter than any songbird and a heart that shines like none other. This is how I say, "Mom".

Teacher: Gina Moberly

Stephanie Hitt   Grade: 03
She has a heart like a ruby. You would want her to be your mom. She is thoughtful and funny. I love her very much.

Brystal Marks   **Grade: 03**
My mom's a rare gem that's hard to find, beautiful, elegant and very kind. She's strong and shiny with lots of class - that's my mom.

Ryan Oliveira   Grade: 03
I love my mom because she takes me roller skating, takes me to get ice cream and takes care of me when I am sick.

Teacher: Jamie Rose

Emily Cook   **Grade: 05**
My mom deserves a diamond because she works hard at work and home, and barely gets a chance to rest, and I love her.

Samantha Frank   Grade: 05
I love my mother very much. She's very kind, generous, wise and of course, loving. Please, my mother deserves a diamond.

Jonathan Nguyen   Grade: 05
Choose my mom. She works hard to take care of me so I would be healthy and smart. My mom loves me just like me.

Nicholas Nguyen   Grade: 05
Fire is ruby. Earth is emerald. Water is sapphire. Diamond is the sun and the world is my mother to me.

Teacher: Denise Trenner

Thuy-Ahn Bui   **Grade: 04**
Her love can lead everyone in peace. Her touch like silk that settles on me. Her laugh is glitter than sprinkles throughout the world.

Brittany Chiang   **Grade: 04**
As loving as a family, as warm as the sun. As pretty as a jewel. I wonder who? My precious mother.

Katelyn Giap   Grade: 04
My mom is like petals on a blooming rose. She is the sparkle on a gleaming diamond. She dazzles in the moonlight.

Courtney Lambe   **Grade: 04**
My mom is so unique and beautiful. She is so loving and kind. She shimmers and sparkles like a diamond. That's why she deserves one.

Andrew Lee   Grade: 04
My mom is my light. My mom is my warmth. Her love will never change. She loves me no matter what.

Melanie Mitchell   Grade: 04
My mom is the light in my life. Whenever I see her, I think I am looking at a glowing angel.

Michael Peterson   **Grade: 04**
Her eyes are as blue as the sea. She makes me blush as red as a rose. My mom makes my frown turn upside down.

Robin Reyes   Grade: 04
She's an angel who came from above. She's graceful and unique like a dove. This person is like no other. She's my flawless mother.

Nilay Shah   Grade: 04
My mom shimmers like a diamond. She sparkles with silver and gold and is as warm as hot chocolate.

Josh Wada   Grade: 04
She's a flower in bloom. She is as graceful as a swan. She is a flawless, dazzling diamond.

Elizabeth Yim   Grade: 04
My mom is as sweet as sugar. That fulfills my life. She is the warmth in my heart and protects me in the darkest night.

Teacher: Kellie Vella

Mariam Azizi   Grade: 04
My amazing, awesome, fantastic mom deserves a diamond because she cares and wants for my well-being. She is a very kind person, and I love her.

Colt Cantu   Grade: 04
My awesome mom deserves a diamond because she always puts a smile, a big smile on me, and she cleans up the house.

* Amethyst winners in bold.

Sarah Downey   Grade: 04
My mom is spectacular and outstanding at everything. She's loving, caring, intelligent, and wonderful. She's devoted to teaching me to become a better person.

Julie Hopkins   Grade: 04
Mom, as bright as a diamond with a ring and a pin. I wish her good luck. With hope that she'll win a diamond for herself.

Kane Lambe   Grade: 04
My mom is very loving and pretty. She is loving because she always takes care of me, and she loves me. She is very graceful.

Jenna Norton   Grade: 04
My mom deserves a diamond, shiny and bright. One that is shining white. She is so sweet. She deserves a diamond that can't be beat.

Briana Portales   Grade: 04
My mom is the best mom ever. She is always there for me. When I am sick, she is right there.

Katie Ramer   Grade: 04
My mom deserves a diamond because she is really nice. She is also very helpful. She helps me with my homework when I need help.

Ryan Saghatchi   Grade: 04
My mom deserves it because she cleans, cooks and helps me with my homework. When I am sad, she always makes me happy.

Nathan Singiri   Grade: 04
My mom's as sweet as chocolate. If there were lots of chocolates, I'd pick her because she's the sweetest.

Michael Sweet   Grade: 04
My mom is sweet, nice, giving, and she tells me what to do when I need help. She is an excellent mom. I love her.

Northwood Elementary
Irvine

Teacher: Donna Catalano

Clara Choi   Grade: 05
She sparkles like the stars at night. When everything is gloomy, she makes everything shine. She is also like the sky protecting me from harm.

Brandt Heflin   Grade: 05
A star from heaven coming down to Earth. Her touch is like smelling a rose. Her voice is like a breeze that I love, mom.

Serena Junejo   Grade: 05
Graceful swan on a calm, crystal lake. The setting sun shows her beauty, but who is this swan? None but mom, sheltering me from above.

Lia Kang   Grade: 05
Her voice is silky smooth. She is like a diamond, precious and beautiful. She is my entertainer and heroine forever - Mom.

Hak Kim   Grade: 05
My mom is gentle and warm as a candle melting in the middle of the darkness. Her talents are extremely noteworthy. My most thankful parent. Mom.

Julia Lee   Grade: 05
My mom is a shining star that gives love and care. Her love and care are everlasting. Her smile takes away all tears from me.

Nicole Lewis   Grade: 05
My mom is like an angel on top of a Christmas tree who gives me a snuggly hug and keeps me safe day and night.

Hannah Mc Ilrath   Grade: 05
A bright shining sun who gives rays of warm loving care. Her greeting smile cures all despair. An angel sent from heaven, my beautiful mother.

Curtis Nava   Grade: 05
My mom is like a jacket when I am cold. She will make me feel warm and she has a huge heart. I love her.

Sidney Ocampo   Grade: 05
Just like my teddy bear, she's always there to hug. I always feel safe when she's around. She never lets me down. The best mom.

Jane Park   Grade: 05
Her hugs fill me up with everlasting love. When the Earth is dark, her smile will light the world. My mom is forever mine.

Emily Quitoriano   Grade: 05
She's like a rose. She's beautiful and loyal. She makes me warm, safe, and happy. She's a good parent and wife. I love her.

Jared Ruffin   Grade: 05
My mother is like the moon, loving and caring as she sheds her light to light our path through the shadowy darkness in our lives.

Yessenia Virgen   Grade: 05
My mom is like an angel from above protecting me from danger. My mom deserves a gift of pure love and kindness. I love her.

Teacher: Eileen Levy

Anthony Cao   Grade: 06
My mom deserves a diamond because when I leave for college, the diamond will remind her that I was her little boy.

Eric Li   Grade: 06
She's always there helping, reading what I feel but can't say. An angel when troubles accrue. Magician turning things bright. Giving love the world over.

Mira Pranav   Grade: 06
My mom is as flawless and fine as a diamond itself, much better than aquamarine or zircon, and never the less, she will always be mine.

Blaysen Varnadoe   Grade: 06
My mom does for me and everyone else you see. She makes us all happy. She deserves a diamond. Oh, what a surprise it'll be.

Teacher: Lucinda Mroch

Dylan Brine   Grade: 05
My mom deserves a diamond because she does volunteer work. She makes special breakfast on weekends and cares for me. She makes me feel special.

Julia Chung   Grade: 05
My mom is like a star in the night trying to lead me in the light. That's why I wish I'll be with her forever.

Samantha Hornyak   Grade: 05
My mom is an angel from heaven. She is a diamond in the rough. She melts my fears away. She is a true diamond. Mother.

Samuel James   Grade: 05
My mother is unforgettable and beautiful. She is always kissing, encouraging, and caring. Her love and care are like the sun, always there for me.

Matthew Jou   Grade: 05
My mother is as sweet as chocolate. She is always there for me and helps me. She is the best mom you could ever have.

Virda Khalid   Grade: 05
My mom is as sweet as sugar and supportive as a teacher and fills me with happiness - and that's why she deserves a diamond.

MooJim Kim   Grade: 05
The smiles of my mother are like miles of joy that do not run out, and that is how big my love for her is.

Denny Lee   Grade: 05
Mom works like a servant doing her best always to work, never to rest. Tired, be as she may, always ask, "How was your day?"

Monica Leys   Grade: 05
Pure compassion, everlasting love. So beautiful and elegant like a dove. My mother's hug is like a million "yippee." She's an angel taking care of me.

A.J. Lockridge   Grade: 05
My mom deserves a diamond to see her reflection. It'll match her dashingly, beautiful face. Her cooking tastes like heaven. She'll always be my diamond.

Angel Medina   Grade: 05
Mother: a caring, loyal angel who always brings joy to the world and other people around her. She makes the birds sing.

Nathan Navarrete   Grade: 05
My mom is the greatest. Her eyes are sparkly blue like a diamond. She is gentle as a butterfly. I love her for every reason.

Corinne Swigart   Grade: 05
My mom always makes me oatmeal. She bakes cookies too. She loves me and I love her back. She is the greatest mom on Earth.

Alex Thiem   Grade: 05
My mom's smile is like an eternal spark in my heart that will never go out. When I see her, she's like heaven's jewel. She's my life.

Nicole Valenzuela   Grade: 05
My mother, pretty, unforgettable, caring, loving, cook. When she walks in a room, I feel my heart full with joy.

Reanna Villegas   Grade: 05
My mom is loving, caring and is a supporter. My mom is a diamond in the rough. She loves me for who I am.

Oak Middle School
Los Alamitos

Teacher: Darlene Conforti

Karyan Cruser   Grade: 08
From a shelter to a home, mommy has always stayed strong. She deserves the best in the world. I love my beautiful and caring mom.

Jazzmine Garza   Grade: 08
My mom deserves a diamond because she is as pretty as a diamond. She is my best friend and nurtures me when I need her.

Harout Manukian   Grade: 08
My mom deserves a diamond because she takes care of me like her mom used to. She deserves it because she's a hardworking mother.

Samantha Peristein-Merritt   Grade: 08
She gives me tender love and care. She cares for me if I am sick or well. She's everything that a mother should be.

Cory Radtke   Grade: 08
My mom is always there for me with a smile and good advice. I know she loves and helps me without thinking twice.

Rabecka Snooks- Andrade   Grade: 08
My mom is funny and sweet, she can't be beat. Intelligent and nice, and full of spice. Dorky and cool - she really rules.

Teacher: Wendy Hearn

Joey Alvarado   Grade: 06
My grandma's love for me is a strong as the heat from 1,000 suns. Her kindness shines like the moon on a starless night.

Cheryl Bond - DIAMOND   Grade: 06
My mother loves as passionately as a fire in the forge, melting the iron surrounding our hearts, filling us with golden compassion and silver kindness.

Carolyn Fageaux   Grade: 06
My mom is as sweet as candy. She is the one I look up to and is my role model. She's the rose in my life.

Madeline Hanley   Grade: 06
The bright blue of her eyes shine like morning sunlight glistening on the water. Her heart is dipped in strong, tender love for me.

Maria Herrera   Grade: 06
When I see your smile through the morning sun, it makes me think of you helping us with everything to make our dreams come true.

Abby Kurtz   Grade: 06
My mom cares for me and fills my life with joy and glee. Cheers me up when I'm down, picks me up, spins me around.

Sydney Manning   Grade: 06
Nothing in the world can separate us, not time, nor space, or death. We will always carry each other in our hearts.

Kelly Mc Cone   Grade: 06
She taught me to trust in who I am; to aim for goals that are close to my heart. My mom's a piece of art.

Bernadette McConnell   Grade: 06
Ma's love is the best. Her love is stronger than sun, but nothing could be stronger.

Gina Small   Grade: 06
Mommy is beautiful inside and out. Her eyes glisten like freshly melted chocolate. Her personality is just as sweet. She is the best ever.

Hannah Stojack   Grade: 06
Loving, sweet, ever so sharing, nice, kind, always caring. All of these traits describe my wonderful mother.

Bianca Tripp   Grade: 06
My mom deserves a diamond because she is like a diamond. Under tremendous pressure, she shines brightest. She is brilliant like a diamond. Thank you.

Andrew Turner   Grade: 06
My mom is hardworking, caring, and loving. She is always there for me. Who could ask for a better mom than mine. I don't know.

Teacher: Justin Hill

Aliya Alenikov   Grade: 06
Her wavy hair, her twinkling eyes. She does the chores so very wise. She takes care of me with her oversized heart that warms mine.

Naomi Archie   Grade: 06
Her voice as sweet as a melody, her touch nice and warm, she's as beautiful as a blossom, with eyes sparkling like stars shining brightly.

Deshawn Bates   Grade: 06
My mom is bright as a star. She sparkles in the night and twinkles in the day. She is my diamond.

Madeline Bennett   Grade: 06
Her smile lights up all of Hollywood. Her eyes glisten in the sun and in the rain. She listens, she watches, and she cares. Mom.

Chase Camino   Grade: 06
My mom is pretty and bright. Her beauty is clear. She fights off my fears. She sparkles like the stars at night, just like a diamond.

Sierra Cherry   Grade: 06
An angel that dropped from heaven, an open gate leading me to success, teardrops of happiness fulfill my life with enjoyment and excitement. That's mom.

Alexandra Clark   Grade: 06
She's as fast as lightning. She shines just like a star. Each night I know she'll be there watching me from afar.

* Amethyst winners in bold.

Courtney deLeon   Grade: 06
My beloved mother is a bright star leading me on the right path, guiding me on my road to success.

Kassidy Dillon   Grade: 06
Understanding in her mind, compassion in her eyes, like a light bulb who never burns out. Her warm heart never gives out - my loving mother.

Brandon Gandara   Grade: 06
The light in my life, from above and beyond, my heart and soul, my own treasure. My life to mom whose love is forever.

Sarah Garcia- Gonzalez   Grade: 06
She will always be there for you even when you walk away. It is a pretty thought and it's true in every way. She's mom.

Katelyn Gersjes   Grade: 06
Mom is the reason I am living within this world. She is the light in my day. She's the greatest star in my dreaming night.

Brianna Hernandez   Grade: 06
Diamonds can never beat the gaze in her eyes. Flowers can never beat her beauty. My mother who stays by my side truly.

Ane Marie Horton   Grade: 06
Twinkle in her eyes like the stars at night. A smile bright as the sun. A flower that keeps sprouting, calming touch. My loving mother.

Ryan Jenkins   Grade: 06
My mom's heart is a heart of gold from the heavens. Her heart is worth a zillion dollars for what she does for me.

Charles Kaub   Grade: 06
Her eyes are stars that twinkle at twilight. Warmth of her heart beats to my soul. I love her like an angel in Heaven - Mom.

Gretchen King   Grade: 06
As caring as a bear for her cubs, as sweet as candy, a heart bigger than the universe equals one loving and amazing mom.

Katherine Macintosh   Grade: 06
My mom is nice, loving, and hardworking. She cares for me like a black bear protecting her cub. She is as bright as a sun.

Logan McJihon   Grade: 06
She is a shining star from outer space. She is one of a kind. She makes me feel like a sun ray on a cloudy day.

Evan Okuma-Smith   Grade: 06
My mother shines across the sky like a knight in shining armor and protects my heart from harm's way and dries my tears away.

Sage Rodriguez   Grade: 06
My mom more than a diamond. With her dazzling eyes, her lovely soul that comforts me wherever. Whenever she helps me with my problems - my mom.

Ryan Rusin   Grade: 06
Her soul is as bright as two suns shining in the universe and her smile sparkles like the stars in the sky. She's my mom.

Briana Santana   Grade: 06
Her smile is like the sun shining bright in the sky. She's like the rain falling down when I have a frown. She's my life saver.

Christopher Senner   Grade: 06
My mom cooks like a gourmet chef. Her eyes are like the stars of the night sky. Her kisses are like a swarm of butterflies.

Brian Small   Grade: 06
She is the heartbeat of an angel. She is the monarch of the seas. She has a face of kindness when she smiles upon me.

Isabela Soto   Grade: 06
She has a heart full with love. She cuddles like bears with her cubs. She is sweet like candy and she's a gift from heaven.

Taylor Turpin   Grade: 06
She feels my heart with love. She supports me to the leading doors to success. Why am I so lucky to have her?

Victoria Tuttle   Grade: 06
She is wonderful, loving, caring like a lioness always watching her cubs, never letting them out of sight. My mom is so amazing and happy.

Matt Wauters   Grade: 06
Her eyes twinkle like the bright stars. She cares by spending time with me. Together we are like a heart that will never break - Mom.

Ivie Williams   Grade: 06
Her eyes shine like the stars in the moonlight sky with a heart of warmth and love that will always comfort me - my mom.

Teacher: Carrie Martin

Willow Benton   Grade: 06
When I describe my mom, I describe her as bright almost as bright as the sun. She is the most intelligent person I ever met.

Brittany Houston   Grade: 06
My mom sparkles like a diamond, she shines like a jewel. She's a heck of a mom. Oh! She's so cool. I love my mom.

Synthia Rios   Grade: 06
My mom deserves a diamond because she is smart. She is also nice like sugar and spice. Lastly, she is beautiful.

Riley Ritchie   Grade: 06
My mom is the most amazing, beautiful active mom ever. She cooks, cleans, picks up and drops off kids, and rollerblades in her free time.

Nickolas Vengoechea   Grade: 06
My mom sparkles like diamonds. My mom makes me waffles like a restaurant. My mom is kind. My mom helps me find my stuff.

Cameron White   Grade: 06
My mom is as loving as a mother bear. Her soul is shinier than the stars above and her heart loves us all.

Teacher: Carla Olmscheid

Reynaldo Barcelo   Grade: 06
Flawless is a term that applies to jewels and my mom. She sparkles in her kindness and beauty, radiating sunlight, making everyone joyful.

Rachael Chait   Grade: 06
My mom is always there, from when I am little to old and through my life, her name changes from mama to mommy to mother.

Bobby Curry   Grade: 06
As pretty as a princess, as beautiful as a bird. My mother is elegant and flawless. She is a diamond among stones, unique and special.

Robert Finch   Grade: 06
My mom is like a diamond, so beautiful glistening in the sun. Sparkling like an angel from Heaven sent above, she's the world's best mom.

Allison Forbes   Grade: 06
My mom is like a swan, she is full of poise and grace. I get that special feeling when I look into her beautiful face.

Joseph Gomez   Grade: 06
My mom shines with the white hot intensity of one thousand suns. She teaches everyone she meets how to be wonderful. My mom's a diamond.

Hallie Heffern   **Grade: 06**
My mom is a shining star. She's brighter than any stars are. Her heartfelt wishes and morning kisses get us through the day.

Sarah Olsen   Grade: 06
My mom shines like a star. She loves me even when I'm far. I love her that much back, and that is a true fact.

Jon Pajaud   Grade: 06
My mother teaches me how to do everything on my own so I will become successful. I want to thank her for outshining the stars.

Gabriel Quiroz   Grade: 06
She is a graceful swan in the night. She does everything without complaining. She gives everyone a smile. Who is she? She is my mom.

Cassy Wind   Grade: 06
My mom is the sparkle in my eye, the love in my laugh, and the happiness in my smile. A lovely rose.

Jaden Wyszpolski   Grade: 06
My mom deserves a diamond half as pretty as her. She works as hard as her love is strong. My mom deserves a diamond.

Bruno Youn   Grade: 06
My mom deserves a diamond because she warms up hearts. She closes holes in hearts, as if they were doors.

Oka (Isojiro) Elementary
Huntington Beach

Teacher: Heather Hopkins

Allyson Carrillo   **Grade: 05**
The moon lights our path, the stars brighten the night sky, but no star shines as bright as my mother's heart.

Mariana Chavez   Grade: 05
My mom shines like a moon, protects like a tiger. The best thing she does is gives me a hug and says, "I love you".

Dhalila De La Cruz   **Grade: 05**
Her smile covers a blanket of happiness everywhere. Her voice sings out a harmony whispering in the wind. There is no other mother like that.

Aubrey Grandon   Grade: 05
Twinkle, twinkle little star, my mom is the best by far. She sparkles on her very own. All she needs is a diamond tone.

Kristie Hoang   Grade: 05
Sweet chocolate cookies, warm vanilla and mint cake, just a drop of syrup - and that's makes my mom.

Kyle Napier   Grade: 05
Her eyes sparkle like the gleaming moonlight. She hears my cry from a mile away, and I can always go to her for help.

Mikaila Pacis   Grade: 05
My mom is a gemstone. She helps me with everything and supports me also. I think she deserves a diamond.

Vanessa Ruiz-Joya   **Grade: 05**
My mom deserves a diamond because my mom is like the sun and air I breathe. Without her, I will not be.

Teacher: Cheryl Loukides

Kevin Agustin   **Grade: 01**
My mom is very caring. She always helps me when I am sick and takes me to fun places. I love mom very much.

Kyle Chapman   Grade: 01
My mom is very caring. She always takes me to fun places and cooks great food. My mom is 1. I love my mom.

Gabby Torres   **Grade: 01**
My mom is always happy. She does everything for my family. I love her.

Cassie Torres   Grade: 01
My mom is very kind. She always cooks food I like to eat. I love my mom. My mom is the best.

Teacher: Jeanne Moussa-Zahab

Joshua Cortez   Grade: 04
My mom deserves a diamond because she's never owned a real diamond before. I appreciate her very much because she watches all my baseball games.

Delaney Hewett   Grade: 04
My mommy deserves a diamond because she's great and she does so much for me. So I want to do something for her.

Sydney Highter   **Grade: 04**
My mom deserves a diamond because she is a rose especially when she's happy and is tickling my toes.

Cameron Scanaliato   **Grade: 04**
My mom deserves a diamond because she should have something beautiful as she is. I wouldn't want any other mom.

Alyssa Telepnev   Grade: 04
My mom deserves a diamond because she loves me and takes care of me, like a busy bee. I love my mom, she loves me.

Jenny Tran   Grade: 04
My mom is caring and very nice. She does not spoil me. My mom is great to look up to.

Teacher: Dawn Rose

Taylor Belk   Grade: 05
My mom deserves a diamond because she can be more than a mom. She can be a hero to a person who needs help.

Alexis Bennett   **Grade: 05**
My mom deserves a diamond because she doesn't break her promises. She calls my close friends her family. She is there when I need her.

Olivia Harrigan   **Grade: 05**
My mom shines like a beautiful star, sparkling in the sky. She is that lovely rose in the field of daisies. She deserves this diamond.

Nichole Marie Lewis   Grade: 05
I think my mom deserves a diamond because she helps people through the good and bad times in their lives, and she gives homeless people money.

Vivan Lu   **Grade: 05**
My mother touches my heart because she clears a pathway for me to walk through life, guiding me every step of the way.

Harmony Menier-Schierholtz   Grade: 05
My mom is the best mom because she helps the homeless shelter and helps me learn about God. That's why my mother deserves a diamond.

Manuel Merdinoglu   **Grade: 05**
My mom is special because when I'm ill, she snuggles me by her side and gives me comfort and love.

Alex Nguyen   Grade: 05
I think my mom deserves a diamond because she is caring and shares with people. She donates clothes. That's why she deserves a diamond.

Koray Sahinyilmaz   Grade: 05
One reason why my mom deserves a diamond is because she walks me to school every day to make sure I'm safe.

Jose Sanchez   Grade: 05
My mom deserves a diamond because she teaches me how to be a caring and clean person. That is why she deserves a diamond.

* Amethyst winners in bold.

Joey Underwood — Grade: 05
My mom deserves a diamond because she always asks people if they need anything when we go places and she always cares about other people.

Sierra Wager — Grade: 05
My mom deserves a diamond because she donates clothes and blankets we don't need and gives to people who need them. My mom is caring.

Olita Elementary
Whittier

Teacher: Carie Cruz

Benjamin Ayers — Grade: 02
My mom is as pretty as the moon, bright as the sun, almost like a gem. I love my mom like a wonderful star.

Kaylee Ayers — Grade: 02
My mom's eyes are like a diamond. Her hair is soft like a pillow. My mom is sweeter than a cake. My mom is like an angel.

Nicolas Correa — Grade: 02
My mom has crystal eyes. Her hugs give me love. She is so sweet I can't stand it. Her heart is as shiny as treasures.

Melissa Gardner — Grade: 02
My mom is a mother bird that protects me, but she's not just a mother bird, she's my heart and my angel.

Isabella Lasoya — Grade: 02
Her eyes glow like glitter. She is lovely like a blossom. Her hugs are warm like a teddy bear. I love her very much.

Kameron Matua — Grade: 02
My mom is as beautiful as a diamond. She is as shiny as one too. Her heart is as bright as the sun.

Nayah Pola — Grade: 02
My mom has beautiful eyes. Her hugs are as warm as a teddy bear. I love her a lot like a diamond.

Amanda Quinonez — Grade: 02
My mom is a pearl. She watches me in a place called "I love my daughter". She takes me on adventures. I love my mom.

Alexandra Sandoval — Grade: 02
My mother is like a diamond each day in every way. I always mean this more each day to say my mother deserves a diamond.

Olivewood Elementary
Lake Forest

Teacher: Helen Rushbrook

Leodan Aragon — Grade: 05
She sacrifices herself for us. She helps me. She will never stop working. She is a good mom. That's why she deserves it.

Stephanie Loyola — Grade: 05
My mom deserves a diamond because she works a lot for me and my whole family, but most of all, she loves me a lot.

Kirsten Mauban — Grade: 05
My mom's hardworking, loving, fighting, breast cancer, and Avon manager. Even busy, she always sets time for me. She has a happy side to all situations.

Gabriela Salsgiver — Grade: 05
My mom deserves a diamond because she shines like a diamond. When she meets somebody, they are friends instantly. She is a great person.

Our Saviors Lutheran Sch.
San Clemente

Teacher: Thomas Barbara

Lily Aasland — Grade: 03
My mom deserves a diamond, she's precious like one too. I know she'll get the best one because the love is true.

Lewis Ahola — Grade: 03
My mom deserves a diamond as she is like a star twinkling in the night. She glitters and she's the biggest diamond ever.

Christopher Baker — Grade: 03
Why my mom deserves a diamond is because her eyes are like a diamond's shine, and she is as beautiful as a diamond.

Jessica Cramm — Grade: 03
My mom deserves a diamond because she means everything to me. She helps me with my homework and she loves me. I love my mom.

Kacie Faris — Grade: 03
My mom deserves a diamond because she is so sweet and so funny. Diamonds are so valuable. Just like her wonderful and beautiful eyes.

Noah Hammond — Grade: 03
My mom deserves a diamond because she is so sweet. My mom deserves a diamond. She really is a treat. The diamond would be neat.

Hannah Reese — Grade: 03
My mom deserves a diamond because she's very sweet. She's the hero in my heart and she's always there for me.

Kiera Thornton — Grade: 03
My mom deserves a diamond. She brings me many places and never seems to mind. She is the best mom you can have.

Hunter Wade — Grade: 03
My mom deserves a diamond. I think she really does. It should sparkle like her eyes. It should also be really pretty.

Madison Wilson — Grade: 03
My mom deserves a diamond. She is so nice to me. She sparkles like a diamond. As bright as you can see.

Gabrielle Wilson — Grade: 03
My mom deserves a diamond like the sparkle in her eyes and she shines in the sky. That's why.

Oxford High
Cypress

Teacher: Diane Erickson

Victoria Castillo — Grade: 07
Her sparkling eyes like diamonds in the sky. Her smile filled with happiness, her arm heart full of love, she is my mom, my angel.

Journey Chen — Grade: 07
Through a cold winter night, her warmth wraps around me. Her lips sing a lullaby, leading me into a dream filled with endless love.

Phi Do — Grade: 07
Through pounding rains and booms of thunder, through the coldness of nights, shines a candle like no other. Warm and bright, my mother.

Kevin Flores — Grade: 07
Mother, a cozy sweater against frigid air, my broken heart she'll repair. If she's there, I won't grieve, I work hard, a diamond she'll receive.

Crystal Foutris — Grade: 07
My mom, a brown eyed beauty with long black waves. My mom, a flawless angel sent from heaven and above. My mom, forever, my savior.

Ignacio Garcia — Grade: 07
Lovely as a sparkling diamond. She is as beautiful as spring, has a caring heart that is always open, for she is my mother.

Angeline Hernandez   Grade: 07
She is an amazing mom and wife, The coach that guides me through life. Through good times and bad.   Mom is always there, I'm glad.

Sabrina Khuon   Grade: 07
Her eyes full of understanding.   Her heart as beautiful as the waves of the sea.   My mother is a treasure as rare as can be.

Gracee Kim   Grade: 07
Brighter than the sunshine, wider than the skies, deeper ;than the ocean and taller than the greatest trees is my mother's precious love for me.

Samantha Kim   Grade: 07
`Her sound, a melody, her skin, field of silk, her heart, overflowing with love. Her kisses, butterfly wings, Mom, a perfect diamond. Queen of Hearts.

Mai Le   Grade: 07
Rays of sunshine hold me close. Her crystal eyes are filled with hope. A shining diamond lights the dark, which was non the less, my mother's heart.

Hyeon Lee   Grade: 07
With a heart as ward as a blazing fire and a voice of an angel. This is what makes a true diamond. My Mother.

Samantha Lim   Grade: 07
Like a puzzle, missing a piece. Like a flower missing a petal.   Like a pen missing ink. I am incomplete without my mother.

Joel Martinez   Grade: 07
Her smile sparkles brightly. Her love shines out for me.   Her beauty keeps her glowing. That's why my mom's my star.   I love you Mom.

Evan May   Grade: 07
She is the diamond in my eye. She is one who'll never die. She is the one who'll wipe away my tears, when I cry.

Jennifer Montano   Grade: 07
Every day my mom's face brightens up my morning like the sun brightens up the sky. Her smile is the moon of my dark, stormy night.

Jonathan Musngi   Grade: 07
Her love for me is like an unending river. She is my past, present and future. She is my life, my guiding light, my mom.

Isaac ngo   Grade: 07
With wisdom like an owl, the strong spirit of an eagle, the love of a mother bird, my mom is a treasure, forever and ever.

Amy Nguyen   Grade: 07
The precious smile that I see every day. The valuable lessons that she taught me and her sparkling attitude makes her the treasure of my life.

Gabrielle Oh   Grade: 07
She's a statuesque, heavenly lighthouse. I, a lost ship in the raging sea. Her light is my guidance, the most precious thing to me.

Obinna Omeirondi   Grade: 07
Her love, deep endless sky. Her hands, soothing, caressing clouds.   She gave life, love, beauty to me. I give her twinkling stars from the sky.

Carolyn Pak   Grade: 07
My mother is the sun and clouds showering me with love.   My flowers of life can bloom, completing everything, my sky, my world, my soul.

Michael Parsons   Grade: 07
Through days of selfless giving, she never gets to rest.   She's my one and only mother. She's undoubtedly the best.

Karla Rodriguez   Grade: 07
Her caressing hands calmly lift my heart with warmth. She eliminates my burdens and holds my life's pieces together by sewing in love's missing threads. Crystal

Timothy Rodriguez   Grade: 07
Her eyes sparkle brighter than stars.   Her aluminum better than mine. Her heart richer than every gold bar. Her love more valuable than a diamond.

Rachel Wahhab   Grade: 07
My guardian angel. Loving sparkle in her turquoise eyes.   Like the ocean, she is pure, comforting me like the soft waves. Love is my mom.

Jason Yang   Grade: 07
Shadows fall upon my life, enshrouding me with utter darkness.   Mom i8s here to guide me through. Light prevails and I'm safe in Mom's arms.

Sarah Ziemer   Grade: 07
Beauty, Aphrodite gave.   Athena put wisdom in her eyes.   Each Greek god bestowed blessings upon her.   Truly making my mom a diamond in the rough.

Jorge Barajous   Grade: 09
Her beautiful black hair, smooth and silky. Her big brown eyes watching over me. Her soft red lips that say I love you, my mother.

Kelly cheung   Grade: 09
She's everywhere when I look up, embracing me with her heated sun rays, guiding me through darkness with her moonlight.   She's my sky, always there.

Michelle Choi   Grade: 09
Comforting words after a nightmare. Rushing with Band-Aids when I fall.   These little acts of kindness speak her love through it all.

Mahak Goel   Grade: 09
On a dark chilly night, Mom lovingly wraps my shivering body in another blanket, never asking, but always deserving thanks for her caring gestures.

Hyesu Han   Grade: 09
The heart she gave to me, full of love, full of life will stay with me forever and will never stop giving me her heart.

Rashad Jubran   Grade: 09
She is the sun that brightens the day and kills the darkness of the night. She is watching from a distance and lighting my path.

Hyunji Jung   Grade: 09
First to see in the morning, seeing me off to school.   Last to see in the evening, waiting for me to finish homework and say good night.

Andi Kim   Grade: 09
Spreading her branches of love, closing in tight to give a warm hug, giving all she has for me, my mother, the genuine giving tree.

Priscilla Kim   Grade: 09
Her heart is carved of real gems that shine through her sparkling eyes.   Her bubbly nature, her charming smile and best yet, her genuine love.

Joshua Lanzona   Grade: 09
There are only a few things that last forever. One is my love for my mother and the other is the diamond that she deserves.

Phillip Minott   Grade: 09
George Washington says he never tells lies, he only speak truth. Now, I shall speak of no lie, My mother's love knows no boundaries forsooth.

Gil Olaes   Grade: 09
My brain, a dim flashlight flickering in the dark.   My mother, a diamond refract in my beam lighting up the night revealing my true abilities.

Haley Trinh   Grade: 09
Mommy, you're always doing things for free, cooking, cleaning, chores galore.   A diamond? You deserve much more.

* Amethyst winners in bold.

Brian Yang — Grade: 09
My ray of hope, my foundation of support, my drive of inspiration. My light of motivation, through the good times and the bad - my mom.

Teacher: Melissa Galvan

Tiffany Huang — Grade: 07
You can put a price on a beautiful diamond, but you can't put a price on a beautiful mom.

Ronni Park — Grade: 07
My friends are gold, my home is marble. When my mother is near, I see diamonds, the world's beauty in a very small package.

Linda Shih — Grade: 07
Your heart beat is a lullaby. Your smile is strength. Your eyes are encouragement. Your hands are support. Your love is the reason that I live today.

Amanda Simpson — Grade: 07
She forgives me when I mess up, supports me when I fail, still loves me when we fight and accepts my imperfections. She's God's gift.

Anna Toma — Grade: 07
Loving, caring, and deserving mother making sacrifices, you treat me like a precious diamond, but you fail to see what a beautiful diamond you are.

Teacher: Cathy Larson

Jesse Chavarin — Grade: 07
Her eyes twinkle like a luminous star. Her smile, brighter than the sun. Her personality, full of color and her heart, bigger than the world.

Sarah Choung — Grade: 07
Her brilliant smile illuminates the dark room of negative emotions. Her voice protects from welling tears. Guardian angels work behind her heavenly soul.

Ali Farooqi — Grade: 07
Eyes of diamonds and hair as black as obsidian. Love gently flowing through her shimmering eyes. Her soothing voice gently caressing me to sleep.

Ayla Hermoso — Grade: 07
In a dreary room of gloom, I lay afraid, until my mom comes in, glistening shining as bright as the sun, just to comfort me.

Benjamin Hoang — Grade: 07
A blazing fire of heartfelt warmth, a calming peaceful sound, a sweet fruit of compassion and an enormous barrier of protection, that's my Mom.

Jason Hur — Grade: 07
Shining brighter than any diamond, my mother is my goddess and my life, making the boulders weighing down on me, disappear, as she comforts me.

Alexander Huynh — Grade: 07
My mom, a flare in the cave of darkness, the priceless gem everyone wants. One glimpse, my pain is relieved, my wish just came true.

Saksham Jain — Grade: 07
A diamond is unbreakable just like mom. Diamonds come at a price, but she is priceless. She is pure and divine like a true diamond.

Michelle Jang — Grade: 07
From ear to ear, a grin appears. Her twinkling eyes shine along. Her face a glow with delight, her smiles just as bright.

Irene Kao — Grade: 07
An array of love, smiles sweet as powdered sugar. Her eyes glittering like fields of golf. Laughter fills the room, a radiant one, my mother.

Prescilla Lee — Grade: 07
So huggable and cuddly, she slowly embraces me. Her hugs are, I know more soothing than hot cocoa. Gentle and calm, I love my mom.

Adriana Macias — Grade: 07
Loving mother, bearer of life, sculptor of character, bright diamond light in my darkness. Enlightened by my success. Provider of confidence. Fair and unconditional love.

Alicia Martinez — Grade: 07
Her gentle voice lets you know everything is going to be alright. A hard worker who's worth more than the world to me. She's my mother.

Adriana Murillo — Grade: 07
Carved out of crystal with a heart made of gold. Shines bright in the darkest shadows. This treasure is mine forever to hold, my mom.

Mitchell Nguyen — Grade: 07
The lilac flower buds open as the crimson sun shines above welcoming a new day. Her love opens up flowers and makes the sun rise.

Robert Niscior — Grade: 07
My mom, a waterfall of bursting happiness and uncontrollable love, the air that I breathe. Her warmth and care are diamonds caressing my heart, eternally.

Justin Noh — Grade: 07
The greatness of blazing stars in the night. Warmth of living fire, the sun's solar flare is only a fraction compared to my mother's care.

Joyce Pan — Grade: 07
My mom, the northern star, out shines all the others guiding me through the dark endless night. She is the light of my life.

Paige Pickler — Grade: 07
The delicious taste of freshly spun cotton candy melting to sweet sugar by the kiss of your lips as my mom's love melts my heart.

Carlos Quintana — Grade: 07
One who's heart is gold with many stories to be told. I'm stuck to mom like a ribbon to a present. My only on - Mom.

Xitlaly Ruelas — Grade: 07
Your radiant smile makes me smile. Your love makes me warm. The twinkle in your eye and big bear hugs makes me love you forever.

Brandon Santamaria — Grade: 07
A silent protector watching over me, guiding me through life's journey. The glimmering light with loving arms, my mother is a priceless gem.

Claudia Son — Grade: 07
The most extravagant star in my evening sky. Her divine radiance illuminating like no other. Drawing me in the stardust, she is my gracious mother.

Anas Subhi — Grade: 07
Past, present, future. A mother is forever. Heaven at her feet. The diamond deserves no other. I love my life, thanks to my mother.

Brittany Vill — Grade: 07
Her hair shines like morning sun. Her eyes glimmer like moonlight. However, her heart wakes me in the morning and tucks me in at night.

Jonathan Vo — Grade: 07
A drop of honey, and a bit of lemon. The twinkle in her eyes could cheer a child. My mom, more precious than any diamond.

Pacifica High
Garden Grove

Teacher: Melissa Patterson

Karen Chung — Grade: 11
She's the Leaning Tower, falling yet strong. She's strict, yet unable to hide her gentleness. She's Wonder Woman, making the impossible possible. She is...my mother.

Samuel Han   **Grade: 11**
A pureness above standards. A worth past numeration. A beauty beyond description. My mom is a diamond.

Bethany Lettiere   Grade: 11
I don't know what is required of someone to deserve a diamond. Is not the perpetual sacrifice of being a mother sufficient enough?

Samantha Lum   Grade: 11
Mom sews an important piece onto her quilt - backing, which holds it together. She's the backing to the quilt I know the best - our family.

Christine Park   Grade: 11
A special gift that God gave to me. My dependable source of comfort. My cushion when I fall. There's no love like a mother's love.

Carolyn Powell   Grade: 11
Just as a diamond, she has more strength than any, but effortlessly maintains that timeless beauty which never tarnishes or wears away through life's journey.

Chelsea Sherman   Grade: 11
My mom deserves a diamond to match the sparkle in her eyes, beauty there untouched by the years, love untainted by time.

Molly Andoe   Grade: 12
Miles and miles spent apart. Yet still dear to my heart. When time is a luxury, I am still awed by your love for me.

Alison Ernst   Grade: 12
Without a second thought, my mom is always willing to sacrifice her time to help others, putting them first, never expecting anything in return.

Jessica Locke   **Grade: 12**
Incredible, remarkable, ideal, she is simply perfect. Proud of her future soldier, my mother is the inspiration of my life. I love her forevermore.

Ali Miller   Grade: 12
People say a diamond lasts forever. I'd like to see a diamond compare to my mom's love and patience for me.

Jesse nieto   Grade: 12
My mom deserves a diamond because her heart is flawless. She's the most giving, kind hearted person. Her value is worth more than a diamond.

Leonora Ocampo   Grade: 12
Her smile like pure light. She cares for all around. A true mother to me. Like a beautiful gem. Mom, you are a living diamond.

Niki Potts   **Grade: 12**
An extraordinary woman I have found. Heartbeat with a beautiful sound. A human of much kindness and calm. A friend, guardian angel, my amazing mom.

Tyler Smith   Grade: 12
Don't make the same mistakes I did, she says. Bit if I could be half as good as her, I would take the chance.

Rubi Trujillo   **Grade: 12**
Her rushing waves of benevolent love cradle my being. Encasing me in an everlasting embrace. My friend, my sanctuary, my mother.

Julian Velasquez   **Grade: 12**
Through thick, through thin. My mother endures longer and stronger than stone. To show what she means to me, I will immortalize her in poem.

John Vogan   Grade: 12
My mother is my foundation. She has directly shaped the person that I've become. She has shown me nothing but love, and I love her.

Parks (D. Russell) Jr. High
Fullerton

Teacher: Dina Parker

Alex Aguiar   Grade: 07
My mom is like the sun helping and nourishing everyone. When she gives, she can't hold back. She dese3rves a metal plaque.

Kevin Aguirre   **Grade: 07**
My moms eyes sparkle like a water droplet meeting the suns light. Her soul like an eye-catching diamond.

Christian Balzora   **Grade: 07**
My mom's valuable. Her love always runs full. Her smile shines like the sun. She conceals her love from so one.

Jacob Channel   **Grade: 07**
Dazzling like a glistening drop of water, her gleaming smile is like the ocean at sunset. Her beautiful long blonde hair flows in the wind.

Justin Chien   Grade: 07
Shimmering in the moonlight, dazzling in the day. My mother is so kind. It'll make you say "Hurray".

Brittanie Eraso   Grade: 07
My mom is pure like a consecutive gleam of light. She is my angel, my inspiration that guide me to choose the right

Sarah Fajnor   Grade: 07
My mom is softer than a rose. She shines brighter than any other star. My mom is sweeter than chocolate.

Anushay Fathim   Grade: 07
My mom is like a river, her lush dark hair flows like the sea, her big brown eyes remind me of the stars. I love my mom.

Chris Gamez   Grade: 07
Sparkling eyes look at me like they love me. I love that feeling. She's mine forever, no words needed.

Sarah Gauthier   **Grade: 07**
My mom is like a box of chocolates. She is very sweet. She is as lovely as flowers waving in the wind on spring days.

Monique Gonzalez   Grade: 07
She smells beautiful like a bunch of flowers from a garden. Her smile is like the beautiful sun, as shiny as a diamond.

Erika Gonzalez   Grade: 07
She is as shiny as a water drop on a yellow rose. She is the example for my life. Her heart sparkles like a diamond.

Kimberley Guerrero   **Grade: 07**
Diamonds and mothers, beautiful and elegant...they have so many things in common but this, you can replace diamonds but you can never replace a loving mother.

Jason Heh   Grade: 07
Like a diamond, my mom is a sparkling within a rough piece of rocks - waiting to be discovered.

Vaughn Jackson   Grade: 07
She is as bright as the sun. I know because I'm her son. She guides me when I'm lost. She is nothing less - My mom.

Bhavika Joshi   **Grade: 07**
Sleeping to her soothing lullabies. Waking me up to her dulcet call. Providing me with everything n life, guiding me through it all.

Esther Kang   Grade: 07
My mom's love is make me smile. She is sweet like a candy. She will love me forever no matter what.

Justine Kim   **Grade: 07**
My mom is the sun. I am the Earth. She makes me so happy while shining on me.

Yena Kim   **Grade: 07**
Solid like a rock, when I am tired. Clinging onto her hand, that's when I'm inspired.

* Amethyst winners in bold.

Sandy Kim Grade: 07
Diamonds brilliant body like my mom's bright smile. This sparkling beauty shines like my mom's kind words.

Aimee Kwon Grade: 07
Chestnut eyes that sparkle in the sun, always lively and agreeable to anyone. Yearn for me to be sophisticated. To me, she is the amazing diamond.

Michelle Lee Grade: 07
My mom's smiling face is shining as the sun. Sunlight shines on me. It gives me an energy, full of love.

Peter Lemcke Grade: 07
My mom is my guardian. She is the one who guides me. She's the spark of my imagination. The rose and uphold of my life.

Kelli Lively Grade: 07
Diamonds are a girls best friend. She is my best friend. Diamonds are beautiful, so is she. Can't live without them. Can't live without her.

Erin Malarkey Grade: 07
My mom deserves a diamond because she works around the clock like a museum's hidden camera, watching you. Both diamonds and my mom are priceless.

Alex Moon Grade: 07
She is like the tree providing shade and shelter. She makes me feel comfortable and always waits me for me to come.

June Park Grade: 07
More laughs than the colors in a bag of Skittles, giving off more smiles than the music of fiddles, to be short, she's brilliant.

Julian Ramo Grade: 07
Life with her is an unforgettable journey, like the winter breeze. Shifting, falling leaves drifting under the moonlight. My mom is the diamond.

Nicole Sebial Grade: 07
She is kind and sweet, she cannot be beat, a mom like her is rare, and she is full of love and care.

Andrew Shin Grade: 07
My mom is juicy like a plum, that has a beautiful sound when she hums. Her heart is so full of care spreading kindness everywhere.

Bryan Vargas Grade: 07
My mom is beautiful like a rose. Her smile is like an angel. She guides me like a map.

Abbee Willig Grade: 07
Her love is like a rainbow. It has many different colors. I can always do something wrong, but she still loves me because she's my mother.

Teacher: Orba Smith

Amanda Fenske Grade: 07
My mom deserves a diamond and more. My mom means the world to me, I don't know how I could live without her love.

Pearce Mullins Grade: 07
My mother deserves a diamond because of all the great and wonderful things that she has done for me in my whole entire life.

Jaxiel Rico Grade: 07
My mom deserves a diamond for her hard work in helping others and for her outstanding kindness that shines brighter than the sun.

Natalie Tabatabaeepour Grade: 07
My mom deserves a diamond because it is as if she is one herself. She sparkles in my eyes and is worth so much more.

Parkview
Placentia

Teacher: Darlene Jagger

Linda Rygh Grade: 04
Mom is as sweet as a loving pastry with icing and a great peaceful kiss to begin my day joyfully.

Marissa Mauter Grade: 05
She cares for me like an angel holding a dove, takes me in, holds me tight, and teaches me how to fly. She loves me.

Eric Rygh Grade: 06
Mom's kind and loving heart holds a sweet gift of joy for all. She is delicate like dragonfly's wings, yet as strong as a rock.

Patton Elementary
Garden Grove

Teacher: Diana Mc Bride

Lindsay Aquino Grade: 01
My moms eyes sparkle like the moon and stars. She smells like a new fresh spring, clean, nice flower. I love her very much.

Sadie Barling Grade: 01
Her eyes sparkle like the stars, she's pretty as a new spring flower.

Aidan Fair Grade: 01
I love my mom because she is very thoughtful and loving. Her eyes sparkle like the baby blue sky. She is wonderful.

Justin Jhern Grade: 01
My mom always smiles and never frowns. When she smiles it seems like 1000 dollars. When something wrong, she fixes it.

Andrew Pena Grade: 01
My mom is pretty as new spring flowers. My moms eyes sparkle like the stars. My mom is as gentle as a baby bunny.

Audrey Pham Grade: 01
Roses are red, violets are blue, all my hope is from and to you! If you mind...I call my love, it's all for you!

Brian Portugal Grade: 01
My mom is pretty as a new spring flower, gentle as a baby bunny and loving like a garden of roses.

Morgan Roberts Grade: 01
My mom is wonderful. My moms eyes sparkle like the moon and stars. I love my mom . My mom loves me.

Hannah Robinson Grade: 01
Mom I love you, you love me. You are beautiful I am kind, you look as pretty as a flower.

Alyssa Tadeo Grade: 01
My moms eyes are as green as fresh new grass. She is as pretty as a lamb and she always takes care of me.

Raeanna Torres Grade: 01
My mom loves me and cares about me so much. My mom is beautiful like fresh roses. My mom smells pretty all the time.

Jocelyn Tran Grade: 01
My mom is as pretty as a pink rose. My moms eyes sparkle like the moon and star. My mom cares about me.

Mimi Wilson Grade: 01
My mom is so fabulous even how she looks. Her eyes are as shiny as the blue sky and she puts T.V. on.

Teacher: Barbara Rodermund

Alexandra Casian Grade: 03
My mother how much she shines for the diamond she will soon find. She will shine even more than the moon and stars.

Jerlene Hsueh Grade: 03
A diamond shined in the pine. My mother who was kind, shared it among the fine.

Max Koyama   Grade: 03
She feeds me well. She plays me funny. She cheers me loud. I need her and she needs me.

Kelalani Luong-Kha   Grade: 03
Under the moonlight, stands my mother, she glistens like gems, sweet and nice.

Vanessa Morales   Grade: 03
She is funny, smart and her eyes are so gleams like the light in the moon.

Andrew Park   Grade: 03
I love my mom that is true. Her eyes sparkle in the moonlight. She is all I could want and she is always wonderfully cheerful.

Teacher: Cari Wozniak

Laura Lavigne   Grade: 05
My mom is amazing. She helps us do homework, cooks dinner, and cleans without complaint, even when she is tired or busy.

Phong Nguyen   Grade: 05
My mom should deserve a diamond because she is the best mom. She helps me and my family and she deserves a gift.

Nicolet Sellers   Grade: 05
My mom is wonderful, indeed she is. She can finish any task, please give my mom a diamond that's all I ask.

Callie Smith   Grade: 05
My mom should deserve a diamond because she is the best mom in the world so she needs a reward for all that she does.

Tommy Smith   Grade: 05
Why does my mom deserve a diamond? Well that's easy, she's the most hard working woman I know. She does everything without a thank you.

Joseph Vallone   Grade: 05
My mom teaches at her job but not for the money but to help kids learn information that can help them in life.

Paularino Elementary
Costa Mesa

Teacher: Tom Barr

Kaylee Anderson   Grade: 03
My mom deserves a diamond because she does so much for me and she gives me everything. So I want to give her something special.

Jacob Jones   Grade: 03
My mommy deserves a diamond because she works really hard at work and taking care of our family.   She thinks of others before herself.

Jasmine Nguyen   Grade: 03
My mom deserves a diamond because she's beautiful and smart.   She will always love me and be there for me.

Pegasus School
Huntington Beach

Teacher: Nancy Wilder

Sara Cluck   Grade: 08
Her eyes are the brightest star in my galaxy. Her heart is the warmest blanket upon my soul. Her words are my Bible. My everything.

Dana Fish   Grade: 08
My mom - my life. The reason for my being. The light that guides me. Growing to love her more each day she is with me.

Josephine Jarecki   Grade: 08
My mother raises me night and day and she teaches me to work then play. Even through life's toughest trials, she always makes me smile.

Peters (Ocia A.) Elementary
Garden Grove

Teacher: Katherine Acquarelli

Elsie Ayala   Grade: 06
My mom has diabetes and had fought all her life with it. She inspired me. She also has perseverance. She will keep me going forever.

Edward Castro   Grade: 06
She's an angel from heaven. She watches us, cares for us, but most importantly, loves us. She'll risk her life just for me.

Raul Cazares   Grade: 06
Mom deserves a diamond because she cares, she sacrifices everything for us even though she is not Batman or Superman, she is someone special...mom.

Allison Grennon   Grade: 06
I love my mom because she's worth more than all the diamonds put together, and I hope I'll be with her forever.

Hugo Guerrero   Grade: 06
My mom deserves a diamond because she cares, listens and gives me love in exchange for just a smile.

Keila Soriano   Grade: 06
Because you love me so. You're my mom, because you care. You're my mom because I love and care for you. God put us together.

Evelyn Torres   Grade: 06
I love my mom! She always makes me time for me. She is my hero. No matter what, she will always be 1 in my heart.

Teacher: Mihoko Chida

Ashley Dinh   Grade: 06
My family isn't rich, but mom never tells of how fortunate we could be, just how fortunate we are, but she deserves to be treasured.

Valery J. Gomez   Grade: 06
My mother is the best. I love her so much I would love to give a beautiful sparkling diamond because she is awesome.

Jennifer Hoang   Grade: 06
My mom deserves this because in this world I can only have one true mother. I want to give her something to show my appreciation.

Jennifer Vu   Grade: 06
My mom is the most influential person in my life. She gives great advice. Even words can't describe how much love her. She's my mom.

Randy Vu   Grade: 06
My mom takes care of me and loves me. She is the best precautious mom you could have. She is wiling to do anything.

Wade Whitman   Grade: 06
My mom deserves a diamond because she is always nice to me, she has always been there, has always helped me, and I love her.

Teacher: Joyce Choi

Natalia Contreras   Grade: 06
There is no other way to say I love you than to give the light of your life a diamond. It's her time to shine.

Christopher Escobar   Grade: 06
My mom deserves a diamond because she's smart, cool, and loving, but most of all, she brought me to the world. She's priceless like a diamond.

Celeste Flores   Grade: 06
My mom is the world, my mom loves me, my mom is my life, but most importantly she's mine and she loves it.

* Amethyst winners in bold.

Peterson (John R.) Elem.
Huntington Beach

Teacher: Polly Clenney

Noah Campbell   Grade: 03
My mom deserves a diamond because she helps around the house, makes food, and folds clothes for us and cleans our room for us.

Marina Gibson   Grade: 03
My mom deserves a diamond because she has a loving heart. She does everything in the house. She has to take care of three kids.

Zak Grove   Grade: 03
My mom deserves a diamond because she is the best mom in the whole entire world because when I am sick she takes care of me.

Addison Hogrelius   Grade: 03
My mom deserves a diamond because she very trustworthy, sweet and she wants jewelry. She is respectful and will never start a fight.

Alexandra McDonald   **Grade: 03**
I think my mom deserves a diamond because she ahs a very big heart and she raised four healthy kids.

Kayla Rios   Grade: 03
My mom deserves a diamond because she has done a lot for everybody. She does laundry, breakfast, lunch and dinner. My mommy is always responsible.

Karina Rosas   Grade: 03
My mom should deserve a diamond because she is very responsible. I think that my mom deserves a diamond because she tries to help.

Tani Song   Grade: 03
My mom deserves a diamond because she is loving, kind and cares for me and she does everything to be a great mom.

Kelsey Tovar   Grade: 03
I think my mom deserves a diamond because she is very trustworthy, smart and caring and loving. She is a very good mom, I love her.

Ethan Wright   Grade: 03
I think my mom should deserve a diamond because she is responsible for everything and caring.

Teacher: Deanna Zamiska

Emma Cox   Grade: 02
She is as pretty as a diamond. She is like a beautiful butterfly. My mom is a s wonderful mom. She is the best.

Chloe DiMaio   Grade: 02
My mom is so sweet to me and my brother, even when she is sick. She looks like a diamond. I love my mom.

Andrea Guzman   Grade: 02
My mom is the best mom ever. She looks like a diamond. I love my mom. She is very funny.

Jack Horton   **Grade: 02**
The funniest mom in the galaxy is my mom. She plays with me when I'm lonely. When she is working she is slurping a slurpee.

Ronnie Nawrocki   Grade: 02
My mom is fantastic as a crystal. My mom is beautiful. My mom takes me places and she is the best mom in the world.

Sidney Roberts   **Grade: 02**
Snow is falling like it is my mom. It is graceful but non=t at all a simple snowflake. The snowflake is shaped like her.

Isaac Rocha   Grade: 02
She is as kind as a diamond store owner. She is as smart as a dolphin. She is as intelligent as a monkey.

Jazmine Romo   Grade: 02
My mom is so terrific she always share with you. She never lies. She is like a beautiful diamond butterfly.

Cheyenne Torres   **Grade: 02**
You are the best mom in the world. You are as soft as a teddy bear. I love you. You are as sweet as a rose.

Plavan (Urbain H.) Elemen.
Fountain Valley

Teacher: Andrea Benson

Kacey DeSantis   **Grade: 04**
My mom is an angel who's soft white wings wrap around me and keep me warm. Everyday of the year. I love my mom.

Evelyn Hoang   **Grade: 04**
My mom is extremely beautiful because her eyes shimmer and I am surely certain that my mom is a winner. I really love my mom.

Maria Toubbeh   **Grade: 04**
My mom is like the stars in the sky. My mom is a beautiful butterfly. My mom is the moon, the sun. I love mom.

Sarah Wallace   Grade: 04
My mom deserves a diamond because she's more than just a caring mom. She's a friend and I love her.

Teacher: Julie Boyd

Hank Caprini   Grade: 02
My mom deserves a diamond because she is like a flower, her eyes like crystal clear pools. She is nice. She is my angel.

Alyssa Garrison   Grade: 02
My mom has sparkling eyes. She is an angel, I love my mom more than anything. She is a diamond. I love you mommy.

Jake Hopkins   Grade: 02
My mom should have a diamond because of her crystal, compassionate, gold heart, and her twinkling eyes. I feel good about her.

Sarah Kwon   Grade: 02
My mom deserves a diamond because she reads stories to me and she loves me. My mom is special to me. I love my mommy.

Joseph Matveyenko   **Grade: 02**
I wish mom had diamond roses that she'd water with hoses. She would earn it for her love, she would give me a big hug.

Abigail Perkins   Grade: 02
My mom deserves a diamond because she lights up my world. She loves me more than anything. And I love her back. She is a great mom.

Teacher: Elizabeth Hudson

Louis Caprini   Grade: 03
My mom deserves a diamond because she is loving, kind and spreads happiness throughout the world. My mom is very nice and forgiving.

Kevin Chow   **Grade: 03**
My mom deserves a diamond because she has hands so beautiful, like crystals. Even her eyes glow like diamonds. She really warms my heart.

Sephten Clevenger   Grade: 03
My mom deserves a diamond because she flies like an eagle. She is like a circle, it doesn't stop. She is my life.

Paige Frink   Grade: 03
She has a beautiful smile, sparkling eyes and she always believes in me. I would like to be like my mom when I grow up.

Alexandra Gettman   Grade: 03
My mom deserves a diamond because she helps me and my grandpa. She stays on the topic of conversation. My mom is like my heart.

Kendrich Nguyen   Grade: 03
My mother deserves a diamond for the love she spreads to my family. She is carried in God's hand forever. She deserves a diamond.

William Nguyen   Grade: 03
Her smile is from the heavens above. She's nicer than lemonade on a hot day, she's full of love. Nobody can replace her in anyway.

Zachary Wheeler   Grade: 03
My mom deserves a diamond because her eyes sparkle like diamonds and has a heart full of gold, but none can be loved like mom.

Nathan Wilson   Grade: 03
My mom deserves a diamond because she is an angel. She always comes when I need her. She is my guardian angel. I love her.

Teacher: Becky Jensen

Auryelle Hall   Grade: 03
My mom deserves a diamond because she is really understanding and always knows what's wrong and right. I thinks she really deserves a diamond.

Alayna Lieu   Grade: 03
My mom is very special. She takes care of me even if she is busy. She is a gem. I love her at any cause.

Courtnee Moreno   Grade: 03
Her eyes, a twinkling star. Her hair the slightest breeze. Her voice, a sparrow. Her touch, a swallow's wing. My mom.

Teacher: Eric Morton

Elizabeth Diaz   Grade: 05
My mom is as gorgeous as a rose. She's loving and caring as can be. She has generosity and kindness and of course, she's hardworking.

Andrew Doan   Grade: 05
Her cooking is a masterpiece. She guides me when I am confused. She supplies entertainment when I'm bored. I love my mother.

Harleigh Higger   Grade: 05
My mom deserves a diamond because she's a very special seed. She's loving, she's caring and she always takes the lead.

Crystal Hui   Grade: 05
Her eyes shine like a brilliant star. Her voice, soothing as honey. I love my mom the way she is. My mom deserves a diamond.

Taylor Matney   Grade: 05
Her heart is full of gold. She laughs and my heart loves. She looks and my eyes see twinkling stars. She's kind. She loves. She's my mom.

Randy Schmidt   Grade: 05
Her smile is as bright as the sun. She's as nice as a cinnamon bun. She's fun, I'm glad to be her son.

Lauren Snow   Grade: 05
My mom is an angel with twinkling eyes, she's smart, she's good natured. She's one of a kind.

Tiffany Truong   Grade: 05
My mom is the sun inside my heart. She sparkles, she shines, she's one of a kind. I'm so lucky that she's all mine.

Teacher: Cheryl Panzella

Maggie Carr   Grade: 03
My mom deserves a diamond because she is the angel of my life. My mom's eyes are like two blue crystal diamonds.

Angelina DePersis   Grade: 03
My mom deserves a diamond because my mom is like a moon and I am like the star following her footsteps. I love my mom.

Josilyn Grant   Grade: 03
My mom is the person who I'm following. She helps me when I'm late for school. My mom is the best mom.

Jared Loudenback   Grade: 03
Why my mom deserves a diamond is because she is sweet and kind. She's all angel, all the way to heaven. I love her.

Cameron Nakashima   Grade: 03
You are the angel that guards my heart, the crystal white light that comes up as soon as I see you. My angel, my mom.

Jesse Ranieri   Grade: 03
My mom is a bird in the sky. She turns to a beautiful angel that protects my heart. This is why I love my mom.

Rachel Roberts   Grade: 03
My mom is the light to my path. She is the brightest star in the sky. She is my mom.

Teacher: Mara Rieck

Karin Chao   Grade: 04
My mom's soul is like a beautiful rose. Her eyes are like sparkling crystals. I know she loves me and I do too.

Jack Hughes   Grade: 04
My mommy is an angel and she is the best. She even plays some sports with me and she will never threat.

Lauren LeBouvier   Grade: 04
My mom should get a diamond because right when you see her you'll laugh. Her love and beauty will go into your heart.

Jenna Lieu   Grade: 04
My mom is like a diamond, the sparkles in the light, she is prettier than you can imagine, she sings like a happy hummingbird.

Adam Mancini   Grade: 04
Her eyes are like the morning sky and her smile is more glistening and warming than any diamond. Her heart is as solid as gold.

Sapphire Pham   Grade: 04
She's cheerful, friendly and loving. Her eyes twinkle like the stars from heaven watching me. An angel like her would deserve a diamond from me.

Khoa Phan   Grade: 04
My mom is better than ice cream, chocolate, even soda or chips. She's the best food in the world. That's why I love her so much.

Teacher: Marilyn Ryan

Leandra Doan   Grade: 05
Love, grace, personality - these are the ingredients for an extra special person. My mom is that person. For she is always bringing happiness to everyone.

Natallie Dunckel   Grade: 05
My mom, I love so dearly has kindness and love all over. She is no other than my mother, and that will never change.

Emma Hartigan   Grade: 05
My mom's a sparkling diamond through darkness and light. Without her, my world would shatter. She's a floating dove in the sky.

Nathan Hoang   Grade: 05
My mom completes my heart. When it is cold, she hugs me warm. My heart explodes when she hugs me. I love my mom.

* Amethyst winners in bold.

Ariana Isbell — Grade: 05
Every morning when I wake up, I see an angel. When I clear my eyes, I realize it's my mom. I love my mommy.

Nicholas Malone — **Grade: 05**
Glistening in the night to give me light, holding me tight throughout the night. Sparkling eyes like diamonds in the light. She is my mother.

Lucy Nakashima — **Grade: 05**
A light guiding me through darkness. A gentle breeze in a meadow. A dew drop in the morning. My mother is everything, especially to me.

Kathleen Vo — Grade: 05
My mother is a lovely woman with a warm heart. I love her with all my heart because she's an angel from above.

Plaza Vista
Irvine

Teacher: Scott Bedley

Emily Culbertson — Grade: 05
My mom deserves a diamond because of her kind and loving heart. She cleans up every day and makes my dinner oh so great.

Jordanne Hamilton — Grade: 05
My mom deserves a diamond because her personality sparkles like one and she inspires me in life and shows me how to praise God.

Glenn Parham — Grade: 05
My mom deserves a diamond because she works 24/7 with a lot of stress, plus she got a new jewelry cleaner for Christmas.

Ajay Raj — Grade: 05
If you catch one glimpse of my mom you'll instantly wish you were her. But the genie made another rule; you can't wish to be my mom.

Weylan Wang — **Grade: 05**
While flowers in gardens may falter, you are a rose that shines. Your loving kindness radiant shows you're a mother that's one of a kind.

Teacher: Dawn Burgess

Olivia Liu — **Grade: 04**
Her love penetrates the deepest, darkest places spreading light from her fingertips. Her love is a priceless jewel that will shine even after all ends.

Advaith Rai — Grade: 04
If it were possible to see inside my mother's heart, all you would see would be beautiful colors showing happiness, kindness and purity.

Katelyn Schmidt — Grade: 04
My mom has a heart the size of six Swedish meatballs. Without her love, I would be nothing. That's why she deserves a diamond.

Austin Walters — Grade: 04
My mom gave up a beautiful diamond like body just for me and I think that she deserves a beautiful mineral just like she was.

Teacher: Michelle Rigoli

Momoka Abe — Grade: 06
My mom sparkles everyday and will shine forever like a diamond, so she deserves a diamond.

Ehtesham Ali — Grade: 06
Why my mom deserves a diamond, isn't as simple as it seems. She cooks varieties of foods without changing her mood.

Michelle Bau — **Grade: 06**
Hummingbirds flying busily in the sky. Eagles defending it's territory up high, peacocks filled with rare beauty. My mom is the one and only.

Ron Best — Grade: 06
Diamonds, diamonds are very precious and they should only be given to people like them. My mom is sweet, she deserves a treat.

Annie Chen — Grade: 06
My mom is great. She helps, she cooks. She helps with homework, and when I need her, she'll always be there for ne.

Sheenu Chirackel — **Grade: 06**
Moms are like a diamond, they are sparkly, loving and caring all about. They'll never let you down even if you have a doubt.

Aruba Din — Grade: 06
My mom is the most precious gift from God given to me very similar to how diamonds are flawless and unique.

Attiya Elahi — Grade: 06
How does she do it? She cleans the house, dishes, laundry, cooks meals, helps with projects, and loves us. How can she continue? The diamond.

Cerena Esquibel — Grade: 06
My mom deserves a diamond because she sparkles in the sun with kindness, and her heart shines like a golden chest of love.

Jamie Greenberg — Grade: 06
My mom's always kind to me. She is a mother of three. A hardworking teacher never quits and always tries her best - she's great.

Elise Gwin — Grade: 06
My mom is hardworking. She is always there for me, if mischief's about, she's looking and always is able to see.

Joanna Hsieh — Grade: 06
When I am crying, mom let's me cry on her and that makes me feel better.

Harry Hwang — **Grade: 06**
Anytime I looked at her, I saw a smile on her face. Every time I talk to her, I feel partnership. Mother of happiness.

Selin Karaoguz — Grade: 06
If my mom was next to hundreds of diamonds, she would shine the most. She gives all the warmth she has and cares for everyone.

Maya Kashlan — Grade: 06
Why I believe my mom deserves a diamond? Well to me, that's obvious. She's getting her masters degree and diamonds are a great graduation gift.

Jillian Kido — Grade: 06
My mom's smile is golden; her eyes sparkle and shine as bright as the midnight sky. She is a true gem to me.

Vinay Kumar — Grade: 06
All my mom does is work, work, work. So this is a present from me to her, I hope she'd be with diamond jewelry.

Stephen Lantin — Grade: 06
My mom deserves a shining jewel because she's smart, kind, caring, and cool. She's very creative too, my mom earns the diamond, that's so true.

Timothy Lantin — **Grade: 06**
The civil engineer should receive an applause for working and working without pause. Hardworking and cool, I think my mom deserves a jewel.

Stephanie Lee — Grade: 06
Moms cook, clean and wash but my mom is the hardest worker. Driving us here and there, mom my multi-tasked with love and care.

Mali McKenzie — **Grade: 06**
My mom's face lights the sky. Her smile makes my day. A voice like an angel's. Takes my fears away.,

Bridger Moore   **Grade: 06**
Her roses we trashed, her violets we pounded. Please give her the diamond before I get grounded.

Austin Nguyen   Grade: 06
My mom 's a great parent and doctor. She helps patients get better and when my dad had cancer, she revised him back to health.

Lauren Nguyen   Grade: 06
My mom helps us when she's exhausted, without being frustrated. She is always supporting us. I love her. I wouldn't trade her for the world.

Rana Salem   **Grade: 06**
Diamonds over here, diamonds over there, give my mom a diamond and you'll never despair. She's always there, never far. She's always in the car.

Andrew Schmidt   Grade: 06
I love my mom with all my heart. She is shiny, happy, precious, lasting, golden, beautiful, loving, and she's mine. A diamond can't compare.

Parsa Shaghaghi   **Grade: 06**
My mom, her two eyes are full moons gazing at me. Her voice, the sound of chirping birds. A hardworking therapist, a great mom.

Duncan Shepherd   **Grade: 06**
The only one caring for two sons. Works hard each day, what fun. Spreads her love, without help sent. A diamond makes a nice present.

Achint Singh   **Grade: 06**
My mom deserves a diamond, it is very simple to see. She is the nicest mom there will ever be.

Tanay Singhui   **Grade: 06**
One who cooks, one who helps. One who loves, one who cares. One who is only my mom.

Jonathan Tang   Grade: 06
She cares for me, she makes me food. Each bite, I taste is full of love. She cares for my grandma who is disabled.

Jennifer Tram   **Grade: 06**
My mom deserves a diamond because it reflects her personality. She sparkles and gleams like a diamond, and is just as valuable as one too.

Ben Tuval   **Grade: 06**
How would it be without a diamond. For a mom so sweet, without a necklace to see. She loves you, she feeds you, cares everyday.

Jarod Urrutia   Grade: 06
My mom works hard, everyday of the week, loving and supportive, she helps my family. Although she gets mad sometimes, I know she loves me.

Teacher: Jill Tamminen

Dante Gaz   Grade: 04
My mom has done many things like helping out hurt people and just being there…but her love is what counts to me.

Bob Ko   **Grade: 04**
Mom is hardworking, ever deserving. She loves me with all her heart. My dear mother, you'll be my sun forever and ever.

Kanghee Lee   Grade: 04
My mom deserves a diamond because she is a one of a kind and because she has a sparkle that makes her like no other.

Kitana Mejia   **Grade: 04**
Her shining eyes, her loving heart, is all I need to se. I love her looks like a dreamy path of stars.

Samantha Mickelson   Grade: 04
Glistening eyes in the sun, a big bright smile on her face. Her hair shines like a diamond in the moonlight.

Noah Pacis   **Grade: 04**
Mom's eyes sparkle with gleam. They are like diamonds that have reflecting beams. They sine more whenever she blinks because that is Mom.

Robyn Pollisco   Grade: 04
My mom is flawless and beautiful. She always makes me laugh and smile. When I tripped, she came and said, "Keep moving forward".

Michelle Son   Grade: 04
My mom makes my heart beat faster, faster, and faster because she is my joyful, flawless mother.

Alexa Wallace   Grade: 04
If you were a teacher what would your name be? If you were the 1 mom, your name would be Mitzi because she's the best.

Portola Hills Elementary
Trabuco Canyon

Teacher: Susan LeHardy

Ariana Barry   Grade: 05
My mom always sacrifices for our family and has a fake diamond ring. That is why I think she deserves a real diamond ring.

Brendon Derache   **Grade: 05**
My mom, beautiful as the rising sun, graceful as a swimming swan. She cheers me up when I'm down. She heals me when I'm sick.

Jessie Fischman   Grade: 05
My mom deserves a diamond because she does so much for my family and I. And helps us through tough times. She deserves much more.

Kylie Fulton   **Grade: 05**
My mom doesn't deserve a diamond, she deserves more. As the greatest mom, she deserves a lot. But a diamond just may have to do.

Travis Loranger   Grade: 05
My mom is the best and she needs a diamond because she takes care of three kids and she deserves a gift for her dedication.

Jacklyn Thompson   Grade: 05
My mother deserves a diamond, she would rather give than receive. She helps the less fortunate. She is loving, caring, and a very giving person.

Teacher: Francine Sinatra

Shane Adamski   **Grade: 05**
I'll lasso the moon, I'll lasso the stars, I'll give you my heart, I'll give you my soul. You'll be the mom I'll always love.

Chayley Blaydes   Grade: 05
My mom deserves a diamond because she helps people with medical problems by giving them their prescription. I love her because she's a diamond inside.

Sohaima Khilji   Grade: 05
My mom's heart is a heart of gold. Reach down the rainbow for a pot of gold, wait and you'll win the diamond of caring.

Nicholas Padilla   Grade: 05
Although a diamond is shiny and valuable, with her smile and eyes, I'll bet you my life that my mom is worth more than a diamond.

Ashley Sutphin   Grade: 05
Her hugs and kisses are full of love like a graceful dove. She is very kind with a smart mind. That's why I have her.

Kristen Wisneski   **Grade: 05**
My mom is a gem like me. Her eyes twinkle like stars at sea. Her voice sparkles like sapphire souls. She's the best, I'm told.

* Amethyst winners in bold.

Prince of Peace Lutheran
Costa Mesa

Teacher: Mary Caldwell

Hannah Bradford   **Grade: 05**
She comforts me when I'm scared. She fixes my buttons and combs my hair. One thing I love most, her heart is warm as toast.

Tia Gordon   Grade: 05
She snuggles me when I'm sick. Sings to me when I'm sleepy. Always so involved. I can't wish for a better mom than her.

Jenny Jorgensen   **Grade: 05**
Sometimes I'm happy, sometimes I'm sad. Other times I'm grumpy or mad. Your absolute love never lets me go, whether I'm grouchy or glad.

Olivia Khoury   Grade: 05
My mother's eyes sparkle in the morning light. She cooks and cleans and does everything you could possibly think of. She is a splendid mother.

Elizabeth Sturdy   Grade: 05
My mom is funny, loving, and kind. She picks me up when I'm down. She means the whole world to me. I LOVE HER.

Nathan Wesdell   Grade: 05
Whatever is true, whatever is noble, whatever is right but my mom's eyes are like diamonds.

Teacher: Linda Coxson

Jacqueline Chee   Grade: 04
My mom brings home the money and cleans the house. She's the best mom of the 21st century. She deserves a diamond. She's a wonder woman.

McKenna Covey   Grade: 04
My mom deserves a diamond because she is very giving. She puts me in a lot of sports, a school, and a roof over my head.

Tucker Dye   Grade: 04
Why mom deserves a diamond, she has been worked to the bone at home. She deserves a diamond. She is the best literally.

Madison Galitski   Grade: 04
My mom is caring, kind, loving. She is everything in my life. She knows when something is wrong. I can tell my mom everything.

Dawit Habteab   **Grade: 04**
My mom is sweetly endowed. She will always be remembered. She is like a friend that always grows. She is significantly unique always to me.

Lauren Weisser   Grade: 04
My mom helps me do my homework. Her eyes sparkle like the stars and her hug makes me full of joy.

Teacher: Amy Reed

Karen Bradford   Grade: 03
My mom deserves a diamond because she is the best in the world. She loves me and I love her. She is so beautiful.

Bailey Captain   Grade: 03
My mom deserves a diamond because she is sweet, hardworking, amazing, the best mom ever.

Jon Geiger   **Grade: 03**
Mom cares for me, wakes me gently. She pancakes me, laughs at my syrup and schools me to and from then comfortably to bed with kisses.

Hannah Welsh   **Grade: 03**
Mama, is like many other moms, but there's no mom in the world that loves their daughters as much as my mom loves me.

Guita Afzali, Michael Watson, and Tram Diep search for a Diamond Winner in the 2009 contest.

Rancho San Joaquin Middle
Irvine

Teacher: David Kingsbury

Roya Aghavali   Grade: 07
My mom is the one who would care. All the wonderful memories we share. Joyful moments she brings. For that she deserves a diamond ring.

Egel Auh   Grade: 07
I asked if she love me, she said yes. I asked if she would die for me, she said yes. My own personal Jesus Christ

Melissa Ballard   Grade: 07
My mom deserves a diamond because she's the shoulder I cry on, the person who loves me, and inspires me to triumph over any obstacle.

Melissa Calica   Grade: 07
My mother is always there to confide in, to relieve a nightmare, to nurture my soul. For she is my mother; she is my friend.

Anne Chen   **Grade: 07**
Eyes like diamonds, heart of gold, smile like stars, wisdom she holds. Hand that gives, soul that loves. Mother that guides me beyond and above.

Jordan Freedlander   Grade: 07
Sacrifice, that's how she functions. Kindness, her language. Love, it forms the bond between her and her family. She brings laughter but her laugh, priceless.

Will Glass   Grade: 07
She has shown me the world in such short notice. To see her face filled with joy, in my heart, a diamond would repay her.

Haruka Hatori   **Grade: 07**
An angel fell from the heavens. Broken; destroyed through with the help of her family. She became the strong, loving mother, I know and love,

Tiffany Huang   **Grade: 07**
Eyes twinkling like the moon. Always humming a cheery tune. Her mind is quick and ever so clever. She is my mother, a jewel forever.

Vladi Iotov   Grade: 07
Since the moment I first saw the light, a woman so fine and beautiful picked me up into gentle arms. She kissed me. My mother.

Dakshin Jandhyala   Grade: 07
My mom deserves a diamond because her eyes sparkle as if a diamond and when she speaks, I hear a soft, beautiful and encouraging voice.

Daniel Johnson   **Grade: 07**
Mother, her eyes sparkling bright. Her graceful walk, her glowing smile. The incarnation of loving care. Mother: Diamond of my heart.

Sara Krolewski   Grade: 07
She is the shimmering diamond of beauty and hope on the necklace of my life. Her constant effort helps everyone including myself.

Sahil Lamba   **Grade: 07**
She has love. She has shine. She has skills you just can't find. Please don't let me part, from the diamond of my heart.

Leslie Ledezma   Grade: 07
Rosa, a rose. Mother. Her smile full and soft. Her cheeks rosy as petals. Her helping hands stronger than any stone. Rosa. A rose. Mother.

Jenny Liu   Grade: 07
My mom deserves a diamond for choosing to love me, for choosing to care for me, for choosing to be my guide through life's surprises.

Danni Ovens   Grade: 07
A diamond is pure, something that has many facets. It is always sparkling and glittering. My mom is my diamond. She is rare and special.

Michael Schiffer   Grade: 07
Heart shines, eyes sparkle, her arms are the chain around my neck. Her hands, the clasp, to hold it together. Finest jewelry in the world.

Kyla Scott   **Grade: 07**
If my family is a dress, she is the hem. If it's a flower, she is the stem. This is why mom deserves a gem.

Preethl Seshadri   Grade: 07
My mother's love shines vibrantly our bond glows like a ruby. Even if saddened, her faith is unwavering and her encouragement will always be shimmering.

Stephanie Shi   Grade: 07
Mom, the glimmering parent in my life. Guardian, ping pong player, dancer - mother.

Clara Sim   **Grade: 07**
Diamonds, gold, and lots more. Those are true gems we explore, but deep inside, the more beautiful we see. Your mother's devoted love towards thee.

Annie Tran   Grade: 07
Diamond heart, glowing with love. Her love for me greater than a sea of treasure, can't be expressed. Love like this deserves a diamond.

Haripriya Vasireddy   Grade: 07
Mother deserves a diamond because she has shows me how difficult it is to love, but how meaningless life can be without it.

David Zheng   Grade: 07
I think my mom deserves a diamond because in my heart, she's the greatest of jewels.

Teacher: Pam Otto

Myna Allister   Grade: 07
Her eyes that sparkle. Her ears that listen to my stories. Her smile that lightens up the room. My mother. Oh mother. I love you.

Martin Huang   Grade: 07
The sunlight of my heart. My strength to live. Her love is as wide as from Earth to moon. This person is my mother.

Jennifer Kim   Grade: 07
Shiny, colorful, hard, luminous, bright, lovely, precious, strong, valuable. My mom is the diamond of my life.

Teacher: Shannon Van Dam

Liu Jiang   **Grade: 08**
My mother's affection...livelier than silvery soft moons sailing in the night... brighter than brilliant golden suns scattering penetrating light...a precious gift from heaven.

Alex Jow   **Grade: 08**
Her hands, instruments of work, yet benevolent, considerate, compassionate, steadfastly laboring for my cause, ensuring my future, toiling for my success and not her own.

Karamia Link   Grade: 08
My mom deserves a diamond because she's not really my mom, she's my foster mom and she wanted me when no one else did.

Deborah Ma   **Grade: 08**
A warm embrace, comfort in a night of despair. A springtime gust, love pulls me out of winter shadows. She is my spring.

***** Amethyst winners in bold.**

Angela Park   Grade: 08
My mom is everything I aspire to be. Beautiful, radiant, and hardworking, she never fails to love. She's my precious one of a kind diamond.

Jocelyn Vennat   Grade: 08
My red rose that endows incessant love. My guardian angel sent from above. My mother, my priceless gift of joy, I will cherish forever.

Justin Wang   Grade: 08
Dear mama, if I could repay you, for all your rays of unconditional love that have bled into me, I'd be the richest man alive.

Lisa Xie   Grade: 08
Sweet breeze that caresses my soul that brings life to a lonely stroll. Howling wind that kindles the love, making my heart melt thereof, mom.

Sammy Yoon   Grade: 08
As gentle as a lake and as soft as a cloud, my mom brings awe to other with her kindness and her heart.

Red Hill Lutheran School
Tustin

Teacher: John Dovenmuehler

Wyatt Barclay   Grade: 05
My mother has a belly fluttering sense of humor. She does as much work as one hundred people in one day and asks for nothing.

Eric Chang   Grade: 05
Her beauty lights the night sky. She bursts with kindness. She melts ice with her love. She sparkles like a priceless diamond. She's my mom.

Connor Gowland   Grade: 05
My mom is with me at the hardest time. She is like a butterfly. She's never mean, she is never rude and her heart is true.

Kaitlyn Julian   Grade: 05
My mom can be embarrassing, but she is awesome. She has a really good heart and is the best mom in the universe.

Kaylee Kreyling   Grade: 05
Her eyes are a sparkling pool of diamonds. Even though she is short, she is 100% love and care and always think of me.

Zachary Macadam   Grade: 05
My mom is very considerate and generous. She is like the glistening sun. She does so much work for nothing. She is a great mother.

Reece Meyhoefer   Grade: 05
My mom is as busy as a bee helping me and my two sisters. She loves me more than a diamond because she shows it.

Amanda Raber   Grade: 05
She's loving, caring, her teeth shine like a beautiful diamond. Her eyes are like eagle eyes watching over me. She's a priceless mom to me.

Teacher: Valerie Wilson

Aidyn Carlson   Grade: 05
She cooks, she cleans, she does so many things. She does my hair, she takes me everywhere. She is my mother. She's like no other.

Taylor Craft   Grade: 05
My mom is a diamond. She is my hero and mentor. She is different from any other mother. She can do anything, I love her.

Michelle Manous   Grade: 05
Mommy loves me so. Mommy teaches me everything I know. I hope to be like her someday. Mommy's eyes sparkle and so does she.

Nicholas Robertson   Grade: 05
My mother deserves a diamond because she sings like an angel. She loves and cares about me. Without her, life would be horrendous, she's awesome.

Arabya Royal   Grade: 05
My mom deserves a diamond because she nurtures me. She's always encouraged through rough times. My mom is the most loving person ever.

Sabrina Saenz   Grade: 05
A diamond for my mother who has put a sparkle in the eyes of so many in need would be my dream come true.

Diana Thompson   Grade: 05
My mom is a diamond. She is my hero and mentor. She is different from any other mom. She is the key to all success.

Samantha Waipa   Grade: 05
She is the highlight of my life. I always come to her in times of trouble. She should win because she is my shining diamond.

Reilly (Phillip J.) Elemen.
Mission Viejo

Teacher: Michele Arambula

Reid Berke   Grade: 03
My mom creates happiness wherever she is. I treasure and preserve her love. Her hugs are more precious than anything. She is my diamond.

Nathan Caparaz   Grade: 03
My mom is very thoughtful and nice. She also cooks me orange chicken and rice. I have my moms love. My moms love is eternal.

Tyler Lenning   Grade: 03
The heavens open when she sings. She is my guardian angel that watches over me in my sleep. I know she loves me.

Ann Ruthkowski   Grade: 03
My mom is always looking out for me. She is a golden eagle that can help me when I'm in trouble. Thanks mom.

Bianca Thoburn   Grade: 03
She's always filled with positive energy. She helps me with my wounds. She fills my heart with happiness. She's my loving mom that made me.

Teacher: Roxane Blake

Tanner Boydstun   Grade: 04
Her eyes are as sharp as an eagle, brown like one too. Her love has unlimited capacity. She's just like an angel, an angel to me.

Maddy Cole   Grade: 04
My mom is my soul. She's the reason I'm living. Most people feel fear of growing old. My mom doesn't fear, she constantly shines.

Justin Gierstorfer   Grade: 04
My mom is a dolphin leaping through a sea of happiness. Her kiss is like roses glistening in the moonlight. That's my mega-loving mom.

Paige Jones   Grade: 04
As beautiful as a diving dolphin, her laugh reminds me of crashing waves, her eyes tell her personality. She's as precious as a sprouting rosebud.

Kyle Kelly   Grade: 04
My moms voice touches me like a miracle in the air, her hugs warm my heart like springtime. My mom is a treasured diamond.

Nolan Lee   Grade: 04
She is loving, like a mother swan, I'm not telling lies, and with a beautiful face. It's hard not to notice when you pass by.

Adam Tyler-Smith   Grade: 04
My mom is like a pillow and a piece of candy, soft and sweet. My mom is like a monarch butterfly glistening in the moonlight.

Hallie Tyler-Smith   Grade: 04
If my mom was a poem, her words would flow together like a river under the moonlit sky. Her love emanates through my heart.

Teacher: Maureen Cordina

Garrett Clover   Grade: 05
Emerald eyes, heart of gold, sapphire soul. Delicately forged of diamond. Gazes into your soul, touches your heart. As beautiful as the goddess of Venus.

Adam Debdeb   Grade: 05
Her heart is my companion, her soul runs my train, her love makes me orbit the sun, my mom, the gem of my life.

Robyn Lippel   Grade: 05
Her heart a ruby, her soul a diamond. Caring always, mysterious too. She's as lovely a cherry blossom tree blooming. She's my mom, gladly.

Christopher Orem   Grade: 05
Her face like Miss America's, her movements like a dance, her voice like min, singing a song, my mom's the star of the show.

Amanda Petersen   Grade: 05
Each eye a gleaming gem, each hair a strand of gold, each smile like glistening pearls, she's my soul, my love, my world, my mom.

Alexei Rehern   Grade: 05
My mom is like the flawless universe. Her face is brighter than the stars. She is enlightened by the beautiful sun. I honor her greatly.

Andrew Richmond   Grade: 05
The angel's heart is a fireplace comforting me. Her eyes look down upon me like stars from heaven. She'

Julia Running   Grade: 05
Like a passing shooting star, she is beautiful. She shines like the moon on summer nights. Heart warm, like sun radiance. My mom, the brightest.

Brady Scott   Grade: 05
Into my soul she gazes with sparkling eyes that glisten like the suns reflection on the oceans' choppy surface. Her heart is warm like the summer.

Noah Valdez   Grade: 05
Her eyes sparkle like a diamond, high up in the sky, my mom deserves a diamond, because she's an angel in disguise.

Jean Wu   Grade: 05
She has a heart full of gold, eyes like the moon, a soul as gentle as Hawaiian waves, she's my life, she's my mom.

Teacher: Holly Flowers

Lisa Bilen   Grade: 04
My mom came from heaven with a diamond dress, and a heart of amethyst, and a loving soul. And that's why mom deserves a diamond.

Jenna Brewer   Grade: 04
She is delicate like flakes of gold. Her eyes like diamonds and her heart is like millions of rubies, held together with shines of love.

Olivia Bush   Grade: 04
My mom's heart is like one million diamonds, like one thousand amethysts, one hundred garnets. Her voice is like ten singing angels. Kind and caring.

Kelly Elsperman   Grade: 04
Shimmering sparkles of beauty, your heart like a snowflake, so big and caring. A taste of anything sweet wouldn't change you at all.

Emily Garreton   Grade: 04
My mom is sweet as honey. Her eyes twinkle like the stars at night. She's smart like a cookie and she's cuddly like a kitten.

Hannah Green   Grade: 04
She's diamonds, amethysts, and garnets too. If you mix them all up and add a bit of gold, that is her heart strong and bold.

Trinidad Madrigal   Grade: 04
My mom is like an angel shimmering in the light with skin softer than a snowflake and more beautiful than any diamond. She's a blessing.

Kensi Olsen   Grade: 04
My mom is like a cookie baking in the sun. She shines like a star. Her smile lights up the world. She's a pretty princess!

Cassidy Stewart   Grade: 04
Her love seeps around me, she melts my life into relaxation, shine fills her body like a jewel of many things as she touches my heart.

Bailey Vertson   Grade: 04
My moms eyes are like beautiful diamonds in the sky and when she whispers its like a chorus of angels.

Teacher: Karen French

Hannah Badger   Grade: 04
My mom is a beautiful orchid, she always believes I'm a winner. I think she's the best mom ever because she's a great tucker-inner.

Lauren Bauer   Grade: 04
My mom is like a diamond glimmering, in a cool; sunshine breeze. She has no end from love and kindness she brings from the heavens.

Andrew Cai   Grade: 04
My mom deserves a crown, with diamond and pearl gems. Like the gentle ocean breeze, my mom calms any heart. My mom is an angel.

Matthew Chicoine   Grade: 04
My mom's heart is like the sun, shining it's rays of love from the angels in heaven. My mom has many wonderful qualities.

Tyler Enriquez   Grade: 04
My mom is so caring. She is so loving and kind that she would take care of me every time. She is really lovable.

Delaney Good   Grade: 04
My mom is the gem of my heart and the key to my happiness. She is as bright as the sun, she treasures me, always.

Joseph Kerfoot   Grade: 04
My mom is the angel of my heart, flying up to the glistening stars, flying to the fountain of hope and dreams! I love you!

Hannah Lewis   Grade: 04
The power of love is in her soul. Heavens words are spoken when she sings to me. My mothers love for me is pure.

Kristin Merrill   Grade: 04
My mom is like a dove, as pretty as can be. My moms eyes are like a sparkling raindrop looking down at me.

Jax Mills   Grade: 04
My mom is as bright as the sun. She is a beautiful eagle, she is a caring mother, and beautiful rainbow in the mountains

Sara Neil   Grade: 04
My mother is a rose blossoming with beauty. She is a dove spreading her wings of wisdom. Moms eyes dance like the stars at night.

Alexis Veazy   Grade: 04
Her hugs are like a teddy bears' warm gentle hug. Her voice is like an angels lullaby, so lively, sweet. Her eyes like chocolate. That's mom.

* Amethyst winners in bold.

Teacher: Cheryl Kamphefner

Alexa Aziz   Grade: 05
My mothers bright green eyes for a stem and golden blonde hair for petals make a gorgeous daisy, growing more beautiful each day.

Kaitlin Carroll   Grade: 05
Her eyes, brighter than the North star. Her smile, happiest thing in the world. Her heart as loving and pure as gold. That's my mom!

Daniel Crane   Grade: 05
Her eyes shine brighter than the moon. She treats everyone the same, I think she should be awarded in fame.

Elizabeth Erban   **Grade: 05**
Her spirit soars like an eagle, her hair flies like the wind, her voice is a sparrow singing, her eyes flutter like a butterflies wings.

Allison Giles   Grade: 05
My mom shows she loves me in many ways each day. She loves me lots no matter what and makes my problems go away.

Jake Good   **Grade: 05**
The beautiful planets, the sparkling sea, a caring mother cheetah. My mom's all of these-beautiful, sparkling, caring. But most of all she's my mom.

Kassandra Phan   Grade: 05
Through colds and chills mom takes care of me until I'm well. Through friends and family mom helps me with fundraisers until I sell.

Collin Pimsaguan   **Grade: 05**
Her eyes glow set the depth of the ocean, yet her smile glows with a thousand suns. Her hair shines and puts flowers in boom.

Noah Scherner   **Grade: 05**
My mom is so dear to me , without her I wouldn't be, she fills me up with glee, like a morning cup of tea.

Teacher: Marilyn Marestaing

Rebecca Blyn   **Grade: 03**
My mom deserves a diamond because her generosity is as giving as a tree with apples. Her company fills my life with happiness and love.

Jack Briwick   Grade: 03
My mom deserves a diamond because her cooking is as spectacular as a gourmet chef in a five star restaurant.

Aspen Cunningham   Grade: 03
My mom deserves a diamond because her love is like juicy strawberries. Her voice is like singing baby bells.

Connor Moran   Grade: 03
My mom deserves a diamond because her hair is as soft as a pillow. Her cooking smells as rich as gold.

Sloane Werner   Grade: 03
My mom deserves a diamond because she is as gentle as a priceless diamond during sad times. Her eyes are glittery as a moonlit stream.

Teacher: Debra Sheehan

Benjamin Bendix   Grade: 03
My mom deserves a diamond because her eyes are beautiful. It would be hard without her. Her heart is as big as the forest.

Sabrina Campana   **Grade: 03**
She is as beautiful as a rhinestone. Her smile is as big as the sun. Her heart is as big as the sky. She's special.

Summer Dobbs   **Grade: 03**
My moms heart's as big as heaven, she smiles as bright as the sun, her eyes twinkle and she is as beautiful as a diamond.

Phoenix Goldberg   Grade: 03
My mom deserves a diamond because she is as brave as a noble dragon. I could not live my life without my great fabulous mother.

Carryn O Neil   Grade: 03
My mom has a heart as big as a watermelon. Her eyes twinkle like beautiful stars. She hugs as warm as a stove.

Teacher: Lynn Souers

Nathan Benefeito   **Grade: 02**
My moms eyes are greener than grass, when she smiles I can't look, it's too bright. She is so very pretty! I love my mom!

Tiara Brown   Grade: 02
My moms eyes sparkle like sunlight. She's there for me when I'm sick. She prays with me and I love her. She is the best.

Kristen Ghitea   Grade: 02
My mom has eyes like a sparkling diamond. When she laughs it sounds like a sweet angel. She is kind and giving. I love her.

Naomi Lewis   **Grade: 02**
A glistening dove twinkling in the moonlight, reading me a bedtime story, who is this beautiful light? It's my mother, what a wonderful sight.

Ansley Nguyen   **Grade: 02**
My mom is as beautiful as a flower, her eyes sparkle like rare diamonds. My mom smiles like an angel, she is a loveable mom!

Lillian Ross   Grade: 02
My mom has a perfect attitude, she loves her family with all her heart! She always laughs funny and her eyes glisten like gemstones.

Grace Langan   Grade: 03
My moms eyes are as beautiful as sapphires. Her hair shines like a gold angel goddess. Her face is the thing that keeps me going.

Teacher: Cheryl Van Every

Kaitlin Bigley   Grade: 05
My mom is as pretty as a peacock and as valuable as a diamond. She's as sweet as a blueberry and as kind as Santa.

Samantha Carroll   Grade: 05
My mom is the diamond in the wall of stones. The sharpest knife in the drawer. I'd do anything for her. I truly love her.

Alanna Childs   Grade: 05
She is as elegant as a rose, as beautiful as a parrot, as kind as someone taking in a stray dog. I love her.

Tara Doroudian   Grade: 05
Ten years ago, so bright was the room, her face was aglow. This wonderful person was my mom. My first memory.

Madison Underhill   **Grade: 05**
A dip of sparkle and a dab of diamond with a heart as good as a fairy, an angel from up above, I love.

Sue VanEvery   **Grade: 05**
My mom's eyes are like a gorgeous star during a dazzling night. Her smile is warm and delightful like a sunset over the horizon.

Riverdale Elementary
Anaheim

Teacher: Shelli Burkhart

Justine Bennett   Grade: 05
My mom is hardworking, smart, strong, nice, beautiful. She tries to keep a roof over five kids' heads. She also helps my grandmother a lot.

Rosaura Coronado Flores   Grade: 05
My mom is like a star, that's why I think she deserves the diamond. Also, she takes care of me. Takes me to places.

Rachel Coyle   Grade: 05
My mom is graceful and very pretty. I wish on a star that she would win a diamond. She is the best in the world.

Steven Daskowski   Grade: 05
I want my mom to have a diamond because she is very nice and caring. She is nice to everyone and never mean to anyone.

Nadine Douhal   Grade: 05
My mom is happy, cool, nice and helping. Also, she helps me, cook and helps me with my homework. My mom is very loving.

Katrina Garcia   Grade: 05
My mom is one of the nicest people in the world. She is like chocolate, sweet and lovable. My mom is a wonderful lady.

Cinthya Ledezma   Grade: 05
My mom helps me on my homework. She takes care of me when I am sick. She is very special because she loves me.

Evelyn Martinez   Grade: 05
My mom is hardworking and beautiful mom. She always helps me with everything. My mom gives me things I need for loving.

Gabriella Rios   Grade: 05
My mom does not think about herself, she thinks about others. Now I want to give her the attention she needs. I love my mom.

Jacqueline Rios   Grade: 06
My mom works hard to feed and help us. Mother's Day isn't enough to thank my mother for what she does every year.

Teacher: Art Coony

Gloria Fernandez   Grade: 04
My mom deserves a diamond because she takes care of me, loves me, helps me. She is pretty good at working. She works a lot.

Hayley Leyns   Grade: 04
My mom is a loving, caring, person who works hard each and everyday. She makes my life perfect. I would love it if she won.

Hailey Manliguis   Grade: 04
My mom is really nice. I love her. I want to give her the best gift ever. She takes care of me.

Tui Moala   Grade: 04
My mom deserves a diamond because she works to pay the bills. Even if the economy is going down, she still works hard.

Rachel Roll   Grade: 04
My mom deserves a diamond because she's a great single mother with four kids struggling with money and with a full time job.

Brianna Serrano   Grade: 04
The reason my mom deserves a diamond is because she is nice, pretty, and helps me with my homework. She tells me to study.

Emily Tovar   Grade: 04
My mom cleans, cooks; she does everything. My mom deserves that diamond because she works everyday.

Teacher: Carrie Griggs

Emma Aldrete   Grade: 01
My mom deserves a diamond because she gives me good, helps me with my homework, loves me very much and my brother too.

Jonathan Ford   Grade: 01
My mom deserves a diamond because she makes me do my chores, make my bed, helps me doe my homework, cleans the dishes, and take out trash.

Alex Grams   Grade: 01
My mom deserves a diamond because she is nice to my family and friends and she helps me with my homework and my other stuff.

Teacher: Linda Harestead

Christopher De Paola   Grade: 05
My mom should get a diamond because she is lovable, funny and always happy. She cares for me, and she will always love me.

Megan Garcia   Grade: 05
I love my mom. I'm not going to say, "My mom's great". Every girl will say that. My mom's perfect just for me.

Mandy Jezowksi   Grade: 05
My mom deserves a diamond because she works really hard and doesn't get rewarded. That is why my mom deserves a diamond.

Sabrina Perez   Grade: 05
My mom deserves this diamond because she is the best mom you could wish for and she means more to me than the universe.

Joceylin Rangel   Grade: 05
My mom deserves a diamond because she is kind, loyal, respectful, beautiful, cool and is the best foster mom in the whole entire world.

Vanessa Torres   Grade: 05
My mom deserves this diamond because she means the world to me and she deserves this great diamond.

Tyler VonDenlinger   Grade: 05
I'm 9 years old and my mom means a lot to me. She does hard work. She is pretty and nice. That's why mom deserves a diamond.

Teacher: Gino Self

Yousef AbuNemeh   Grade: 06
My mom deserves a diamond because she loves all my family, because she always takes care of my little brother and sister.

Desiree Alford   Grade: 06
She is pretty, loving, caring, nice, funny, , flawless, exciting, describing, shines like a sun, a star, sassy, different, sharing, and never to be forgotten.

Sandra Cortes   Grade: 06
My mom deserves a diamond because she is a hard worker. Her name is Silvia. She helps me with anything and understands me and the drama.

Brittney Lopez   Grade: 06
My mom deserves a diamond because she works very hard to give us food and clothes. She gets us anything we want. I love her.

Kenneth Malac   Grade: 06
She deserves a diamond because she is nice. I would do anything in the world to see her everyday with a smile on her face.

Philliz Tuvao   Grade: 06
My mom deserves it, she works hard to take are of our family. She always puts the family first. That's why she deserves it.

Samantha Van Ordt   Grade: 06
My mom deserves a diamond because she works very hard and drives to Fullerton to take me to dance class almost everyday.

Robinson Elementary
Trabuco Canyon

Teacher: Nancy Brown

Amy Ausman   Grade: 04
My mom deserves a diamond because she is as sweet as honey and as loving as a cuddly bunny. She's also as pretty as a peacock.

* Amethyst winners in bold.

Noah Bradford   Grade: 04
One reason why my mom deserves a diamond is because she is one of a kind. Her bright brown eyes are brighter than the sun.

Kendell Brereton   Grade: 04
Mom is special and very kind, she loves me even, if I don't mind, time together is so fun, I'm always sad, when it's done.

Megan Busch   Grade: 04
My mom has a smile as big as the world when she smiles at me. Her smile is the most delightful thing to see.

Andrew Calof   Grade: 04
My mom deserves a diamond because she is kind and sensitive. She is one of a kind because she is a sweet as sugar.

Olivia Farrell   Grade: 04
My mother has a smile that fills me with joy; her eyes sparkle like a star in the sky. My mother deserves a diamond.

Will Holf-Hillis   Grade: 04
Mom is awesome because she cares about me and loves me dearly. She is one of a kind and as bright as the morning sun.

Ryan Livesay   Grade: 04
Mom's as pretty as a peacock. Mom's as graceful as a bird. Mom's as kind as a bunny and that's why I love her so.

Madison Lorenz   Grade: 04
My mom deserves a diamond because she is as nice as a dear and when I'm sick she makes my bed all comfy and warm.

Claire McNeal   Grade: 04
My mom's eyes are as pretty as the ocean at night when the sunsets on the water. That's why she deserves a diamond.

Sophia Mirth   Grade: 04
My mom deserves a diamond because she cooks for me and does all my chores; like folding my laundry and cleaning my room.

Dietrich Olischefsk   Grade: 04
My mom deserves a diamond because when I get sick, she's always there for me. My mom is the best mom a kid could have.

Aryanna Pazeky   Grade: 04
My mom as pretty as the ocean. My mom is as loving as a baby dog that doesn't bite.

Ryan Poelstra   Grade: 04
My mom has protected me from death and being sick. She does a lot of helping around the house. She is almost a nurse.

Allyson Randall   Grade: 04
My mom deserves a diamond because she is always so happy. Her smile is as bright as the glowing sun on a bright sunny day.

Teacher: Michon Miller

Ashley Bullock   Grade: 04
My mom is as pretty as a diamond on a sunny day on the beach with the sun shining on her and I love it.

Reece Burt   Grade: 04
My mom is as delicate as a snowflake in the snow. Her eyes are as blue as the ocean at daytime.

Isabel Cookston   Grade: 04
My mom deserves a diamond because she sparkles brighter than any gem in the whole world and she is the diamond of my life.

Mark Eaton   Grade: 04
My mom deserves a diamond because she is like a surfboard in the ocean blue, keeping me from going under because of her loving encouragement.

Emily Esail   Grade: 04
My mom deserves a diamond because her heart is large, filled with love, and she gives it all to me.

Jack Farley   Grade: 04
The reason my mom deserves a diamond is because she has a whole lot of joy and a nice golden heart.

Scott Hickman   Grade: 04
My mom is as beautiful as a swan floating on a lake in the evening and is as fun as a monkey swinging in trees.

Christian Lockard   Grade: 04
My mom deserves a diamond because she is the best person ever. She helped people in need and does the right thing.

Preston Middleton   Grade: 04
My mom's eyes are beautiful and they glisten and sparkle like the twinkling stars above. That's why my mom deserves a diamond. I love you.

Josh Mitchell   Grade: 04
My mom protects me from fear loves me with all her heart. This is why my mom deserves diamond.

Ethan Patterson   Grade: 04
My mom is a fantastic super mom flying through the air; saving us before we're in danger. That is why she deserves a diamond.

Hailey Popma   Grade: 04
A diamond glistens like a star and my mother like the sun, except she glows a whole lot brighter. She brings a smile to everyone.

Sydney Ruppert   Grade: 04
My mom is like my nurse. She heals me when I'm hurt. When I break just like a mirror, she puts the pieces back together.

Elizabeth Scott   Grade: 04
My mom is happy as dolphins and as cheerful as monkey. My mom loves me and I love her. My mom deserves a diamond.

Madison Stein   Grade: 04
My mom is like a shining star. She is sweet as a rose. Her eyes glitter like crystals. She is always there for me.

Rossmoor Elementary
Los Alamitos

Teacher: Katie Smith

Eugene Blackmun   Grade: 05
Her eyes are as bright as the stars. She goes through a lot to help me stay alive. I love her.

Kylan Carpenhoft   Grade: 05
You shine like gold and sparkle like silver. You care for us even when you're made and love us. My mother, who cares for me.

Analeisa Davison   Grade: 05
My mom's eyes shine like gold, she's the diamond in my heart. She shines brightly like a hidden treasure. She is my priceless treasure.

Holden Edmondson   Grade: 05
I look in her eyes that sparkle like diamonds, I see her care for me, she is am important part of me.

Ashten Fitzgerald   Grade: 05
Her heart is pure gold, her eyes sparkle like a thousand jewels put together. She's caring, loving, and always there for me. My mom rocks.

Dalaney Garland   Grade: 05
Mom's eyes are like diamonds sparkling in the moonlight. She shimmers like glitter in the sunlight. Her love and peace at least deserves a diamond.

Sarah Jenson   Grade: 05
Her sparkling blue eyes. Her heart of pure gold. Her sympathetic smile...my mom, the light of my life. The gem of my life.

Jason Kight   Grade: 05
My mom's skin shines like a bright star, deep down in her heart. She cares about me. Her smile is like gold to me.

Emma Leach   Grade: 05
You are a star I keep in my heart. I will never let go even through the bad times. You are the one I love.

Johnny Luyben   Grade: 05
I love her, and she loves me. With her heart made out of gold and eyes made out of diamond she'll always love me.

Kylie Moy   Grade: 05
Mom is a loving ocean, she's open to anyone: Fish- her kids. Coral- hard as her love. My love for her is big as the ocean.

Aven Pradhan   Grade: 05
Her eyes gleam with love and care. When I'm down, her heart of gold picks me up. Her personality shines like the moon.

Ashley Willingham   Grade: 05
Her heart shimmering with love. Her eyes twinkling with joy. Her soul filled with help. Her hands are soft and warm; my mom…my hero.

Running Springs Elemen.
Anaheim

Teacher: Teresa Donovik

Erica Andrande   Grade: 04
My mom is as sweet as a sweet apple shiny as a diamond pretty as a flower and smart as a teacher.

Hannahlei Cabanilla   **Grade: 04**
Your eyes look like a diamond, that's why you deserve a diamond, I love you like a little boy loves chocolate, ruby, garnet, Hannahlei's heart.

Skyler Deutsch   Grade: 04
My mom is like a big wave; she comes and goes, but she's always on my side. She helps me at everything I need.

Tyler Jaworski   Grade: 04
My mom is sweet like an apple, nice as a flower, cool at night and fun at day, clear like water, her love will stay.

Maya Mandal   Grade: 04
I love you one and all, heart and soul, birth until death, day and night, dead or alive, I love you more than like itself.

Jasmine Maya   Grade: 04
My mom 's heart is sweet as a candy. Her eyes shine like a diamond. She works very hard for us three. She's a caring mother.

Brooke Woofter   **Grade: 04**
You are my love, you are the moon in the sky, you've got the biggest and warmest heart, you shine like a crystal.

Saddleback Valley Christian
San Juan Capistrano

Teacher: Elise Bradley

McKenna alvarez   Grade: 01
I think my mom deserves a diamond because she always does the laundry and she makes dinner every night. That is why I love her.

Ben Bergen   **Grade: 01**
I think my mom deserves a diamond because she cuddles with me when I'm scared and loves me so much.

Jake Brown   **Grade: 01**
I think my mom deserves a diamond because she works for us. My mom makes the best grilled cheese.

Anna Goetano   **Grade: 01**
I think my mom deserves diamond because she cleans the house. I think my mom deserves a diamond because she lets me eat cookies.

Joshua McDonal   **Grade: 01**
I think my mom deserves a diamond because she is a good cook. She teaches me about Jesus.

Sierra Rustman   Grade: 01
I think my mom deserves a diamond because she loves me and takes care of me. She loves me to pieces.

Brenden Short   Grade: 01
I think my mom deserves a diamond because she makes me smoothies. Last, she lets me stay up.

Chelsie Siciliani   Grade: 01
I think my mom deserves a diamond because she takes good care of me. I love when we make brownies together.

Cody Sowle   Grade: 01
I love my mom because she buys me toys. I love my mom because she makes nice food.

Teacher: Jane Marshall

Matthew Bunuel   Grade: 03
My mom deserves a diamond because she loves me. She buys me Lego sets. She makes good food. She is a great mom.

Jolie Calvert   Grade: 03
She gives me anything a kid could ever need or want. Her eyes twinkle when she looks at me because of her love for me.

Joshua Chang   **Grade: 03**
My mom deserves a diamond because she makes me laugh. I also like my mom because she takes me to the movie theaters.

Ryan Chudacoff   Grade: 03
My mom deserves a diamond because she stepped up and helped my dad when he fell off a ATV and broke his pelvis and ribs.

Jasmine Hughes   Grade: 03
I think my mom deserves a diamond because she is the best mom in the world. The diamond will shine as bright as your eyes.

Kristin Igawa   Grade: 03
I hope my mom gets a diamond. She words hard at the fire station. She takes me where I need to go. She love my family.

Bryce Laxson   **Grade: 03**
My mom deserves a diamond because she works very hard for my family. She is nice and full of compassion. She is the best ever.

Jarreau McLean   Grade: 03
She takes me out to dinner. She makes me dinner. She loves me. She makes me lunch. She helps me get up in the morning.

Beau Monson   Grade: 03
My mom deserves a diamond because she works hard and she cooks for us. She helps me with my home work and she folds clothes for me.

Ivan Mota   **Grade: 03**
My mom deserves a diamond because If it wasn't for her, I wouldn't be born. When I look in her eyes, I feel like water.

Teacher: Lara O' Brien

Andrew Ashby   Grade: 05
My mom is a gift from god. I love her. I know in my heart she is the best, and is a blessing to me.

Lue Audet —   **Grade: 05**
My mom is a hard worker, she works all day. She is very loving and kind to everyone.

* Amethyst winners in bold.

Shelby Bauer   Grade: 05
Mom is full of love. Her hugs are so soft as a dove. She feeds me, cares for me and loves me every day.

Casey Cunningham   Grade: 05
My mom is a hardworking person. She feeds 5 people and 2 dogs and takes them to sports every day and cleans after them too.

Julia Green   Grade: 05
Mom is my sunshine. She warms my hear. She sings cheerful songs. She opens my eyes to what I need to learn, I love mommy.

Jason Igawa   Grade: 05
She is hilarious, works hard, organizes. She only sleeps for two hours. She helps me build my Lego set. She is very pretty too.

Zoe Kaffen   Grade: 05
Since the day I was born, she loved me. A love so strong not even riches could break and that love still continues, even now.

Dalton Lohman   Grade: 05
My mom has the most beautiful eyes. They shine like the morning dawn. She is the most gorgeous, loving woman in the universe.

Hayden Malone   Grade: 05
My mother's smile is the best you'll ever see, It's like when the sun hits the sea. It glistens and seems to glide to appeal.

Michelle Moloci   Grade: 05
My mom deserves a diamond for she is so very sweet. She gleams and glows throughout the day. She cooks and cleans with a "yay".

Kaitlin O'Brien   Grade: 05
In her I see a smiling, joyful face with love and patience. I see her always looking up to God and doing everything he needs.

Nathon Roberts   Grade: 05
My mom is very blessed, she's also the very best. Her attitude shines afar, just like the Bethlehem star. She is an example of Jesus.

Lauran Thomas   Grade: 05
Her eyes sparkle like the twinkling stars in the night sky. She is caring and patient toward everyone. In her, I see love and Godliness.

Teacher: Elaine Sandberg

Talia Calvert   Grade: 01
My mom is beautiful. She is nice. She is lovely. She takes me to the park.

Tina Chmiel   Grade: 01
My Mom loves me. My Mom likes to go on walks with me.

Carol Mota   Grade: 01
My Mom is nice. My Mom is loving and the best cook.

William Wall   Grade: 01
She goes hiking. My mom helps me with my homework. She plays with me. I love her.

Teacher: Carol Temple

Nikita Adicker   Grade: 04
Because she works really hard for money when she gets money she spends it on us. She gets nothing for herself. I think she deserves something nice.

Marc Audet   Grade: 04
My mom deserves a diamond because she helps me with my homework and she listens to me.

Emma Joy Benis   Grade: 04
Mommy deserves a diamond because she has multiple sclerosis and even so she has an amazing attitude that encourages others to be glad.

Amber Clement   Grade: 04
My mother deserves a diamond because she is a hard worker and everyone in my family is proud of her. She deserves a special gift.

Kayle Hunn   Grade: 04
My mom deserves a diamond because she had gone through surgery and she has a disease called lupus. She had been to the hospital.

Rotimi Kirya   Grade: 04
My mom deserves it because if you are scared she lets you sleep with her. When you're sad, she has the right words to say.

Brandon Laxson   Grade: 04
My mom deserves a diamond because she is kind, loving, forgiving and respectful of others. That's why my mom deserves a diamond.

Ben Samuel   Grade: 04
My mom deserves a diamond, because she helps people who need help, like if they're confused or someone is being sad.

Zach Sherwood   Grade: 04
My mom always helps me with my homework and with my sister.

Amelia Tammel   Grade: 04
My mom deserves a diamond because she always makes sure my brother and I are safe and teaches us about God.

Ian Towles   Grade: 04
I think my mom should win a diamond because she helps me cares for me, and takes care of three kids.

Bryson Westcott   Grade: 04
My Mom deserves a diamond because she tries to make life better for me and everyone in the whole wide world. I love my Mom

Ryan Young   Grade: 04
My mom deserves a diamond because when I have had dreams she helps me fall asleep. She plays games, and she loves me.

Salem Lutheran School
Orange

Teacher: Jim Violette

John Abendroth   Grade: 04
If she isn't driving me to L.A., she's helping me in every way. My mom is so sweet. She is a angel watching over me.

Claire Arnold   Grade: 04
I love my mother's warm hands. They are the best to me. My mother deserves diamonds. She is so loving and will always be.

Raymond Corey   Grade: 04
My mom shines like the moon and the sun. She shines like a dime. She deserves a diamond because she's the best.

Elke Day   Grade: 04
My mom is kind and sweet, her voice is very neat. Her eyes shine like light. Her heart is very big and full of love that's bright.

Lexi Esser   Grade: 04
My mom is like a midnight star that glows like the moon, the beautiful moon and stars. She is the prettiest mom ever.

Andrew McCabe   Grade: 04
My mother's kiss is like a wish come true, her cheeks are like roses that bloom, and the best thing about her is everything.

Desiree Morales   Grade: 04
Her eyes shine in the moonlight like all the pearls in the world. Great thing about her is she loves me and she loves you.

Parker Swoish   Grade: 04
My Mom deserves a diamond because she works hard all year making candy, cleaning the house and taking such good care of my family.

Hanna Wheeler   Grade: 04
My mom, a young girl with diamonds, her eyes, crystals in her long brown hair. Yes, she is a beautiful diamond with beauty and light.

Teacher: Susie Willits

Michelle Alexander   Grade: 04
My mom's sparkling brown eyes glisten in the moonlight. Her shiny golden hair waves like the ocean. She brightens the room up just like angels.

Brenden Avventino   Grade: 04
Her eyes sparkle like the morning sun. The gold in her heart brings me love. She loves me with her pure heart.

Danielle Gutierrez   Grade: 04
Her eyes sparkle in the moon light   Her heart is full of love., kindness and joy. She has a beautiful face like the angel above.

Paige Huffman   Grade: 04
When I look at my mom, she makes me smile like a shining light.   My mom deserves a diamond because she always loves me.

Taylor Jimenez   Grade: 04
My mother's eyes sparkle in the light. Her love is like gold, that I cherish. Her love for me is everything I always wanted.

Derek Noel   Grade: 04
My mom is like a shiny jewel. Her peaceful eyes are like clear blue water. Her face looks like it was made by pretty angels.

Marina Praet   Grade: 04
Your eyes shine so bright like a emerald in the light. When you smile, her teeth are like diamonds smiling through the night .

Caroline Willits   Grade: 04
My mom's eyes shine with love and care when she looks at me. Her hugs fill me with love and joy. I never let go!

Chase Young   Grade: 04
My mom's eyes shimmer like the sea.   Her heart is full of gold. Her love is pure, this I see.

San Joaquin Elementary
Laguna Hills

Teacher: Susan Hammond

James Cooper   Grade: 01
My mom deserves a diamond because she is such a great cook and always gives me hugs.

Palmyra Espinosa   Grade: 01
My mom deserves a diamond because she lets me play with my brother.

Jaime Flores   Grade: 01
My mom deserves a diamond because she takes such good care of our family and she is a great cook who always gives me hugs.

Alyssa Guay   Grade: 01
My mom deserves a diamond because she is helpful and cheerful.   She works so we can eat .

Daniel Hoke   Grade: 01
My mom deserves a diamond because she is my mom and is such a great person.

Hunter Jones   Grade: 01
My mom deserves a diamond because she takes good care of my family and because she is so nice.

Darell Mamahit   Grade: 01
My mom deserves a diamond because she is such a great cook and always gives me hugs.

Jacky Reyes   Grade: 01
My mom deserves a diamond because she is so nice to all of us because she cooks for all of us.

Ian Chon   Grade: 02
My mom deserves a diamond because she always helps me clean my room

San Marino Elementary
Buena Park

Teacher: Hariet Booke

Alyssa Allen   Grade: 06
My mom deserves a diamond because she works hard to get me and my sister where we need to be. She's the best

Efrain Rubalcaba   Grade: 06
My mom deserves a diamond because she has raised me very well and she is very special to me. I'm glad to have a mother.

Teacher: Carol Workman

Nathan Drinkwine   Grade: 06
My mom's heart is as lovely as a rose, her smile is like the sun light anyone who meets her gets a smile.

Miles Galang   Grade: 06
My mom is like a shooting star beautiful and unique in many ways and this is why she deserves a diamond as bright as her.

Ryan Gurmel   Grade: 06
Because she sparkles like the morning sun. When she speaks to me she sounds like a angel. She is caring, loving and protects me.

Santiago Elementary
Lake Forest

Teacher: Deedre Kingdon

Carissa Andrus   Grade: 06
The sun is bright, the moon is grand, but if there was anything more enchanting than both, it's my mother. My extraordinary mother.

Danaya Bullapa   Grade: 06
This special mother, the heart of me. She shines like the evening star watching and protecting me, flowing like the river slowly and calmly.

Teresa Camarillo   Grade: 06
Shooting stars across the moon, my mom glows in the night. She's like a crystal clear pool of blue. My mom is the gem of me.

Felicity Clark   Grade: 06
The sun rises just to see her pure beauty. The moon gets sad when it sets. To me, she is brighter than any star.

Nathan Corado   Grade: 06
Angels gaze upon her lovely soul. Her eyes are like a sparkling star. She's like a horizon with a beautiful warm heart.   ….My Mom.

Matthew Cummins   Grade: 06
Her eyes glisten in the light when she looks at me.   It feels like she can see my heart inside me. Mom deserves a diamond.

Gabriela Flores   Grade: 06
The sun rises just to see her flawless face. Her eyes sparkle in the moon light. Entirely forged of gold is my mother's heart.

David Garcia   Grade: 06
The sun rises just to see her loveable and huge heart. Her personality is more valuable than all the diamonds being cracked from the ground.

Ian Jurak   **Grade: 06**
She found a humongous bus crawling across the bedroom rug and caught it. Just so I could see. That's how much my mom loves me.

Matthew Lindermuth   Grade: 06
Every time I look at her, twinkling eyes look back. Her spirit makes gold look bad. All the gems are nothing compared to my Mom.

Valeria Lopez   **Grade: 06**

My mom is a strong person, she is unbeatable, just as a diamond and my love for her is worth much more than a diamond.

Camila Martinez   Grade: 06
Shooting starts flying by seem to go slower then they see her eyes. More valuable than diamonds. She's the heart of my heart..... My Mom.

Maddie Moreen   Grade: 06
The queen of my heart, the gem of my life, the sunshine in my eyes. My mom is the role model of my life.

Manuela Rivera   Grade: 06
My mom is as beautiful as a diamond. When you look in her eyes, you see two glowing pearls. Always, she looks like a star.

Madeleine Rosier   **Grade: 06**
She has a personality more valuable than anything. She would help anyone in the world.

Delani Taft   **Grade: 06**
As she looks at me with her glistening eyes and extraordinary heart and tells me she loves me, I know my mom is perfect.

Monica Thompson   Grade: 06
Her eyes, like a clear blue pond with lily pads floating among the surface so beautiful, my mom, the diamond that lays inside my soul.

Sumaira Torres   Grade: 06
Flowers giggle as she walks past flawlessly. Her voice is as gentle as a bird's song. She is the reason the sun rises. ...My Mother.

Santiago Middle
Orange

Teacher: Patti Hayden

Razan Abuhasan   Grade: 07
My mom is like fire, fierce and strong, but gives me warmth and light. Mom is my sun, brightens my day, everyday.

Fernando Aguilor   Grade: 07
My mom is like a diamond shining and glistening so bright. Shine, glow, shine, glow, my mom is the bright light in my lift.

Tristyn Berman   Grade: 07
Hush, she crooned when I fussed. Hush, she said after I cut myself. She still whispers hush when I cry. That's my Mom extremely loving.

Tim Cao   **Grade: 07**
Lighting up the way. Shining down on me. My mother is the star that guides me through my life.

Joseph Chacon   **Grade: 07**
My mom is my soul. She's like a lion protecting her cubs. She shelters and protects me because of my mom, I am alive.

In-Fee Choi   Grade: 07
My mom deserves a diamond because my mom works hard to care and protect me like I am my mom's most valuable and rare treasure.

Caroline Corp   Grade: 07
Her sapphire eyes, her ruby hair, even her pearly smile, cannot compare to her diamond soul, that hovers in the heavens.

Christopher De Guzman   Grade: 07
My mother is a rare, shining lion within the jungle of life. Her heart is filled with courage, beauty and love.

Jenna Duncanson   Grade: 07
She's like a penguin, full of love and is hilarious. She's like a rainbow. She fills my world with color. She's my Mom I love.

Pascal Ellis   Grade: 07
Sounding like bells, as she goes along, all down the halls, singing a song, kind as can be, I love her and she loves me.

Colleen Flinn   Grade: 07
My mom is the essence of me. She brings the sunshine into my life on a cloudy day. When she's gone, I feel empty, incomplete.

Patricia Flores   Grade: 07
My mother is like my armor. She shields me from harm protecting me from danger, coming to my aid when I'm injured, protecting me forever.

Amber Garcia   **Grade: 07**
She is like a flowing river, lively and sparkling in the sun; as pretty as the fish that swim around. That person is my mother.

Azure Gomez- Robinson   **Grade: 07**
Kisses like butterfly wings, Hugs like loving bubbles. She is happiness and sunshine; fearless and careful, protecting me from silly things. She is my mother.

Emily Hull   **Grade: 07**
My mother's smile shines brighter than a thousand white suns. Her creative heart is sunshine in my world and her luminescent eyes are moonlight.

Kearsten Kain   **Grade: 07**
She's a river of sunshine flowing through the fountain of wisdom, ready for any battle, ready to comfort my loneliness. Spirit of the purest gold.

Nick Kuchta   Grade: 07
My mom feeds us every day and lets us go out and play. Her happiness is like the sun and shines upon everyone.

Robert Lamb   Grade: 07
Apples are red, acorns are brown, My Mom should be wearing a crown. She keeps earth clean; she even recycles to keep the earth green.

Sam Livingston   **Grade: 07**
My mom is the blazing fire who burns all obstacles in my way as I walk through the long winding path of life.

Melissa Lopez   Grade: 07
A mother, my mother is the rarest of all stones who's soul is so illuminate. It radiates rainbows of happiness that is debonair and thankfully mine.

MacLane Mattert   Grade: 07
Her eyes shine with the brightness of the sun. Her face twinkles like the stars. Her body glows with the precious gleam of the moon.

Mitchell McKhann   Grade: 07
My mom is exciting. She is like the pages of a book. Every page you turn there is something spectacular to learn about her personality.

Ryan Nagel   **Grade: 07**
My mom….She is a nuclear reactor of love. She provides a constant flow of protection and care. She supplies all that for me unconditionally.

Mason O' Grady   Grade: 07
Her heart is filled with gold, her eyes sparkle in the light. Every time she smiles, a rainbow appears. She fills my heart with happiness.

Loren Oh   **Grade: 07**
Thump, thump, my heart is beating. I gaze into my mother's eyes and find sparkling crystals of love. She is the key to my heart.

Noah Phillips   Grade: 07
She sparkles like a diamond, she always finds a way to lead you down the path to who you want to be.

Jack Riley   **Grade: 07**
Mom, as graceful as a ballerina. More beautiful than the sunset. Rarer than a diamond. Her love is like a fountain of gold.

Angel Salazar   Grade: 07
My mom is the food that gives me life, she is the spirit that encourages me. She is the soul guide that says right or wrong.

Malenie Salsman   Grade: 07
My mom beautiful brown eyes sink through me. Her kindness flows through my heart. There is no comparison. I love her more than the world.

Allie Salsman   **Grade: 07**
The love in her heart shines like the stars in the dark night to me. She is more valuable than a diamond. She is amazing.

Joseph Sanchez   **Grade: 07**
She is caring and loving. Her smile is contagious and her words are truthful. She is a friend and a mentor. She is the best.

Katherine Shepherd   Grade: 07
My mother is priceless. No piece of artwork or gem could match how much she's worth to me. Her heart is all of gold.

Rebecca Soto   Grade: 07
My mother's love and courage, big as the galaxy itself, brings warmth and joy, and lights my way through darkness. The angel in my heart.

Justin Suter   Grade: 07
My mom is an angel, hidden in disguise. My mom is an angel, especially in my eyes. My mom is the angel of everyone's lives.

Brenna Thomas   **Grade: 07**
So many words to label her. Mom, Mommy or Mother. Me? No, I call her something even better: precious, rare, one of a kind…..diamond.

McKenna Torell   Grade: 07
My mom….as graceful as a tiger, as calm as the sea, as loving as a panda, her heart as beautiful as a moonlight sky.

Anthony Vasquez   Grade: 07
My mother's love is like an open fire, it warms my soul. Not even all the water in the world can put it out.

Ramario Vasquez   Grade: 07
My mom deserves a diamond, maybe even more, for all those years and so, she is worth the world.

Tiffany Zand   Grade: 07
My mom is like the sun as she brightens my day and gives me energy. Without her, I cannot live, as if without the sun.

School Of Our Lady
Santa Ana

Teacher: Susan Dixon

Emanuel Alvarado   **Grade: 05**
My mother is a sweet and gentle soul who gives her love unselfishly. She's always in my heart, no matter where I am every day.

Giovanni Barron   **Grade: 05**
She is the sun of my day and the moon of my night. She helps me whenever I ask. My mother is everything to me.

Alfonso Bravo   Grade: 05
She shines like a diamond. She looks like one too. Whenever she shows her love, it sparkles all over you.

Camilo Cancino   **Grade: 05**
My mom is a beautiful star who shines throughout my day. She watches over me, nurtures me and helps me to be a good person.

Domenique Cardenas   Grade: 05
She's prettier than a rose. She's brighter than a star. I love my mom, she inspires me to be all that I can be.

Victor Casarin   Grade: 05
When my mom is near me, I feel like she's my guardian. When I give her love, she gives me her hugs.

David Garcia   Grade: 05
My mom deserves a diamond, because she is beautiful like a rose. She is like a star to me, my mom shines like a star.

Jonathan Gautier   **Grade: 05**
You are as beautiful as a rose and a radiant diamond that glows. You are more than the moon and the stars above. You're my angel

Isaias Herrera   Grade: 05
My mom deserves a diamond because she taught me the faith of God, and told me to do what is right to the best.

Annie Luna   **Grade: 05**
My mom i9s like a rose, kind and gentle. She's the one I ask for help. She's the one I love. She is my mom.

Andrew Mares   Grade: 05
My mom lights up my life like a glowing candle. Her smiling eyes sparkle like diamonds. There's nothing in the world she can't handle.

Guadalupe Orozco   Grade: 05
My mother is the light of my life, who brightens up my day. In everything she does and what she has to say.

Mariano Ramos   **Grade: 05**
Higher than the mountains, warmer than the sun, brighter than the stars is my beautiful mother's love.

Kelcie Salgado   Grade: 05
You're like an angel who keeps me safe. Your eyes are like diamonds that shine each day. Your love is never far away.

Anthony Servin   Grade: 05
My mother's love always cheers me up, even when I get a cut, she takes care of me. She's the one that loves me.

Yvette Zepeda   Grade: 05
My mom is a special gift from God. She is a reflection of her mother. She is my inspiration for whom I want to be.

Teacher: Cheryl Johns

Miguel Bravo   Grade: 04
My mom deserves a diamond because she gave birth to my brothers and me. She works hard to pay the bills, like rent and school.

Jose DeLaRiva   Grade: 04
My mother deserves a diamond because she gave birth to 14 children and raised them like a jewel. She gives us all her love.

* Amethyst winners in bold.

David Guzman   Grade: 04
My mother deserves a diamond because she's a very hard worker. She pays all the bills. She has good credit. She always cooks dinner.

Daniella Leyva   Grade: 04
My mother deserves a diamond because she is special, unique, cool, wonderful and great. I think she is the fairest and prettiest mom of all.

Daniel Maestas   Grade: 04
My mom deserves a diamond, because she is always polite to everyone she knows. She is always protecting me. She is the best mom ever.

Nataly Perez   Grade: 04
My mom deserves a diamond because she has taken care of my brother, sister and me and does all her chores. She really deserves one.

Mariah Roa   Grade: 04
My mom deserves the diamond because she is helpful. Her heart is full of love for everyone. She loves to bake.

Ethan Smiggs   Grade: 04
My mother deserves a diamond because she loves me and she is kind to others. Also, she cares about me, my family and everyone else.

Teacher: Linda Suarez

Angela DeLaRiva   Grade: 06
My mom deserves a diamond because she's a non=stop hard working mother of fourteen kids and never asks for anything in return.

Jose Mercado   Grade: 06
My mom deserves a diamond because she would go to great lengths to keep me safe. Words can't explain how loving she is.

Lisa Torres   Grade: 06
My mom deserves a diamond because she is a hard worker, not just that, but she is the sweetest friend and Mom to me.

Maria Vasquez   Grade: 06
Because she's the sun that lights my way, also, because she's the reason why I wake up with a smile on my face. That's why.

Thomas Villa   Grade: 06
My mom deserves a diamond because she is loving. She is kind, generous and always gives love for my family. I love my mom.

Kevin Delatorre   Grade: 07
My mom deserves a diamond because she has done so much for me, and I want to give her something special in return.

Diego Franco   Grade: 07
Why my mom deserves to win a diamond. My mom is an idol for me.   She did everything to get me in this good school.

Sofia Lomel   Grade: 07
There's an angel who loves, cares for me. The angel is beautiful.   She makes me happy. Who is this sparkling unique angel? My Mom.

David Ocampo   Grade: 07
My mom deserves a diamond because she is the best mother in the world. She takes care of me and feeds me without complaining.

Paloma Oropeza   Grade: 07
My mom has two big brown eyes. When I see them or when she hugs me, I feel her sweet love. I love her.

Joseph Zamora   Grade: 07
She is the sun that lights my way.   The rose in my garden.   The reason I get up in the morning.

Sequoia Elementary
Westminster

Teacher: Isabelle Karsh

Vanessa Alvigo   Grade: 06
My mom deserves to win because I've never seen anyone else care so much about their children. It's not because she's my mother, it's very true.

Connor Beaudoin   Grade: 06
Why my mom should get a diamond is because she works hard with little rest and comes home to do more chores.   That is why.

Brianna Hallman   Grade: 06
Some moms are just moms, but my mom's a friend.   She's great, pretty and smart and that's why she's a perfect ten.

Hayley Houdeshell   Grade: 06
A Diamond can put no price on my mom for what she means to me. She may not be perfect, but who can?

Joy Kiehl   Grade: 06
My mother is so great.   She works so very hard.   Even when she is away. I know she misses me so.

Crystal Lostaunau   Grade: 06
My mom deserves a diamond because she helps everyone in our family.   She cooks dinner every night and saves money so we could enjoy vacations.

Halie McKee   Grade: 06
My mom is the best and is as beautiful as a rose. She cleans house and keeps it nice. She deserves diamonds for being awesome.

Jasmin Moss   Grade: 06
Kind, giving, thankful for life, my Mom is just that and more.   Sweet like sugar.   These are the reasons why my Mom deserves a diamond.

Brigette Sanders   Grade: 06
My mom is always hard at work. She starts at dawn and ends at night and does everything she can to help my family.

Teacher: Angela Schiffner

Jewel Carrera   Grade: 06
Her flowing red hair and deep chocolate eyes, her smile drains away my sorrows. Her voice and compassion fill my heart. There is no greater love.

Frankie Edeza   Grade: 06
My Mom's beauty is like the first bloom in spring.   Her smile is brighter than any diamond.   My mom has a golden heart.   She cares.

Robert Guzman   Grade: 06
I think my mom is special because I don't have a Dad. To me, my Mom is like my mom and Dad.

Haley Kindstrand   Grade: 06
My mom is as beautiful as a rose blossoming on a warm summer day.   She is the best mom a kid could ask for.

Mikaela Malsy   Grade: 06
She outshines the stars.   She's brighter than any gem.   She is my dazzling Mom.

Tristin Ondrejik   Grade: 06
My mom is beautiful as the morning sun. She helps me with everything.   She takes care of me like there is no tomorrow.

Sharidyn Pointer   Grade: 06
My mom is as soft as the wind.   She is a gentle as a feather.   She is sweet as a rose. She is my inspiration.

Thi Trinh   Grade: 06
Gentle as pure wind, my mom is very kind. Her cheeks are red as beautiful blooming roses. Like the sun and sky, I love her.

Daniel White   Grade: 06
My mom deserves a diamond because you can tell her a problem and she can fix it.   If you need help with homework, she will help.

Kaley Winegarner — Grade: 06
Always telling me you'll always love me. Opening my eyes and making me see. Life is short and I can be whatever I want to be.

Shoreline Christian School
Fountain Valley

Teacher: Iris Herr

Diane Chu — Grade: 05
When I cry, my mom comforts me with her lovely ruby heart and makes me smile with her glowing love.

Haydyn Kimball — Grade: 05
My mother's heart is like a pink pearl. Her sacrifice and love are as red as a ruby. I love her and I appreciate her.

Aubrey Patterson — Grade: 05
I feel like my mom deserves a diamond because her heart is as red as a ruby and her eyes are like smoky topaz.

Valerie Sharp — Grade: 05
Her skin is as smooth as a pearl. Her eyes glisten like an emerald in the morning sun. Her soul is as pure as a diamond.

Cole Swain — Grade: 05
My mom deserves a diamond because she sparkles like a diamond, and she is soft as a pearl. She loves me and my brother.

Teacher: Marcella Smith

Mark Azer — Grade: 07
My mom's a pearl found in the sea. She's more precious than a diamond to me. Her eyes in the night, give me my light.

Wyatt Colvard — Grade: 07
My Mom is my all. My Mom is my everything. Her eyes sparkle like a diamond and she glows like a gem. I love you Mom

Lauren Lavender — Grade: 07
Roses are red, violets are blue, my Mom is sweet, her eyes diamond blue, she loves me so much and I love her too.

Christopher Nguyen — Grade: 07
She shines like the sun and sparkles like a jewel. She is an angel sent down from heaven. She turns dark times into unforgettable memories

Calvin Nguyen — Grade: 07
My mom has glistening eyes. When I look into them, I see shiny gems. More mesmerizing than a burning fire, she's pretty like a sapphire.

Nathan Otto — Grade: 07
My mom is my everything. She is my cup to my cake, my macaroni to my cheese, my gem to my stone. I love her

Kyle Sakamoto — Grade: 07
My Mom is the gem of my life. Her surface shines with brilliant colors. Her love gleams light on the path of my life.

Teacher: Judy Yonkers

Eunice Bala — Grade: 06
I have someone who loves me very much. She cleans and cooks too much. Oh, it's my mother, the sparkling diamond in my heart.

Joey Yonkers — Grade: 06
My mom is a ruby in the sun and sparkles like rays from the sun. She shines bright, like a beautiful day.

Silverado Elementary
Silverado

Teacher: Cass Clagg

Jaya Girard — Grade: 05
She is as beautiful as sparkling gold, as loving as an angel, and her smile is as bright as the sun.

Liliana Hernandez — Grade: 05
My mom is a shining light in the darkness. A golden treasure. She cares for me and teaches me. Best of all she loves me.

Velta Mansfield — Grade: 05
My mom's eyes are like diamonds. Her heart like gold. She is as sweet as sugar and very bold.

Faith Metzger — Grade: 05
My mom's eyes twinkling stars in the night sky. Her smile comforts me when I'm down. Her touch is like a soft cloud.

Ariana Moore — Grade: 05
A shining star, glimmering glow, a soft breeze, a gentle blow. A calming touch to my skin, my mom, how I love my beautiful gem.

Maricruz Salgado — Grade: 05
Eyes that twinkle like the stars, a smile warmed my the sun, as beautiful as the fallen snow - my Mom.

Nikolas Schilling — Grade: 05
My mom is a strong willed person who never lets me go. Even though, she works hard all day, she still finds time for me.

Griffin Stellhorn — Grade: 05
My mother, my mother sparkles like crystal salt in the beautiful blue sea. She makes life priceless and she makes my life worth living for.

Jaymi Wilson — Grade: 05
Her eyes, how they sparkle, her hair, so fine. Her smile, how radiant. Her heart, so caring. She is gentle and loving, My mom.

Emily Wood — Grade: 05
Her eyes like stars from heaven, her whisper, a gentle sound of comfort. Her heart, a place filled with compassion, love, and protection. My Mom.

Teacher: Celeste Ivory

Max Bennett — Grade: 04
Her hair is as soft as velvet. Her crystal heart twinkles with mine. My Mom.

Calvin Coffee — Grade: 04
My mom's heart is like a pearl shining in the ocean, her eyes shimmer like a rainbow fish swimming in a river. I love you.

Cristian Colgan — Grade: 04
My mom shines like a star in the sky. Her eyes shine like a diamond. She's as sweet as a flower. I love you mom.

Brooke Derache — Grade: 04
My mom is as strong as a tree, as pretty as a flower, as nice as a bird. She smells like vanilla - my mom.

Brianna Di Maggio — Grade: 04
Mom, your eyes shine better than the moon. Your face is softer than a blanket. You look like a angel. I love you sweet Mom.

Malorie Shald — Grade: 04
She is gentle as a dove, lovely as a sweet pea flower. Glowing in the sun, she is my beautiful diamond.

Tyler Shrieves — Grade: 04
Her hairs as blonde as a daisy. Her teeth are as white as the clouds. Her eyes sparkle like a star.

Christian Torres — Grade: 04
Her eyes glow in the dark like the spirit in heaven. She is so powerful she brings people back to life. She is a diamond.

Elyse Wilson — Grade: 04
Mom, she's lovely as an aura and graceful as a wave. She's as elegant as a ruby, beautiful as an emerald, more lovely than diamonds.

* Amethyst winners in bold.

Elizabeth Wood   Grade: 04
My mom shines like a star that guides me and she's is as beautiful as a butterfly.

Smith (Agnes L.) Elemen.
Huntington Beach

Teacher: Amanda Anderson

Morgan Aranda   Grade: 04
My mom deserves a diamond, because when she tucks me in and say "good night" her eyes gleam like the beams of twilight.

Charlee Blanthorn   Grade: 04
My mom is like a sunflower shining in the sun. She's always laughing every day and she's never boring always fun.

Adi Goren   Grade: 04
Her heart is full of love. Her eyes twinkle in the sun like diamonds. She is so sweet and amazing. My mom deserves that diamond.

Jared Kurth   Grade: 04
My mom has a heart of pure gold which is my prize. I can see love through her diamond eyes. She is my gem

Summer Lu   Grade: 04
She is as flawless as a bird flying through the sky. My mother is a beautiful reflection of the diamond she deserves the most.

Malia McDonald   Grade: 04
My mom is great! She has a heart as big as the earth. She is caring to anyone she meets. She deserves this diamond.

Michelle McLean   Grade: 04
Little twinkle star eye, a dab of mother earth, her hearts, the sunshine, I'm glad she is mine.

James Odin   Grade: 04
My mom deserves a diamond because she is as bright as a dragonfly. She is sweeter than sugar. She is nicer than the waves.

Everett Pirtle   Grade: 04
My mom's eyes are as beautiful as emerald colored diamonds and her hair is golden silk. So, I think my mom really deserves that diamond.

Jacob Saude   Grade: 04
Her eyes are glimmering stars. Her heart is made of love. She loves me and is always listening. My Mother is as beautiful as a dove.

Max Seirsen   Grade: 04
Her smile is like the sun. Her eyes are like diamonds glimmering in the sun. Her voice is the sound of music.

Tanner Southern   Grade: 04
My mother deserves a diamond. She teaches me street smarts and making food I can eat.

Amanda Wheeler   Grade: 04
My mother is warm as a fire, she is kind as a baby, she lifts me up with encouragement until I feel I can fly.

Teacher: Devon Broussard

Tim Angelosanto   Grade: 05
My mom deserves a diamond because she is a single mother with four kids. She is also so protective as Jackie Chan.

Meredith Burke   Grade: 05
My mommy deserves a diamond because she had to take care of seven kids and she should get a present for all the hard work.

Connor Dahl   Grade: 05
My mom smells as sweet as a rose. My mom is as sweet as a chocolate bar. My mom is as smart as a computer.

Smantha Eliades   Grade: 05
My mom deserves a diamond because she is as beautiful and magnificent as a swan. She is the most wonderful Mom in the world.

Karay Henderson   Grade: 05
My mom is my hero. She gave me my life. She is as magnificent as a diamond. I love my mom more than the world.

Kennedy Kuper   Grade: 05
Her eyes are pearls that sank to the bottom of the ocean, but still glistens in the nighttime sky.

Griffin Leener   Grade: 05
I think my mom deserves a diamond because she works so hard at the things she does. Please give the diamond to her.

Kylan Mann   Grade: 05
My mom deserves a diamond because she is a loving and caring person. I love her so much. She lets me play basketball and football.

Presley Merrick   Grade: 05
My beautiful mom deserves a diamond because she is nice, cool, funny and smart. I would never trade my mom for anything. I love her!

Madison Merrick   Grade: 05
My mom deserves a diamond because she is the best. She is worth more than a trillion dollars and I wouldn't replace her for anything.

JJ Mufatore   Grade: 05
My mommy deserves a diamond because she has tried her whole life to raise 5 kids. I think my mom deserves a diamond.

Jadeylan Ngo   Grade: 05
My mommy deserves a diamond because my mom is very hard working. She has two jobs and she is very beautiful, kind and helpful.

Sydney Preston   Grade: 05
My mom deserves a diamond because she is as pretty as a butterfly and as smart as a scientist. She loves me so very much.

Justin Quinn   Grade: 05
My mom deserves a diamond because she cares for my family. She helps us when we're hurt, and makes us happy when we're sad.

Cody Rohifing   Grade: 05
My mom deserves a diamond because she has to clean up after me and my friends after she just cleaned up.

Leon Sandeberg   Grade: 05
My mom deserves a magnificent, sparkling, glamorous diamond because she is so sparkling with an enormous bunch of love and passion for me. She's beautiful

Daniel Schwab   Grade: 05
My mom deserves a diamond because she is nicer than any trophy and more extravagant than a crystal. Mom, another word for love.

Evan Steiner   Grade: 05
I believe my mom deserves a diamond because she is graceful like a bird. She loves me to the moon and back. I love her.

Brooke Wilson   Grade: 05
My mom deserves a diamond because she is magnificent. She is as beautiful as a peacock. She gave life to me. She's a wonderful person.

Teacher: Lain Collins

Gaby Anderson   Grade: 01
My mom is beautiful and funny. My mom has blue eyes and brown hear. My mom is cool. I love her.

Faith Bourret   Grade: 01
My mom deserves a diamond. She is the best mom ever. She gives me good luck. She is the nicest mom.

Jacob Caballero   Grade: 01
My mom deserves a diamond because she is nice. She gets a diamond because she is funny. My mom makes me food.

Billy Canalett   Grade: 01
My mom deserves a diamond. My mom sneezes when dust is around. My mom is nice to me. My mom cooks me food.

Joey Chau   Grade: 01
My mom deserves a diamond because she does my chores. She is very smart. She give me surprises. My mom is the best and most beautiful

Ella Davison   Grade: 01
I think my mom deserves a diamond because she teaches me words. My mom cooks me dinner every night. She took us to Disneyland

Grace Houchen   Grade: 01
My mom deserves a diamond. She gives me everything she can because she loves me.

Tyler Kurth   Grade: 01
My mom deserves a diamond because she loves me. My mom helps me go to sleep, because my mom is the best. She takes me home

Brian Reed   Grade: 01
My mom deserves a diamond because she teaches me lessons and plays with me. She really is cool. She is a really good cook. She helps.

Josh Rosow   Grade: 01
My mom deserves the diamond because she does almost everything for us. She is very nice to people. She cooks food for us.

Teacher: Shannon Edwards

Arianne Bloore   Grade: 03
Her heart beating with love in every beat. Her eyes blue, peaceful and loving. Her hair long and full of courage. My mom is mine.

Sachiko Brown   Grade: 03
The sun will shine among the earth, shining with it's glee. but my mother deserves it most, because she cares so much for me.

Brigette Butler   Grade: 03
My mom deserves a diamond because she saves people's lives. She also get food so we're not poor. That's why mom deserves a diamond.

Abbey Coopman   Grade: 03
Her eyes are as a brownie. Her hair is blond as a golden star and that's why she deserves a diamond so far.

Ashley Drake   Grade: 03
My mom is the missing diamond to my life. Her heart is made of diamonds sparkling bright. She's the one. I'm glad she's here.

Sarah Grant   Grade: 03
She's sweet, she's loving, she cares for me. Through good and bad, she's there for me, through cancer, through sadness. Yes, she's my mom.

Kade Hicks   Grade: 03
Her soul is brighter than gold. Her eyes are dark grass green. Her hair is soft like a fluffy pillow. I love her so much.

Thomas Massey   Grade: 03
My mom's heart is strong like a pure crystal rod. She never lets me down. Her eyes sparkle like the crystal blue ocean.

Makayla Milligan   Grade: 03
My mom deserves a diamond because she is beautiful and her eyes sparkle like the moonlight.

Joseph Ruiz- Steiskal   Grade: 03
She helps me with my homework. She gave me life and accessories. She tries as hard as she can for me and my sister to have food.

Corrin Smith   Grade: 03
My mom's eyes are as bright as a diamond. She is as beautiful as a flower. My mom is the best.

Denisa Tudorache   Grade: 03
Her eyes sparkle as bright as a twinkling star. She comforts me with her pure heart of gold. She's the precious gem in my life.

Sophia Woolsey   Grade: 03
My mom always has a hug to share whenever I'm sad. She always helps me learn new things when I'm studying. I love my mom.

Teacher: Melissa Eisenrod

Kyle Atlas   Grade: 05
My Mom is the best mom. My mom gives me good food. My mom is as nice as a flower. I like my mom.

Michaela Fazio   Grade: 05
My mom is like a beautiful crystal shimmering on a crystal necklace out on the balcony. She is a beautiful gem. She is the best.

Olivia Fernandez   Grade: 05
My mom is like a box of chocolates , sweeter than you think. One thing I know is that inside her she loves me.

Nicholas Hillas   Grade: 05
Her voice sounds like the ocean. Her eyes twinkle like the full moon and her skin as soft as sand. She is amazing.

Chloe McKinish   Grade: 05
You deserve a diamond, because you're filled with love and when you take me places you're like a crystal ball. Mom, you're like a hundred bucks.

Rex Reevesq   Grade: 05
My mom is breathtaking both inside and out. She is why I live. Her eyes are beautiful like doves in the sky.

Elijah Wilcox   Grade: 05
My mom's smile is gold with sprinkles of silver. She is as kind as can be and she loves everybody she knows. She is a God.

Teacher: Juliette Greyshock

Mason Fulp   Grade: 05
She is a blossom in the sky. Her hard labor makes me cry. She makes me very proud. She is a heart in a cloud.

Claire Grimes   Grade: 05
Her eyes sparkle like the sea. I look into them and what do I see? Love, strength and beauty. She's my mom.

Maxwell Holley   Grade: 05
A friend for life and when I'm stressed out, she's always there to shake off the doubt. My mom, she is Queen beautiful and lean.

Anna Howard   Grade: 05
My mom is like a diamond. She sparkles in the sky. Whenever I need her she is always nearby.

Dora Lee   Grade: 05
My mom has a special place in my heart. We share so much love. My mom is a wonderful person that cannot be replaced.

Alexis Loya   Grade: 05
My mother shows lots of care. Her touch is like a mother bear. Protecting me through thick and thin, encouraging me to win, win, win.

Breanna Mormion   Grade: 05
Mom warms the heart. Mom's heart is so big, she spreads love around the world without even trying. She loves everyone , that includes me.

Emma Reed   Grade: 05
Mom shows me lots of love. She's as graceful as a dove. Her hair is dark, her eyes are green. She is really very keen.

* Amethyst winners in bold.

Riley Reid   Grade: 05
My mom deserves a diamond because she nurtures me and supports me on everything I do.

Lauren Swintek   Grade: 05
Face of a goddess, but has to use a mop. Doing all the household chores, but pretty as a dew drop.

Collin Wilhelm   Grade: 05
Her eyes are like the grass in the meadows. Her lips are like beautiful roses. She cooks like a five star restaurant. She's my mother.

Joyce Wu   Grade: 05
My mom has always cared for me. Her love is like the secret key to happiness, excitement and glee. She's as perfect as can be.

Zoe Zacharopoulos   Grade: 05
What a fine fragile vase, my dear mother is filled with violets and bows, yet is full of adventure and fiery frizz. She always knows.

Teacher: Debbie Harris

Tatem Bounting   Grade: 02
My mom has a big heart and the crystal will shine in her eye. My mom is really nice.

Max Grimes   Grade: 02
Your eyes sparkle upon the sea just like a flower. When I look in your eyes, I see strength, love, and beauty.

Grace Larey   Grade: 02
She smells like roses. She melts into my soul. Her eyes twinkle like the stars.

Sierra MacDonald   Grade: 02
My mom is as sweet as honey. She makes my heart full of love and she makes my eyes sparkle.

Alana Tait   Grade: 02
My mom has sparkly eyes. She is nice and cute. Her face has pride. I love my mom.

Megan Tams   Grade: 02
The sparkle in her eye looks like a star. She brightens my heart with love and joy.

Bastian Tobar   Grade: 02
Your eyes are bright like a soul, like a sun shining in the sky, like a piece of gold. You are a special woman..

Raquel Ycaza   Grade: 02
My mom has twinkling eyes. She has the kindest smile. She's nice. She's pretty that's why my mom deserves a diamond.

Teacher: Lori Hiltbrand

Evan Athey   Grade: 04
My mom deserves a diamond because she cares for me with all the love and care in her heart and I wish to thank her.

Katelyn Castillo   Grade: 04
My mom's as kind as a fawn and her smile reminds me of dawn. She is like the ice beneath my skates. She deserves a diamond.

Tanner Davis   Grade: 04
My mother is as calm as the Dali Lama, she is as caring as the whole Peace Corps put together. She is beautiful.

Crystal Dean   Grade: 04
My mom is as pretty as a tulip. My mom is like a bursting flower of sweetness, I love my mom.

Susanna Dugmore   Grade: 04
My mom is as beautiful as the sunset at the beach. She deserves a diamond like a winner deserves a trophy.

Jake Griner   Grade: 04
My mom is as sparkling as a diamond. She is as nice as a nurse. She is very smart. She especially deserves a diamond.

Cassandra Moan   Grade: 04
My mom is as awesome as a blossom. She works as hard as the president. She cooks, cleans and takes care of me.

Arianna Satler   Grade: 04
My mom deserves a diamond. She is beautiful and full of loving care. She looks like a tree peony. That's my brilliant Mom.

Joseph Schlesinger   Grade: 04
My mom is caring, loving and helpful she's too good to be true. She treats me like a king so please give her some bling.

Jordan Stark   Grade: 04
My mom hugs, makes be warm inside. She shares her love with me anytime. She makes my day with a big smile ..That's my mom.

Ben Tappeiner   Grade: 04
My mom is as thoughtful as a baby giving his sucker to another baby. She keeps me warm when there is a storm

Brayden Wood   Grade: 04
My mom is as beautiful as a rose, as sweet as a kiss, as smart as a scientist, because she's my mom.

Amory Yagar   Grade: 04
My mom is terrific. She is as jolly as Santa. Skittles are as sweet as my mom. She is as pretty as a rose.

Teacher: Norma Jean Janssen

Rachelle Addam   Grade: 05
Her hugs, warm. Her smile shines like the sun. Her eyes twinkle like a star through a glistening diamond. Most of all, she is precious.

Sidney Farrar   Grade: 05
My mom is a diamond in a sea of gray. Her radiant smile holds behind enchanting words. Her silhouette is a gallery of love and hope.

Micah Hawkes   Grade: 05
My mom's extraordinary smile glistens in the sunlight like a diamond being shined to perfection. Her eyes sparkle like the ocean water. She's beautiful.

Nicholas Karidakis   Grade: 05
My mom's eyes are like shining stars in the sky. All her teeth glisten like snow. She loves me with all her heart. Moms are great.

Alec Lowman   Grade: 05
This is why mom deserves a diamond. Her smile sparkles like a star. She dazzles everyone with her shiny attitude and I love her.

Briana Martin   Grade: 05
My mom shines and glows from her beauty. She is very attractive, caring and loving. She deserves a diamond for her kindness.

Drake McKinish   Grade: 05
My mom is beautiful and loveable too. She is smart and I know she does so much for everyone. That is why she deserves a diamond.

Michelle Meledy   Grade: 05
My mom is my heart and soul She brings me out of the shadows. She makes me happy and smile. My mom deserves a diamond.

Zac Moore   Grade: 05
My mom is brighter than me. She is sweet as cotton candy. She rises over the sun and sparkle. My Mom dazzles like a diamond.

Nathan O' keefe   Grade: 05
My mom is a gentle blooming rose. Her eyes sparkle with delight. She has a laugh that mends broken hearts. My mom deserves a diamond.

Guadalupe Ordaz   Grade: 05
My mom glows like an angel. She glistens in my soul. Her kisses are very sweet and her heart is filled with love and compassion.

Amber Schlindwein   Grade: 05
My mom deserves a diamond, she sparkles like a gem in the moonlight, she dazzles like a diamond. I love my mom.

Vivien Tran   Grade: 05
From the day I was born, in my mother's tender arms,   I realized she was an irreplaceable diamond that will guide through my life.

Teacher: Carol Krogstad

Lara Falcao   Grade: 01
My mom is fun to play with and she gives me good food. She is the best mom and I kiss her all the time.

Sydney Galls   Grade: 01
I think my mommy deserves a diamond because she helps me go to sleep at night and because she feeds me.   I really love her.

Lauren Petroff   Grade: 01
My mom deserves a diamond because she cooks healthy food for us. She cleans our rooms for us. She even cleaned my book shelf.

Bret Vardeman   Grade: 01
My mom is the best. She goes to school. She reads and plays with me. She gives me hugs and takes care of me.

Benjamin Walker   Grade: 01
She buys me school supplies. She walks me to school. Sometimes after school, she walks me to the park. I love my Mom.

Aubrey Williams   Grade: 01
My mom deserves a diamond because she is always there for me. When I am scared, she shows me where my brave heart is.

Teacher: Tammi Samaniego

Trinity Andrews   Grade: 01
My mom deserves a diamond because she works really hard. She takes me places. She makes me dinner.

Emily Bailey   Grade: 01
My mom deserves a diamond because she works really hard because she wants to make the house clean.

Elle Bluhm   Grade: 01
My mom deserves a diamond because my mom works really hard at work. She is nice to me and my brother.

Cali Dopp   Grade: 01
My mom deserves a diamond because she works hard at work. She loves me very much.

Emma Graf   Grade: 01
My mom deserves a diamond because she loves me and she plays with me.

Jonah Henderson   Grade: 01
My mom deserves a diamond because she tucks me in bed and she is nice.

Rachel Houchen   Grade: 01
My mom deserves a diamond because she works hard to let us live. My mom takes me to meetings.

Noah Near   Grade: 01
My mom deserves a diamond because she is nice and she is cute. My mom helps the baby too.

Jake Piekarski   Grade: 01
My mom deserves a diamond because she's nice. She takes me places. My mom buys me things. My mom gave me a computer.

David Ross   Grade: 01
My mom deserves a diamond because she loves me and I love her.

James Zouras   Grade: 01
My mom deserves a diamond because she is nice. My mom deserves a diamond because she takes good care of me.

Teacher: Dee Sheahan

Zachary Abraham   Grade: 05
Smells like cookies.   Works too hard. She deserves a diamond in thorough the night. Flows like a butterfly through the light. Works overtime - My Mom.

Jon Canter   Grade: 05
My mom is like a dove on the silky sea. Her white feathers always hugging me, giving kisses.   I love my mom with hugs and kisses.

Jade Chandler   Grade: 05
My mom is a sweet as a sugared strawberry. She watches over me like sparkling stars at night. I love my mom.

Madisson Christine   Grade: 05
My mother deserves a diamond for her loyalty. Her heart beams like the sunshine is rising. Her eyes shine and I feel so toasty warm.

Jacob Heard   Grade: 05
My mom deserves a diamond. She is always there for me and gets me through the hard things in life.   She definitely deserves a diamond.

Kyle Hughes   Grade: 05
She puts a smile on my face. She always makes me laugh all the time. No mom can ever replace her.

Nicholas Klukken   Grade: 05
My mom is caring and loving. My mom loves me now and forever, even though I get her mad sometimes.   I will always love her.

Samantha Morales   Grade: 05
My cousin is loving and considerate. She also loves me like the beautiful orange colored sunset along the horizon of the amazingly glorious ocean.

Tifany Nguyen   Grade: 05
My mom deserves a diamond, she's happy and full of glee, even though she lost someone she loved.   She still has a loving family.

Hannah Switzer   Grade: 05
Mom deserves a diamond , her beauty shines like the morning sun. Even when she is gone, her beautiful soul will shine in mine.

Ryan Wesleyson   Grade: 05
She is a caring and loving mom.   She is always there for me.   Her eyes sparkle as she keeps an eye on me.

Cassandra Winch   Grade: 05
My mom is like a bright shining star. When I see her, I knew the first thing she will say is "I love you"

Teacher: Elena Spencer

Rhett Blackwell   Grade: 03
My grandma's eyes shine like the moon. She fills my heart with gold and she is my hero. She is a diamond. Also, she gleams.

Ali Churchin   Grade: 03
My mom deserves a diamond because she is so beautiful, I know every soul of her is sparkling my Mom is my special gem.

Hunter Dickey   Grade: 03
Mother how your eyes glisten and your voice is like a diamond in the sunlight. You are very special to me like dark purple amethyst.

Michael Dunn   Grade: 03
My mom deserves a diamond because she is the coolest, and loving and most beautiful mom in the world. That's why my mom deserves a diamond.

* Amethyst winners in bold.

Jonathan Martinez   Grade: 03
My mom deserves a diamond because she is nice to me and she helps me with my homework. She buys me stuff at stores and malls.

Malia McMillan   Grade: 03
My mom deserves a diamond because she is as bright s the sun. Se deserves something special. She is as beautiful as a flower.

Melissa Nguyen   Grade: 03
She's beautiful like a butterfly and shines in the light. She is my mom, oh, can't you see. She is the love of my heart.

Owen Olivieri   Grade: 03
My mom deserves a diamond because her eyes are like them. They gleam and glisten in the sunlight.

Lauren Rollings   Grade: 03
My mom deserves a diamond because of the very hard work that she's done. She does the dishes, clothes, cooked food and cleaning the beds.

Stone Sharp   Grade: 03
Her eyes glisten like diamonds. They look like pools of blue. She loves me and I love her too. She deserves a bright shiny diamond.

Marissa Torres   Grade: 03
My mother deserves a diamond because she is the diamond in my soul . My mother's eyes sparkle like the stars in the sky.

Traver Vincent   Grade: 03
The reason my mom deserves a diamond ring is that she works hard and she's always there for me and my brother and sister.

Savana Wood   Grade: 03
My mom's eyes twinkle like stars. My mom's heart is as light as the sun, her words come out with love. She's a joy.

Teacher: Tom Watt

Evan Baker   Grade: 04
My mom always cheers me up and I love it when she smiles. It's like a mouth full of sunshine. She always helps me with my homework.

Robyn Brown   Grade: 04
My mom deserves a diamond because she is very loving. My mom always goes out of her way for other people.

Tessa Churchin   Grade: 04
You're as delicate as a flower. You're as patient as a leaf waiting to finally fall after the seasons pass. You are my wonderful mom.

Ariel Gallo   Grade: 04
My mom deserves a diamond because she is perfect as can be. She snuggles up with me like a giant bear. I love her.

Joe Gieser   Grade: 04
My mom deserves a diamond because she is kind and she fills my love garden with life. She is filled with happiness, joy, and love.

Georgia Mulligan   Grade: 04
My mommy is as sweet as sugar, but she still calls me "booger" She's as pretty as a butterfly. That's why she deserves a diamond.

Sonora High
La Habra

Teacher: Toriann Lee

Christian Acuna   Grade: 09
She's smooth to the touch, but stern as a rock during rough times. She's the twinkle in my eyes. She deserves so much more.

Amanda Blazey   Grade: 09
A mother's love is limitless. A sparkling gem of hope she has to give. More precious than any jewel. My shining star.

Nicole Chang   Grade: 09
To me, my mother is a Teacher, a helping hand, an inspiration but she deserves a diamond because she loves me for who I am.

Chanel Chi   Grade: 09
Such charm, essence of care and compassion. One glance brings a blink of hope and safety. A diamond, such motherly love.

Jessica Cole   Grade: 09
Mom knows what to say with her caring heart, she makes sure I'm okay. Even though at time we fight, our relationship is still tight.

Monica Cortez   Grade: 09
My mom deserves the diamond because when I was sad, she is always with me and she is my best friend.

Rene DeLaFuente   Grade: 09
She is the one who brought me into this world. She is the one who raised me well. Wouldn't you say, "Mom deserves a diamond."

Stephanie Diaz   Grade: 09
My mom deserves a diamond because she is a hard working woman. She cooks, cleans and helps me out. My Mom is special to me.

Clarissa Faner   Grade: 09
My mom deserves a diamond. She sparkles and shines like no other. She is brighter than any other gem. Her smile lights up the world.

Brianna Flores   Grade: 09
The warmth of her heart radiates to others. Her glowing personality brightens the night. I wouldn't wish for a different mother because she's just right.

Rebecca Huerta   Grade: 09
"Diamonds are a girls best friend" My mom is my best friend. Her voice, her heart, her love…a gem, I will treasure forever.

Brenna Hughes   Grade: 09
Her shining spirit lights my heart, nurtures me through my days. She loves me always - Mother.

Maria Jurado   Grade: 09
I love you more that I can express. You have my total respect, Mom. Every time I look at you, I can see a walking miracle.

David Kang   Grade: 09
My mother is like the golden sun and I am her one and only son. She loves and embraces me , for that you are precious.

George Khamo   Grade: 09
Your unconditional love will never sleep. Your forgiving nature will always be. Your support will never fail. You are genuine love. You are my mother

Rachel Kim   Grade: 09
Her eyes are topaz, her lips ruby red, her skin pearly white, her heart a sturdy diamond. My mother's unbreakable love pours out for me.

Julia Kleemann   Grade: 09
The golden sun, moon of night, a diamond shining radiantly bright as the stars in the heavens above, a marvelous symbol of motherly love.

Fatima Lopez   Grade: 09
Mom is wonderful and shines like the light of God. She always has love in her heart. She gave birth to her own gem - me.

Jair Lupian   Grade: 09
My mom deserves a diamond because she is very special, creative, she tells me what's right and wrong. I could count on her anytime.

Javier Martinez   Grade: 09
Her voice so sincere. She makes life seem so clear. She is wise with no fear. If it weren't for her, I wouldn't be here.

Cynthia Montes — Grade: 09
Without my mommy, life wouldn't be the same. She keeps me living and makes sure everything around me is okay.

Shannon Nolte — **Grade: 09**
A precious thing she is glowing with radiance and spark, shining on a cloudy day forever my best friend. My prized jewel, my mom.

Camellia Oepomo — Grade: 09
Mom upside-down spells "WOW' She wows me with everlasting love. She wows me with hugs and kisses. Thanks for being the "wow" in my life.

Ashley Orozco — Grade: 09
My mother a diamond in every way, beautiful, strong, has love that lasts forever. The sparkle in her eye speaks without words. "I Love you".

Nikole Padgett — **Grade: 09**
She makes me smile when I am sad, she fills my heart with joy, I love her now and always will.

Tim Park — Grade: 09
My mom never gives up on me. She gave me life and lights my way and never asks for anything back, after all she does.

Justine Penrose — Grade: 09
Though a diamond is not what she seeks for all the hard work she puts in during the weeks, her hard work deserves something special .

Nicklaus Piraino — Grade: 09
My mother's gaze is like a drop of gold. Whenever she smiles, it is like a pool of crystal immersing my body.

Manuel Pucheco — **Grade: 09**
My mother deserves a diamond because, in my eyes she is the best mother. The one great things about her is. She loves so much.

Robin Read — **Grade: 09**
Mom deserves a diamond for working extremely hard, always cleaning house, putting groceries in the car. She never stops to rest, so she deserves the best.

Angie Reyes — Grade: 09
My mom's eyes shine, just like a diamond. Everything she touches turns nice. You' can't compare her to anything. Smiles bright like a diamond.

Kyle Roberts — Grade: 09
I'd like to give my mom a gift. A gift as precious as her, a diamond that shines so brightly like stars of the night.

Brian Rodriguez — Grade: 09
She has supported me, protected me and has fought to keep me with her. I love her and harsh times always seems to bring us together.

Angie Ruplas — **Grade: 09**
Mom is smart and beautiful. She takes care of me when I'm sick. She's there for me when I'm lonely. She is my best friend.

Jasmine Sauser — **Grade: 09**
The one who loves, the one who cares, the one who's gentle, the one who will cherish me for all of time, my mother, forever.

Kevin Sheridan — Grade: 09
Her sparkling eyes, her glinting smile, her precious features. I wonder if there is a diamond as valuable as my mother.

Angela Valencia-Gowing — Grade: 09
A gentle heart, a strong outer layer, fun and laughter come next and at the center, a diamond encrusted soul.

Ruben Valle — Grade: 09
The sensation of your touch heals my pain. The blooming of your face, love I gain. You're my best friend, Mom.

Kayleen Velasquez — Grade: 09
She is witty, intelligent, down to earth, honest, my charming mom deserves a smidgen of something extraordinary every now and then, like a precious gem.

Luis Vera — **Grade: 09**
My mom deserves a diamond because of her pretty smile. She also deserves a diamond because of her good cooking and she's nice looking.

Maria Villalobos — Grade: 09
She is wonderful, humble and nice, patient, strong, optimistic and kind. She illuminates my darkest nights. Without her, I cannot image my lift.

Adan Zamora — Grade: 09
My mom deserves the diamond because she is a kind person, she also treats me well. This is why I think she deserves a diamond.

Ana Zaragoza — Grade: 09
My mom deserves a diamond because she is the best mom and she does every thing to see a smile on my face.

Danelle bu — **Grade: 11**
An infinite love, flaming like a sun; She raised six children with her heart and soul. The mother that I'm proud of deserve a diamond

Sowers (Isaac L.) Middle
Huntington Beach

Teacher: Michele Albaugh

Stacey Asis — Grade: 06
My mom deserves a diamond because she never asks for anything and does all the work in the house. She always loves my family.

Lauren Barker — Grade: 06
My mom deserves a diamond because she is spectacular and she does am enormous amount of things for me and my family. I love her.

Jordan Kirkenslager — Grade: 06
She gives me much and easily. She makes my life perfect. Through everything, she is always proud of me and I'm proud to be her son.

Madelyn Kish — **Grade: 06**
Describing my mom in 25 words is close to impossible, but when I think of her, I think of three. Hope, sacrifice, and most of all - LOVE.

Guinevere McLin — Grade: 06
My mom is a diamond. My mom means the world to me, and I know she will never let me fall. I love her much.

Victoria Sneddon — Grade: 06
My mom deserves a diamond for a million reasons. She works hard to earn a living for us and never complains. Mom, you're number one.

Teacher: Anna Dow

Jessica Cox — **Grade: 06**
A single sentence can make my day better when it is from my mom. I love you. That is why my mom deserves a diamond.

Chaz Gendry — Grade: 06
My mom deserves a diamond because she's the most beautiful and special mom in the world and she doesn't have a diamond. Deserves a diamond.

Elise Peregrin — **Grade: 06**
Mom - though times were tough, and the road was rough, we made it through just me and you, now more than ever. I love you.

Katie Peterson — **Grade: 06**
Neither I or you deserves the diamond as much as my mom. She helps people and asked nothing in return. Best part, she loves me.

* Amethyst winners in bold.

Teacher: Cindy Thompson

Garrett Babbitt   Grade: 06
My mom deserves a diamond because she saves lives and loves the people but the only thing she loves more is me with her crystal heart.

Adam Cavecche   Grade: 06

My mom deserves to win a diamond because no matter how exhausted she is, she will help me to solve any problem. She is selfless.

Taylor Conner   Grade: 06
My mom is my hero. She makes my life perfect. My mom takes me everywhere and makes sure I'm smiling at all times.

Shelby Defeo   Grade: 06
She weathers the storm for me. She is strong, but she is also loving. She has an amazingly warm smile and a heart of diamonds.

Olivia DeSalvo   Grade: 06
My mom deserves a diamond because she volunteers for every activity I do and stays at home to take care of my sister and me.

Elizabeth Irving   Grade: 06
Mom, she always smells like sunflowers. She always looks like daisies and treats me like gold. I would definitely choose her for a diamond.

Jessica Leas   Grade: 06
A smile as bright as the sun. Warm as an open fire. Smart as an encyclopedia. I love my mom.

Kalista McCauley   Grade: 06
My mom's the best, she carts my brother and I around following our crazy schedules without a single complaint. She loves us very much.

Keith McCord   Grade: 06
My outstanding mother of three smart, bright children and two playful pets, is loving, caring, supportive in everything I do. She deserves a diamond.

Garrett Mullins   Grade: 06
My mom deserves a diamond because she has taken great care of me for 11 wonderful years.

Chelsea Russell   Grade: 06
My mom deserves a diamond because she works hard. She takes care of my family and learned to speak and live in America.

Vanessa Stevens   Grade: 06
When I look at my mother, I see her sparkling eyes burning with such intensified love. Her unfailing love is our flame that never dies.

Spring View Middle
Huntington Beach

Teacher: Pamela Clark

Eddie Anwell   Grade: 06
Her love means more to me than the sun, moon or galaxy. She's as sweet as a chocolate cake covered with frosting.

Lauren Ayala   Grade: 06
My mom's smile is as bright as the sun. No words can describe how much she loves and cares for me. She is priceless.

Kolby Bingham   Grade: 06
You took me from the stars. You are the land ,the sea, the air. You are strong. You bring me life.

Jared Dube   Grade: 06
My mom is radiant like a rose in a beautiful garden. Her eyes sparkle like a star in midnight's sky. She loves me like summer.

Trevor Erickson   Grade: 06
Her love is like the depth of the ocean. She is as pretty as the light glimmering on the waves. I love her very much.

Antonino Flores   Grade: 06
Her arms are soft like a blanket. Her touch makes everything ugly seem beautiful. With her, I am always surrounded in love.

Ariana Galeana   Grade: 06
Her feet are like the stars that dance with the moon light for she is my ballerina that shines from above.

Steven Gingery   Grade: 06
My mom is like the sun warming me up any time I see her. Everything beautiful in the world I see. I think of mom.

Cameron Gorman   Grade: 06
I love you because you are so loving and nice. You are like a jewel, so beautiful, fragile, and magnificent. I love you Mom.

Michael Henien   Grade: 06
My mom's hugs are like the whole ocean filled with love. When she puts her arms around me, it's the best thing I could ever get.

Zach Lombardo   Grade: 06
My mother's eyes sparkle like the sun's reflection shining down on the ocean. She is always with me, directing me with gentle care.

Evelyn Martinez   Grade: 06
What makes my mom special is the warmth of her embrace, the taste of her cooking and her gentle advice and direction.

Kaitlyn McCollum   Grade: 06
No one could ever know how much I love you. You are like a blossom blooming in the spring. So beautiful and loving. I love you.

Brandon Merchant   Grade: 06
My mom's love and beautiful eyes are the thing that makes my world go around. She's with me for all the ups and downs.

Jayme Morrow   Grade: 06
My mom is the sweetest person I know. She comforts me when I'm scared and warms me when I'm cold. Without her, I'm nothing.

Kevin Nguyen   Grade: 06
My mom has so much wisdom that when I get tired, she will lull me to sleep and let my imagination soar while I'm dreaming.

Shadow Patterson   Grade: 06
My mother is an angel and a superhero too. Her love is my food, her kiss is my healing, and her hug is my home.

Bailey Ranck   Grade: 06
My mom is like a lady bug, delicate and beautiful. Her hair is like a lagoon. Her love and comfort are like a paradise of contentment.

Michael Sekaly   Grade: 06
My mom is the refrigerator and I am the magnet. Although we push against each other, our love will keep us together.

Kristen Sosa   Grade: 06
My mom is the moon and bright stars in my charcoal black skies. She's my cheerleader, right behind me, always cheering me on .

Joey Stillwagon   Grade: 06
I love my mom and she loves me. Her heart is pure gold and her eyes are like jewels. She's the perfect mom for me.

Brandon William   Grade: 06
'When she goes to church, I listen to her beautiful voice that sounds like an angel. Her words soothe my soul and encourages my path.

Teacher: Nancy Hoyt

Tyler Buhman   Grade: 07
She sparkles like a gem, shining, glistening, and dashing. A heart of gold and eyes like diamonds. A valuable, loving treasure.

Miguel DiSanzo-Graham   Grade: 07
Mom, humble sweet, playful, silly loving. The coolest and most helpful mom their could be always looking out for me. Such a loving mom. Awesome.

Zoe Fresques   **Grade: 07**
Underneath her tired eyes. Lies a heart purer than gold. She's loving, caring, and worriless. She is my diamond, gem, my precious.

Justin Goodman   Grade: 07
My mom, she is nice, kind. She is loving, caring and sweet. She is the best mother.

Kevin Honsberger   Grade: 07
My mother has a crystal heart, delicate and fragile, yet, worth gold. A diamond in a mountain just for me to love.

Craig Huff   **Grade: 07**
Mom, beautiful and magnanimous, entertaining, caring and wholesome. My mom, flawless like a diamond with many faucets.

Kevin Huff   Grade: 07
My mom is like a diamond. She has more value than gold. Twinkling like the starry night sky. You are my mold of love.

Brijin Jensen   Grade: 07
Her tired eyes hide her shining soul. She is my rock, my foundation. But slide underneath the granite, and there waiting is a diamond.

Brooke Lockhart   **Grade: 07**
She opens the door into my soul. Making me laugh all day long. Warms my heart with goodnight kisses. Home is where she belongs.

Dominic Matias   **Grade: 07**
The charming smile, the beautiful face. The understanding eyes, the sparkling brown diamonds on her face. The gleaming emerald, in my life, my dear mother.

Ryan Nguyen   Grade: 07
Her eyes sparkle like a gem. She is the loving, caring mom that I adore. She is the light that brightens my day.

Trini Nguyen   Grade: 07
Mom, shimmering and flawless. Sparkles, shines and glows. Scintillating but not in the store window. My precious gem.

Kendyl Riley   Grade: 07
She supports me through everything. She loves me and makes me succeed. My mom sparkles and shines. In my life, my mom is a diamond.

Allison Rymer   **Grade: 07**
Her eyes, hollows of compassion. Her voice, a tender melody. Her heart of gold mends your aches. My mom, the most dazzling diamond of all.

Richelle Son   Grade: 07
Her tired soul shows. Hiding, the shimmering gem. That lies underneath her. Just waiting to radiate.

Megan Stewart   Grade: 07
Mother that loves me so her heart shines like the moon. Love that radiates from her eyes. She is the best I have ever known.

Shanida Telfer   **Grade: 07**
Mother, who shines like gems. A beautiful woman with artistic talent. A flower who touches my heart. A cook, a giver, I love my mother.

Bobbie Wilkinson   **Grade: 07**
She shines like the facets of a rare diamond. The twinkle in her eyes light the room. She brightens my life with love.

Tanner Worrell   **Grade: 07**
She is nice and caring. She does many things like clean, shop and work. She is an awesome person. She's also an amazing mother!

Jaclyn Yamasaki   Grade: 07
She is a diamond in the rough. A love that can't be seen but felt. Her love is everlasting and her name is mom.

Teacher: Sharon Knobloch

Amanda Christidis   **Grade: 07**
Her voice soft as the sea, her golden eyes gaze at me, her beautiful brown hair sways in the breeze. My mom loves me.

Bailey Erickson   Grade: 07
Even at her worst, she shines. Even when she's down. She can make me smile. She needs something her own…for all her hard work.

Mackenzie Jeter   Grade: 07
A rose in a field of daisies, a moon in the starry sky, she is a life not worth living without. She is my Mom.

Cassie Macy   **Grade: 07**
Why my mom's great, you ask? She does one simple and wonderful task. Mom loves and cares for me every day. I love Mom in every way.

Coral Martinez   Grade: 07
My mom is really special to me because she is the one who gave me life I can't think what life is without her.

Jennifer Snyder   Grade: 07
Her eyes will glimmer like crystals with one around her neck. She will feel more special. She takes care of me and my sick grandfather.

Nina Tran   Grade: 07
Mom, you deserve a diamond because you put so much effort in keeping this family healthy and strong. I will and always love you Mom.

Maria Troncoso   Grade: 07
My mom, the woman who gave me life, who brought me into this beautiful world. The person I love with my heart and soul.

Teacher: John Morgan

Amanda Abernathy   **Grade: 06**
My mom's personality sparkles like the north star. She's always generous and positive, no matter how many problems there are. My mom, my role model.

Joseph Cardoos   **Grade: 06**
I love my mom's eyes. She is beautiful. When she has a smile on her face, my heart feels good. I owe her my life.

Lexi Castillo   Grade: 06
Hazel eyes, heart of golf, golden smile, always has a hug waiting for you at home. Loves her kids more than the sun loves shining.

Elijah Edwards   **Grade: 06**
When I hug my mom, I feel her heart, her affection, but more importantly her love.

Elizabeth Guillen   **Grade: 06**
Her eyes are beautiful as the seamy body melts with love like chocolate cupcakes. This person is my mother, the rose of my paradise.

Caleb Heartsill   Grade: 06
Your eyes are the stars of the galaxy. Your heart is bigger than the sun. Your love is a river, your smile warms my heart.

John Holmes   Grade: 06

Your love is sweeter than candy, your eyes glisten more than the sun. You're an angel from heaven. I'll always be your son.

David Peters   **Grade: 06**
I love the way your brown eyes twinkle in the moonlight. Your heart is as big as the moon. I love you, You're perfect.

* Amethyst winners in bold.

Sabrina Rogers-Hofbauer Grade: 06
Her heart as colorful as a rose.   Her eyes glows the stars and moon.   Your heart as open as the big blue ocean.

Clint Shephard Grade: 06
Her eyes twinkle sun and birds start to chirp. Everything starts to bloom all around her.   A diamond will be perfect for mom.

Christelle Walker Grade: 06
Her eyes twinkle like the store in the night sky. She smiles and hugs me with her loving arms.   The best mom ever is mine.

Teacher: Jeannine Rowe

Sam Ahern Grade: 07
My mother deserves a diamond because she is kind, strong, witty and nice. She has the shine of a flawless diamond, but doesn't get arrogant.

Luamy Aquilar Grade: 07
I love my mom very much. She knows when something is wrong with me.   I owe her my life. I love you mama bear.

Ariel Hamel Grade: 07
In the heart, my Mom's selfless beautiful. She's a giver. She should receive this diamond in return, showing she's pure and flawless like this diamond.

Noah Jackson Grade: 07
My mom deserves a diamond because she is as fine as one.   She is amazing and will make you smile even when you're sad.

Jessica Johancsik Grade: 07
My mom deserves a diamond because she bakes my favorite pumpkin bread. My mom deserves a diamond because she wraps everything in thread.

Andrew Lam Grade: 07
My mom is the best she deserves a diamond cause she is everything you would look for. She also loves to joke and play around.

Cristal Mariscal Grade: 07
My mom deserves a diamond because she is the nicest mom I could ever ask for and she is very beautiful, loving, caring and supporting.

Katia Mejia Grade: 07
My mom deserves a diamond because she is nice, caring . Responsible. She is helpful and she always has time to hear my problems.

Mailan Pham-Ada Grade: 07
She's quiet, smart and beautiful. She's too stubborn to listen, but she's my mom and I love her.

Kayla Sweeney Grade: 07
She's the sun, stars and moon that light my road of life. She's my hopes and dreams. She's my guardian angel made just for me.

Rebecca Tran Grade: 07
My mom deserves a diamond because she is like a sparkling light in the sky to guide to where I am right now.

Nicholas Wannall Grade: 07
I think my mom deserves a diamond because every time I'm with her I feel safe. When I'm being bullied or left out, she's there.

Michael Whitley Grade: 07
My mom deserves a diamond because she is really nice and wouldn't hurt anything. She would give for them and help people in need.

Springbrook Elementary
Irvine

Teacher: Kathy Covington
Meher Bhullar Grade: 01
She love me and always hugs me and tells me that she loves me.

Kent Dana Grade: 01
My mom cooks breakfast for the whole family. I love her and she loves me.

Ryan Harrison Grade: 01
She goes to work and she does some work on her computer and she gives me kisses and hugs.

Jake Jameson Grade: 01
When I was in mom's tummy, she worked and when I came out, she took care of me.

Jackie Ni Grade: 01
My mommy cooks me food and helps me read books.

Sierra Shaver Grade: 01
I like the diamonds that she makes and I like that she reads me a book and I like that she makes my breakfast too.

Kathryn Strombeck Grade: 01
My mom should get a diamond because it looks pretty, just like her!

Victoria Vaswani Grade: 01
She loves me by hugging me and she plays with me a lot.

Maria Webster Grade: 01
My mom does water aerobics. She shows me that she loves me by being kind and loving me and making my lunch.

Jennifer Zhang Grade: 01
My mommy helps me when I get sick and she plays with me.

St. Angela Merici School
Brea

Teacher: Diana Brandt

Scarlett Aiello Grade: 06
My mom deserves a diamond, she's loving as can be. When I need her the most she's always there for me.

Mackenna Alvarez Grade: 06
My mother is a mother to everyone. She is hospitable to strangers. She is always there to talk. My mother has a beautiful open heart.

Olivia Amezoua Grade: 06
My mom shines like a diamond, sparkles like a sun, glitters in the light, and shimmers with love. She's generous and caring above all.

Angelica Consunji Grade: 06
My mom, cooling like water, but strong like fire.   Soothing like the wind, but full of life, like the earth. My mom, the harmonious elements.

Kaylie Dascanio Grade: 06
My mother's love is like counting stars, it's never ending. I would give her the world if I could, but she deserves so much more.

Madeline Hurst Grade: 06
Her voice is the waves soothing and serene she's always there for me when I fall upon my knees. We never fail as a team.

Madilyn Kelly Grade: 06
The love of my mom is as big as the sun, my mom is as generous as God, I would never wish for another mom.

Matthew McCloskey Grade: 06
She is kind, she is nice like a calm shine. She is beautiful like a log of butterflies. She comforts anyone who is hurt.

Tara Ribisi Grade: 06
Like a diamond, my mom sparkles uniquely. Her love is crystal clear. Her example is a strong, sharp point. She deserves millions of diamonds.

Adam Rooney Grade: 06
My mother deserves a diamond. A jewel to grace her finger. To make her working hands quicker a second and to make her smile linger.

Marissa Vaccher   Grade: 06
My mom is so gentle, she is so special. She is like the sun and we're the planets, she deserves the diamond without any hesitation.

St. Bonaventure
Huntington Beach

Teacher: Erin Dobrowolski

Jake Armstrong   Grade: 03
She shines like light, what makes me faint, my heart will really break, she is the best. What makes me cry, who can't delay.

Tram Bui-Vu   Grade: 03
She's pleasant and humored, she owns a heart that shines of pure love. No mom as loving as she, would come around very often.

Sophia Carr   Grade: 03
Her eyes glitter just like diamonds. Her cheeks are red as a rose. The sun always reflects on her face like gold.

Lauren Castaneda   Grade: 03
When I look at my mom's eyes, I see a gold color. When I hug my mom, it's like I'm hugging Jesus.

Nicole Cochran   Grade: 03
Caring and loving are her best things. She stands out of everyone. If she has a sparkle for every excellent deed. She has the most.

Alyssa Dizon   Grade: 03
Her cheeks are red like an apple. Sparkles are in her eyes. Her smile is filled with butterflies. Her heart is full of fireflies.

Katie Frei   Grade: 03
My mom's heart is pure gold. It reaches out and grabs my soul. Her eyes twinkle crystal blue, I will always love her too.

Alexandra Grosse   Grade: 03
A drop of chocolate, a pinch of vanilla. My mom makes everyone's day. She has sparkles in her eyes. She talks in a magnificence way.

Katherine Hernandez   Grade: 03
Her voice is like a beautiful song. She has sparkles and stars in her eyes. Never has she gave up on me, but did the opposite.

Alessandro Juliano   Grade: 03
My mom's heart twinkles like a shining star. Her smile is worth a thousand dollars. She has lots of love, she'll give any one a hug.

Mike Kincade   Grade: 03
In my mom's diamond heart and believing in her crystal soul and a pinch of love and a cup of rareness and I love her.

Sean Meyerhofer   Grade: 03
My mom's eyes look like gold, she lightens up and warms my soul. She also helps me with my stuff, she's never mean or rough.

Kaylin Miller   Grade: 03
My mom's eyes twinkle like a diamond. She is as nice as the sparkle in the center of the diamond. She gives a glowing smile.

Vyvyan Nguyen   Grade: 03
A ruby heart shines in my mother's body like a crystal in the diamond sky. The colors of the wind will lead my mother home.

Maily Nguyen   Grade: 03
My mom is the sparkle of my eye. She is always mine. Everyday, every night, she guides my way. She always brightens my special day.

Natalie Smale   Grade: 03
Mom is always protecting me. Heartwarming love gazing into her eyes. Nothing can go wrong helping me when I'm down. Mom lights my world.

Romie Smith   Grade: 03
Her heart is made out of gold, it is molded in prettiest of ways. Her eyes gleam like stars. Her smile twinkles like the sun.

Jack Uribe   Grade: 03
My mom is like a ray of golden sunlight who tastes like a Hershey's candy bar. My mom - my whole wide world.

St. Catherine School
Laguna Beach

Teacher: Maureen Dube

Jack Fuhrman   Grade: 02
My mom is like a daisy. She is pretty, sweet and delicate. She helps me whenever she can. I think she deserves a diamond.

Joseph Oursler   Grade: 02
My mother deserves a diamond because she helps people. She lets everyone have their good times. She always does laundry and cooks for us.

Grant Ristoff   Grade: 02
Her soul warms my heart. Her eyes twinkle at night. If I'm hot, she cools me with her heart. She always makes me happy.

Sydnie Soucek   Grade: 02
My mom reminds me of Jesus. She is my guardian angel. She is the best mom in the universe. She is my diamond.

Sam Stapinski   Grade: 02
My mother is fabulous. She's like an angel to me. She floats in the sky like a star.

Christopher Thomas   Grade: 02
My mother is like an angel sent from heaven. She's kind hearted and knows that to do.

St. Jeanne De Lestonnac
Tustin

Teacher: Laurie Martin

Claire Couyoumjian   Grade: 04
My mom has a sparkle in her eye like a butterfly. My mom is wise and always surprised. That's why she deserves a beautiful prize.

Rachel D' Eramo   Grade: 04
You are beautiful from head to toe, In the dark, I see you glow. You, Mom deserves a big red bow, tied around a diamond.

Tien Dang   Grade: 04
When it is night, my mom shines like a glistening diamond. She is not old. She's shining gold.

Sarah Politiski   Grade: 04
Mom, you're the diamond in the sky. You shine so brightly, you're the boldest of all. So you deserve the greatest of all.... A Diamond.

Chandler Pollett   Grade: 04
My mom is a flower, her root is her prettiness. Her stem is politeness, her leaves are sweetness. Her blossoms are how awesome she is.

Taline Ratanjee   Grade: 04
In my eyes she is beautiful. She always shows me love. I'm the most important person in her life. My mother is my light.

Sofia Sanchez   Grade: 04
My mom is a ruby from her head to her toes. She is as beautiful as a diamond. She glows in the sky like fireflies

Carine Sayyur   Grade: 04
My mom has two eyes that glow, in the light below, morning and night, she is so bright, like a diamond.

* Amethyst winners in bold.

Catherine Vu Grade: 04
Diamond in the night, diamond in the light. When I'm outside, stars are like diamonds sparkling in the sky.   Mom's eyes sparkle like diamond's rays.

Hailey Worden Grade: 04
Her eyes twinkle like stars in the night. Her crystal heart is as bright as the big white sun. She is my mother, my "gem".

Kylie Yeung Grade: 04
This pretty person I know, is like a diamond that glows. She sparkles in the light and glows in the night. She's my Mom.

Ariana Zambrano Grade: 04
Alexandrite and aquamarine make a perfect combination, because you love me. You're like the sea, beautiful and calm just like me.

Cristina Zapata Grade: 04
My mom is a bright light that glows in the night.   Mom should earn a diamond that is bright.

Teacher: Renee Sandoval

Ivy Delgadillo Grade: 04
My mom's smile is like a shooting star, ready to blast out with happiness.   I want my mom to always have a smile

Alden Hodgdon Grade: 04
My mom is as graceful as a swan.   She is sweeter than honey. Oh, she is so funny. My mom is more than amazing grace.

Ava Marinelli Grade: 04
Mom is a gleaming star. The glow in her smile, the sparkle in her eyes that's beauty, the star, She's on and is watching me.

John Nagel Grade: 04
Mom, you shine like the sun. You are my hero. I couldn't ask for a better mom. You are the best. Love you.

Catherine Nguyen **Grade: 04**
My mom's love is as far as the ocean, her eyes sparkle like the night stars. Her hug warms my heart forever. She's the best ever.

Juliette Nguyen Grade: 04
She's as bright as the sun, cause she is number one.   She has love stronger than all of nature. She's such a pretty picture.

Cristian Ochoa Grade: 04
My mom's cheeks are red as rubies. Her hair golden brown. Her eyes sparkle in the moonlight. My Mom's love: endless as the horizon.

Matt Peabody Grade: 04
My mom's eyes shine like a diamond glowing in the moonlight and her face is amazingly beautiful like the horizon. I couldn't live without her.

KayLee Porter Grade: 04
She's as sweet as an apple. She's as pretty as a flower. She's as happy as a clown. She deserves to have a crown.

Sydney Snyder Grade: 04
My mom's like a butterfly flying in the air. She loves me anywhere I go and anywhere I am. I love my Mom!

Kelly Trujillo **Grade: 04**
My mom deserves a diamond because her eyes sparkles like the moonlight stars, her smile warms my heart, her kisses make me smile inside.

St. Joseph Elementary Sch.
Santa Ana

Teacher: Mackie Cardoos

Cesar Carrera Grade: 07
My mom deserves a diamond because she does everything. She cooks, cleans, and helps my brother and I with homework. We don't thank her enough.

Xavier Gutierrez Grade: 07
I think my mom deserves a diamond because she works so hard for me and takes care of me. In my eyes she is a diamond.

Rogelio Jurado Grade: 07
my mom is a very hardworking and independent woman. She is very dedicated to finishing school and giving us a better life.

Ratima Orozoo Grade: 07
My mom deserves a diamond. She does everything I can ask for; helps on homework, advice, helps on a project. I can't thank her enough.

Claudia Ruesga **Grade: 07**
My mom is extraordinary in many ways. She's the brilliance in my life. She always loves me. She will always be the one I love.

Sierra Siebert **Grade: 07**
My mom is a giving person. She bought new chairs for the first   Grade   that needed them desperately. She also helps box food for the hungry.

St. Paul's Lutheran School
Orange

Teacher: Janette Mattoon

Hannah Alston Grade: 06
My mom is my light, she guides me all night. She brightens my day.   I wish I could stay with her forever!

Benjamin Blowers **Grade: 06**
Your eyes twinkle like the moonlit sky. When I hear your beautiful voice, I sit back and sigh. My mom, a cherished treasure to me.

Emily Dudeck Grade: 06
She is my heart of gold.   Someone who will never stop loving me.   She is filled with compassion. My caring Mom.

Ian Kent **Grade: 06**
Mommy: She gives hope and peach to all. She gives the homeless happiness, gives beauty a new meaning and wins the hearts of millions.

Hye- Lin Kim Grade: 06
My mom is smart. She has a big heart. She is full of love and as elegant as a dove.

Matthew Le Crone Grade: 06
Her love is golden. Her heart is diamond. She never leaves my side. She even comes and finds me when I hide. I love Mom.

Shelby Mattoon Grade: 06
My mom is beautiful in every way.   When she is near, the light shines through the day. My mom is valuable like gold!

Molly Pascale **Grade: 06**
My mom deserves a diamond. She has done so much for me.   My mom already sparkles, but she deserves to shine bright like a star.

Emily Pratt Grade: 06
She deserves a diamond because she is my friend.   She is the jewel of my heart. Her eyes sparkle like the stars, she's my Mom.

Patrick Reardon Grade: 06
Beautiful eyes, amazing hair, lips like roses, so humble and so fair, her teeth shine like a billion diamonds.   I lover he so much.

Haley Rupe-Salazar Grade: 06
Who is beautiful, so brilliant and smart? Who shines in my heart like a crown of gold? Who loves me so much? My loving Mom!

Lindsey Spindle Grade: 06
Her eyes twinkle like the moonlight shinning down on a rushing river. Dancing flowers on a meadow make her smile so mellow. That's my Mom.

St. Pius V School
Buena Park

Teacher: Amy Gomory

Marissa Cabral Grade: 04
My mom deserves a diamond because she's there for me through the tough times. My mom has a heart full of love!

Alexandra McLellan Grade: 04
Mom deserves a diamond because of all her work. She has done all for us. But, we have done non for her. I love you Mother.

Matthew Parnham Grade: 04
Mom deserves a diamond because she taught me when I was 3 years old. She comes to all my school events. She is just awesome.

Jorge Santiago Grade: 04
My mom deserves a diamond because she is a great mother to me. She cares for me and loves me and I love her.

Sierra Schimmel Grade: 04
Mom deserves a diamond for everything she's done. She brings smiles to everyone's face and is so much fun. That's what makes her my number one!

Kimberly Vergara Grade: 04
She twinkles like a star, her eyes are like the sun. Out of all the moms in the universe, she is the very best one.

Brian Yoo Grade: 04
My mom deserves a diamond because my mom is special to me. She gave me something that's more precious than a diamond and it's love.

Teacher: Jayne Steen

Elizabeth Craig Grade: 05
She has a rainbow opal in her eyes. Her smile like a topaz sun. Playing with her under a sapphire painted sky.

Gregory Kim Grade: 05
My mom's eyes sparkles more than a gem. My mom's heart is harder than a diamond. My mom's face is prettier than a emerald.

Kiana Navarro Grade: 05
Your brown sparkling eyes, your loud, wonderful laugh, your wonderful smile and most of all you're perfect for me.

Loisa Paz Grade: 05
Your lovely smile, sweet heart, and your patience any daughter would be lucky to have you, so I guess I'm the luckiest girl in the world.

Veronica Perry Grade: 05
At sunrise, at sunset, I will never forget the gentle hugs, the loving kisses and beautiful smiles that fill me with bliss.

Stanford Elementary
Garden Grove

Teacher: Heather Bergman

Lilian Hernandez Grade: 05
My mother is gentle and opened hearted. Her dark eyes twinkle upon a diamond. My graceful mother and the gleaming diamond are both brightening figures.

Alyssa Aragon Grade: 05
Mother, mother you are like no other. I'm so lucky God gave me you. My brothers and sisters are too.

Maria Nguyen Grade: 05
True love shining in her eyes. Taking care and loving her children with all her heart. Also, a very loving person with a kind heart.

Kyduyen Nguyen Grade: 05
I think my mom should deserve a diamond because she is the queen of my life and her sparkly diamond eyes protect me every day.

Becky Nguyen Grade: 05
Gems are beautiful as my mom. She helps me from the morning all the way till night. It would be hard without her.

Star View Elementary
Midway City

Teacher: Kristy Magee

Shea Amame Grade: 03
I think my mom deserves a diamond because she is the nicest and most loving mom in the whole world.'

Jarvis Bui Grade: 03
My mom is like gold to me so precious, so nice. It's like my mom can fly like a glitter fly. She is so nice.

Luan Nguyen Grade: 03
My mom's eyes are like a blue diamond of the sky in the middle of July. She is a diamond star.

Avery Pham Grade: 03
My mom is very special to me. She is always caring about people. I love her very much. She is my heart.

Vivian Pham Grade: 03
My mom is beautiful as the taste of sugar plums. The white snow twinkles with love going around the world.

Mykenna Vandermarlierre Grade: 03
My mom's pretty eyes glittering as a diamond in the sunlight as the day passes by. She is the diamond of my heart.

Teacher: Alice Mariano

Karl Barrett Grade: 05
My mom deserves a diamond because she is encouraging and has an enormous heart. She sacrifices everything for our family.

Zach Coo Grade: 05
My mom deserves a diamond because she is a supportive and a nice person to the family and the homeless.

Gina Le Grade: 05
Diamonds sparkle reflecting light. My mother's soul is just as bright. Her best virtue would probably be how much she loves my brother and me

Annie Ngo Grade: 05
My mom deserves a diamond because she is sweet and loving. She is the warmth in my heart.

Catherine Nguyen Grade: 05
My mom deserves a diamond because she always has time for love and family. She has a kind and brave attitude. She deserves that diamond.

Katie Sauer Grade: 05
My mom is the very best, but her heart is even better, it sparkles and shines and I want her to know I love her.

Thkao Tran Grade: 05
My mom deserves a diamond because she is a compassionate and kind-hearted person, who will go through the hardship just to help her loving family.

Sunset Lane Elementary
Fullerton

Teacher: Elaine Cox

Joseph Ferraro Grade: 06
My mom cares for everyone she sees. She also is always equally nice to her 5 kids and is sometimes driving her crazy by us - Loving her.

* Amethyst winners in bold.

Eun Sol Han   Grade: 06
My mom deserves a diamond because of her loving actions. She deserves more than what I give her in the fractions. To me, she's just perfect.

Cherry Myung   Grade: 06
My mom deserves a diamond because she never gives up on taking care of me. She loves me and does everything to keep me safe.

Matthew Reyes   Grade: 06
She deserves a diamond because she works so hard for me and I want to give something back. She deserves something so nice like her.

Susanna Suh   Grade: 06
My mom always does Mommy chores, cooking, cleaning, scolding, working and more. My mom gives us both loving care.

Taft Elementary
Santa Ana

Teacher: Annie Kensinger

Destinee Cisneros   Grade: 03
My mother is a present from the heavens. Without my mother, I would not exist. My mother is as pretty as a shining star.

Deven Deleon   Grade: 03
My mom is a flower. I can smell her. She smells like cherry and blue berries. She is my heart.

Fredy Gomez   Grade: 03
My mom is an angel sent from above. She compliments me. My mom's heart is bigger than the world. She is my angel.

Destinee Manzo   Grade: 03
She is beautiful as a diamond and the rock of our family. There's no rock or diamond in this earth like my Mom.

Priscilla Mendoza   Grade: 03
Mom, You're a wonderful mother, so gentle, yet strong. The many ways you show you care makes you the one I love.

Eunice Nacho   Grade: 03
My mom is so sweet, sweeter than a marshmallow. Her heart is the diamond, I am the gem. We will stick together forever then.

Madeline Napier   Grade: 03
My mom is beautiful, like a diamond in the sky. She loves me. Her shining smile looks like white pearls. I love her very much.

Jasmine Nguyen   Grade: 03
My mom is my shining sun. When you kiss me the sun shines on you. That's why I love you very much.

Maggie Quiroz   Grade: 03
My mother is beautiful like a red shiny apple. She is the love of my life. I love her very much. My mom is the best.

Trevor Tran   Grade: 03
My mom shines like a star in space. She's the sun, but brighter and better. She's as beautiful as Saturn's rings. She shines like bright gold stars.

Teacher: Cindy Vaughn

Katya Anaya   Grade: 02
My mom is very special. Her eyes twinkle in the sun. My mom is very nice, she hugs me whenever I'm sad.

Sean Le   Grade: 02
My mom deserves a diamond because she does all the work. I love her when she cooks for me and my dad.

Tyler Lopez   Grade: 02
My mom deserves a diamond because she is so special. Her eyes are sparkly like diamonds.

Tamura (Hisamatsu) Elem.
Fountain Valley

Teacher: Lopez

Crislyn Beltran   Grade: 03
Why mom deserves a diamond because she cooks me meals. She plays games with me when I'm lonely. She loves me with all her heart.

Matthew Caha   Grade: 03
My mom deserves a diamond because she helps me with my home work. She corrects my paper when something is not right. I really love my mom.

Travis Henderson   Grade: 03
My mom deserves a diamond because she helps me with my homework. She takes me places I like. When I get hurt, she will help me.

Jordan Tran   Grade: 03
My mom deserves a diamond because she lets me hold my baby sister. She gives me toys and helps me with my homework. She washes dishes.

Teacher: Nicole Schlosser

Nicole Boardman   Grade: 03
My mom is like sunshine on a rainy day. She is my hero who swoops in and saves the day. She deserves a diamond

Grace Burnett   Grade: 03
My mom deserves a diamond. She does all she can to make me feel good, but I feel just grand.

Kira Clark   Grade: 03
My mom has always been a inspiration for my life that's why she deserves a diamond. I will always love her.

Jessica Nguyen   Grade: 03
I always depend on my mom, she's taught me everything stored in my brain. She's also nicknamed the "legendary super mommy". My mom is awesome.

Taylor Nguyen   Grade: 03
My mom deserves a diamond because she works very hard for us every day and the beautiful diamond would be a special reward for her.

Top of the World Elemen.
Laguna Beach

Teacher: Marie Bammer

Adam Champ   Grade: 04
My mom deserves a diamond because she taught me to add, subtract, multiply and divide before my teachers even taught it. She is the best.

Kirsten Landsiedel   Grade: 04
My mom deserves a diamond because she is always by my side and picking me up when I'm down. She is my sparkling star.

Bayley Thomas   Grade: 04
I think my mom deserves a diamond because she has taught me so I can write this letter and she holds our house in shape.

Lucas Toro   Grade: 04
My mom deserves a diamond because she is a very beautiful and generous person. She will also give you the best hair cut ever.

Luke Winter   Grade: 04
My mom should win a diamond for many reasons. My mom always forgives me when I do something wrong and always loves me no mater what.

Teacher: Cory Day

Crystal Curras   **Grade: 04**
Mom, the diamond in my eye, the crystal in the sky, the one I adore the most, she deserves the most.

Teddy Malpass   **Grade: 04**
My mom is a star in the night sky. She flies me through my dreams. She is the most flawless spectacular diamond in the night sky.

Ryan Meisberger   Grade: 04
A diamond is pretty, the sun is too, you deserve a diamond just for being you.

Madison Sinclair   Grade: 04
My mom looks like a diamond. She is calm like a silent, beautiful swan and deserves to be a princess.

Russell Thomas   Grade: 04
The night sky is pretty, so is the moon. A diamond would be beautiful, but not as much as you.

Trabuco Mesa Elementary
Rancho Santa Margarita

Teacher: Kathy Adair

Annika Braaksma   **Grade: 04**
My mom is the angel that protects me when I'm sleeping. She is the one with the twinkling eyes that reach keep into my heart.

Nicole Clayton   Grade: 04
Her voice so soft, her cookies so sweet, I love her, I love her, that's why she deserves a treat.

Kendall Davies   **Grade: 04**
My mom is the mom who has the shiny bright blue eyes. The soul of an angel. The song of the birds. She is perfect.

Hayden Engelbrecht   Grade: 04
She is the brightest in my heart, her heart is as big as the world. Her eyes sparkle like the great God.

Timothy Fayollat   Grade: 04
Her eyes sparkle like the moonlight shining into my soul. If she would leave, I'd really plead, come back and please don't leave my soul.

Fatima Hagverdiyev   **Grade: 04**
Her hair shines, her eyes glow, she's the diamond in my soul. She's the star at the ball because she's the crystal of them all.

Dylan Hull   Grade: 04
She is the light of my life and she sparkles in my eye. She sparkles in the water, like a dolphin in the sky.

Mitchell Jennings   Grade: 04
My mom sparkles like a diamond She's like a graceful bird in the sky. When she looks at me, I smile. She is the best.

Makenna Joels   Grade: 04
The sparkling light in her eyes makes me feel joy. She has a grand laugh. We love one another.

Emma Jones   **Grade: 04**
A kiss from mom shines so bright, her heart twinkles with love. She's as kind as an angel and my mom is my star.

John McCook   Grade: 04
Necklaces with gems and paintings is what she likes, going at the Jacuzzi and talking on the phone, but loves me the most.

Amanda Seelbinder   Grade: 04
My mom's eyes sparkle like the sky as my reflection on her. She is my diamond.

Teacher: Sheila Jones

Austin   **Grade: 01**
My mom deserves a diamond because she protects me and reaches in my soul.

Brenda Aguilar   Grade: 01
My mom works hard to get money to buy food and clothes. She catches butterflies and bugs and she collects shells.

Jake Conerty   Grade: 01
She loves us so much. She cares about us so much. Mom is the best in the world. I love her.

Jack McConnell   Grade: 01
My mom deserves a diamond because she cooks s'mores with me and cleans the car.

Christoher Paz   Grade: 01
My mom deserves a diamond because she reads with me.

Lauren Plesac   **Grade: 01**
My mom deserves a diamond because she has a kind heart. She helps other people in need. My mom is very faithful

Travis Ranch
Yorba Linda

Teacher: Helen Davis

Tommy Aragone   Grade: 05
My mom is as beautiful as a hot summer's day. Her heart is as big as the sun. I would buy her the world.

Nick Owens   **Grade: 05**
For all the ways, you've cared for me, for all the love you've shared with me, for always being there for me. Thanks, Mom.

Raymond Rejon   Grade: 05
My mom is sweet, kind and her heart is open to anyone who needs help and she is just a loving person.

Delaney Von Iderstein   **Grade: 05**
When I'm with my mom, my heart feels like a yummy, sugar cookie that just came out of the oven. I love my mom.

Teacher: Susan Martin

Sammy Krausse   **Grade: 04**
My mom's eyes are two blue paths that wind into a glowing meadow filled with pink poppy flowers.

Daniel Rune   **Grade: 04**
Red for love, yellow for happiness, green for delicious cook, blue for kindness and purple for beauty. My mom, my rainbow of my life.

Sedona Sinclair   **Grade: 04**
My mom is like a gem on a angel that shines in the light, but even in the dark, you can see a bright light

Adam Carrillo   Grade: 05
Roses are red, diamonds are clear. My mom deserves a diamond because to me, she's so dear.

Angela Chuang   Grade: 05
My mom's eyes are like the night sky, so bright and beautiful. She has a gentle heart, her cooking is like a gourmet chef's.

Drew Dahlson   Grade: 05
My mom is the light of my day. She is the hardest working woman I know. She makes me feel loved down to my soul.

Jason Hellebrand   Grade: 05
My mom is like a rose in a rose garden. When it comes to night, she hugs me tight and is full of delight.

* Amethyst winners in bold.

Lauren Smith — Grade: 05
My mom deserves a diamond because she gave life to me. I can look up to her and I can see a diamond shining.

Michael Uranga — Grade: 05
Her eyes are shinier than the sun. She's light in the darkest hour. She's made every day worth getting through.

Teacher: Debbie Mc Donald

Emma Allen — Grade: 05
My mom deserves a diamond because she loves me. Her heart is so tender and filled with love. Nothing could take her apart from me.

Allyson Blomgren — Grade: 05
My mom is loving, she loves our family so much, with a twinkle in her eyes, she lets me know she loves me so much.

Evelyn Chan — Grade: 05
Because she loves me so much that there's nothing that will make her leave me, so I want to tell her thanks. I love you.

Raquel Davidson — Grade: 05
My mom deserves a diamond because of that sparkle in her eyes. I know I love her because my heart breaks every time I say goodbye.

Kyle Drees — Grade: 05
My mom deserves a diamond because her love's bigger than the sea. She deserves a diamond because she's always there for me.

David Garfunkel — Grade: 05
My mom deserves a diamond because she always thinks of me, she always does everything for me, and she always loves me dearly.

Amanda Gold — Grade: 05
My mom deserves a diamond because she's always there when I'm feeling sad or scared, she really truly cares.

Mileah Hugins — Grade: 05
My mom deserves a diamond because her love for me is as huge as the sun. She's so active and gives me lots of fun.

Lyanne Lalunio — Grade: 05
My mom deserves a diamond, there is no contest to see, how much I love her, and how much she means to me.

Sam Malhas — Grade: 05
My mom deserves a diamond…even though she's prettier than a diamond. She would pick me over an ocean of diamonds.

Morgan Mateus — Grade: 05
My mom deserves a diamond because she is so kind. She keeps me out of trouble and never leaves me behind.

Allison Newman — Grade: 05
My mom deserves a diamond because she helps me work out my problems. She helps me out with things. That's why she deserves a diamond.

Timothy Pawlovich — Grade: 05
My mom deserves a diamond because she's like your mom, she adopted me with love. An angel in heaven, a jewel of my own.

Michelle Polen — Grade: 05
My mom's eyes sparkle like the sea, she fills her heart just for me. The Lord shines on everything she does. Mom, I love you.

Nicole Ray — Grade: 05
My mom deserves a diamond because she always helps me when I'm sad, and never really will get mad.

Melanie Sanchez — Grade: 05
My mom deserves a diamond because she always helps me with things and because when I do the wrong things, she helps me correct it.

Blake Schriever — Grade: 05
Because she's caring to people and me, greets people she doesn't know always supports people and roots me on and the other team I play.

Teacher: Nancy Mullen

Brandon Acero — Grade: 06
My mom is the star in the sky, the twinkle in my eye. The angel in my life and the treasure of a thousand kings.

Faika Awkal — Grade: 06
The wrinkles of her laugh enlightens me. Her spirit shines through melancholy an exciting days. Even with mistakes, my mother is perfect.

Eugene Barbeau — Grade: 06
My…her eyes glow like the moon. When I hug her, I know nothing will happen to me. I am complete with my mom.

Megan Bothwell — Grade: 06
My mother is a busy bee. She works so hard for you and me. To me, she is a bird so free.

Raphael Caliolio — Grade: 06
My mom, a bible teaching us right and wrong. A falcon, wise in actions. A mother bear, guarding her family. This is my mom.

Amber Camerena — Grade: 06
My mom is a sparkling gem in the morning sky. But, as the sky becomes nightfall, she shines like a dark amethyst.

Alexis Cugini — Grade: 06
My mom is wise as an owl, brave as a bear, protective as the tiger, beautiful as a butterfly, she is more perfect than anything.

Austin Cullen — Grade: 06
My mother deserves a diamond because she fills my day with joy and happiness, and she shines like the evening star at dark.

Carly Curtis — Grade: 06
My mother, a se of never ending compassion, a rose always in bloom. A rock of never wielding guidance, a sparkling diamond of bright happiness.

Ashley Does — Grade: 06
If my mom were a diamond, her price would be infinite. She would be the most gorgeous, and nobody would love her more than I!

Zach Gage — Grade: 06
My mom is as sparkling as a gem. She is the sun that starts a brand new day. That's why she deserves this diamond.

Jaeda Gogerty — Grade: 06
Your eyes are like sparkling jewels. Your heart is made of pure gold. Your true personality shines and glows, like a diamond, you are beautiful.

Ryan Guerrero — Grade: 06
My mom is a beautiful shining light of love that guides me through the path of life when I have lost my way.

Leah Heyman — Grade: 06
Mothers - people who are physically made to care for you. A mother - a certificate of authenticity, proven to love you. My mother - my everything.

Alyssa Hosford — Grade: 06
My mom is like jewels skipping across a pool of silver water. She shines in the day and glimmers in the night.

Brianne Hosford — Grade: 06
My mom is like a waterfall, overflowing with love. Her heart is filled of diamonds that make her more perfect than anything.

Dana Jacobs   Grade: 06
My mom's heart shines like the jewel she is. She is the North Star in the world. She isn't a oyster, she's a pearl.

Lindsay Jameson   Grade: 06
Her eyes glisten like a full moon in the dazzling sky. Every time I look at her it brightens up my day. She deserves a diamond.

Merisa Kanzaki   **Grade: 06**
My mom is like the sun glistening all day long. Your words are comforting, just like a timeless song. I've loved you all along.

Cheyenne Kotick   **Grade: 06**
My words echo your voice, you're the road of my choice. You've mapped my way to heaven above, teaching me kindness and teaching me love.

Kevin Krausse   Grade: 06
My mom's eyes sparkle like a mountain lake at sunset. Her teeth glisten like new snow. Like a diamond, my mother is perfection.

Trip Moore   **Grade: 06**
Her comforting touch is like an angel's. A lion's strong and brave heart is in her, yet her tears of happiness shine like a diamond.

Chad Morris   Grade: 06
My mother is like a wolf, she shares pride in what she does. She is the leader of the pack, she deserves something wonderful.

Alison Porras   Grade: 06
Her eyes sparkle like gorgeous emeralds. Her beautiful blonde hair shines like the sun. But most importantly she has a heart of gold. She's mom.

Brandon Powell   Grade: 06
My mother is like a garnet, she's beautiful and red. When she smiles, her perfect smile, it makes anyone want to say friend.

Kallie Puentes   **Grade: 06**
My mom is the sun peeking out behind the moon after it has been eclipsed, the breath in my lungs, she deserves a diamond.

Cameron Rehmani   Grade: 06
Mom, you are the stem of our family's flower, you deserve a diamond because you sparkle like a ruby and you keep everyone happy.

Rima Romolia   Grade: 06
Mother - a flower that blooms or a shimmering moon. My mom - a diamond as clear as crystal water. I am glad to be your daughter.

Kiana Sarad   Grade: 06
Mom, I love you so much. You warm my heart with your touch. Helping me with every endeavor. Memories of you will last forever.

Austin Shih   **Grade: 06**
She's a sparkling diamond in the sky like a beautiful delicate dragonfly. She lets me soar through the night beaming like a firefly.

Olivia Tewksbury   Grade: 06
My mother, an unselfish caregiver. As lovely as the morning sun whose rays throw the warmth of golden sunshine over everything she does.

Elizabeth Tipping   Grade: 06
My mom is a gem. Her face shines with love and care like the facets of a diamond. My mother has a heart of gold.

Brigette Waldrup   Grade: 06
Protective, supportive and loving. As a mother bear with her cubs. Giving, caring, expecting, nothing in return. My mom, as flawless as a precious stone.

Teacher: Helen Nelson

George Abdallah   **Grade: 05**
My mom is more beautiful than a diamond. She makes my ears disappear. When she smiles, it turns sunny. Her beautiful face makes flowers bloom.

Parisa Ahadiat   Grade: 05
My mom is the sparkle of my life. She gives me love, happiness and care. She is always there for me. She deserves a diamond.

Kayla Amini   Grade: 05
My mom is like a star in the sky. She lights up the sky at night. Stars can be different colors. Just like my mom.

Evelyn Chan   **Grade: 05**
My mom shines like the north star which leads me to her heart. She warms my heart with joy which makes me brave and strong.

Lily Clark   Grade: 05
Sparkling like a rainbow, shinning in the sun. Always laughing and having fun. A diamond on her finger show our love to everyone!

Farah Daghestani   **Grade: 05**
For times when I weep, my mother is always there to wipe away my tears. Whenever I look in my mother's eyes, I see love.

Raquel Davidson   Grade: 05
She's my gummy life saver, the best candy of all, but this special one cannot be found in my store or mall. Mmmm…yummy.

Sarah Edmunds   Grade: 05
A star at midnight. My Mom's smiles and shines bright. She's the light of life.

David Garfunkel   Grade: 05
My mom shines like a sparkly diamond in the glowing sea and she always thinks about me and loves me so dearly.

Kenzie Graham   Grade: 05
My mom is the center of my life, just like a diamond upon a ring. She deserves a diamond. Mother is the guardian angel to me.

Lyanne Lalonio   Grade: 05
My mom is pretty like the angels above. She's also a grace to one dove. My one true symbol of her true love.

Jessica Mabry   **Grade: 05**
Bright, shiny, full of fire. Brilliant and strong that's my mom love endures like a precious gem. My mom's my radiant rock.

Michelle Polen   **Grade: 05**
Mom, you're a gift from heaven above. You have all of God's love. God sent you for everything you always do. Mom, I love you !

Nisha Rao   **Grade: 05**
A shimmering lake, a shining star. My mother shines from afar. She helps other people, not only me. Her medical talent has meaning to thee.

Riley Rose   Grade: 05
My mom is an angel from heaven above. She is so full of love, as gorgeous as a dove. My mom is from heaven above.

Teacher: Bernadette Osborne

Giana Borelli   Grade: 04
My mom deserves a diamond because I love her and I am happy that she's my mom. She's the best mom anyone could have.

Fallon Gallant   Grade: 04
My mom deserves a diamond because she's done a lot for me and now it's time for me to do something for her kindness.

Teacher: Nicole Rodriguez

Isabella Paulus   Grade: 01
My mom deserves a diamond because she always helps me with my homework and when she helps me make my bed.

* Amethyst winners in bold.

Nicholas Pienatos — Grade: 01
My mom deserves a diamond because she is beautiful and special and last but not least, good to me.

Sophia Smith — Grade: 01
My mom deserves a diamond because she works hard and makes me happy.

Trinity Lutheran School
Anaheim

Teacher: Terah Atwell

Mackensie Ferguson — Grade: 05
My mom is very caring, her hair is shiny like a ruby ring, her personality shimmers like a jewel. My mom is so very cool.

Justin Quong — Grade: 05
My mom's eyes gleam like moon light. Her special cooking skills are better than scrumptious food the cook makes. She is as wise as a genius.

Derek Vollero — Grade: 05
My mom's eyes are like two emeralds. My mom's love is like all the rubies put together in the world.

Min Yu — Grade: 05
My mom is as valuable as a diamond. Her eyes sparkle and shine like a glimmering diamond. She has a smile that shines the way.

Teacher: Julia Diorio

Rachel Hedman — Grade: 04
My mom flutters like a butterfly and always spreads her wings. She flies like a butterfly. She is a diamond to me.

Jenna Lehn — Grade: 04
My mom's eyes sparkle brightly in the moonlight with the stars shining down on her. During the day, she is like a ray of sun.

Maddy Nimeh — Grade: 04
My mom brightens the sky on cloudy days. She simmers and sparkles as I look in her eyes. She is a diamond to me.

Kylie Palacios — Grade: 04
My mom is as sweet as sugar and as delicate as a rose. My mom is there as time comes and goes

Benjamin Rausch — Grade: 04
Her eyes gleam like amber. Her face shines like gold. When I am with her, she makes me feel bold.

Kristin Snyder — Grade: 04
Her life does not last forever, although her love surely does. When she laughs, I see sparkles in her eyes.

Mollie Wright — Grade: 04
Mom is a diamond in the sky. She twinkles in sunlight and lights up my path on foggy days. She gleams in my soul.

Makeala Zeran — Grade: 04
My mom's eyes are like beautiful diamonds. They sparkle like them too. They are more beautiful than crystals. So she deserves a diamond.

Teacher: Linda Grana

Allie Gerard — Grade: 01
My mom is special as a diamond. My mom sparkles like a diamond. Her eyes sparkle like a diamond.

Kaela Gonzales — Grade: 01
She is nice to me and she is special to me and her eyes sparkle like sunshine.

Allison Romo — Grade: 01
My mom cares for me. Her eyes shine like diamonds. My mom shines like the sun. When my mom shines, she loves me.

Kylee Williams — Grade: 01
My mom is silly and she loves me. I know when she cares for me cause her eyes shine like a diamond.

Teacher: Kathi Myers

Katherine Honkham — Grade: 03
When you see the sunset, that's my mom's sun like face. Her smile is like a shining diamond. That's why I love you!

Hannah Rahn — Grade: 03
My mom's eyes sparkle with glee! She smiles like a gem, and laughs like a sparkling diamond that is hard to find, a special mother.

Xander Rogers — Grade: 03
She has a gleaming heart so delicate. What eyes! They glow heavenly ! You're crystal clear - you'll never break. That's why I love you so!

Jessica Streuer — Grade: 03
First comes moonlight in her gem-like eyes. A gratifying heart makes my mother shine like a glistening diamond.

Danielle White — Grade: 03
You are the jewel of my life. Your eyes shimmer in my soul. You and your heart are as bright as a diamond.

Noel Yamamoto — Grade: 03
My mother is a perfect diamond at night, I see her eyes sparkling. If the diamond breaks, I still think my mom is grand.

Carol Smestad

Thuy-Tien Bui — Grade: 02
My mom shines like a star. She shimmers, she glows and sparkles. She is an angel to me, sparkles like a diamond.

Ronnie Coates — Grade: 02
My mom deserves a crystal heart, because she cares and helps me for whatever I want. She also shines like a star

Lucy Gallagher — Grade: 02
My mom is the pride of jewels. Her crystal heart is as bright as the sun. She shines when she smiles, her eyes are gems.

Megan Han — Grade: 02
My mom shines like an angel. She's a star that leads me through life. How much I love her like a diamond of my own.

Sarah Lawson — Grade: 02
My mom has glowing eyes in the night. But in the light a dot of light shines on her. So that's why I love her.

Samantha Rocke — Grade: 02
My mom is so pretty, she shines like a star, crystal eyes and a ruby heart whatever I'm a crystal to her.

Turtlerock Elementary
Irvine

Teacher: Birgie Glassen

Trinity Cha — Grade: 01
You look at her heart, it captures your soul. She loves me so much. She looks at my face, her eyes sparkle like diamonds.

Karen Cho — Grade: 01
My mom is a glowing night. She sparkles all over her body. My mom is a star with a beautiful face.

Christina Denlinger — Grade: 01
A rainbow doesn't sparkle . Books and birds don't sparkle and the ocean doesn't sparkle, but my mom sparkles.

David Lee — Grade: 01
A piece of wind, a piece of snow. The wind blows the snow. It really sparkles and crunches like my mom.

Anna Lim   Grade: 01
A little dab of moonlight and a dab of sparkling water which is like a mom's eyes.

Alyssa Rave   Grade: 01
My mom is like gold. Her eyes like glitter. She sparkles like pink and white. She's full of love.

Iman Syed   Grade: 01
My mom is happy when I am home. She glows every night like a diamond.

Sirgid Torsvik   Grade: 01
My mom's eyes glitter like snowflakes high in the sky. Her smile is following me.

Jordan Wheeler   Grade: 01
A drop of diamond golf, like the sun shining down. The eyes of God hitting the eyes of my mom. She is so, so beautiful.

University High
Irvine

Teacher: Margaret Segala

Jane Heur   Grade: 11
She tries concealing it, but I see her blood, sweat and tears for me. These hardships she swallows when I am in the smallest sorrow.

Brigitte Kirshman   Grade: 11
Mom is the eternal gemstone of my life. My love is like a diamond, nothing can break it.

Andrew Le   Grade: 11
She instilled life into me; she never ceased to protect me. She insured my future, and sacrificed hers. She is my mother, and guardian light.

Teacher: ThereseSorey

Tiffany Cheng   Grade: 11
My mother, cheerful and fun. My mother, warm and maternal. My mother, the melody to the music of my life.

Laurel Clare   Grade: 11
My North Star lighting up my sky when dark. My compass, guiding me when lost. My mother, there when I need her most.

Elizabeth Dinh   Grade: 11
Stars pale in comparison to her eyes. Choruses of angels are nothing to her voice. Billions are worthless to her love. My mother: My everything.

Ryan Dobis   Grade: 11
My mother's benevolent character is like an angel's descent from heaven; sweet and virtuous. Her relentless and courageous efforts insurmountable, deserving a diamond.

Ifrah Hassan   Grade: 11
I am blessed with my mother whose tender love I will never surrender. A radiant smile shines from her face, with every kiss and embrace.

Irene Joo   Grade: 11
The kindness of her heart, the beauty of her soul, the sacrifices she makes radiate true love that deserves more than just a thanks.

Clement Kao   Grade: 11
Mother, as soft as the rose petal. Yet also diamond hard, shimmering sanctuary against the dark shadows of the world. The ultimate embodiment of love,

Sara Martinez   Grade: 11
Her love can move mountains out of sight. She truly has no kryptonite. This real life superhero is none other than my strong, loving mother.

Stephanie Nguyen   Grade: 11
You cook meals with love, and give me hugs as warm as a glove. Constantly drinking tea, you protect me like a tall oak tree.

Jacob Rubalcava   Grade: 11
My mother is simply amazing, a true gift from God, a blessing in my heart. I couldn't ask for anything more. She's my only need.

Anup Sarakki   Grade: 11
Mom: The embodiment of morals and values on the earth. Mom: An ocean of love to engulf me. The one, the only, Mom.

Boanne Song   Grade: 11
A beacon of light, she shows her might warning me when there is trouble. She guides me through obstacles, one after another, my beloved mother.

Emily Tian   Grade: 11
Mom, though your radiant smile invigorates, and your comforting voice relieves, your priceless love is most precious to me. You are truly my guardian angel.

Joyce Tseng   Grade: 11
My wisest teacher, my most spirited cheerleader, my best friend. My mom, her inner beauty sparkles like a true diamond for the world to see.

Caroline Wu   Grade: 11
To mom. Thank you for trying so hard everyday, for smiling through your dreadful days, for caring for us even when we fight back.

Olivia Yeh   Grade: 11
Her gentle touch and soothing voice reminds me I am loved. Three hugs, two kisses, one warm smile. I often forget she's only here awhile.

University Park Elementary
Irvine

Teacher: Hazel Alvarez

Sangwen Ahn   Grade: 03
My mom deserves a diamond because she buys, fries it for me. My mom eats fruit with me. I like fruit and my mom.

Cindy Arellano   Grade: 03
My mom deserves a diamond because she helps me with my homework. She cooks delicious chicken noodle soup for me.

Bethany Goto   Grade: 03
My mom loves me and makes my food. She is helpful to me and everybody. She gives me toys like Webkinz and Bokugan.

Matthew Mindiak   Grade: 03
My mom deserves a diamond - she cooks food for me and I like it a lot. She lets me go on bike rides.

Darin Murphy   Grade: 03
My mom deserves a diamond because she tucks me into bed and reads to me at night. She helps me with homework. I love her.

Madeline Parr   Grade: 03
My mom deserves a diamond because she takes me ice skating and she helps me with my homework. She cooks me dinner.

Brandon Sanchez   Grade: 03
My mom deserves a diamond because she takes care of me when I am sick. My mom is always there for me.

Andrew Vidaurreta   Grade: 03
My mom deserves a diamond because she helps me with my homework. She cooks delicious tacos for dinner. She helps me clean my room.

Tag Kahlon   Grade: 04
My mom deserves a diamond because she is nice to me, helps me with my homework, makes me dinner, let's me ride my dirt bike.

Teacher: Kathleen Lui

Shadai Garcia   Grade: 01
I love mom because she is kind to me and she is always hugging me. My mom is the best mom in all the world.

Shinya Ishimura   Grade: 01
I love mom because she helps me to my English and Japanese homework. I love mom because she plays with me.

Sang Soo Lim   Grade: 01
I love mom because my mom helps me do homework. I love my mom because she's kind and gives me lots of hugs.

Jun Hyang Lim   Grade: 01
I love mom because she is still taking care of me. I love mom because she cooks me cheese pizza.

Rin Matsuura   Grade: 01
I love mom because my mom plays with me and makes me good cakes. I like mom because my mom helps me do homework.

Jae Kyung Shin   **Grade: 01**
I love mom because she is still taking care of me even though I am seven years old. She is kind and gives me hugs.

Tenghe Wang   **Grade: 01**
I love my mom because she gave me life, and mom cooks for me, helps me, and buys almost anything for me.

Kaori Kimura   Grade: 02
I love my mom because she helps me do my homework and cooks the best food. I love mom because she buys me presents.

Valencia Elementary
Laguna Hills

Teacher: Jill Bennet

Noah Anderson   Grade: 05
My mom is the sun to my day, her eyes as sparkling as a diamond and her heart as big as a mountain. My mom.

Katie Christiansen   Grade: 05
My mom deserves a diamond because her smile reflects one. She should be awarded with one because her loving heart is clear as one.

Danielle Grace   Grade: 05
She's the warm sea breeze that's in my every thought, always doing things for me, I tell her thanks a lot. She's my mom.

Bridget Gramling   Grade: 05
She makes me feel in paradise. She makes me feel in bloom, she makes me feel tons of things. I wish you'd feel them too.

Tessie Maraki   Grade: 05
She seems to be a river overflowing with affection. But really, she's a stream, calm and passionate.

Emma Mc Clellan   **Grade: 05**
When wishes are whispered, who's ear is to hear. The secrets inside me, the hopes and the fears. Our hands meet, holding each other: Mother.

Vivian Nguyen   Grade: 05
Dazzling hazel eyes watch me. Sweet voice lulling me to sleep. Her everlasting path of love. I'll be my mother's sacred treasure to keep.

Angeline Tran   Grade: 05
Diamond Haiku. Mother's a diamond. She's bright just like a diamond. She is number one!

Teacher: Janice Mecham

Ryan Bishop   **Grade: 04**
My mother's eyes are as beautiful as a sunrise. Her smile is like a lantern leading the way. Her love is all I'll ever need.

Chloe Flora   Grade: 04
My mom is always there for me when I am sad or lonely. Her eyes are like blue sparkling pools that uplift my spirit.

Elizabeth Haugan   Grade: 04
My mother's eyes are two stars glistening in the moonlit sky. Her kisses, tiny rainbows. Her smile lights up my very soul with magic.

Skylar Holder   Grade: 04
Her love as hugs as the ocean. Her eyes like a diamond. Her kisses as magical as a mermaid. My mom definitely deserves a diamond.

Alexander Huynh   **Grade: 04**
My mother's eyes glisten like morning dew. She sounds like the most soothing bell, but her true beauty is she's the light in my world.

Cassandra Kays   **Grade: 04**
Her eyes are as shiny as crystals. Her beauty is prettier than butterflies. Although those things are important, they're nothing compared to her heart.

Rachael Kim   Grade: 04
Her love comforts me when trouble comes. Her love never stops. Her cup can never overflow. There's always enough room for anyone. Love is there.

Erinn Lee   Grade: 04
My mother's eyes sparkle in the sun. Her voice is as sweet as birds chirping in the spring. I wouldn't trade her for the world.

Michael Mc Clellan   Grade: 04
Her eyes - sparkling, glistening diamonds. Her hugs - blanket of love. Her voice - the sound of joy. Her love - a priceless gem.

Sean Smith   Grade: 04
She's as beautiful as she is smart. Her laugh, a cheerful song and her smile can lighten every soul. For my mother is the best.

Nicholas Steffenhagen   **Grade: 04**
My mom's eyes are like two fireflies dancing with the moon. She is the flashlight that shines my way through the forest called life.

Cole Weidenhammer   Grade: 04
Mom's sweet, kind and funny. She's the best mom I could have, worth more than money. Pick her please and knock her off her knees.

Teacher: Dean Steidle

Cristina Alosio   **Grade: 05**
My mom is my best friend and she will be until the end. Her eyes shine like the sun. My mom is the best one.

Sarah Bresler   Grade: 05
My mom is as sweet as a cup of sugar. The sun rises to see her pretty face. She can't be compared. I love her.

Stephen Grant   Grade: 05
My mom's eyes are like diamonds because when you look at her, they sparkle so much. It's impossible to say what my mom does everyday.,

Dominique Gray   Grade: 05
She's like a crystal, always sparkling. In my heart, she's always knocking. Her heart stretches over to mine. She always puts my life in line.

Rebecca Krajeski   Grade: 05
Mom will never be compared to a diamond, she is more beautiful. Her hugs are warm and comforting. She's the one who gave me life.

Teacher: Mare Stephens

Paola Aviles   Grade: 05
I love my mom. She is a calm as the ocean, as sweet as honey, and guides me through my journey of paradise.

Venika Bibra   **Grade: 05**
My mom is the sparking ocean at sunset. She is the twinkling stars at night. She is my imagination when dreaming. She is my life.

LaRyn Florentine   Grade: 05
My mom is a sparkling bright yellow sun that brightens up my day when I am down. She is the greatest hero to me.

David Hunt   Grade: 05
Everyday and everyway, my mother is there for me. She lifts me up when I am down and gives me hugs for free.

Ellis Puscas   Grade: 05
My mom is like a diamond twinkling in the sky forever and ever. She will be an angel lighting up a path, everywhere I go.

Skyler Sather   **Grade: 05**
My mother smiles like a diamond. Her laugh is music to my ears. Though she has three kids, she has lots of love for me.

Moriah Tago   Grade: 05
My mom has brown hair, she really does care. Her eyes are green as grass. Every time she tickles me, I laugh.

Teacher: Kristen Svensson

Madison Smith   Grade: 01
She is loving and giving. My mom buys me new clothes when I need it. She reads me a bedtime story at night.

Emily Steffenhagen   **Grade: 01**
My mom is nice. When it is my birthday. She lets me go wherever I want and do whatever I want.

Kaitlin Vu   **Grade: 01**
She takes me to school everyday. My mom buys me toys and she helps me with my homework. I love my mom.

Logan Wilson   **Grade: 01**
My mom makes me special dinners and she helps me with my homework. At night, she tucks me in my bed.

Valencia High
Placentia

Teacher: Maleah Dhenin

Roberto Castro   Grade: 09
My mom enjoys the shine of a diamond. She carries the sparkle of my life.

Robert Escodara   Grade: 09
My mom deserves a diamond because she fills my heart with joy and the way she sparkles into my eyes just like a diamond.

Shirley Lara   Grade: 09
Beneath the full moon and the sparkle shine of the bright stars, my glamorous mother gave me birth. A diamond is how I'll say thanks.

Jose Franco   Grade: 10
I like the way you love me. Every time you kiss me it lifts me up. There will be no one else like you.

Mariana Penaloza   **Grade: 12**
There are not enough words to explain why my mom deserves a diamond. She's my treasure, the light of my life, the reason for my victories.

Teacher: Beth Mazurier

Maria Carrasco   **Grade: 11**
She's the star that I look up to for advice. She is the sun in my cloudy sky. She is my mom.

Laura Pilawski   Grade: 11
Moms are there for those hard times in life as well as those unforgettable moments and I'm proud to say you've been there for all.

Victory Christian School
Anaheim

Teacher: Valerie Birge

Joshua Amasula   **Grade: 04**
My mom is like a ruby and sometimes calls me cutie, and when she tucks me in at night, her face glows so bright.

C. J. Marshall   Grade: 04
My mom deserves a diamond because she is my mom. She cleans and cooks and makes me study books and looks like a beautiful woman.

Kaitlyn Peters   Grade: 04
My mom is a diamond. She's cute with sparkles. She's my love. Her love is never-ending and she's pretty like a flower. She's my mommy.

Viejo Elementary
Mission Viejo

Teacher: Mike Rager

Ella Eddy   Grade: 04
Her eyes twinkle, so does she, just like a shiny, beautiful diamond she deserves to be.

Brett France   Grade: 04
My mom's eyes shine like diamonds in the sun. She is as beautiful as a mountain meadow. She smells like a dandelion in a field.

Christina Gonzalez   Grade: 04
Her eyes are like crystals shining in the bright sun. But her heart is like a ruby filled with love. Nothing is like my mom.

Edward Julian   Grade: 04
The eyes on your face looks like a beautiful light, like a diamond should shine.

Rachel Leon   Grade: 04
She is as sweet as sugar, her eyes are like diamonds, but most of all, she is the sweetest mom ever.

Elizabeth Turner   **Grade: 04**
A little bit of moonlight. A dash of sun. The diamond shines like your eyes in the sunlight. You sparkle like the star that shines bright.

Gisela Villalobos   Grade: 04
Diamonds are clear and shiny as you. I hope you like this diamond because I love you.

Teacher: Staci Smith

Caddy Aguirre-Stanton   Grade: 04
My mom helps me when I'm blue. She cares for everyone in our family, even friends as well. My mom is one of a kind.

Taylor Bell- Ellis   Grade: 04
My mom deserves a diamond because I only see her every Saturday. She's beautiful, she's wonderful, she's my mom.

Steven Bodenhoefer   Grade: 04
When you're home, I love you. Eyes like quartz, I love you. You are beautiful, I love you. Thank you for being my mother.

Ann Chavarria   Grade: 04
My mom deserves a diamond because she is a lovely mom and because she works so hard to be a fine mother and she is.

Miranda Chavis   **Grade: 04**
Her smile lights my heart. Why would she need gems? When she is one!

* Amethyst winners in bold.

Kellie Dixon   Grade: 04
My stepmom deserves a diamond because she cooks, she cleans. When I miss my real mom, she is always there for me.

Stefany Fernandez   Grade: 04
We kids need our moms from morning to night. Since the moment we were born. Without our moms where would we be. I wonder?

Faith Floyd   Grade: 04
My mom deserves a diamond because she is beautiful , nice to everyone, and has the hardest job ever which is taking care of our family.

Christian Garcia   Grade: 04
My mom deserves to get a diamond because she is spectacular, awesome, fabulous - every word I could think of, and because she is intelligent too.

Gustavo Gonzalez   Grade: 04
I know my mom deserves a diamond because she is so generous to other people and tries to help them or us no matter what.

Amber McKernan   Grade: 04
My mom deserves a diamond because she is like one. Caring, gorgeous, amazing, loving, and special. She is everything I ask for.

Alysa Ochoa   Grade: 04
My mom deserves a diamond. She's a really, really hard worker. She loves me and I love her because my mom is my hero.

Izziak Perezcastaneda   Grade: 04
I think my mom deserves a diamond because no matter how much she has to do, she never quits, and I love her

Vanesa Ramirz   Grade: 04
She has been through a lot of things and has no time for herself. But I will still love her in my heart.

Vanessa Rosas   Grade: 04
Mom deserves a diamond. Her eyes are two shining stars. Her hair is made of soft silky dreadlocks. She has a heart made of gold.

Luciana Taviras   Grade: 04
The only woman who's fought for me is my mother. She's really brave. I'd love for her to have something that means thank you.

Villa Park Elementary
Villa Park

Teacher: Tammy Williams

Cambria Gibb   Grade: 05
I think my mom deserves a diamond because she does so much for us that we should do something for her. She cooks and cleans. Thanks.

Sabrina Godinez   Grade: 05
Despite suffering with MS, my mom helps me with school and all other activities. Even though physically difficult, she's never missed any of my games.

Connor Hein   Grade: 05
My mom deserves a diamond because she helps my sister and I to get to school on time and ready and helps us with homework.

Emily Hong   Grade: 05
My mom deserves a diamond because she helps my family to cook, wash the clothes and dishes. She treats us very nice and rocks.

Lauren Jones   Grade: 05
My mom deserves a diamond because she always does things for other. She is always helping people.

Maddie Kato   Grade: 05
My mom deserves a diamond because she is like a rose and has the heart to make her child a happy as can be.

Michelle Palacios   Grade: 05
My mom tries her best to take care of me even though I only get to see her twice a day. She deserves a diamond.

Ryan Robinson   Grade: 05
My mom deserves a diamond because she is nice, loving, hardworking and stressed out at work. She makes dinner, does dishes and designs freeways.

Regan Schmid   Grade: 05
My mom is just like a kid. She plays with me on the trampoline, doing flips and playing games. She plays tetherball until she's bruised.

Matthew Wilson   Grade: 05
My mom deserves to get a diamond because she helps me manage my diabetes. This is to be her reward.

Vineyard Christian School
Anaheim

Teacher: Ingrid Wilkinson B.

Tonia Bayakzan   Grade: 06
I praise my mother for the dirty work around the house. Loving and promising, she never got what she deserved. My mother rocks my world.

Jessica Cobb   Grade: 06
My mom is like a bear because she cares for her cubs. She goes through hard times, but she stays strong through it all.

Taylor Hoppe   Grade: 06
My mom deserves a diamond because she has been there every single time. I shed tears, giggled and desired somebody to be with me.

Rachel Moyes   Grade: 06
My mom deserves a diamond because she helps me through the thick and thin and she will love me until the end.

Adelaide Truong   Grade: 06
Mom sparkles brighter than any diamond could possibly be. With a helpful and loving heart, she is always there for me.

Blake Zamora   Grade: 06
My mom deserves a diamond because when I am sad or down. She uses love and care to pick me off the ground.

Diana Aranda   Grade: 07
My mom deserves a diamond for being a kind-hearted woman. There is no way I can thank her, but let's start with a diamond.

Dylan Britt   Grade: 07
She brings a shine to those around her and a sparkle to the ones she loves. She is a priceless diamond.

Kolton Freck   Grade: 07
She deals with my teenage stage, but yet she stays beautiful and strives forward every day.

Jeremiah Martin   Grade: 07
I love my mom in every way. She's always there to help, but what I love the most about her is her love for me.

Connor Matz   Grade: 07
Mom's polished and beautiful. She is hard when she needs to be. Mom makes everything look better. When she is around, just like a diamond.

Christopher Brooks Grade: 08
My mom deserves a diamond because she is one. Pretty and beautiful, she always will make me smile and I will always love her.

Joshua Case Grade: 08
My mom is a great influence in my life. Steadily showing me ways to be successful and prosperous. But most of all, happy.

Lesly Ann Collins Grade: 08
My mom deserves a diamond because she's like a diamond in the rough. She is starting college to improve herself and to help our family.

Tara Cuff Grade: 08
I love my mumsy, so. Cleaning up wherever she may go. She's as graceful as a doe. She keeps the family in perfect harmony.

Kevin Darmstadt Grade: 08
Caring, loving, selfless, these are the words I would use to describe my mom. If anyone, my mom deserves a diamond. I love my mom.

Norman Hasso Grade: 08
The lighthouse burns bright but one day it will fade away, my mom's light guide me but hers will always shine through.

Zachary Neenan Grade: 08
My mom deserves a diamond, that's so true. It would be unfathomable to tell all she does for me to you.

Alex Park Grade: 08
My mom deserves a diamond unthinkably. So as her life goes back and forth, side to side, and to and fro.

Mario Reyes Grade: 08
My mom deserves a diamond because she loves and cares for me. She brought me into this world and I cherish her deeply for that.

Timothy Rowe Grade: 08
My mother deserves a diamond because she always was understanding when hearing my fears and she always tried to stop my tears.

Kristine Schmidbauer Grade: 08
My mom treads through teenage spontaneity, messes and dramas. And yet, here we both are, shining with perseverance. That's why my mom deserves any prize.

Parker Stanley Grade: 08
My mom deserves a diamond because she lets me follow my dreams. Really she deserves everything. That's why I want to give her a diamond.

Vista del Mar Elementary
San Clemente

Teacher: Brenda Dahlgren

Cole Dorris Grade: 04
She should get one because she is helpful, hardworking and caring. She only gets a break when she sleeps. She is very special to me.

Julia Hockemeyer Grade: 04
A kind hearted, hardworking, and loving mother deserves something for giving us her love and support. She deserves a flawless, beautiful, shining, Brazilian amethyst.

Elsonray Maxwell Grade: 04
My helpful mom has three kids. She takes care of all of them very well. Mom does not make yucky microwave dinners.

Scott Royer Grade: 04
She is peace loving, hind-hearted and caring. I think of her as a strawberry dipped in warm chocolate.

Michaela Schwartz Grade: 04
Because my mom is like a diamond; if you shine light on mom, she will produce a sparkling rainbow.

Ellie Winklemann Grade: 04
My loving mother as good s can be, her name is Sue and you will soon see… Sine, shimmer, sparkle, useful, understanding, unique, excellent, elegant, exciting.

McKenna Brownell Grade: 05
Mom is a diamond herself. In the shallow waters of diamond bay, she is the best diamond, shiny, beautiful and magnificent.

Sydney Davis Grade: 05
My mommy is a beautiful diamond waiting to glisten in the bolting sun. Her hazel eyes sparkle with the one and only diamond she deserves.

Josiah Howard Grade: 05
Mom, her eyes are shimmering diamonds in the dim moonlight, hair as smooth as the finest silk spun from a silkworm. My mom is flawless.

Andrew Lane Grade: 05
My mom, the nicest of people, would help me fight the measles. Whether I'm blue or covered in glue, she fills me with love.

Grace Perry Grade: 05
Taking care of a family of four, plus a puppy is hard work. But that is my mom's life. Anyone would want my mom.

Jacob Phillips Grade: 05
My mom deserves a diamond because she gets out of bed to do anything she can to help us and the Lord.

Teacher: Nicole Davis

Parsa Ali-Hemati Grade: 05
Her beautiful voice is as sweet as a robin that keeps on sharing her lovely voice in my head.

Jake Bettinelli Grade: 05
An eloquent and attractive woman, a charismatic and relentless worker. A roaming angel, bringing super times to everyone, especially my flawless family. That's my mommy.

Alexis Dimond Grade: 05
My devoted mom cares so much for me. She works early to late, then comes home and cooks dinner. Her only breaks are on weekends.

Taylor Dunlevie Grade: 05
My mom is a good role model and I would like to repay her in a nice and beautiful way. I love my mom a lot.

Rachel Hughes Grade: 05
My graceful mom sparkles like a polished diamond, and sometimes, I think of her as my very own glittering star that I look up to.

Christopher Mastracchio Grade: 05
My mom is as flawless as the waves that wipe the sea. She is as impeccable as the soft, flowing, vacuum of space and time.

Marisa Miller Grade: 05
My mom's unique. She's a teacher, so she touches kids lives every day, including mine. She's also optimistic, caring, and very, very, very loving.

Chloe Moodie Grade: 05
My mom has a shimmering and glistening smile watch it glow. Her radiant eyes are the gemstone topaz. She is so beautiful. I love her.

Mallory Moody Grade: 05
Kindness, caring, loving too. Who's this person? It's my mom, that's who. Is best of all she does, her heart is filled with warm fuzz.

Andre Pallante Grade: 05
My caring and extraordinary mom is so nice and sweet. She never gets really mad and she helps me with anything from math to reading.

* Amethyst winners in bold.

Maxton Wallett   Grade: 05
A sparkling scuttle fish in the gentle waves, a glimmering magenta ruby in the moist cares, a true work of art she really is - Mom.

Alyson Wazny   Grade: 05
My mom's eyes glitter like the diamond I'm wanting to win her. Also, when I see her grin, she sparkles like the sun itself.

Teacher: Stacy Eltiste

Madison Gordon   Grade: 05
My mom deserves a diamond because she goes non-stop driving me everywhere I need to go like dance. I think my mom is the best.

Michael Guillotte   Grade: 05
My caring mom deserves a precious diamond because she's always cleaning around our house (without jewelry) to let us live in a clean environment.

Malia Helbling   Grade: 05
My mom deserves a diamond because she loves every single one of us in my family equally. She deserves this because she works hard.

Amber Navarra   Grade: 05
My mom deserves a diamond because she is a wonderful, loving, hard worker and she is caring, pregnant woman with one baby boy.

Jessica Raitz   Grade: 05
My mom deserves a diamond because she is caring. She adopted me without a man; that is why my mom deserves a diamond.

Sarah White   Grade: 05
Mrs. White-Horne deserves a diamond because she's as sweet as a strawberry and loves her family more than anything. She works so hard, she rocks.

Teacher: Vernon Gries

Taylor Blitch   Grade: 05
My mom deserves a diamond because she has brown, glossy hair, is also really nice, and arrives at work like a shining sun in the sunset.

Evan Cappadocia   Grade: 05
The mom without flaws in mine. She has a beautiful voice like a whistling bird. She's a funny mom, and the most beautiful.

Hunter Hawkins   Grade: 05
Rubies are red, sapphires are blue, my mom likes diamonds so please give her two (or one), she works very hard, for my family.

Summer Meltvedt   Grade: 05
My mom deserves a diamond because she's very loving and kind. She stays by my side all day while I'm ill. I love her a lot.

Jennifer Mendoza   Grade: 05
Mom deserves a diamond because she is kind, caring, and she helps me. Also, even if she had a bad day, she still loves us.

Cambria Mogavero   Grade: 05
My mom deserves a diamond for she shines like a shimmering sun among the shadowed world which is now light, peace and sunny.

Andrew Orozco   Grade: 05
My mom is the best. I can't ask for her to be the tiniest amount better at anything. She's such a great mom, yeah, mom.

Mirabal Secretario   Grade: 05
Her marvelous, extraordinary personality gleams brightly and she's a very dedicated hard worker. When I need her, she's there for me with her arms opened.

Andrew Wilk   Grade: 05
My mom glows like a star in the sky, she fills the room with happiness, she deserves everything because she works so hard.

Weaver (Jack L.) Elemen.
Los Alamitos

Teacher: Heidi Kwalk

Elora Camacho   Grade: 05
A haiku for my mother. Loving as a puppy. Wise as the tiny owl's heart. Always believing in you.

Anthony DeMarco   Grade: 05
My mom deserves a diamond because she is like a hero to me. She is also like a diamond because she brightens up the room.

Laurence Ferrufino   Grade: 05
Mom deserves a diamond because she looks out for us. She feeds us and helps us follow the right path that she took.

Ashley Geller   Grade: 05
My mom deserves a diamond because she works more than any other mom. She also gets involved in all parent school projects.

Krista Hayakawa   Grade: 05
My mom deserves a diamond for she cares for two independent eleven year old daughters. She also supports me in every way she possibly can.

Andie Kotani   Grade: 05
My mom deserves a diamond because she is like a best friend to me and I love best friends like her.

Madeline Medby   Grade: 05
My mom deserves a diamond because she loves me and hugs me tight, and because she cuddles me at night. She is extraordinary.

Kaitlyn O' Gara   Grade: 05
Imagine a mom like this; exciting, creative with our games, encouraging with homework, a magnificent wife and an extremely beautiful woman. My mom totally rocks.

Brittany Taga   Grade: 05
My mom deserves a diamond because she does more work than you can give her. My mom's brain holds much information about computers. Go awesome mom.

Teacher: Dominic Nguyen

Lia Arambula   Grade: 05
My mom deserves a diamond because I did not get her a very good Christmas present, but she loves me anyways and no matter what.

Brian Beal   Grade: 05
She is kind, caring, sweet as a plum and cheers me up when I feel bummed. I love her and she loves me too.

Danielle Beaudreau   Grade: 05
My mom deserves a diamond because she supports me. She stopped working just for me. She is always behind me to catch whenever I fall.

Katrina Brunter   Grade: 05
My mom deserves a diamond because she has been with me through the ups and downs and I have never given her something so special.

Mark Kim   Grade: 05
My mom is a special person. She gets me ready for the future. She deserves a diamond so she can have a good future.

Jordon Taibi   Grade: 05
My mom deserves a diamond because she was brave enough to go across a 300 ft. zip line and she always strokes my hair every night.

Vivienne Youn   Grade: 05
My mom can sew holes in hearts closed and has always helped everyone around. She can make anything, something amazing and I am really grateful.

Western High
Anaheim

Teacher: Karen Clark

Mouminat Damer   Grade: 11
A mother's kindness shines. She's a hundred carats of perfection that gives off her diamond's reflection.

Noland Mayor   Grade: 11
Because she was always there for me, from my struggles and devastation. Her sacrifices shaped my personality and taught me to walk in other's shoes.

Soondus Yammout   Grade: 11
All I can give mom is love; and although that's immensely greater than diamonds, I'd appreciate showing my sincerity with the greatest symbol of all.

Noemi Gil   Grade: 12
She is the best in me. The strength when I have none. A beauty divine. A diamond in the sun.

Westmont Elementary
Westminster

Teacher: Becky Murphy

Emily Burr   Grade: 04
I would like my mom to win a diamond because she really likes diamonds. She's in Scotland and would also like a really special gift.

Haley Mindrum   Grade: 04
My mom is really deserving, we need it because we're going on a road trip to Idaho, a castle, and San Francisco and we need gas.

Marissa Rodriguez   Grade: 04
My mom should deserve a diamond because she's always wanted a diamond and because she always wanted something sparkly. My mom would like $600 dollars.

Peter Tran   Grade: 04
My mom deserves a diamond because she's done lots of things for me, and I want to do something for her. Lastly, thank you.

Teacher: Marsha Sipkovich

Ivan Alcazar   Grade: 04
My mom is like the bright moon in the sky at night. Her hugs are like puffy clouds. Her smile is like shining stars.

Travis Anthony   Grade: 04
My mom shines like heaven's angels come upon me. She has words of wisdom and unlimited compassion.

Marcello Cannon   **Grade: 04**
My mom tucks me in like a mother bird laying on her eggs. She takes care of all my needs. She does a lot for me.

Jacob Crist   **Grade: 04**
My mom is more beautiful than the sea. She will take your breath away. She is more beautiful than a manta ray gliding away.

Marcus Flum   **Grade: 04**
An inspiration in my life, sweet and caring. Smiles like sparkling water. Always there caring for me, my loving mother.

Yissel Garcia   **Grade: 04**
My mom is a warm wind flying in my life. She has beautiful eyes and a smile that lights my world.

Skye Geraud   Grade: 04
My aunt is like a rose in spring, the one I can count on for anything. The most special flower of all.

Ixchel Gomez   Grade: 04
My mother is rose and a caring person that fits in the garden of my heart.

Connor Lu visi   Grade: 04
My mom's the glowing star that lights my life. She's the one who brightens my world.

Brandon Moreno   Grade: 04
My mom is so kind to me because she loves me. She says that I am the one to eat first.

Alexander Oprer   Grade: 04
My mom's golden blonde hair is made from the shining sun and her eyes are made of the stars in the night sky.

Chase Rupe   **Grade: 04**
My mom is a rose in a garden of weeds. Her eyes shine in the sun and her smile shines on the earth.

Myreya Tahay   **Grade: 04**
My mom is like a star in the sky that grants wishes. She cares about me. She is nice.

Maritza Tlatenchi   Grade: 04
Beautiful and caring, sweet and loving, always giving loving hugs to the world. A bright star near the planet, my beautiful mother.

Westpark Elementary
Irvine

Teacher: Cynthia Martinez

Jonas Berry   Grade: 03
My mom is a beautiful crystal who can overwhelm the most vivid bright light. Her perfect connection with me shines inside like marvelous gem.

Henry Chen   Grade: 03
My colorful mom is like a rainbow who shines in the sky. She sews beautiful pillows and wonderful clothing for my family. I love her.

Casey Dallman   Grade: 03
My mom is like a dazzling stone who flickers under the sun. Mom makes my life glow. She encourages me regularly to create polished homework.

Emanuel Goffe   Grade: 03
My mother's love reflects the rays of the sun. Her eyes look like green crystals warming me tender, twenty-four house everyday of the week.

Sarah Jin   Grade: 03
My mom gleams brightly like Rudolph's famous red nose. She's a treasure, loved and classic. Her amazing Korean and American cooking tastes like priceless jewels.

David Ma   Grade: 03
My mom is more priceless than a million dollars. I wouldn't trade her for anything in the world. She's the money being paid into my heart.

Ryan Paqlacio   Grade: 03
My mom is a gleaming diamond who shines like a priceless crystal. She gives me cold fruit every night, so I'm healthy, ready for life.

Olivia Vir   Grade: 03
My mom is like crunchy fruit that is tough on the outside, yet sweet and priceless inside. She is prized for her loving, helpful way.

White (George) Elementary
Laguna Niguel

Teacher: Sally White

Gavyn Bailey   Grade: 05
My mom deserves a diamond because almost everyday she flies in an airplane as her job. She has no time to shop.

*Amethyst winners in bold.

Kaylee Bashor   Grade: 05
My mom deserves a diamond because she has been a gratifying teacher long enough to have great patience with her curious children. She is considerate.

Kaylee Finnegan   Grade: 05
My mom deserves a diamond because even though she gets frustrated with me sometimes I always know that she loves me. She's exceptional to me.

Garrett Giltner   Grade: 05
My mom does a lot for the school and Red Cross. She gives blood and saves a life every day that goes and gives blood.

Justin Huitema   Grade: 05
My mom deserves a diamond because she forgives me no matter what and provides me with more love than a sad homeless kid desires.

Jack Jumer   Grade: 05
My mom deserves a diamond because she works full-time at a pharmacy and she really deserves it. She is a great mom, thank you.

William Kendall   Grade: 05
My mom deserves a diamond because whenever my brother and I get in trouble. She is strict, but open minded and caring to us.

Maya Landa   Grade: 05
My mom thinks about me first. Her life's spent taking care of me. She gives me what I need before she gets something for herself.

Cole Smith   Grade: 05
My mom deserves a diamond because she appreciates everyone, sees the brighter side of things, and will love me no matter what path I choose.

Samantha Williams   Grade: 05
I love my mother very much, she warms me by her every touch. She never lets me cheat; she's the one no one can beat.

Wood Canyon Elementary
Aliso Viejo

Teacher: Robert Bridwell

Gavin Anderson   Grade: 05
My mom deserves a diamond because she works hard to keep my sisters and I healthy. I want her to know she deserves it.

Ashley Edson   Grade: 05
My mom deserves a diamond since the day I was born. She's loved me tight and kept me close at her side. I love her.

Caroline Fleishman   Grade: 05
When smiles her eyes twinkle seek stars and her teeth sparkle. My mom deserves a diamond because it would match her sparkly personality.

Dillon Hallex   Grade: 05
My mom deserves a diamond because it's her birthstone and she loves jewelry and she would treasure it forever.

Gabriel Hernandez   Grade: 05
My mom deserves a diamond because she solves the problem even if she is mad., and kisses me when I'm blue.

Ethen Ibarra   Grade: 05
My mom deserves a diamond because she helps when needed. She works hard and is attending school to earn her B.A. For a better life.

Kennedy Mangum   Grade: 05
She is a working mom but she still has time to care for my two sisters and dad, and she is organized and loving.

Grant Morel   Grade: 05
My mom deserves a diamond because she is as beautiful as a rose on a hot summer day. She is also very honest and respectful.

Bibi Quasem   Grade: 05
My mom deserves a diamond because she keeps me safe from danger. She has four children in the house that she loves and cares about.

Lainey Westfall   Grade: 05
She's my mom and that's good enough for me; my mom deserves a diamond-it's as simple as can be!

Teacher: Ann Dockins

Mysoon Afridi   Grade: 03
My mom deserves a diamond because she is nice, better than mice! She is cute and uses a flute. She is attractive and very active.

Kabreah Anderson   Grade: 03
Mom's tall and pretty. Don't underestimate her because she always protects me. But the diamond must be as pretty as mommy.

Isaiah Dalden   Grade: 03
My mom deserves a diamond! She cleans everything and cuts my hair. She is smart, cute nice and helpful. She makes me go to bed early.

Hannah Fleischman   Grade: 03
When my mom laughs her eyes twinkle. Her hugs feel like you swallowed a gulp of hot soup. That's why she deserves a diamond.

Raya Hijazi   Grade: 03
Mom deserves a diamond, not just because she's sweet but also because she's fun to meet. She's creative and funny, and doesn't care about money.

Meelad Mozayanfar   Grade: 03
My mom deserves a diamond because she is very nice. My mom has a very nice name. Her name is Sahara. She is smart.

Katie Penn   Grade: 03
Nice, sweet and helpful, well that's my mom. I can't give her my things but I need something special that will make her smile.

Teacher: Kristi Hebbard

Bryan Beltran   Grade: 03
The morning sun shines like a diamond; it's lovely as a mom wearing a piece of sun which shines in the sky.

Maile Earlywine   Grade: 03
If you put a bunch of moms together, you will know which one is mine. Here eyes glow and her heart is like a ruby.

Kristin Farrell   Grade: 03
My mom is one million colors; she's purple, blue green, and more. She loves me and cares and helps me with nightmares.

Rebecca Martinez   Grade: 03
My mom makes problems go away. She lights everything up. Her hands are like smooth paths. She smell like strawberries.

Mason Moreland   Grade: 03
My mom's eyes melt in the skies of my heart. So beautiful you are drifting through the sky keeping my heart happy. You're a dazzling mom.

Leilani Ruiz   Grade: 03
My nana has the best soul. Her heart is made out of pure gold. She is very sweet. She helps me with everything I make.

Rachel Williams   Grade: 03
The stars shine on that pretty face of yours. You glow in my heart. You have gems in your eyes, they look just like emeralds.

Teacher: Eliana Koutroulis

Andrea Gonzalez   Grade: 01
My mom deserves a diamond because she is nice to us. She loves her husband and she goes to work when I am in school.

Nicholas Horner   Grade: 01
My mom deserves a diamond because she had four babies at the same time. She is gorgeous. She takes care of us.

Lauryn Horner   Grade: 01
My mom deserves a diamond because she had four babies at once. She takes good care of us and helps us stay healthy.

Alexandra Iemsisanith   Grade: 01
My mom deserves a diamond because she works at the gym all day when I'm at school. My mom likes her husband and her family.

Belen Meza   **Grade: 01**
My mom deserves a diamond because she helps people and my sister. She likes me. When I go to school she gives me a kiss.

Victoria Vernaza   **Grade: 01**
My mom deserves a diamond because she is cute and she wears nice clothes. She plays with me. I love my mom.

Andrew Vieta   Grade: 01
My mom deserves a diamond because she is nice and she is good. She is beautiful. She helps at my school.

Teacher: Mcall Lee

Conner Beekman   Grade: 05
My mom deserves a diamond because she is very sweet. When anyone sees her , they get swept off her feet!

Jorge Castillo   Grade: 05
My mom is sweeter than candy, braver than a knight, stronger than a mountain, more beautiful than a flower, and more loving than floating hearts.

Gordon Demeter   **Grade: 05**
My mom deserves a diamond because she is a maker of jewelry and loves gems. Her dream is to be a gifted gemologist.

Emily Eloedes   **Grade: 05**
My mom does everything for me, but as don't have enough money to buy her anything. This will make her smile (and me too!)

Skyler Nicoli   Grade: 05
My mom deserves a diamond because she's as sweet as nectar, as pretty as the stars... she loves me so much and that's worth a diamond.

Wyatt Robertson   **Grade: 05**
My mom deserves a diamond because she helps me with my homework. She plays with me and when I'm bored we play Wii together.

Teacher: Liz Martin

Rocco Biondi   Grade: 04
Because it will look nice on her finger and she would look pretty if my mom had a diamond.

Schuyler Deomampo   **Grade: 04**
My mom is as lovely as a rose. She shines like a star and her eyes are like the moon. My mom is my heart.

Catherine Dimapilis   Grade: 04
Red and purple are the colors of the prizes. My mom might like one of them. She will be happy when the diamond comes.

Vanessa Jimenez   Grade: 04
My mom has love like a dove. She is precious like a diamond. Real rare. A smile of stars in the sky.

Daisy Quintino   **Grade: 04**
Roses are red, daises are white, just like my mom on her anniversary night

Teacher: Miss Nelson

Henna Jahangiri   Grade: 02
My mom deserves a diamond because she is really nice. She always buys me stuff and she always lets me play outside. It's fun!

Leslie Nava   **Grade: 02**
My mom gives us food every day and she is very nice. When I was little, she helped me to stand up by myself.

Diana Perea   **Grade: 02**
My mom deserves a diamond because it would make her happy and she will keep it in her pocket.

Chanyang Song   Grade: 02
My mom deserves a diamond because she disciplines me, but she always forgives me with love, truth and with hope.

Teacher: Carla Nerney

Kennedy Dragon   Grade: 04
MY mom deserves a diamond because she's so nice. She cleans the house and does the cooking. I hope she's not looking. "Hi mom!"

Alexis Llamas   Grade: 04
My mom deserves a diamond because she is always cooking, cleaning, kind, beautiful, makes my lunches, does my hair and drops me off at school.

William Sidaris   **Grade: 04**
My mom deserves a diamond because she completes my family, she gives me joy and cheers me up. Without her, I'm incomplete.

Teacher: Jo Ann Punelli

Leena Alsowaigh   **Grade: 03**
My mom deserves a diamond because she is helpful, respectful and loveable. She is helpful because one time she helped me with Mario Cart.

Cosette Garzon   **Grade: 03**
My mom deserves a diamond because she loves me and helps me learn new things. When I'm sick , she lets me come to her job.

Jasmine Johnson   Grade: 03
My mom deserves a diamond because she's a hard worker, unique, graceful, pretty, grateful, honest, protective, and responsible. She makes good cinnamon apples.

Heila Manely   **Grade: 03**
She is grateful. One time when I gave her a gift she said "thank you" so many times and hugged me.

Ryan Rodriguez   Grade: 03
My mom is responsible because she makes me food. My mom is loveable because she tucks me in bed. She deserves a diamond.

Elanor Zierhut   Grade: 03
My mom deserves a diamond because she has us clean our room. She also goes on walks with us. I think she is very responsible.

Julie Robertson

Hailee Aguilar   **Grade: 03**
My mom deserves a diamond because when I'm sick her smile makes me gleam and her rosy cheeks make me cry.

Maddie Boyer   Grade: 03
Roses are red, violets are blue, My mom is careful, loving and true. My mom is nice, clean and beautiful, I hope yours is too.

Lindsi Kleppe   **Grade: 03**
Roses are red, violets are blue, My mom is a good citizen and yours is too.

Brianna Llamas   Grade: 03
My mom deserves the diamond because she works so hard and she always has a smile on her face every day and she is a sweetheart.

Erica Plomen   Grade: 03
My mom is cleaner than me. My mom is smart. My mom is loveable. My mom is a herd-worker. My mom is really terrific.

Teacher: Jessamy Tran

Noah Armstrong   Grade: 01
My mom deserves a diamond because she takes me to amusement parks all the time and lets me sleep in her bed.

Sydney Karimi   Grade: 01
My mom deserves a diamond because she loves me and she lets me eat whatever I want and she's the most important person I know.

Jillian Graham   Grade: 02
I think my mom should have a diamond because she takes care of me and nobody told her to. She makes us food. She loves us.

Woodcrest Elementary
Fullerton

Teacher: Ronette Merrihue

Eric Garcia   Grade: 05
My mom's eyes shine like diamonds. Her heart is bright as the morning sun. She is beautiful as a spring morning, and I'm so grateful.

Ashlea Grabau   Grade: 05
My mom is always there to support me at school, dance, and everything I do. She stands out from everyone else with her humorous personality.

Jazmin Martinez   Grade: 05
My mom is the best because she supports me throughout my life. If I need help with girl problems, she is always there for me.

Thomas Morrison 3rd   Grade: 05
My mom is nice and always helps me. She cooks for me and always buys me clothes to wear. She doesn't embarrass me at all.

Miguel Rojas   Grade: 05
My mom is the best mom ever. She gives me food in the morning. She lets me go outside to play and have fun.

Teacher: Rochelle Wolf

Anthony DeLeon   Grade: 05
My mom's hands are warm like an oven. My mom is as beautiful as a yellow rose. My love for her grows and grows.

Candy Hernandez   Grade: 05
My mom is as beautiful as a red rose. My mom's hair is as brown as a chocolate bar. I love her like a guitar.

Oscar Herrada   Grade: 05
My mom's hugs are as soft, like a pillow. My mom's hair is as soft as a peacock's feather. She'll always keep our family together.

Alicia Morales   Grade: 05
My mom's eyes are like pots of honey. Her heart is as big as the universe. She is the best woman I have ever met.

Daisy Morales   Grade: 05
My mom's hair is as curly as spaghetti. Her eyes are sparkling as a diamond. I love her and always will.

Uziel Perez   Grade: 05
My mom is as sweet as candy cane. Her heart is as big as three galaxies. I love her more than she sees.

Jose Placencia   Grade: 05
My mom's heart is as red as a ruby. Her eyes are as bright as shooting stars. I love her more than candy bars.

Giselle Ruiz   Grade: 05
My mom's hair is as curly as a curly fry. Her personality is as loving as her heart. We will never be apart.

Adam Trujillo   Grade: 05
My mom's hands are as soft as a velvet blanket. Her earrings are as light like the sun. I love her and always will.

Woodsboro Elementary
Anaheim

Teacher: Amy Livergood

Dorian Apitz   Grade: 05
Like a lion's mane, her hair blows in the wind. Her eyes like diamonds. No matter what the weather is, she will be smiling.

Jared Bogler   Grade: 05
She's one like no there. She's kind and sweet. Her heart is the center of a warm cookie. She deserves a sparkling diamond,

Scott Burn   Grade: 05
Her eyes glimmer and shine, she works like it's a mine, to keep us all happy and fed, she's worth every bead.

Adrika Chakraborty   Grade: 05
Her solid gold heart will melt into mine because of compassionate love. The moonlit sky drops silvery tears at the sight of her hard work.

Justin Dionne   Grade: 05
You shine in my heart like the sun itself. You glow like the moon, you make me shine mom.

Aurora Donaldson   Grade: 05
Heart as big as the world. Soul as big as the heart. I love mom and mom loves me. We would never tear apart.

Tiffany Hoang   Grade: 05
Her eyes twinkle like stars in the dim light of the moon. Her heart, warm and mushy, always caring for me.

Tiana Huynh   Grade: 05
Her heart warms my soul. Her smile walks me through. She helps me pursue my goal. There are only few...in the world like her.

Jacob Leiken   Grade: 05
Through sports galore and carpools even more. My mom's the best and wouldn't ever miss an inning or a goal.

Kenzie Lombard   Grade: 05
My mom shimmers in the moonlight, shines like a star. Her eyes sparkle like the morning sun. Everyday I tell my mom, I love her,

Rubin Patel   Grade: 05
My mom...her diamond eyes sparkle with compassion. Her golden heart filled with affection. Her love flows through me like the air that I breathe.

Nathan Shube   Grade: 05
Loving and compassionate, with a heart of gold, two crystal eyes and a soul of silver. She is the jewel of my life.

Angela Tsai   Grade: 05
Her eyes as dark as night, but in them sparkles life. She teaches me things I don't know. She is my role model.

Yermo (Glen) Elementary
Mission Viejo

Teacher: Lois Connors

Danielle De la Cruz   Grade: 05
A gem is a heart. A heart is a gem, but my only gem is my mom who I love.

Kevin Esquivel   **Grade: 05**
My mom's eyes glow in the light of the moon in the sky and her heart is as hot as the sun in space.

Kimberly Flores   Grade: 05
My mom is the gem in my heart. She is the one that I love from the start. She cares everywhere.

Jocelyne Flores   Grade: 05
Her eyes twinkle like a beautiful star that gazes like the moon. Her soul is a gorgeous flower. Her heart is a diamond she deserves.

Caitlin Jaggli   **Grade: 05**
My mom's heart shines like the moonlight and stars. Her smile is as bright as the sun. That's why she gets the love from above.

Jordan Loya   Grade: 05
The gazing eyes of the person I love. Her exquisite face makes me feel warm inside. A diamond would be the key to her heart.

Samuel Manzo   Grade: 05
My mother is like no other. Her eyes shine like the stars that watch over me. Her hands are as gentle as her voice.

John Pope   **Grade: 05**
My mom is like a sunset at a beach that shines in the water like a pearl.

Zoha Qadeer   Grade: 05
The river reflects against the moon as much as your eyes shine in the sky. Your eyes are gleaming diamonds, which you positively deserve.

Naomy Servellon   Grade: 05
Her soul is my sunlight. Her eyes are the stars…that's how I describe her. I love her so much, you're my soul mom.

David Valerio   **Grade: 05**
Your gleaming eyes are like a sun shining brightly. My heart is like a dove waiting to be free from it's cage. She's my gem.

Teacher: Linda Smith

Nikki Calloway   **Grade: 05**
My mom has a heart of gold. It's her blood in my veins that helps me live. My mom deserves a diamond.

Shane Cringle   Grade: 05
A precious look in your eyes. You strengthen me in life. On the days that I cry, you say "I love you" and I'm alright.

Juan Gomez   Grade: 05
You bring sun on my cloudy day, promised me you'd always stay. Your strength took my fears away, your hand wiped my tears away.

Joshua John   Grade: 05
My mom is cool even when I act like a fool. She is always there when I need her near. She is my mom.

Viridiana Medina   **Grade: 05**
I wrote your name into the sky, but the winds washed it away. I wrote your name into my heart and forever it shall stay.

Sebastian Reyes   **Grade: 05**
I have two things in my life: A rose and my mom. The rose is for one day and you are forever.

Dillon Sherman   **Grade: 05**
You stood by me through thick and thin, even when I didn't win. You carried me long miles when I was sad and restored my smiles.

Zach Stidham   Grade: 05
A diamond is a stone, a grandmother is a heart. I love her with my soul. When she talks, I hear a beautiful sound.

Danna Vasquez   Grade: 05
My mom is a rose spreading love around me. My mom protects me when I'm scared. My mom's hugs make me feel better.

Emily Vollert   Grade: 05
I know that my mom is watching over me and watching my every move. Thanks for being there, I am happy that you care.

Sandra Zamora   **Grade: 05**
I think of you when I'm at school. I think of you when I'm sleeping. I think of you in my heart. I love you.

Teacher: Judy Weed

Raven Burns   Grade: 06
My mom deserves diamonds. That's because the labor of her love is very good to give. And each and everyday she gives it away.

Jessica Chavez   Grade: 06
My mom is precious like a diamond and she is my moonlight that guides me.

Emma Chiecchio   Grade: 06
Why mom deserves a diamond because I love her and she loves me, more than the clouds you see up to the sky, up high.

Yorba (Bernardo) Jr. High
Yorba Linda

Teacher: Don Gebler

Andrew Chang   Grade: 07
She shines brighter than any star, lighting up my way. She is a queen of touching love within my heart. That's mom, precious and sweet.

Jennifer Do   **Grade: 07**
To say she's made of gold and silver… blasphemy. She shimmers with brilliant shards of fire and life, foremost in the heart of a diamond.

Maxwell Ellington   **Grade: 07**
Mother bird keeps her young warm, in the harshest wind and harshest storm. Though her young she does warn, still they wander, hopefully home by morn.

Lauren Escalante   Grade: 07
Roses are red, violets are blue. I will miss my mom when she leaves for school. I can't wait for my mom's hugs at last.

Troy Gaghon   **Grade: 07**
My mom is the best queen rabbit. She gives up her clear carats so we can have our orange carrots. She deserves a shiny diamond.

Jack Gillespie   Grade: 07
My mother deserves a diamond for her compassion, but not just towards me, to all people who deserve a loving hand on their heart.

Paige Gulley   Grade: 07
Moms do a list of things, but the best thing mom can do is inspire you to love her, and in return, she loves you.

Nikelle Guzman   **Grade: 07**
Dreaming, a mother who desires me, nourishes me, and inspires me…then it dawned on me, this isn't a dream, she's mine.

Mackenzie Holst   **Grade: 07**
Superman's flaw is kryptonite. Spiderman's is Mary Jane. But my birth mother has no weaknesses; yet she performed the ultimate act of heroism; she gave me up.

Zane Padilla   Grade: 07
She has been loving for as long as the sky of day has been blue.

Katalina Park   Grade: 07
Candy is good and sweet, but it doesn't last forever like the warm, beating heart of my mother.

* Amethyst winners in bold.

Sarah Robison   Grade: 07
I think my mother deserves a diamond because my mother tries her best to teach me right from wrong, so I won't be evil.

Nichole Romero   Grade: 07
My mom participates in Girl Scouts, Boy Scouts, Brownies (girls) and she loves to be a mother to every kid and she deserves this.

Sierra Schinhofen   Grade: 07
She works more jobs than anyone I know. She's a taxi driver, cook, house cleaner, laundry washer, coach, teacher, friend, and she's my hero.

Brady Smith   Grade: 07
My mom deserves a diamond because she has a time consuming job at church and can still be an amazing mom to three proud kids.

Jacob Stevens   Grade: 07
My mom deserves a diamond because she has worked for over 13 years to make sure all 5 of her children were taken care of.

Justin Whittaker   Grade: 07
My mom is always there whether it is a scraped knee or a broken heart; she never leaves my side.

Heba Zanayed   Grade: 07
Her eyes look in my heart. Her passion is loved. The voice she calls, sound like an angel from Heaven above.

Teacher: Kristin Riles

Cole Flowers   Grade: 08
She carried and cared for me when I was young. She wiped away tears and washed away blood. I will never forget her motherly love.

Sarah Shawki   Grade: 08
My mom is always thinking of others before herself. She is always thinking of me first; for once she deserves something for her.

Rylee Wilmeth   Grade: 08
She never gives up. She frequently knows what to say to make my heart mend. My mom is a magnificent friend and she's my stimulation.

Teacher: Margaret Silver

Zach LeDoux   Grade: 07
My mom deserves a diamond. When we came home for the weekend, our beds were made. She cleans our rooms. She is caring and funny.

Brandon Shimoide   Grade: 07
My mom deserves a diamond for all the things she does for me. She makes my breakfast in the mornings. She loves me everyday.

Yorba Linda Middle
Yorba Linda

Teacher: Melanie Carmona

Kendra Horsfield   Grade: 07
Inspirational, beautiful, angel. Glistening star. Works hard. Loving mom. Like a unique song. Precious jewel. My world she rules. Her smile enlightens loved one around.

Adam Jankowski   Grade: 07
Amazing, outstanding, kind as can be. My mom is always there for me. She is beautiful, hardworking and sincere. She deserves a big cheer.

Ashley Nichols   Grade: 07
Every diamond is unique just like my mom. She shines and stand out over all the others. My mom is a true work of art.

Alyssa Oertwig   Grade: 07
My mom is a powerful source of encouragement. Plus, she scrapbooks everything in my life so I can look back later. I love her graciously.

Ramesha Patel   Grade: 07
My mom deserves a diamond because as a daughter, it's job to keep her frown upside down. Appreciating her with a diamond will last long.

Jake Wagner   Grade: 07
Beautiful, flawless, and dazzling. Brilliant, breathtaking, and unique. I'm not talking about a diamond, but instead my loving, one of a kind fantastic mom.

John Yi   Grade: 07
As my mom immigrated from Korea at high school, she had to do all the house chores and study hard to make her life successful.

Teacher: Cathy Hinson

Lauren Hernandez   Grade: 08
Aunt Sue deserves a diamond because she loves to take in foster kids. I am one of her foster kids. She will always love me.

Libby Magargee   Grade: 08
Mom always helps me with my horses. She greatly loves me and I greatly love her. In my eyes, she really deserves this great prize.

Vanessa Panizo   Grade: 08
She deserves it for all her hard work. She is a good person. All she does is give, never takes.

Teacher: Cameron Paulin

Zedam Borrie   Grade: 07
I think my mom deserves a diamond because she saved my life. I was choking and she dropped everything to save me.

Hansen Cohen   Grade: 07
My mom's always there for me. She stopped doing dangerous things like skydiving because she wants to stay safe to be with me.

Steven Galvan   Grade: 07
My mom deserves a diamond because she has taken care of me for twelve years and I haven't been able to buy her anything expensive.

Brandon Eickhoff   Grade: 08
My mom: My role model, my inspiration, my friend. She is the glistening gold in a treasure chest. She is a diamond.

Brieanna Gray   Grade: 08
She's the one there to Band-Aid your boo boos. There for our first heart break. But mostly, there for our first breath and our last.

Kathy Nguyen   Grade: 08
My mom is someone who always makes sure we're going down the right path, even if that means sacrificing her happiness. She is my hero.

Shane Shahrestani   Grade: 08
The qualities of diamonds are rare in people. Not everybody has beauty, elegance, value, uniqueness, rarity, and being irreplaceable. Qualities like this deserve a diamond.

Zion Lutheran School
Anaheim

Teacher: Judy Bakalyar

Joey Adamson   Grade: 05
My mom is the meaning of love to me. Forever we will always be. I'm happy when she watches me perform. I love my mom.

Trevor Bengston   Grade: 05
Mom is sweet, kind, and very generous. I hardly get to see her. I want her to have a diamond in remembrance of me.

Steven Fick — Grade: 05
My mom is an awesome mom. Whenever I see her eyes, I feel better. She always burns with excitement. Nothing can describe my mom.

Benjamin Flores — Grade: 05
My mom is my sunshine on a cloudy day. She picks me up when I am down. She makes me smile when I frown.

Camden Lowe — Grade: 05
My mom is a star shining greater than all. She is like an angel with a voice so beautiful. She is loving, kind, and graceful.

Brianne Martinez — Grade: 05
My mom is wonderful. My mom is great. She is the best mom in the whole United States.

Corrie McClees — Grade: 05
Her eyes shimmer like crystal light. She's loving as can be. She's a beautiful diamond. Her cheeks are ruby red. Who is she? My mom.

Monique Villicana — Grade: 05
Peace, care, love, making greeting cards, making her laugh, makes my mom's heart open. Her eyes sparkle like the sun sets on the ocean water.

Teacher: Elizabeth Noriega

Netana Christiansen — Grade: 03
My mom deserves a diamond because she is very nice. My mom has many talents, like working hard, cleaning house, being a psychologist and art.

Alyssa Flores — Grade: 03
My mom deserves a diamond because she makes me shine when I wake up, she makes my day.

Brent Lowe — Grade: 03
My mom is very loving. She cooks for my family. My mom helps my class. That's why my mom deserves a diamond.

Andrew Macias — Grade: 03
My mommy deserves a diamond because she tucks me in at night. She spoils me a lot. She always plays with me. She works hard.

Lauren Ware — Grade: 03
My mom deserves a diamond because she is a good singer. She is a nurse who cares for me. She deserves at least a small diamond.

* Amethyst winners in bold.

Martha Velia Watson

1925　　　**1938**　　　**1939**　　　**1940**　　　**2001**

Martha Velia Watson was the adoptive mother of contest founder Michael Watson. She was born March 15, 1920, in Lily, Kentucky. During World War ll, Martha worked in Cincinnati, Ohio, sanding molds for airplane parts. She married in 1944 and moved to New Albany, Indiana. Martha was a cub scout den mother and loved to actively participate in school PTAs. Martha was a compassionate listener and one who forgave easily. She was slow to criticize, yet quick to encourage. Martha also loved kids.

In 1993, the WHY MOM DESERVES A DIAMOND® contest was established in her name to give kids the opportunity to express their appreciation for their own moms. Since then, the contest has positively touched millions of people in our nation. Because of her courage and support in her son's search for his biological origins, Martha will always be known as the first mother to inspire this legendary contest.

Following is a poem written the day before her funeral. Martha died on September 14, 2006.

Because She Loved Me First

Mom woke me softly in the morning
And readied me for school
Speak kind words to everyone
Obey the Golden Rule

With a gentle hug and kiss
She handed me a sack
Potato sticks, with snacks and fruits
Were very neatly packed

Her endless love embraced me
Even while at play
She was the warm sun glowing
As I ran throughout the day

"I hope you like my art," I said
"I made it just for you"
My mom was always proud of me
Despite the smears of blue

Although I'd drawn outside the lines
She praised me anyway
And on the table by the door
She framed it for display

With open ears she sat to hear
My worries of the day
The problems seemed to disappear
With caring words to say

Then adventure burned my soul
To search for distant lands
She spoke three things before I left
I held her wrinkling hands

Remember that I love you
And before I closed the door
Remember to love others
And there was just one more

Remember that I chose you
To be my very own
Now my dear adopted son
Into a man you've grown

The tears I cry are from joy
For my mom will never die
Because she'll live within my heart
As long as I'm alive

Now in every face I meet
My mom smiles back at me
Her priceless gift was her flame
Of blinding Light, you see

Through every desert I may walk
My soul will never thirst
I learned to love you and myself
Because she loved me first

Famous Diamonds

The Golden Jubilee. 545.67 carats.

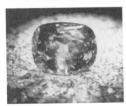

This enormous yellow-brown diamond was cut by Gabi Tolkowsky, and was presented to the King of Thailand in 1997 for his Golden Jubilee - the 50th anniversary of his coronation. Prior to this event, the stone was simply known as the Unnamed Brown. The Golden Jubilee is the largest cut diamond in the world.

The Cullinan. 3,106 carats in rough!

One of the largest diamonds ever found, the Cullinan originally weighed about 1 1/2 pounds. It was cut into 105 beautiful diamonds, one of which is the 530 carat Star of Africa. In 1907 this diamond was given to King Edward VII of England and set into the Royal Scepter. It is currently displayed with the British Crown Jewels in the tower of London, and is the second largest cut diamond in the world.

The Incomparable. 407.48 carats.

Formerly called the Golden Giant, this diamond was found in Zaire in the 1980's by a young girl playing in a pile of rubble outside her uncle's house. Its rough shape was extremely irregular, with many gaps, cavities and cracks. The inside, however, was virtually free from inclusions. After four years of studying the stone, The Incomparable was eventually cut by Louis Glick into an internally flawless, brownish-yellow shield shape. It is the third largest cut diamond in the world.

The Centenary. 273.85 carats.

This diamond was discovered on July 17, 1986. It took a select team of master cutters almost three years to complete its transformation into the 273.85 carat diamond it is today. The Centenary Diamond, which is now the world's largest top color, flawless, modern cut diamond, was unveiled appropriately at the Tower of London in May 1991.

The Orlov. 194.75 carats.

Legend says this stone, which served as the eye of an Indian idol, found its way into the Court of Russia in the 1700's, where Prince Orloff gave it to his ex-lover, Catherine the Great. This stone is currently held in the Diamond Treasury in Moscow.

The Regent. 140.50 carats.

Found on the Kistna River, India in 1701, this diamond weighed 410 carats. The stone was cut into a brilliant cushion shape. In 1717, it was sold to the Duke of Orleans, regent of France. The royals used the stone in many ways, including being set in the Crown of Louis XV, as a hair ornament of Queen Marie, and as an adornment in the hat of Marie Antoinette. After the French Revolution the stone was set in the hilt of Napoleon Bonaparte's sword. Napoleon's wife, Marie Louisa, carried the Regent back to Austria upon his death. Later her father returned it to the French Crown Jewels. Today, it remains in the French Royal Treasury at Louvre.

The Premier Rose. 137.02 carats.

A spectacular pear-shaped diamond boasting a grade of D flawless, the Premier Rose is one of the largest perfect diamonds in the world. It was discovered in 1978 at the Premier Mine in South Africa. Robert Mouawad has recently added the Premier Rose to his great collection of diamonds. The stone is now valued at over $10,000,000.

Koh-I-Noor. 105.60 carats.

This oval-shaped diamond is one of the most famous diamonds in the world. Historically, the first mention of it is in India in 1297. It has been said that whoever owned the Koh-i-noor ruled the world. It is now among the British Crown Jewels.

Taylor-Burton Diamond. 69.42 carats.

This pear-shaped diamond was sold at auction in 1969 with the understanding that it could be named by the buyer. Cartier of New York successfully bid for it and christened it "Cartier". However, the next day Richard Burton bought the stone for Elizabeth Taylor, renaming it the "Taylor-Burton." In June 1979, the stone was sold for nearly $3 million and was last reported to be in Saudi Arabia.

The Hope. 45.52 carats.

The Hope Diamond is a natural blue diamond that was once owned by Louis XIV. After being stolen during the French Revolution, it turned up in London in 1830 and was bought by the Hope family. While in their possession, the stone acquired its gruesome reputation for bad luck and the entire Hope family died in poverty. It is now in the Smithsonian Institute in Washington.

Memories

2009. Searching the world to find a Diamond Winner. Guita Afzali, Michael Watson and Tram Diep.

2000. Buried in essays! Carmen Watson, Chuong Pham, and Jo Christian.

1997. Jessica Barraco and Genevieve Slunka present $3,000 to the Orange County Public Library. Mothers Dianne and Sherry.

Memories

1998. Sandy Fredlund, Terry Ogles, Carmen Watson and Carmen Ogles pose beside contest entries.

1998. Front: Jason Kirstein, Vicki Ann Blood, Tawnya Ravy, and Jennifer Plankenhorn. Back: Mothers Heather and Kathy, Michael Watson, mothers Nancy and Janet.

2000. L to R. Cathy and Rachel Tomberlin, honored guest Ruth Ketchersid- our first 1993 Diamond Mom! Tiffany Lamanski and mother, Pauline, Sandy Enriquez and her aunt, Emma.

Meet Our Jewelry Professionals

Michael Watson
CEO, G (GIA)

Watson spent most of his life in New Albany, Indiana, and graduated with a business degree from Indiana University. After working as a diamond merchant for an Indianapolis jewelry chain, he moved to California and founded Gallery of Diamonds in 1991. Watson is a member of the American Adoption Congress and is a Gemological Institute of America-trained gemologist. He is the author of *Adopted Like Me*.

Tram Tiffani Diep
Creative Director

Tram earned a BA in Arts from UCI, majoring in Studio Arts, with a double minor in Digital Arts and Educational Studies. Tram is highly skilled in graphic and visual arts, and has created a multitude of professional marketing brochures. At a major non-profit institution, Tram developed the Art and Illustration program, taught students, created instruction manuals, and trained instructors. Tram illustrated the 2009 Mother's Book.

Life starts with an idea and continues with an imagination.

Janey Perone
Contest Staff

Janey is a native of Southern California. She has trade experience in a variety of fields including jewelry. Janey makes sure the contest is a positive and rewarding experience for every mother and child. Her creative talent is an asset of our industry. Janey loves crafting and cooking. She especially loves to fish. Her true passion is her children. Janey understands what a gift it is to be a mom.

Sandra Babic
Contest Staff

Sandra received her Bachelors degree in French and English from the Univsersity of California, Santa Barbara, and her teaching credential from California State University, Fullerton. She has taught from preschool to graduate school and her areas of expertise are foreign languages and English. She joined the teaching staff in the Saddleback Unified School District in 1989.

It is with great pleasure and pride I have joined the panel of judges for this most worthwhile contest.

Carmen Watson
CFO, Diamond Consultant

Born in Guatemala, Carmen was an administrator for her native city. She came to the United States after receiving her teaching degree. Since our inception, Carmen has been responsible for the daily accounting and merchandise buying for the company. She has proven many of her remarkable talents, such as hand-selecting every gemstone prize and scheduling thousands of winning families to come and receive them.

What I love about the Why Mom Deserves a Diamond® contest is the smiles on the winners faces when I say, 'Today you are going to honor your mother.'

Guita Afzali
Jewelry Consultant

Guita was born in Tehran, Iran. She came to the United States in 1978 and studied at the Academy of Arts in San Francisco. She also worked as a jewelry consultant for a major jewelry chain.
Guita moved to Orange County in 2001.

I am so happy to work for a company that encourages every kid to express what they feel about their moms.

Jeanette Rodriguez
Contest Staff

Jeanette was born in Los Angeles and moved to Orange County when she was in High School.
She enjoys traveling and sight-seeing.
You can often find Jeanette riding bikes with her son in Newport Beach.

I believe there are no accidents. Being part of Gallery of Diamonds has inspired me to be a better mother and daughter to my own mother. My desire is to share that inspiration with other families.

Michael Campus
Contest Staff

Michael graduated from Loara High School in Anaheim and won C.I.F. for Wrestling. He was the top loan officer for a major mortgage company and he has also been a merchant account manager.

I want to excel in everything I encounter.

Meet Our Jewelry Professionals

Doretta Debrick
Contest Essay Typist

Doretta grew up in Arcadia, California. During her first typing session in junior high school, she cut her thumb on the electric typewriter return bar. She always wondered if she would get the momentum to type fast. Well, Doretta now types up to 85 wpm! She raised her two children in Laguna Beach and currently works in San Diego as an Administrative Associate. When not typing, she enjoys golfing, walking on the beach, and reading.

It is a joy to get all of those words formatted for the final stages of publishing.

Claudio Canestro
Computer Specialist/Graphic Designer

Claudio was born in Pto. Ordaz, Venezuela, and lived in Sanremo, Italy for twelve years. He has worked for renowned companies such as Yahoo, Adobe, and Google and has been a computer consultant specializing in the graphic and advertising industries. He is also a Macintosh computer expert and a master graphic designer. Because our contest requires extreme organization, Claudio makes sure operations run smoothly with efficient systems.

Sergio Cruz,
Information and Technology Specialist

Sergio is a Macintosh expert and a FileMaker Pro expert. Sergio has been an Independent Database and Computer Consultant since 1995. His clients have been Apple, FileMaker Inc., and Netscape,

Sergio has a Bachelor of Arts in English from Rutgers University in New Brunswick, New Jersey.

Sergio is the genius that makes sure the computer system works efficiently.

Claudia Elliott
Contest Staff

Claudia was born the night day before Easter in the middle of a blizzard in Fargo North Dakota. With twenty years of natural resource management and business experience - she values her family, friends, plants and animals the most.

Eileen O'Hearn
Vocalist

Eileen is the mystery vocalist of the Why Mom Deserves a Diamond® song! Her captivating voice has charmed thousands of families from the in-store video and the Internet.

Eileen teaches voice, beginning piano, and other music courses at various colleges and universities. She teaches a summer musical theatre camp for kids up to eighteen years old and is a frequent soloist with the local symphony and local chamber music groups. Eileen is also a mom with two kids.

The Lyrics

Why Mom Deserves a Diamond

I read these words from my heart
And place this prize in her hand
Wanna let her know, I love her so
She's the greatest mom in the land

Why mom deserves a diamond
Why mom deserves my love
Why mom deserves a diamond
From Gallery of Diamonds

More Diamonds

You are the sparkle in my eyes
You are the memories that I prize
You remind me of my good times

I want diamonds
More diamonds
More diamonds
From Gallery of Diamonds

© 2006 Gallery of Diamonds

The 2009 Contest Panel Judges

Jennifer Ferrara, Teacher
Charles Emery, Buena Park, CA.

Ferrara has been teaching for 16 years in the Buena Park School District. She has taught all grade levels, and is currently teaching sixth grade at Charles G. Emery Elementary School. Jennifer received her bachelors and masters degrees from California State University, Fullerton. She received Teacher of the Year from her colleagues in both 1995 and in 2002. This is the ninth year that Miss Ferrara's class has been participating in the WHY MOM DESERVES A DIAMOND® contest, and her fourth year as a panel judge. There is a poetry section located in her classroom where all the past poetry books are located, which the children enjoy reading.

Writing about the one you love most is so natural. That is why every poem is truly a winner!

Valarie Ruig, Teacher
Courreges, Fountain Valley

Ruig received her Bachelors degrees in Journalism and in Communications from the University of Southern California and her teaching credential from Concordia University. She continued her graduate studies and earned a Masters in Education from Concordia as well. Ruig is currently teaching fifth grade G.A.T.E. in Orange County.

I'm thrilled to participate in the WHY MOM DESERVES A DIAMOND® contest. What an amazing way to ignite creativity in our children and offer gratitude toward Mom!"

Cristina Coello Barber, Teacher
MacArthur D. Fund., Santa Ana, CA

Cristina was born in Inglewood, California, the descendant of two hardworking Cuban parents. She grew up in Huntington Beach, California, and graduated from California State University, Long Beach with a Bachelor's Degree and earned a Master's Degree in Reading and Language Arts. She has worked as a fifth grade teacher, a Spanish teacher, an English language development teacher, and is currently a sixth grade Language Arts teacher.

I enjoy the excitement of telling my students that they've won a precious stone from Gallery of Diamonds. It's rewarding to give students the opportunity to participate in a contest that honors their mother through the expressive poems they are inspired to write.

Jan Bryant, Teacher
Mariners Christian Sch., Costa Mesa

As a veteran teacher of over thirty years, Mrs. Bryant has inspired many students to express themselves through their writing. As an author of two books, Mrs. Bryant credits her earliest writing experience to her 4th grade teacher, who compiled her own classroom book of Poems Written by Children on a Rainy Afternoon. Mrs. Bryant still has some of those poems she wrote as a child, and she encourages all of her students to save their poems and writing ideas. *You never know when that idea can be turned into a published story or poem!*

I love it when students who never thought they could write begin to learn the joy of creating beautiful and expressive words.

Jeff Chien
W.R. Nelson Elementary, Tustin, CA

Jeff is a 4th grade teacher and the chair of the school writing committee. He is currently his school's Teacher of the Year. He has been awarded two grants for writing. Jeff has created a college scholarship endowment for his former students that are supervised by the Tustin Public School's Foundation.

Danielle De Frank, Teacher
Plaza Vista, Irvine, CA

Pink roses wrapped in aluminum foil. A collection of sea rocks in a Ziploc. Baked goods burned on the bottom. What does a child give her queen? Already an adult, Danielle De Frank still tries to find the right gifts to express appreciation for her mom, knowing none could ever match in comparison with what has been provided.

As an Elementary Science Specialist for the Irvine Unified School District, running science labs at two schools, she learned about the WHY MOM DESERVES A DIAMOND® contest last year.

Jennifer Ahn
Fern Drive Elementary, Fullerton, CA

Jennifer received her Bachelors degrees in Psychology and Sociology from Biola University and her teaching credential from California State University, Fullerton, with a BCLAD in Mandarin-Chinese. She continued her graduate studies and received a Masters degree from National University. Jennifer has been teaching for seven years in the Fullerton School District and is currently a second grade teacher at Fern Drive Elementary School.

Thank you again for the amazing opportunity to serve as a judge. I truly enjoyed the experience!"

The 2009 Contest Panel Judges

Hazel Alvarez
University Park Elementary, Irvine, CA

Hazel Alvarez is currently a Special Day Class teacher for 3rd and 4th grades at University Park Elementary School in Irvine. She received her Education Specialist and Multiple Subjects credentials at Chapman University. Prior to teaching at University Park, she taught special education at Lake Center Middle School in Santa Fe Springs.

"The WHY MOM DESERVES A DIAMOND® contest was a great experience reading about how the students appreciate their moms".

Marina Baltazar, Teacher
Lincoln Elementary, Santa Ana, Ca

Marina has taught 4th grade at Lincoln Elementary in Santa Ana for the past three years. She received her Bachelors degree in Liberal Studies from Cal State Fullerton as well as her Bilingual CLAD teaching credential. Her most important achievement has been having a family to share her accomplishments.

I enjoy teaching because I believe that every child has potential to become great leaders and as a teacher I provide the educational tools to achieve their goals. This is my first year being a judge and I had a great time reading about what they felt about their mother. I am glad I was part of this wonderful acknowledgement for mothers.

Orlene Burd
Linda Vista Elementary, Orange, CA

Orlene Burd has been teaching for thirteen years. Her B.A. in Child Development, and her teaching credential are from Cal. State Univ. at Fullerton. She has taught 3rd, 4th and 6th grades. She enjoys her upper grade Math club on Wednesdays after school. The object is to help these (students) learn that Math is important in everything we do, and can be fun to play with.

I have been enjoying the WHY MOM DESERVES A DIAMOND® contest with my students, and my own children for 14 years. I am helping judge, as a way of giving back to a program that gives so many people a chance to tell and hear just how deep their love goes.

Paulette Dunn
Lincoln Elementary, Santa Ana, CA

One of the most rewarding tasks in life is to teach children, and in teaching them, I've learned a simple truth. The Mother-child bond is the strongest link to family that there is. The genuine love that children feel for their mothers is written so tenderly in their essays. I so enjoy reading the sincere and innocent beauty of the words they express so sweetly.

Karen French
Reilly Elementary, Mission Viejo, CA

Karen French is a veteran teacher of 22 years with the Capistrano Unified School District. She has participated with her students in the WHY MOM DESERVES A DIAMOND® contest for over ten years. Karen was also an honored Diamond Teacher in 2001 and 2004 and was a Diamond Contest Panel Judge in 2009!

I simply love the WHY MOM DESERVES A DIAMOND® because it gives the opportunity for my students to reflect on the love they have for their moms and to express it creatively in words. As a mother, wife, and teacher, I am honored to participate in the judging and to read each child's amazing words of love.

Gail Gilpin, Teacher
Barcelona Hills Elem., Mission Viejo, CA

Gail Gilpin has been teaching for 30 years for the Capistrano Unified School District. She received her Bachelor degree from the University of California, Riverside and her Masters in Education from the United States International University. The highlight of her teaching experience has been the past five years teaching in a collaborative second grade program that mainstreams students with special needs with the regular education program.

As a mother and a teacher I treasure the WHY MOM DESERVES A DIAMOND® contest as a highly motivating writing experience for my students and a life long memorable event for the winners and their mothers.

Mrs. Debbie Igram
Trinity Lutheran School, Anaheim, CA

Debbie has been a teacher for 23 years, teaching grades 2, 3, 4, and 6 and teaching both children and adults in Sunday school. She loves kids and enjoys helping them learn new and exciting things in every subject, especially history and the Bible. Her hobbies include traveling, camping, scrapbooking, arts and crafts, and playing with her 2 labrador retrievers.

I love the Why Mom Deserves a Diamond® contest because it gives the students the chance to think about, verbalize, and write about why their mothers are special to them. We have a really good time discussing why moms are important.

The 2009 Contest Panel Judges

Kathi Manuel
Cox Elementary, Fountain Valley, CA

I have been teaching for over 35 years in the Fountain Valley School District. I am currently the Coordinator for the School Improvement Program at James H. Cox School. Several summers ago, I participated in the U.C.I. Writing Project. It changed my life. Participating teachers were expected to write a selection each week to share with their writing group. It revealed to me the power of words and of writing.

That's why I am so impressed with the WHY MOM DESERVES A DIAMOND® contest. By participating in it, many young writers will feel the power of their words. They'll be able to pay tribute to their mothers and experience how their words touch the hearts of their wonderful moms. I am sure there are lots of tears and hugs that follow the reading of each piece of writing. I enjoyed reading each and every entry and encourage everyone to keep writing!

Janette Mattoon
St. Paul's Lutheran School, Orange, CA

It is amazing to see the growth in small children, and the amazing abilities in older students. The WHY MOM DESERVES A DIAMOND® contest is a wonderful experience to be a part of. To see the reflection in writing of how lucky we are to be mom's. I have two wonderful children who loved participating in this contest!

Anna Smith, Teacher
Los Coyotes Elementary, La Palma, CA

Anna received her Bachelor's Degree in Liberal Art from Pepperdine University and her Master's degree in 2006. She has been teaching either the fifth or sixth grade for seven years in Centralia School District. Anna loves working with young learners and always enjoys her students' delight in writing for the Why Mom Deserves a Diamond® contest. Her classes have participated in the contest for the past 5 years. Anna credits own mom for helping her become a teacher and discover the joys of teaching others to learn.

I feel one's relationship with their mother is one of the most valuable and important aspects in life, and the WHY MOM DESERVES A DIAMOND® contest is a wonderful outlet for students to express their gratitude.

Jan Richards
College View Elementary, Orange, CA

Jan received her Bachelors degree in Sociology from the University of California San Diego and her Teaching Credential a few years later from Cal Poly Pomona. She also received her Masters degree in Education from National University. *I have been teaching for 18 years and have loved every minute of it. I am currently teaching fourth grade at College View Elementary in Huntington Beach.*

As both a teacher and a mother the WHY MOM DESERVES A DIAMOND® contest touches my heart. I value the opportunity to provide a forum for my students to extol the virtues of the women so important in their lives - their moms.

Ms. Marianne Stewart, Teacher
Lexington Junior High School, Cypress, CA

Marianne Stewart has been teaching in Orange County for the past 10 years. There has been nothing in her life that has been as fulfilling as helping young people in their journey of discovery.

Marianne began teaching at Drama at Pacific School of Music and the Arts in Costa Mesa.
Marianne earned her BA in English from University of California, Irvine. Later, she returned to UCI to earn her Masters of Arts in Teaching. She is grateful everyday to share her passion for writing with her students.

I was moved to become a judge for the Why Mom Deserves a Diamond® contest as a tribute to the love I have shared with my own mother. My mother was also a teacher, and has always inspired me to make the world a better place, one day (and one student) at a time.

Parts of the Diamond

Table
The table is the largest facet that is on the very top of a diamond.

Crown.
The top portion of a diamond extending from the girdle to the table.

Pavilion.
The bottom portion of a diamond, extending from the girdle to the culet.

Culet
The facet on the bottom of a diamond. Usually the culet is very small and nearly impossible to see. A large culet is common in diamonds that were cut in the early part of this century.

Girdle
The outer edge of a diamond, and is graded by its thickness. A girdle that is too thin may be more prone to chipping in case of an accidental blow. Extremely thick girdles usually produce extra depth and less brilliance. Girdles may be faceted or polished.

Depth.
The height of a gemstone measured from the culet to the table.

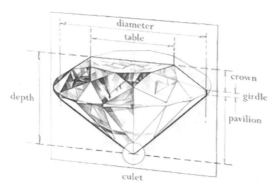

Evolution of Diamond Cutting

Modern Cut Diamond
by Ravi Kewalramani

Rose Cut
Early diamond cutters were unable to polish rough diamonds. However, they found out that they could polish or grind diamonds into a point by polishing almost parallel to the diamonds rough faces. They also realized that only diamonds cut diamonds. Hence they used a wooden table covered with diamond dust to achieve any kind of polishing. This resulted in the rose cut. It was a primitive and non-symetrical shape and derived its name because it resembled a rose. The rose cut came into existence in the early sixteenth century and was widely used till the early nineteenth century.

Old Mine Cut.
A direct ancestor (grandfather) of the modern cut round diamond is the old Mine Cut, which came into existence in the late seventeenth century. The old Mine Cut was the first diamond cut that had all the facets of the present round brilliant cut. However, the facet alignment and sizes were in a different manner as compared to the current round brilliant. The old Mine Cut was also more of a square or cushion cut, rather than being round.

Old European Cut.

The direct descendant to the old miner is the old European Cut. This cut is the father of the present round brilliant cut. The Old European cut was more evident in the late eighteenth century till the early twentieth century. Many experiments were done on the old European Cut during the early twentieth century regarding it's various facet positioning and angles. Most notable were the one done by Henry Morse and Marcel Tolkowsky. They ultimately gave birth to the present round brilliant cut and the ideal cut diamond proportions.

Rose Cut   **Old Mine Cut**   **Old European Cut**

Grading Considerations

Symmetry
Symmetry is an important element of a quality finished diamond. Symmetry means the exactness of the shape and the balanced arrangement of the facets.

Polish
Polish influences how well light is able to pass through a diamond and is important to a diamond's brilliance. Diamonds that have poor to extremely poor polish are less brilliant because they have microscopic polish lines that blur the surface of the diamond. These polish lines reduce the amount of light that enters or exits a diamond.

Depth
The depth of a diamond is important to its brilliance and value. Diamond cutters must remove more weight from the original rough diamond crystal to cut a diamond with proportions that produce great brilliance.

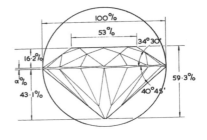

Every year, thousands of mother's appreciation essays invade Gallery of Diamonds. When stacked on top of each other, 20,000 essays reach the ceiling! Photo from year 2000 contest.

PREMIER ISSUE

Oct. -2008. By Michael Watson. G (GIA)

Natural is *Beautiful!*

Just before I dashed into my car, I noticed the sky was bluer than normal. For a quick moment I wondered if the subduing color was real or computer enhanced. I don't think that was crazy. Nowadays, it seems everything that comes across our senses has been altered in some way. Landscapes in real estate ads are always more lush than in real life, and fashion models may not be as thin or shapely as they appear on television. Did you wonder why the hamburger glowing from the lighted marquise is never quite the same as the one you open from the wax paper? Cardboard and pins are used to fluff the lettuce, a mister will spray that one drop of water running down the side of the tomato, and a hairdryer may be used to melt the cheese just before the final glamour shot.

We live in a different world than when I was a young diamond merchant. Today diamonds are drilled with lasers, filled with plastic, bombarded with atoms, and even grown in a laboratory. Processes are used to change brown diamonds to white, yellow diamonds to red, and near colorless diamonds to pink. And, like the computer hacker that makes it necessary for someone else to cure his virus, the gemologist must discover new treatments, be able to identify them, and disclose them to the public.

There is nothing wrong with any alteration or treatment, just as there is nothing wrong with using software to make products appear more attractive, alluring or appetizing. The problem is that there are some jewelers who do not disclose these alterations. Some salespeople do not disclose from the fear of losing a sale, others simply do not have the knowledge or resources to know of the latest treatments.

I'm not saying that one must disclose the enhanced crunch of an apple for a radio ad, or an enticing fragrance sprayed inside a car before the test spin. No problem here. The product was not altered.

The beautiful word we use at Gallery of Diamonds is *natural*. The rainbow colors that burst from our diamonds are not the result of irradiating, injecting, or special lighting. And, as long as you allow us to keep your jewelry clean, this sparkle will never lose its luster. You see, there is really nothing more beautiful or perfect than nature.

Perhaps that is why a natural diamond has become a perfect symbol of love. It is eternal, unchanging, and beautiful to the eye. It is also virtually indestructible. Isn't that the definition of love? When given as a gift, each succeeding glance at the gem will certainly evoke the wonderful memory of the giver.

Unless it is a special vintage or unusual piece of jewelry, Gallery of Diamonds only sells diamonds that are created by the awesome forces of nature. From there, it is the skill of the master diamond cutter who fashions the gem into its magnificent splendor that has fascinated us throughout history.

What does VS mean?

VS stands for "very slightly" included. This means a diamond will have minor inclusions that are difficult for a trained grader to see when viewed under 10x magnification. Gallery of Diamonds offers every grade of diamond up to internally flawless.

I saw a sign in a jewelry store saying "half-off ". Should I check them out?

Many times "half-off" or "half-price" is simply the regular price a jeweler wants to sell the item for. A person may receive a feeling of satisfaction from thinking he or she got a bargain, but many times it is more of a gimmick to bring shoppers into their store. Whether you invest $1,000 or $100,000, we will make sure you get the best and biggest diamond with your purchase.

Should I spend three months of my salary on her engagement ring?

Twelve months is even better! Think of this, gentlemen, is your yearly salary too much to spend for something that lasts forever?

Just kidding. My opinion- the size of a diamond, the grade of a diamond, or the amount one invests has no indication of how much you love someone. Don't worry about these things. But to give you a tip – no matter the size, the grade, or the price, girls love all diamond jewelry from Gallery of Diamonds!

What is white gold?

White gold is made by mixing gold with different alloys, such as silver, zinc, and palladium. Since the natural color of white gold is actually yellowish gray, a rhodium finish is used as a final touch to make the metal gleam sparkling white.

Rhodium is a metal in the platinum family and shares many of its properties. Although very white and hard, it does wear away eventually. To keep white gold jewelry looking its best it should be re-rhodiumed every one to two years.

Do I get an appraisal with my purchase?

Yes. Every piece of diamond jewelry comes with a free detailed certificate of evaluation from a GIA gemologist. This comes with a photo and description of the item, color and clarity of the diamond, and the estimated retail replacement value. This document is important for insurance purposes and to assure you about the quality of jewelry you now own. You may want to obtain a separate rider on your insurance policy if your diamond or ring gets lost, stolen, or mysteriously disappears.

Tell me about a diamond's clarity.

A diamond is born deep within the earth. When you combine unimaginable heat and pressure for about one million years, you beget a coveted gem that remains the hardest natural substance in the universe: crystallized carbon. (Believe it or not, the carbon in a diamond is the same element as the graphite in your pencil, with the atoms arranged differently.)

Moon Over Mountains™

The symbol of love that spells "**MOM**."

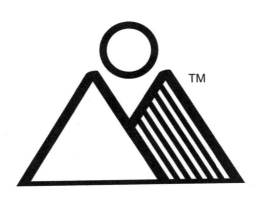

Gallery of Diamonds wanted to create an image that would be an eternal reminder of a mother and child's love. First, we started with the most sacred word of the contest, mom. Then we brainstormed to see what "mom" could be an acronym for. Following are some of our ideas.

Milk Overflowing Meadows

Melody of Motion

Model Of Miracles

Moon Over Mountains

Memory of Melodies

Master Of Motion

Mind Over Matter

My Only Mission

When Moon over Mountains was discovered, we realized that the letter "M" in mountains resembled mountains. When the circular "O" for "Over" was placed above the M, we saw the moon. The word "mom" appeared miraculously before our eyes!

Thich Nhat Hahn once said, "The moon is always expressing something deep, calm, and tender, like the love of a mother for her child." Now, whenever we gaze into the moon, especially as it peeks above the mountains, we will think of our mothers.

Gemologists are still not sure, but we think the inclusions (or flaws) in diamonds are caused by the gradual temperature and pressure changes during the diamonds formation. Inclusions should not be regarded as bad, for it is these natural imperfections that give every diamond the uniqueness of a snowflake.

GIA has determined that the highest clarity grade is flawless, which means a trained eye will not detect a single flaw when viewed under 10x magnification. The grading scale descends, determined mostly on the ease of detecting inclusions at 10x, then continues downward on the ease of seeing inclusions with the naked eye.

How do I find a jeweler I trust?

Trust is something that is earned. Trust takes time and time cannot be rushed. I believe a history of returning happy customers who refer their friends is a great indication that you have earned trust.

Most people are not diamond experts. In fact, many jewelry customers have never had the opportunity to enjoy the mysteries of a diamond by peering through the 10x loupe. Have you ever been to a jewelry store that never invited you to view their diamonds with a loupe? I wonder what they did not want you to see? Then again, many jewelry salespeople are simply not properly trained on diamond qualities.

Honesty and trust are critical to every diamond merchant. In fact, trust is so vital because they realize one mistake could be the end of their business. And even though at some point in your life you might find a dishonest salesperson, I believe that people in general are honest-natured. Has anyone ever come up to you from behind and said, "Pardon me, did you drop this one-dollar bill?" (Just recently, a clerk at a local eatery made the effort to return to my store saying, "Here is your change that you left on our counter.")

Gallery of Diamonds believes that trust is the greatest honor a jeweler can achieve. Since 1991, our goal has been to maintain a symbol of expertise while creating thousands of happy memories. To date, we have helped over 20,000 customers receive a lifetime of enjoyment from our designs.

Stop by or call ahead for an appointment. You'll be surprised about the diamond you can get for your money.

Carmen Watson sorts through thousands of gemstone prizes for essay winners.

©2008 Gallery of Diamonds. No part of this publication may be reproduced in any form without the expressed permission of Gallery of Diamonds.

In the News!

Los Alamitos Middle School Student Wins Mom diamond

20,000 students compete in annual Gallery of Diamonds' writing contest

April 21, 2009. The Orange County Register.
By Jaime Lynn Fletcher

LOS ALAMITOS– A local seventh-grader won a diamond for writing a poem about her mother as part of the 17th annual Gallery of Diamonds writing contest.

Nearly 20,000 students submitted essays in the "Why Mom Deserves a Diamond" contest and winners were chosen by a group of local teachers.

Cheryl Bond from Oak Middle school was chosen as the winner for students in grades 6 through 12 for her poetic essay describing her mother's love.

San Juan Capistrano fourth-grader David Duplissey won in the first through fifth-grade division.

Bond and Duplissey each received a quarter-carat diamond valued at $600 from Newport Beach-based Gallery of Diamonds.

The students, along with other contestants, are expected to visit the store and recite their poem to their mothers as a Mother's Day gift.

If every essay received were stacked, they would reach one half the height of the Leaning Tower of Pisa, or 77 feet high!

COLORADO

Sixth Grader's Poem Proves it's a Real Gem

ANDREA BROWN. Colorado Springs, CO.
March 7, 2005.

A simple poem had a fairy tale ending for sixth-grader Emily Magers. She turned a 27-word verse into a quarter carat diamond.

The poem was selected from 22,629 entries in the national WHY MOM DESERVES A DIAMOND® contest created by Gallery of Diamonds jewelers.

She won a diamond for her mom.

"I was just doing homework," 11-year-old Emily said. "I didn't think I'd win anything."

It took her about three days and three tries to get the words to sparkle.

She came up with this:
"Her voice, a nightingale. Her touch, butterfly wings. Her heart, overflowing with love. Her kisses, flawless bubbles. Mom, a perfect gem . . . a gift forever."

Her mother, Kyong, a lunch lady at Sand Creek High School, was touched by the sentiment from her only daughter.

"I didn't think she felt that way," she said. "Sometimes I give her a hard time. Being a mom, I want her to do a little better."

Timberview Middle School language arts teacher Bridget Burdan said the assignment was optional. She said Emily is an exceptional student.

"My mouth dropped open. It was such a beautiful poem," Burdan said. "I thought she had a chance."

Three diamond winners were selected, two from Orange County and one from the national pool.

"My teacher said, 'I have a huge announcement: You won!'" she said.

TEXAS

Hernandez's Words Earns Sparkling Gift
Condensed articles by Rich Clark and Kristi Rangel-King. Houston Chronicle. May 10, 2001.

Senior Jesus Hernandez recently won the WHY MOM DESERVES A DIAMOND® poetry contest, sponsored by Gallery of Diamonds in Costa Mesa, CA.

There were two California state winners but Hernandez was the only national winner.

Gallery of Diamonds owner Michael Watson said he wanted to find a way to show the value mothers have in our lives.

Winning first place...has not made Hernandez forget the spirit of Mother's Day.

"The diamond does not mean anything to me," said Hernandez. "It's the fact that people will read my poem and see I love my mother."

"I love my son," said Hernandez's mother, Carmen. "The words that he used, it came from his soul."

INDIANA

Sixth-Grader's Essay a True Gem
Jackie Sheckler. The Herald Times. Bloomington. April 17, 1999.

For close to four hours, Chris Olsen-Phillips worked on his essay. He would cross out a word, add another one. Being limited to 30 words made it tougher, as did the subject matter. The 11-year-old was writing about his mother.

"I wrote it six times," he said. Finally, he was satisfied. And so were the judges.

The sixth-grade student at Binford Elementary School was a grand prize winner in the annual WHY MOM DESERVES A DIAMOND® essay contest. The contest received 14,150 entries this year, including 1,500 from 65 Indiana schools.

But being a grand prize winner was not something Chris or anyone else expected. Watson called Binford Elementary with the announcement.

When Deb Olsen picked her son up after school, "his friends were so excited, Chris almost didn't get to tell me himself."

CALIFORNIA

Mom's a Gem

Brenda Rees. The Tidings. May 7, 1999.

In Rosa Marrero's fifth grade class at St. Malachy School in Los Angeles, Mothers Day - and moms in general - are a pretty big deal.

In honor of the upcoming holiday, banners, signs, poems and various selections from prayer books were scattered around the classroom, which Marrero said was probably inspirational and made the students motivated to write their essays."

She's referring to essays her 21 students wrote and submitted as part of an annual contest that challenges kids to compose, WHY MOM DESERVES A DIAMOND®. Winners of the essay will receive a diamond for their mothers.

When her student, Roberto Ruiz, was announced as one of the five winners of the contest, Marrero said she was pleasantly surprised. "

Written with poetic flair, Ruiz's essay is a simple homage to his mother, Margarita.

Margarita said the winning essay is merely the latest example of her son's academic accomplishments. "I feel very proud of him," she said. "He surprises me more and more each day. I ask God to help him remain on his path."

Professional Jeweler Magazine.
June 2006.

On Diamond Day, March 4, two Orange County, California Diamond Winners received a quarter-carat diamond valued at $500 in the 14th annual WHY MOM DESERVES A DIAMOND® writing contest.

Gallery of Diamonds was founded in 1991 as a specialist in diamonds. The ministry of the mothers contest, however, has become deeper than the business itself. What started as a humble dedication to moms has grown into a national tradition in which thousands of kids can express their feelings, while taking the time to reflect on the importance of their moms.

Boy Wins His Mom a Diamond
20,000 students compete in annual Gallery of Diamonds' writing contest

May 8, 2009. The Orange County Register.

By Peter Schelden

If a picture is worth 1,000 words, what are 25 words worth? If you're David Duplissey, a fourth-grader at Ambuehl elementary in San Juan Capistrano, the right 25 words are worth a one-fourth-carat diamond.

The diamond was given to David's mother, Deanne, as part of Gallery of Diamond's 17th annual Why Mom Deserves a Diamond® contest.

Students wrote short poems describing their mothers. David's poem was chosen from more than 20,000 entries from first- through fifth-graders.

To claim the prize, David had to read his ode to his mother inside the store.

"He was embarrassed as heck," Deanne said.

David is an athlete. He has played soccer and Little League baseball for five years, and is competing to be on an elite soccer team this year.

He said his success as a writer comes from third-grade teacher Marillee Carroll and current teacher Jennifer Sullivan.

In the summer of 1993, seven of Michael Watson's friends got together. Realizing the rich differences of their backgrounds, they decided to have a dinner in which each person would bring a dish from their native country. Since Watson's most treasured memories were those precious times he sat with his adoptive parents at the dinner table, he felt this was a wonderful idea.

One friend brought chicken with peanut sauce. Another brought exotic Persian rice. Still another brought pita bread and humus made from sesame seed. Carmen, Watson's wife-to-be, fried platenos and black beans. Watson flipped hamburgers. They never forget that magical day.

Being adopted, Watson spent many years searching for the definition of mother. The greatest consequence of his quest was the creation of the WHY MOM DESERVES A DIAMOND® contest. To date, thousands of kids whose origins trace to the far corners of the world have expressed their appreciation for their mothers. Watson feels if one's true mother is one who nurtures and gently instructs our footsteps, then our beautiful earth must also be our mother.

Watson and his friends now celebrate the International Dinner every year. He encourages other people to start this tradition.

The World Table

Today we bring food
To the World Table
As we sit and eat with
People from all nations
It is easier to see our
Sameness than our differences
And that we are all
Wonderfully interwoven

As we savor our fellowship
And the flavors of our cultures
We can see the reflection of
Ourselves in each other
At the World Table
Our hearts define all things

At the World Table
We know a single torch has
Ignited our sparks
The universe gave birth
To the stars
Our Earth gave birth to us

At the World Table we are all
Children of the same Mother

Until we meet again
At the World Table
We will remember our
Joyous Feast
We will do all things
With great love
And we will love and care
For our Living Mother
Who has so perfectly loved us

© 2006 Michael C. Watson

ConTesT Quiz™ Answers bottom of page.

1. The contest was started in honor of the contest founder's adoptive mother. What was her name?
A. Hazel   B. Martha   C. Violet

2. When was the first contest held?
A. 1862   B. 1943   C. 1993

3. What was the name of the first DiamondWinner?
A. Margaret   B. Clifford   C. Herbert

4. What words are used the most when describing mom?
A. smile & face   B. hands & touch.   C. eyes & heart

5. How many essays have been submitted since the contest began?
A. 10,000
B. 50,000
C. Over 250,000

6. Finish the Song:
I read these words from my heart
And place this prize in her hand
Wanna let her know, I love her so
She's the greatest mom in the ____.

7. How many essays are submitted every year?
A. 1,000   B. 7,000   C. 15,000- 20,000

8. Who reads all those essays?
A. Teachers
B. Secret agent moms
C. Principals

9. How many kids have been a DiamondWinner?
A. 22   B. 46   C. 88

10. Why is there a 25-word limit?
A. Judges get dizzy reading too many words.
B. 25 is a magic number.
C. Increases the challenge to honor mom in a few chosen words

11. On Diamond Day, 2003, Mr. Watson-
A. Forgot to give corsages to DiamondMoms
B. Tripped over a ring box
C. Lost voice. Could not give ceremony speech.

12. If every essays submitted were stacked in a single pile, how high would they go?
A. Top of your school.
B. The Eiffell Tower.
C. 1/2 height of Leaning Tower of Pisa.

13. What shape of diamond was awarded to the DiamondWinner in 2007?
A. heart   B. princess   C. marquise

Gallery Glossary

Diamond Winner: The grand prize student who is chosen to receive a quarter-carat diamond to give to mom. This is the highest prize of the contest. Three Diamond Winners are chosen per year from over twenty thousand submissions; two from Orange County, California, and one from the United States.

Contest Winner: A student who is chosen to receive an unmounted African Amethyst or garnet. It is a great honor to be a Contest Winner, because only the best contestant will win one of these beautiful prizes. Entrants must be creative and catch the attention of the Contest Panel Judges.

Diamond Mom: The mother of a Diamond Winner. The highest honor a mother can receive. On Diamond Day, Diamond Moms are given a red rose corsage to wear over their hearts.

Diamond Teacher: The teacher of a Diamond Winner. The highest honor a teacher can receive. Diamond Teachers are awarded a 14K African garnet necklace.

Diamond Day: The date to commemorate the Diamond Winners, their Diamond Moms, and their Diamond Teachers at Gallery of Diamonds. The first Diamond Day in 1993 was held on Mother's Day.

Contest Panel Judges: These are teachers who spend countless hours thoughtfully grading each essay for creativity and uniqueness. A Contest Panel Judge is only allowed to grade essays outside of his or her own school.

Martha Watson Award: This is a 14K garnet necklace that is awarded to a mother who exemplifies strength, courage, or has greatly benefited society and the world.

The Legendary Contest®: This is a registered trademark and has the same meaning as the Why Mom Deserves a Diamond® contest. This is defined as a "writing contest in which kids can honor their mothers and have the chance to win a diamond or gemstone."

Mission Statement

To provide a positive and magical experience for every customer with excellent service and quality jewelry.

Company Vision

To give the opportunity for every child in the nation to express their written and spoken words of love to their mothers.

JOB OF A LIFETIME! If you would like to use your special talents to help us grow our contest nationwide, contact Gallery of Diamonds for employment opportunities at 1-800-667-4440.

Answers to ConTesT Quiz™.

1. B.	7. C.
2. C.	8. A.
3. A.	9. B.
4. C.	10. C.
5. C.	11. A.
6. land	12. C.
	13. A.

WHY MOM DESERVES A DIAMOND® and THE LEGENDARY CONTEST® are registered trademarks of Gallery of Diamonds.

Patent Pending.

What others are saying about the WHY MOM DESERVES A DIAMOND® contest.

Thank you for including the students of Ladera Vista in your Why Mom Deserves a Diamond® essay contest. Students from so many different backgrounds sharing their love, caring and respect for their moms through writing is awesome.

I have been on the Fullerton School Board of Trustees for 11 years. Your contest is the most selfless and encouraging I have experienced. You are a shining example for others in our community.

On behalf of all the teachers, students, moms and extended families whose lives you have touched, thank you.

Hilda Sugarman, president
Fullerton Excellence In Education
Foundation

Dear Michael,
Your perseverance from your personal past, your warmth, love and generosity have made the most wonderful impact not only on the children, but also on all the mothers and fathers as well. We all know that the thought of "mother" cannot be separated from that of "love". Most of us are lucky enough to swim in a world of that tender love for many years, and, without even knowing it, we are quite happy there. Only after it is too late do we become aware of it. With your encouragement, a child would take time to realize what the greatest gift God has been given him/her:

A mother- a foundation of love.

With your irresistible rewards, a child would willingly learn to express his/her innermost feelings.

From that overwhelming feeling of love, that child will undoubtedly try his/her best to reach for the stars. I have seen that effect on all four of my children who have been lucky enough to receive your awards ,who have not failed to make time to give me hugs and kisses every time we pass each other's way. As for me, a mother, you have not only created fond memories between my children and I, but also embraced me with such a marvelous acknowledgement of my hard work, dedication and love. I feel so humble and honored.

You inspire me to be nothing but the best role model and best mother I can be for my children. You are an extraordinary human being who selflessly brings joy to the lives of people you have never met.

Bich Ngoc Nuyen, Winning Mom
Fountain Valley, CA

What a wonderful opportunity you have given my students! I wish you could have seen and heard their reactions. During the call to Eric, he accidently hung up on me because he was jumping up and down so much! Linda, was screaming joyfully and hugging mom! Marissa, just left my office hugging her mom,

who tearfully was embracing such a tender moment! Wow! Thank you for allowing students to hold up their moms in such a special way. What a gift to the world! Thank you from the bottom of a teacher's heart!

Darlene Jagger , teacher
Placentia, CA.

Thank you for having the contest. As an adoptee, myself, I appreciate the significance of a mother. What a wonderful tribute this is...

My students were thrilled to learn they had won a wonderful gemstone for their mothers. Thank you so much

Jennifer Turner, teacher
Buena Park, CA
Dear Mr. Watson,

...I do not want any more time to pass without thanking you and Gallery of Diamonds for your very generous Why Mom Deserves a Diamond®" Contest. ...What a lovely way to pay tribute to moms...thank you for this wonderful contest and your thoughtful and generous sponsorship.

Susan Vescera, teacher
Christ Lutheran School, Costa Mesa.

Gallery of Diamonds began the contest 17 years ago giving children the opportunity to recognize the love their mothers bestows upon them.

Anthony Bogle, Principal
Crown Valley Elementary
Laguna Niguel, CA

Thank you for the beautiful garnet and diamond necklace that you gave me for being a teacher of the Diamond Winner. It is a treasured necklace and I wear it with such love and pride for what it means in my life. Thank you for the opportunity to help you with the judging, and be part of the WHY MOM DESERVES A DIAMOND® contest. You are such a generous humanitarian. I admire you greatly. Thank you for all you give to the youth and their mothers. It is truly awe-inspiring. You are an unusual man- "one in a million." The Diamond Day ceremony was the highlight of my teaching year!

Laura Little, teacher
Capistrano Valley High School, CA

2002. The Final Decision. The National Diamond Winner is chosen out of 14,375 essays.